WAVE GENERATION AND SHAPING

McGraw-Hill Electrical and Electronic Engineering Series
FREDERICK EMMONS TERMAN, *Consulting Editor*
W. W. HARMAN and J. G. TRUXAL, *Associate Consulting Editors*

AHRENDT AND SAVANT · Servomechanism Practice
ANGELO · Electronic Circuits
ASELTINE · Transform Method in Linear System Analysis
BAILEY AND GAULT · Alternating-current Machinery
BERANEK · Acoustics
BRENNER AND JAVID · Analysis of Electric Circuits
BRUNS AND SAUNDERS · Analysis of Feedback Control Systems
CAGE · Theory and Application of Industrial Electronics
CAUER · Synthesis of Linear Communication Networks, Vols. I and II
CLEMENT AND JOHNSON · Electrical Engineering Science
CUCCIA · Harmonics, Sidebands, and Transients in Communication Engineering
CUNNINGHAM · Introduction to Nonlinear Analysis
EASTMAN · Fundamentals of Vacuum Tubes
EVANS · Control-system Dynamics
FEINSTEIN · Foundations of Information Theory
FITZGERALD AND HIGGINBOTHAM · Basic Electrical Engineering
FITZGERALD AND KINGSLEY · Electric Machinery
FRANK · Electrical Measurement Analysis
GEPPERT · Basic Electron Tubes
GLASFORD · Fundamentals of Television Engineering
HAPPELL AND HESSELBERTH · Engineering Electronics
HARMAN · Fundamentals of Electronic Motion
HARRINGTON · Introduction to Electromagnetic Engineering
HAYT · Engineering Electromagnetics
HESSLER AND CAREY · Fundamentals of Electrical Engineering
HILL · Electronics in Engineering
JOHNSON · Transmission Lines and Networks
KRAUS · Antennas
KRAUS · Electromagnetics
KUH AND PEDERSON · Principles of Circuit Synthesis
LEDLEY · Digital Computer and Control Engineering
LEPAGE · Analysis of Alternating-current Circuits
LEPAGE AND SEELY · General Network Analysis

LEY, LUTZ, AND REHBERG · Linear Circuit Analysis
MILLMAN · Vacuum-tube and Semiconductor Electronics
MILLMAN AND SEELY · Electronics
MILLMAN AND TAUB · Pulse and Digital Circuits
MISHKIN AND BRAUN · Adaptive Control Systems
MOORE · Traveling-wave Engineering
PETTIT · Electronic Switching, Timing, and Pulse Circuits
REZA AND SEELY · Modern Network Analysis
ROGERS · Introduction to Electric Fields
RÜDENBERG · Transient Performance of Electric Power Systems
RYDER · Engineering Electronics
SCHWARTZ · Information Transmission, Modulation, and Noise
SEELY · Electron-tube Circuits
SEELY · Electronic Engineering
SEELY · Introduction to Electromagnetic Fields
SEELY · Radio Electronics
SIEFERT AND STEEG · Control Systems Engineering
SISKIND · Direct-current Machinery
SKILLING · Electric Transmission Lines
SKILLING · Transient Electric Currents
SPANGENBERG · Fundamentals of Electron Devices
SPANGENBERG · Vacuum Tubes
STEVENSON · Elements of Power System Analysis
STORER · Passive Network Synthesis
STRAUSS · Wave Generation and Shaping
TERMAN · Electronic and Radio Engineering
TERMAN AND PETTIT · Electronic Measurements
THALER · Elements of Servomechanism Theory
THALER AND BROWN · Analysis and Design of Feedback Control Systems
THALER AND BROWN · Servomechanism Analysis
THOMPSON · Alternating-current and Transient Circuit Analysis
TOU · Digital and Sampled-data Control Systems
TRUXAL · Automatic Feedback Control System Synthesis
WILLIAMS AND YOUNG · Electrical Engineering Problems

Brooklyn Polytechnic Institute Series

ANGELO · Electronic Circuits
MISHKIN AND BRAUN · Adaptive Control Systems
SCHWARTZ · Information Transmission, Modulation, and Noise
STRAUSS · Wave Generation and Shaping

Wave Generation and Shaping

LEONARD STRAUSS

ASSOCIATE PROFESSOR OF ELECTRICAL ENGINEERING
POLYTECHNIC INSTITUTE OF BROOKLYN

McGRAW-HILL BOOK COMPANY, INC.

New York Toronto London

1960

WAVE GENERATION AND SHAPING

 Library of Congress Catalog Card Number 60-9861

THE MAPLE PRESS COMPANY, YORK, PA. 62160

TO ROSEMARY

PREFACE

Time and time again during the last fifty years the electrical engineer has been called upon to generate a signal having some specified geometry. Either through intuition and experimentation or on the basis of a detailed analysis of the specific problem, the first crude circuits were designed, improved, and modified. With the advent of the transistor, not only were many of the vacuum-tube circuits adapted, but new ones, making use of the special transistor characteristics, were devised. Thus today hundreds of oscillators, multivibrators, and linear sweeps are described in the literature; usually each one is treated as a separate entity.

When only crude methods of analysis were at the disposal of the engineer and when the number of useful active circuits was small, it was necessary for the texts to discuss them all in detail. But with the current state of the art, an encyclopedic study becomes prohibitive, if, in fact, such a work would even be desirable.

The objective of this text is to present a logical, unified approach to the analysis of those circuits where the nonlinearity of the tube or transistor is significant. A developmental treatment is followed throughout as we focus on the essential features of practical wave-generating and -shaping circuits. To this end, the text is arbitrarily divided into five sections: models and shaping, timing, switching, memory, and oscillations. It is, of course, impossible not to step across these bounds in discussing specific circuits and examples have been chosen so that the basic ideas will arise naturally from the discussion. In most cases the analysis is sufficiently detailed so that the techniques may be applied to other existent, and not as yet existent, circuits. Transistors and vacuum tubes are used almost interchangeably to support the contention that the basic mode of operation is independent of the active element employed.

The organization, which is described in some detail below, is a result of experimentation with class notes over several years. Because this work is primarily a text, designed for a senior or graduate course of one or two semesters, it is assumed that the reader is familiar with the transient analysis of linear networks and with simple vacuum-tube and transistor amplifiers. However, since the viewpoint presented may be somewhat different from that previously encountered, some review material is incorporated in the body of the text at the point where it is first needed.

Part 1. *Models and Shaping.* Since we are interested in the transient response of the piecewise-linear models to various excitations, the first chapter presents approximation methods which can be employed for the rapid solution of linear circuits.

In Chapter 2 a grossly nonlinear element, the diode, is introduced. Once its volt-ampere characteristic is approximated by an ordered series of line segments, linear algebraic equations may be written to define the behavior in each region. Most of the problems met in more complex circuits make their initial appearance when the diode is combined with an energy-storage element. Combinations of diodes and resistors can be used to represent, in a piecewise manner, almost any arbitrary characteristic. For solution, the complex circuit is reduced to a sequence of linear networks and the complex problem reduces to finding the boundaries between the various regions (break-point analysis). Chapter 3 reinforces the concepts of Chapter 2 with additional examples of multiple-diode networks.

The piecewise-linear model is extended to multiterminal devices (the tube and transistor) in Chapter 4, relying on the conduction or back biasing of ideal diodes to differentiate the regions of operation. In order to represent the inherent amplification of the active element, the model includes one or more controlled sources.

Part 2. *Timing.* The next four chapters deal with the linear sweep. Since the essential portion of any timed circuit is the exponential charging of an energy-storage element, the problem of analysis resolves itself into finding the time-constant, the initial, the steady-state, and the final sweep voltage.

In the simple voltage sweep of Chapter 5, a gas tube is used as the switching element. This choice makes it possible to treat synchronization without having recourse to the more complex circuit configurations of the later chapters.

Linearization of the sweep always involves some form of feedback. The aim is to approximate constant-current charging of the sweep capacitor. Vacuum-tube circuits are analyzed in Chapter 6, but a discussion of the transistor equivalents is deferred until Chapter 7. In the Miller sweep of Chapter 6, the calculation of the initial jumps, overshoots, and recovery exponentials, from the individual circuit models, lays the groundwork for the later analysis of the multivibrator and the blocking oscillator. Furthermore, the separate consideration of the recovery time and the switching problem leads to the construction of a sweep system, the phantastron. Chapter 8 applies the same techniques of analysis to the current sweep.

Part 3. *Switching.* When a closed-loop system contains active elements and when the loop gain is positive and greater than unity, we call it a switching circuit. If any timing networks are included in the transmission path, the circuit exhibits quasi-stable behavior. The same effect can be obtained by shunting a negative-resistance device with an energy-storage element.

Chapters 9 and 10 discuss a closed-loop regenerative switching circuit, the multivibrator. We are mainly concerned with where and how to begin the analysis. A guess serves as the convenient starting point, and the circuit calculations are checked to see if they yield consistent results. If a contradiction arises, it simply indicates that the first guess was wrong. In the multivibrator both tubes and transistors are active only during the switching interval. At all other times one is cut off or the other is saturated. Hence the exponential timing, which sustains the limiting, occurs within the cutoff zone, and recovery usually depends on the saturated tube or transistor. After the appropriate models are drawn, the calculations involve finding the initial and switching points of the timing network.

Many devices exist whose driving-point volt-ampere characteristic exhibits a negative-resistance region. The most useful treatment of switching circuits containing these elements is from the viewpoint expressed in Chapter 11. Switching and timing are first treated with the aid of a postulated ideal device. Even though the waveshapes and trajectories obtained are approximately correct, the use of an ideal negative resistance leads directly to a stability criterion that is inconsistent with the physical device. Since the reasons that the contradictory results arose are pointed out later, this chapter also illustrates the dangers inherent in overidealizing a model.

The ideas presented in Chapter 11 may well be considered as unifying concepts. These are presented rather late in the text so that the student may better appreciate the limitations as well as the advantages of this viewpoint. The negative-resistance treatment is useful for understanding the operation of all sweeps and switching circuits even where it is difficult to isolate the two terminals across which the negative resistance is developed. It is, however, a convenient design method only for those circuits which employ such special devices as the unijunction and *p-n-p-n* transistors and the tunnel diode.

Not all circuits can, in fact, be solved completely. But the methods developed in the earlier sections of the text, when applied to one which cannot be, for example, the blocking oscillator of Chapter 12, do yield a considerable understanding of how the circuit behaves.

Part 4. *Memory.* Since a hysteresis loop indicates memory, magnetic and dielectric materials are ideally suited for information storage.

Chapter 13 examines briefly the terminal characteristics of a core constructed out of ideal square-loop material. Furthermore, a clearly defined time is needed to saturate the core, and although not representable in a piecewise-linear manner, the driving-point impedance exhibits two distinct regions. This enables us to use either a core or a ferroelectric device as the timing element in a switching circuit.

Part 5. *Oscillations.* Although most of the circuits previously discussed depended for their timing on a single energy-storage element, at least two are necessary in order for the system to have a pair of complex conjugate poles located in the right half plane.

The sinusoidal oscillator is first treated as an almost linear feedback system (Chapter 14) which allows the separation of the frequency-, amplitude-, and gain-determining element. The role of each oscillator essential is individually examined, with emphasis on minimizing the distortion and maximizing the stability. Since the signal produced is almost sinusoidal, the amplitude is readily found by plotting a system-describing function.

Chapter 15 returns to the negative-resistance viewpoint and describes the solution of a specific nonlinear differential equation. Here topological constructions, which supplement analytic methods, yield the waveshape and amplitude of oscillations. Hence the text ends by introducing a new topic and not by saying the last word on an old one.

While preparing the manuscript, I received a great deal of assistance and encouragement from many people. I should like to acknowledge the contributions made by those colleagues who taught sections of the course for which this text was written. In stimulating technical discussions, I received the benefit of their ideas and thinking on many topics, much of which caused me to modify the original treatment. They also corrected errors which inadvertently crept into the original class notes, and they prepared some of the problems. The secretarial and drafting assistance made available by the Polytechnic Institute of Brooklyn is greatly appreciated. Finally, I wish to thank all members of the Electrical Engineering Department of the Institute for their generous encouragement during the project. The friendly and cooperative atmosphere made the writing of this book almost a pleasure.

Leonard Strauss

CONTENTS

PART 1

MODELS AND SHAPING

CHAPTER 1

LINEAR WAVE SHAPING

1-1. Introduction. Often the control and instrumentation engineer finds himself faced with the problem of producing a designated complex waveform. Usually his simplest approach is to divide the problem into two parts: first, the generation of simple waveshapes and, second, some type of operation on them to achieve the desired final result. If the required waveform is of a sufficiently complex nature, several substages of shaping may be needed, with combination taking place in the final stage. Generation always involves the use of active elements, and although they also perform a function, shaping is predominantly effected by the circuit's passive components. One might even go so far as to say that a major portion of the process of wave generation itself consists in passive element shaping.

In this chapter we shall examine the behavior of linear passive circuits with a view to solving for their time response to various input waveshapes. Exact analysis is, of course, possible, but often so tedious that the competent engineer looks instead for reasonable approximations. Our aim, therefore, is to set up conditions whereby solutions may be obtained rapidly, almost by inspection, avoiding involved algebraic manipulation. This, in fact, becomes possible only under very specific circumstances, which must be clearly delineated. Particular emphasis will be placed on the treatment of circuits containing only a single-energy-storage element, not only because these appear quite frequently, but also because it is here that the approximation techniques are most fruitful. Sometimes even multiple-energy-storage circuits may be reduced to a number of separate single-energy circuits, which are then individually solved. The solutions are finally combined, yielding the approximate total response of the original complex circuit.

In our effort to develop facility in utilizing simplifying approximations, i.e., how to make them and when to make them, we shall start by considering some very basic circuits. Since we already know methods of finding their exact response to simple inputs, we can concentrate attention on the methodology of the solution.

1-2. Initial Conditions. We shall first consider the transient response of a passive linear network, i.e., the response to some abrupt change in either the external excitation or the internal circuit. We know that the solution will be directly related to the poles of the system transfer function, and for poles at p_1, p_2, and p_3, the response to a step will always have the form

$$r(t) = A_0 + A_1e^{p_1t} + A_2e^{p_2t} + A_3e^{p_3t}$$

One exponential term is due to each energy-storage element included in the network. This type of response is readily found by the classical method of writing and solving the system's integrodifferential equations or by modern transformation analysis.

If, however, we restrict our interest to relatively simple systems, i.e., those containing one, or sometimes two, widely separated poles, then these may often be found by direct inspection of the circuit. They will correspond to the negative reciprocal of the time constants.

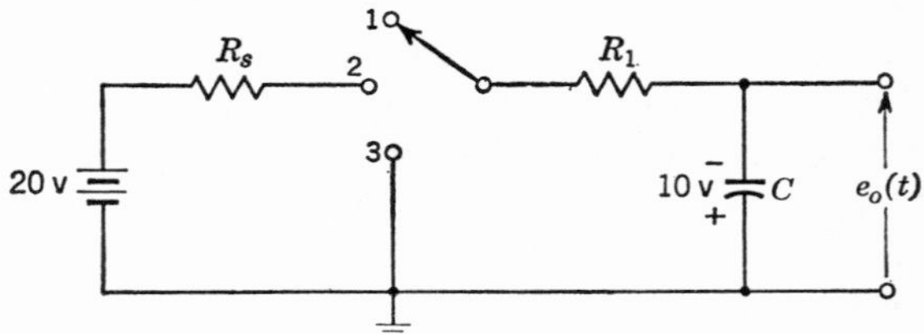

FIG. 1-1. Single-energy-storage-element circuit.

In a circuit containing only a single-energy-storage element, such as the one shown in Fig. 1-1, the response to a unit step will be given by

$$e_o(t) = A + Be^{-t/\tau} \tag{1-1}$$

The first parameter of interest, the time constant, is simply the product of C and the total resistance seen by the capacitor. When the switch is in position 2,

$$\tau_2 = (R_1 + R_s)C \qquad p_2 = -\frac{1}{\tau_2} \tag{1-2}$$

Upon switching to position 3, both the time constant and pole location change; they now become

$$\tau_3 = R_1C \qquad p_3 = -\frac{1}{\tau_3} \tag{1-3}$$

The time response is of the form given in Eq. (1-1); coefficients, of course, will differ.

Since a prerequisite to the complete solution is the value of the various coefficients, a slight digression as to the means of their evaluation is in order before proceeding to the general solution of this circuit. But these coefficients depend upon the initial conditions; therefore the first question to ask is, What determines these conditions? Obviously, one part of the answer is the known external constraints imposed on the circuit, i.e., the excitation function and the various circuit changes. The second half of the answer is the internal constraints determined by the energy-storage elements present within the circuit, in this case a single capacitor.

The voltage drop across any capacitor is related to circuit current flow as expressed in the differential equation

$$e_c = \frac{1}{C}\int i\,dt = \frac{Q}{C} \tag{1-4}$$

This equation says that, in a physical system, the accumulation of charge takes finite time unless an infinite current flows. Consequently the terminal voltage cannot change instantaneously. In an ideal system such instantaneous changes may be forced by placing a short circuit or an ideal battery across the capacitor terminals or by injecting an infinite pulse of current. These do not exist in practice, but sometimes the charge or discharge time is so very fast compared with the total time range of interest that the small time interval involved may be ignored, and we can say that the capacitor voltage has jumped to its final value. From the above discussion, the first circuit constraint can now be stated: *the voltage across the capacitor must be continuous across regions of circuit or excitation change.* Carrying this argument a step further leads us to the additional conclusion that all sudden changes in circuit voltage will be distributed across the various noncapacitive portions of the circuit—across the resistors and inductances. The manner of division depends on the particular circuit configuration under investigation.

One can derive a second condition from Eq. (1-4) by noting that the voltage across C continues to change as long as any current flows. The final steady-state voltage is reached when $i_c = 0$. In a simple network it will always be the d-c Thévenin equivalent voltage appearing across the capacitor.

We conclude that the constant A in Eq. (1-1) represents the steady-state response and may be evaluated by considering the behavior at $t = \infty$. The coefficient B is related to the behavior at $t = 0$ and would be found from the initial conditions.

As an example, consider the time response of the circuit of Fig. 1-1. Its behavior is the following: at $t = 0$ the switch is thrown from position 1 to 2; once the voltage across the capacitor reaches the predetermined final value, $E_f = 15$ volts, the switch is moved to position 3, remaining there.

Rather than attempt to solve the entire problem in a single step, it is advisable to divide it into three simple parts and to solve each in proper time sequence. The complete solution will then be the aggregate of the individual answers. The three parts are:

1. Behavior at $t = 0^-$
2. Response from $t = 0^+$ to the time t_f at which $e_o(t_f) = E_f$
3. Response from $t = t_f$ to ∞

Note that the change of state determines the problem division, with each part holding for a specific circuit configuration. In proceeding, the solution of each part will start from its own zero time as if it were a completely independent problem. Numerical subscripts corresponding to the particular part indicate the time region under examination.

1. Solution for $t < 0_1$:

$$e_{o1} = -10 \text{ volts}$$

2. System response for $0_2 < t < t_{f2}$. In this region the solution is given by Eq. (1-1). We are now ready to evaluate the coefficients from the specific initial conditions holding.

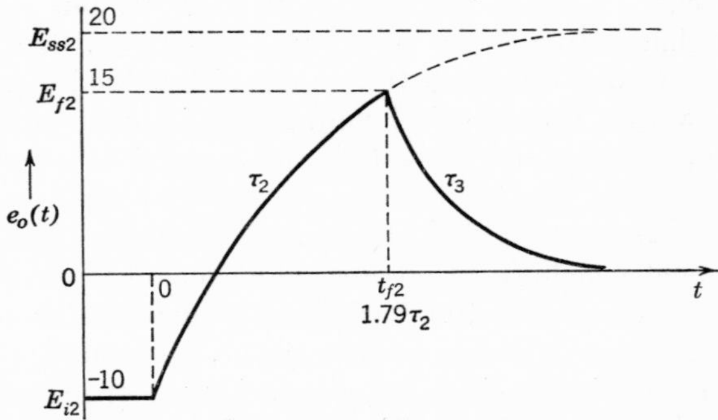

FIG. 1-2. Total time response of the circuit of Fig. 1-1.

Because the voltage of C must be continuous across the switching interval (circuit change), the initial value in this region (E_{i2}) will be the same as the final value of part 1 (E_{f1}). At $t = 0^+$,

$$e_{o2}(0^+) = E_{i2} = E_{f1} = -10 \text{ volts} = A_2 + B_2 \tag{1-5}$$

Furthermore, the output now charges toward a steady-state value E_{ss2}, found at $t = \infty$.

$$e_{o2}(\infty) = E_{ss2} = 20 \text{ volts} = A_2 \tag{1-6}$$

Solving Eqs. (1-5) and (1-6) and substituting into (1-1) yields

$$\begin{aligned} e_{o2}(t) &= E_{ss2} - (E_{ss2} - E_{i2})e^{-t/\tau_2} \\ &= 20 - 30e^{-t/\tau_2} \end{aligned} \tag{1-7}$$

The final value of part 2 is found by substituting t_{f2} into Eq. (1-7).

$$e_{o2}(t_{f2}) = E_{f2} = 15 \text{ volts} = E_{ss2} - (E_{ss2} - E_{i2})e^{-t_{f2}/\tau_2}$$

Solving for t_{f2} yields

$$t_{f2} = \tau_2 \ln \frac{E_{ss2} - E_{i2}}{E_{ss2} - E_{f2}} = \tau_2 \ln \frac{20 - (-10)}{20 - 15} = 1.79\tau_2 \tag{1-8}$$

3. System response for $t_{f2} < t < \infty$ or $0_3 < t < \infty$. By the same methods used for part 2, the new defining equation becomes

$$e_{o3}(t) = E_{ss3} - (E_{ss3} - E_{i3})^{-t/\tau_3} \tag{1-9}$$

The initial and steady-state voltages in region 3 are

(a) $t = 0_3 \qquad E_{i3} = E_{f2} = 15$
(b) $t = \infty \qquad e_{o3} = E_{ss3} = 0$

Substituting these conditions into Eq. (1-9) results in the final decay equation

$$e_{o3}(t) = E_{f2}e^{-t/\tau_3} = 15e^{-t/\tau_3}$$

Figure 1-2 is the plot of the total solution, with the response of each portion beginning immediately after that of the previous part.

In the solution for part 2, the circuit responded as if no change were scheduled. It could not predict the future, and therefore, in solving the problem, we must be careful lest our foreknowledge lead to fallacious reasoning, i.e., the incorrect substitution of E_{f2} instead of E_{ss2} for the steady-state value. Upon entering region 2 the response is toward the final value calculated as if the circuit were invariant.

When the circuit contains an ideal inductance, additional constraints appear.

$$e_L = L\frac{di}{dt} \tag{1-10}$$

From Eq. (1-10) it may be seen that an infinite voltage is required to change the current instantaneously. As this is an impossible situation in any physical circuit, our first conclusion is that *the current through the coil must be continuous across circuit or excitation changes.* A second constraint, also derivable from the above equation, is that steady state is finally reached when there is no further time rate of change of current, i.e., when $e_L = 0$. These conditions are just the duals of the ones found for the capacitor. The overlapping constraints of the two energy-storage elements forbid any instantaneous changes of current, and of capacitor or resistor voltage, in a series *RLC* circuit. Because of the physical nature of the various circuit elements, they will all have associated stray capacity and lead inductance. Therefore all circuits contain more than one type of energy-storage element. These parasitic elements act to slow down the rapid changes found when we consider a simple ideal *RL* or *RC* circuit. But if the time range of interest is sufficiently long, the second-order effects may be neglected.

1-3. Solution of Periodically Excited Circuits. After the sudden application of a periodic input to a passive network, the output itself will eventually become periodic in nature. The transient dies out in four time constants, leaving the steady-state response. The time required for this, in terms of the number of cycles of the input waveshape, depends upon the relative values of the time constant and the period of the excitation function. If the time constant is much smaller than the input period, the periodic output appears within one or at most a few cycles and it can be found by following the behavior cycle by cycle.

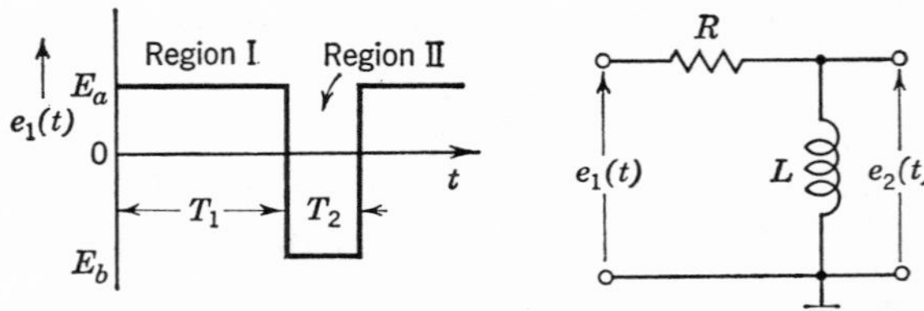

FIG. 1-3. Circuit for the study of recurrent boundary conditions.

On the other hand, when the ratio of the time constant to the period of the input is relatively large, periodicity will not be reached until an extremely large number of cycles have passed. During the build-up, the capacitor charges to the average level of the voltage appearing across its terminals and the direct current through a coil increases from zero to the average circuit value. To attempt to start at zero time and follow the response cycle by cycle until final periodicity is a ridiculous approach to the solution of this class of problems—it will only lead to frustration.

A more judicious treatment would be the application of the results of the previous section, with the addition of the known periodicity of the solution. This enables us to write recurrent initial conditions; i.e., the starting point of any one cycle is the same as that of the next cycle. As an example, we shall now examine the *RL* circuit of Fig. 1-3. The rectangular input shown has been applied for a sufficiently long time so that the output has already reached the final periodic form shown in Fig. 1-4.

The solution during either portion of the input signal is

$$e_2(t) = A + Be^{-t/\tau} \qquad \tau = \frac{L}{R}$$

Except for the time constant, this equation is of the same form as the one found for the RC circuit [Eq. (1-1)]. Since the inductance prevents abrupt changes in the current, the resistor voltage will be invariant across the discontinuities of the input and any abrupt jump in the driving voltage will be reflected across the coil. We can show this by considering the voltage drops around the loop:

$$e_1(t) = e_R + e_L = iR + e_L \tag{1-11}$$

Across the boundary of the two regions the input voltage jumps, and by considering this change as $\Delta e_1(t)$, we see that

$$\Delta e_1(t) = \Delta iR + \Delta e_L$$

But since the inductance constrains Δi to be zero, the complete jump in the input voltage must immediately appear across the inductance.

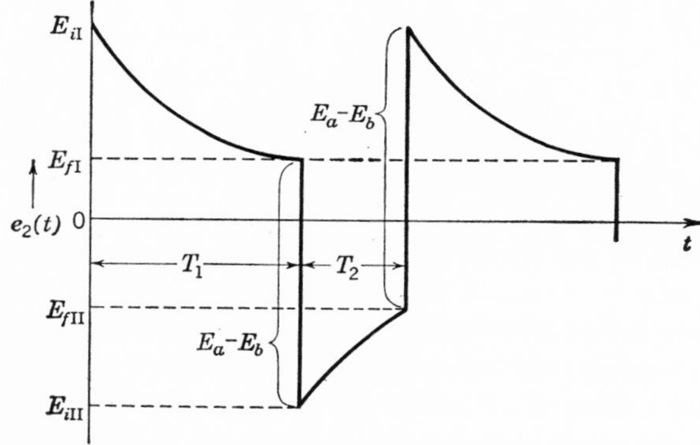

FIG. 1-4. Output voltage across L in the circuit of Fig. 1-3.

Starting the solution at the beginning of region I, which holds for $0_1 < t < T_1$, the first set of initial conditions is

$$E_{ssI} = 0 \qquad E_{iI} = \text{unknown}$$

Therefore the solution in this region is

$$e_{2I}(t) = E_{iI}e^{-t/\tau} \tag{1-12}$$

and the final value, occurring at $t = T_1$, may be expressed as

$$E_{fI} = e_{2I}(T_1) = E_{iI}e^{-T_1/\tau} \tag{1-13}$$

Upon entering region II, the input voltage drops from E_a to E_b, with the same change immediately appearing across the inductance. The final output of region I was E_{fI}. The initial value of region II must be

$$E_{iII} = E_{fI} - (E_a - E_b)$$

In region II, holding for $0_2 < t < T_2$, $E_{ssII} = 0$. The equation for the time response can be written

$$e_{2II}(t) = [E_{fI} - (E_a - E_b)]e^{-t/\tau} \tag{1-14}$$

At $t = T_2$,

$$E_{fII} = e_{2II}(T_2) = [E_{fI} - (E_a - E_b)]e^{-T_2/\tau} \tag{1-15}$$

But the initial voltage of region I, and all other voltages which have been written in terms of it, are still unknown. We must now apply the known conditions of periodicity in order to find the final answer. At the end of region II the input voltage jumps from E_b to E_a and the output voltage changes by the same amount. Periodicity tells us that the new value upon reentering region I is the original assumed E_{iI}.

$$E_{iI} = E_{fII} + (E_a - E_b) \tag{1-16}$$

Substituting Eq. (1-16) into (1-13) results in

$$E_{fI} = [E_{fII} + (E_a - E_b)]e^{-T_1/\tau} \tag{1-17}$$

Equations (1-15) and (1-17) each involve only the two unknowns E_{fI} and E_{fII}; all other terms are constants of the input waveshape or the circuit. The simultaneous solution of the above equations completes the analysis.

If the output of interest were taken across the resistor instead of the inductance, the technique of solution would still be the same, the principal difference being in the initial conditions over each portion of the cycle. Current is continuous, and therefore resistor voltage must also be continuous in the RL circuit. RC series circuits are treated in a similar manner, applying, however, their special boundary conditions; i.e., all voltage jumps appear across the circuit resistance.

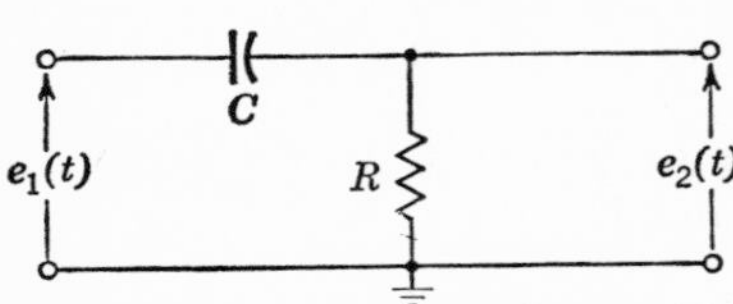

FIG. 1-5. Differentiator.

Even when the inputs are nonrectangular, the shape and equation of their response over any period or portion thereof usually can be obtained by many convenient methods. The known periodicity supplies the additional information necessary for a complete solution.

1-4. Differentiation. A series RC circuit (Fig. 1-5) will, contingent on the satisfaction of certain conditions, have an output approximately proportional to the derivative of the input. These conditions may best be determined by examination of the circuit differential equation

$$e_2(t) = Ri = e_1(t) - \frac{1}{C}\int i\,dt \tag{1-18}$$

Since the voltage across a resistor is directly proportional to the current flow through it, for the output to be proportional to the derivative, the current must also have this relationship. Satisfaction of this necessary condition is made possible only by maintaining the output voltage small with respect to the input. Then from Eq. (1-18),

$$e_1(t) \cong \frac{1}{C} \int i\, dt$$

Therefore

$$i \cong C \frac{de_1(t)}{dt}$$

and

$$e_2 \cong RC \frac{de_1(t)}{dt} \tag{1-19}$$

The major portion of the circuit voltage drop is developed across C only when the time constant is small compared with the time range of interest. At discontinuities the total change of input voltage appears at the output and the circuit only roughly approximates a differentiator.

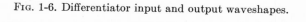

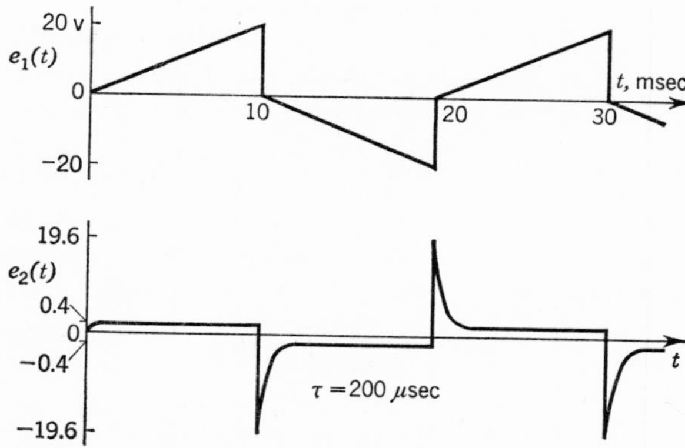

FIG. 1-6. Differentiator input and output waveshapes.

With a sufficiently small time constant, the exact output waveshape is reasonably close, except at the discontinuities, to the one found by assuming a perfect differentiator. The exact derivative at a discontinuity of the input waveshape is infinity. Since instantaneous jumps do not exist in nature, the full change in the input voltage, which appears across the output at the input "discontinuities," is so very much larger than the normal small output signal that the circuit may well be said to approximate the derivative even here. Thus, after checking the time constant against the input waveshape, the output can be drawn by inspection and the voltage values calculated later. Figure 1-6 illustrates this process for an RC circuit having a time constant of 200 μsec.

Because the capacitor will not pass direct current, the periodic response to periodic inputs must have zero average value. The capacitor will store a charge proportional to the average level of the input signal, and its voltage will fluctuate almost between the input extremes.

An RL series circuit having a small time constant also differentiates. Here the output must be taken across the inductance because the basis of differentiation in this circuit is the proportionality of the inductive voltage to the time rate of the circuit current change. By maintaining almost the full input voltage drop across the series resistor, we ensure the current's dependency only on this resistance and guarantee good differentiation.

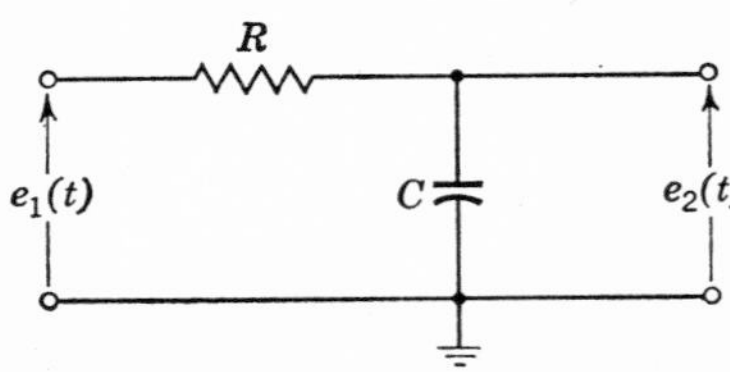

FIG. 1-7. Integrator.

1-5. Integration. Provided that the time constant is very long, the capacitor voltage in a series RC circuit is proportional to the integral of the input voltage (Fig. 1-7). Again the required condition may be found from an examination of the circuit differential equation

$$e_2(t) = \frac{1}{C} \int i \, dt = e_1(t) - Ri \tag{1-20}$$

When the output is small compared with the input, the approximate relationship

$$e_1(t) \cong Ri$$

results, and therefore

$$e_2(t) \cong \frac{1}{RC} \int e_1 \, dt \tag{1-21}$$

If the output voltage rises above a relatively small value, the current, $i = (e_1 - e_2)/R$, becomes dependent on e_2 and the circuit will no longer integrate satisfactorily. An excessively rapid rise in the output voltage within any period is directly dependent on the rate of charging of C. A slow charging rate remains possible only through keeping the time constant long compared with the time over which the integral is desired. C eventually charges to the d-c level of the input with the circuit time constant, and the output voltage shifts accordingly. For a signal impressed at $t = 0$, Fig. 1-8 shows both the input and its integrated output. Eventually the output will shift down until it has a zero average value.

The output voltage, at any time, is proportional to the area under the curve of the input signal from zero to that point. Consequently its shape may be sketched directly from the curve and the coordinates found from Eq. (1-21). In order to calculate the voltage change at the output over any time interval, the input volt-time area is simply divided by the time constant.

A large-time-constant RL circuit also integrates with the small output voltage now appearing across R. Physical inductances always have associated winding resistance and, for large coils, appreciable stray

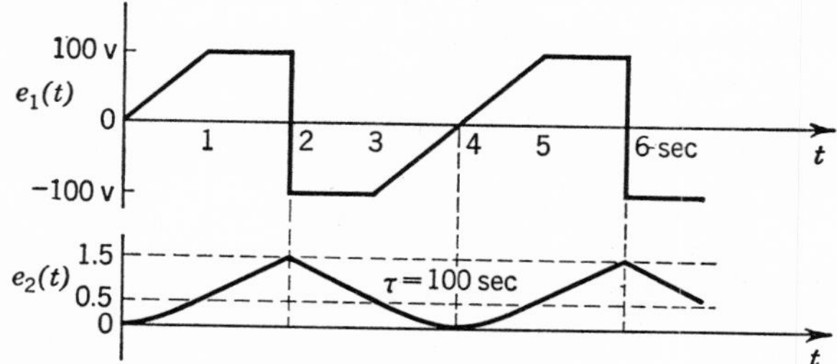

FIG. 1-8. Input signal and integrated output. Input applied at $t = 0$.

capacity. The impossibility of obtaining an ideal element usually precludes the use of RL circuits for many wave-shaping functions. On the other hand, almost ideal capacitors are readily available. Using the new plastic dielectrics, leakage resistance, the major parasitic element, is of the order of 10^5 megohms, a value so large that it may be ignored in most circuit calculations.

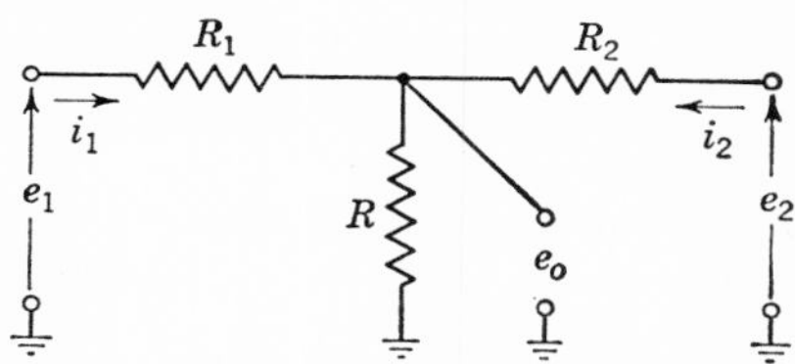

FIG. 1-9. Summation circuit.

1-6. Summation. After independent wave-shaping operations have been performed on various signals, combination is accomplished by summing the individual results. Of the several available methods, the simplest, shown for two inputs, uses the resistor network of Fig. 1-9. From the circuit we see that the two input currents are

$$i_1 = \frac{e_1 - e_o}{R_1} \qquad i_2 = \frac{e_2 - e_o}{R_2}$$

Provided that the output level is kept low compared with each of the inputs, the current through each input resistor is approximately independent of the output voltage. But this is possible only if $R \ll R_1$ and $R \ll R_2$. Almost the complete voltage drop appears across the input resistors, and

$$i_1 \cong \frac{e_1}{R_1} \qquad i_2 \cong \frac{e_2}{R_2} \tag{1-22}$$

The output becomes

$$e_o = R(i_1 + i_2) = \frac{R}{R_1} e_1 + \frac{R}{R_2} e_2 \tag{1-23}$$

Even when R is not small compared with the other resistors, the output voltage can still be found by the linear superposition of the individual terms. The circuit operates by converting the input voltage into a proportional current and then summing all the individual independent currents. Equation (1-23) shows the output's proportionality to the sum of the individual inputs, each of which is multiplied by a scale factor. Determination of this factor is through a choice of the input resistors R_1 and R_2. Summation may be extended to multiple inputs by simply adding additional input branches.

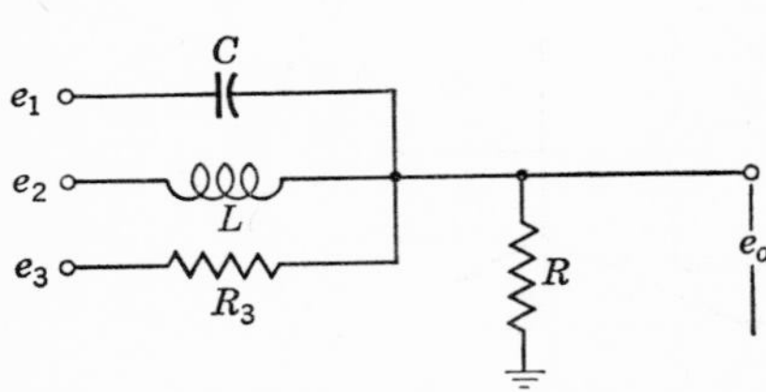

FIG. 1-10. Combined operations (differentiation, integration, summation).

The condition for summation, i.e., the output voltage small compared with each input, is exactly the same as that required for integration and differentiation, and all three operations may conveniently be combined in a single circuit as illustrated in Fig. 1-10. The output, expressed by Eq. (1-24), is found by calculating and sketching each term individually and summing the results; this is often carried out graphically.

$$e_o(t) = CR\frac{de_1}{dt} + \frac{1}{L/R}\int e_2\,dt + \frac{R}{R_3}e_3 \tag{1-24}$$

CR must be small and L/R very large compared with the time interval of the various signals. The inputs, if desired, may be supplied from the same source.

1-7. Approximate Solutions of the Single-energy Case. The results of the previous sections are quite valuable in that they open up two classes of single-energy-storage-element circuits to rapid solution. The first group consists of those with short time constants, the differentiators; the second, those with long time constants, the integrators. These two cases, representing only about 10 per cent of the possible range of RC or RL circuits, include, however, a much larger portion of the important engineering problems.

In handling a problem of this nature, our first step is to compare the time constant with the input signal and on the basis of this comparison to classify the circuit response. If it is a differentiator, the voltage across the resistor or inductance may be sketched by inspection, and the drop across the other circuit element is simply the difference between the applied input and the now known branch voltage. In an RC integrator, the voltage across C is the easily found quantity, with the resistor voltage remaining the single unknown. This is illustrated in Fig. 1-11, where the signal is assumed to be applied at zero time and where we shall apply the techniques of integration in finding the voltage across both R and C. Because C cannot pass direct current and e_R has a d-c level, the

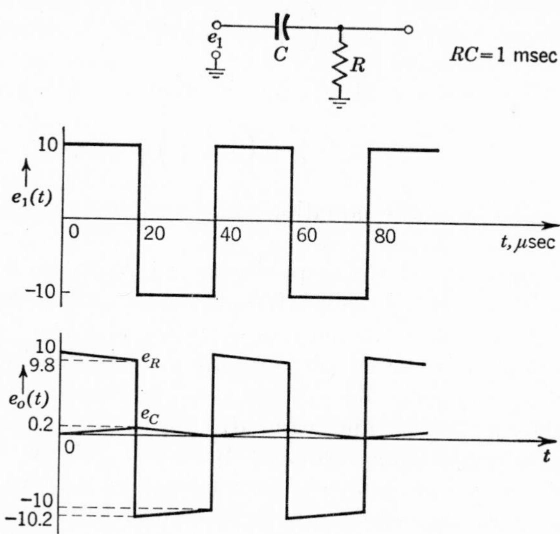

FIG. 1-11. Integrator circuit and approximate output.

output waveshapes sketched (Fig. 1-11) require a minor correction. The voltages must be shifted slightly until both have zero average value. Figure 1-12 shows the final periodic solution.

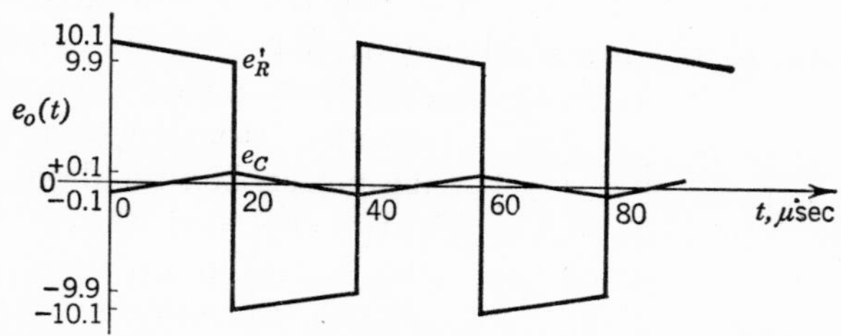

FIG. 1-12. Final periodic solution of the problem of Fig. 1-11.

It is often convenient to be able to express the response of a long-time-constant circuit to square or rectangular inputs as an equation. The exact solution of any single-energy-storage-element circuit is, of course,

$$e_o(t) = A + Be^{-t/\tau} \tag{1-25}$$

Substitution of the series expansion [Eq. (1-26)] for the exponential simplifies the final result. Since the time constant is long, provided that we restrict the ratio of the maximum interval to the time constant, t_m/τ, to less than 0.1, an error of less than 5 per cent is introduced by the neglect of the higher-order terms of the expansion.

$$e^{-t/\tau} = 1 - \frac{t}{\tau} + \frac{1}{2!}\left(\frac{t}{\tau}\right)^2 - \frac{1}{3!}\left(\frac{t}{\tau}\right)^3 + \cdots \tag{1-26}$$

Therefore, for $t/\tau < 0.1$, Eq. (1-25) may be approximated by

$$e_o(t) \cong A + B\left(1 - \frac{t}{\tau}\right) \tag{1-27}$$

which is recognizable as the equation of a straight line having a slope $-B/\tau$.

If the exact expression of the response [Eq. (1-25)] were differentiated and evaluated at $t = 0$, the slope found would be the same as that obtained from the first term in the series expansion. The interpretation which follows is that if the circuit response is restricted in time to the beginning of the exponential decay, this small portion of the curve may be represented by a straight-line segment.

1-8. Double-energy-storage-element Systems. Many circuits containing two energy-storage elements have poles separated widely enough so that the transient response can be approximated by treating them as two isolated single-energy circuits. Of course there must be continuity across the boundary between the two individual response curves and they must satisfy the original system. The pole which is located far from the origin (small time constant) will determine the circuit's behavior with respect to any fast changes in the input excitation. It predominantly controls the initial rise. The pole which is located close to the origin is related to the low-frequency response of the system and will contribute a slow exponential to the output. It will determine the holding power, i.e., the decay rate.

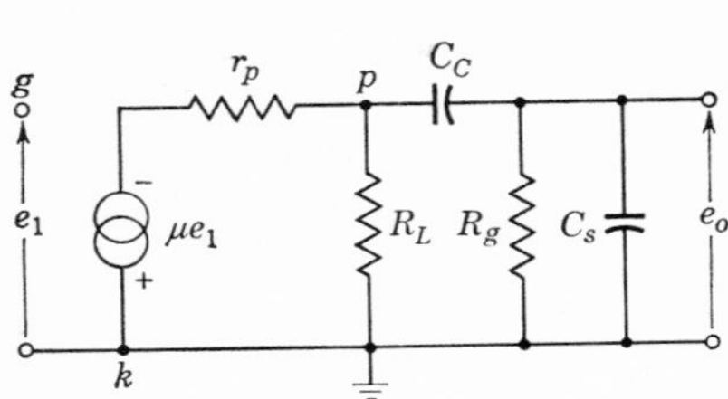

FIG. 1-13. Incremental model for an RC-coupled amplifier.

In effecting the separation of the system response into two time regions, we shall have to depend on the physical characteristics of the energy-storage elements for clues as to the permissible approximations. This technique is best illustrated by an example, and to this end we shall analyze the simple RC-coupled amplifier whose incremental model is shown in Fig. 1-13.

Consider the application of a voltage step of height $-E$ at the grid of the tube. The output is constrained in its time rate of rise primarily by C_s. We see from the circuit (Fig. 1-13) that the full charging current of C_s together with any current through R_g must also flow through C_c.

If, as is normally the case, R_g is very large, the total charge flow just after the excitation is applied is essentially determined by the uncharged shunt capacity C_s. The same charge is also accumulated in C_c. Since $C_c \gg C_s$, the voltage across C_c will change but slightly while C_s charges fully. Thus the coupling capacitor may be assumed to be a short circuit during this entire interval and the equivalent circuit is reduced to one containing a single-energy-storage element (Fig. 1-14).

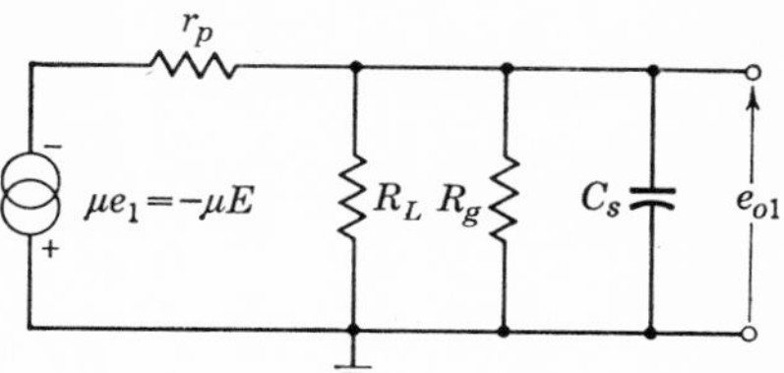

FIG. 1-14. Rise equivalent circuit.

The final steady-state output and the circuit time constant are found by taking the Thévenin equivalent across C. They are

$$E_{ss1} = \frac{\mu R_L \parallel R_g}{r_p + R_L \parallel R_g} E \qquad \tau_1 = C_s(R_g \parallel R_L \parallel r_p) \tag{1-28}$$

The parallel lines indicate that the adjacent elements are in parallel; for example, $R_L \parallel R_g = R_L R_g/(R_L + R_g)$. This notation will be used throughout in an attempt to keep the circuit-element relationships apparent in any equations which will be written.

We are now in a position to write the equation defining the initial portion of the output response.

$$e_{o1} = E_{ss1}(1 - e^{-t/\tau_1}) \tag{1-29}$$

In four time constants, the output rises to 98 per cent of the steady-state value E_{ss1} and the initial rise may be assumed complete.

During this whole interval, C_c is charging, even though it is doing so very slowly. The relatively large current required (because of the large value of C_c) will now control the output voltage and swamp any contribution from the discharge of C_s. We are justified in ignoring C_s and in removing it from the circuit. If the initial value of the output across R_g, upon the sudden excitation of the system, is now calculated, we also find it to be E_{ss1}. As C_c charges, the output decays toward zero, with the new time constant

$$\tau_2 = C_c(R_g + R_L \parallel r_p) \tag{1-30}$$

Thus the equation defining the final portion of the response may be written by inspection.

$$e_{o2} = E_{ss1}e^{-t/\tau_2} \tag{1-31}$$

The only question remaining unanswered is, At what point will the decay take over from the initial rise? If we compare Eqs. (1-28) and (1-30), we see that both the capacity and the resistance terms of τ_2

are much larger than τ_1. Since the decay time constant is so very much longer, the error introduced by starting the decay anywhere in the vicinity of zero will be negligible. We might just as well choose the most convenient point, the end of the initial rise, that is, $4\tau_1$. The total output is sketched in Fig. 1-15.

The exact solution, the dashed line, shows the greatest deviation at the peak asymptotically approaching the approximate solution at both long and short times. By the very nature of the assumption made, i.e., complete charge before any discharge, the exact answer will always lie below the approximate one. As the separation of time constants increases, agreement between the two answers improves. For $\tau_2 > 100\tau_1$, as is normal in this type of amplifier, agreement is extremely good.

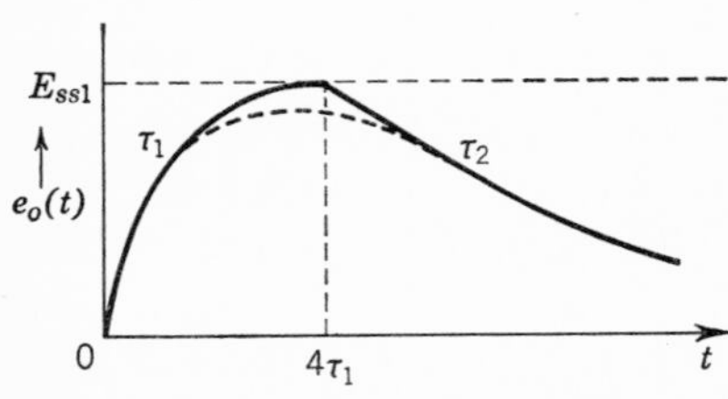

FIG. 1-15. RC-coupled amplifier output—step excitation.

When an amplifier is used in pulse applications, the time response, rather than the related high-frequency 3-db point, is used to characterize its quality. Even if the amplifier transmits all signals faithfully, it may still delay them by a fixed time interval; this delay will also be considered as a defining quantity. Generally, the shape of the output will be affected, and in order to separate the rise time from the inherent delay, we choose the 10 per cent value as our lower reference point. Moreover, the applied pulse makes its presence known long before the output reaches steady state; the 90 per cent point is therefore arbitrarily chosen as the upper reference value. An amplifier's rise time is defined as the time required for the output to rise from 10 to 90 per cent of the final steady-state voltage, after the excitation by a unit step. Substituting these limits into and solving Eq. (1-29) gives the rise time of a single stage as

$$t_r = 2.2\tau_1 \tag{1-32}$$

The smaller the time constant, the faster the initial rise rate. The rise time ranges from several microseconds in an audio amplifier down to a few millimicroseconds in systems designed primarily for pulse amplification.

When the input is a square wave, the amplifier output must eventually become periodic. The stray capacity present slows the rise of the leading edge, and the coupling capacity introduces some tilt on the flat top. The rise time of each half period will be the same as that given by Eq. (1-32) for the unit step. However, the amount of tilt depends on the duration of the half cycle and must be defined in terms of the wave period. If the half period $T/2$ is small compared with the decay time constant

τ_2, only a very small decay will occur over each half cycle, and this may be approximated by a straight line. From Eq. (1-27), the linear representation of this region, we find that the initial value of the top is B (A represents the steady-state value, which in this case is zero). The final value, at the end of each half cycle, becomes $B(1 - T/2\tau_2)$. Tilt is defined as the relative slope of the top of the square wave and is

$$S = \frac{E_i - E_f}{E_i} = \frac{T}{2\tau_2} \tag{1-33}$$

S is often expressed as a percentage. Measurement of the tilt for a given square-wave input serves as a convenient method of evaluating the holding response of an amplifier, just as a measurement of the rise time characterizes its high-frequency response.

1-9. Compensated Attenuators. Attenuation of signals through pure resistive networks generally proves unsatisfactory because of the stray capacity loading of the output (C_2 in Fig. 1-16). Instead of the rapid response to a step expected from a resistive attenuator, the output rises with a time constant

$$\tau = C_2[(R_1 + R_s) \parallel R_2]$$

toward the final value

$$E_{ss} = \frac{R_2}{R_1 + R_s + R_2} E$$

In order to prevent the source impedance from affecting the signal division, usually $R_1 \gg R_s$; otherwise a change from one network driving source to another would also result in a new attenuation ratio.

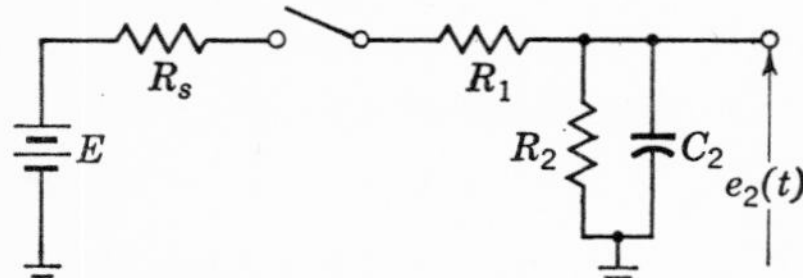

FIG. 1-16. Uncompensated attenuator.

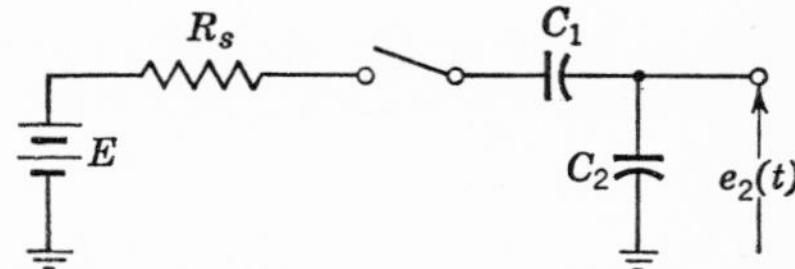

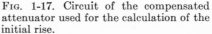

FIG. 1-17. Circuit of the compensated attenuator used for the calculation of the initial rise.

The attenuator response can be greatly improved by shunting R_1 with a small capacitor C_1. Since it furnishes a low-impedance path to the initial rise, the output will reach steady state much sooner. At the instant of closing the switch, the two uncharged capacitors are effectively short circuits. Since most of the current will flow through them, rather than through the parallel resistors, we shall remove R_1 and R_2 from the circuit while investigating the initial rise (Fig. 1-17). The output now rises with a time constant

$$\tau_1 = R_s \frac{C_1C_2}{C_1 + C_2} \tag{1-34}$$

toward

$$E_{ss1} = \frac{C_1}{C_1 + C_2} E \tag{1-35}$$

By assuming that steady state is reached before the decay begins, we can draw the model of Fig. 1-18 to represent the final portion of the response. In this circuit the initial charge on each capacitor is indicated.

The output now rises or decays from its initial value toward a steady-state value E_{ss2}.

$$E_{ss2} = \frac{R_2}{R_1 + R_2} E \tag{1-36}$$

The new time constant becomes

$$\tau_2 = (R_1 \parallel R_2)(C_1 + C_2) \tag{1-37}$$

Comparison of Eqs. (1-34) and (1-37) indicates that τ_2 is much longer than τ_1. C_1 and C_2 in parallel are obviously larger than the same two capacitors in series. R_s had been assumed small, so that the parallel combination of R_1 and R_2 will probably be the bigger term.

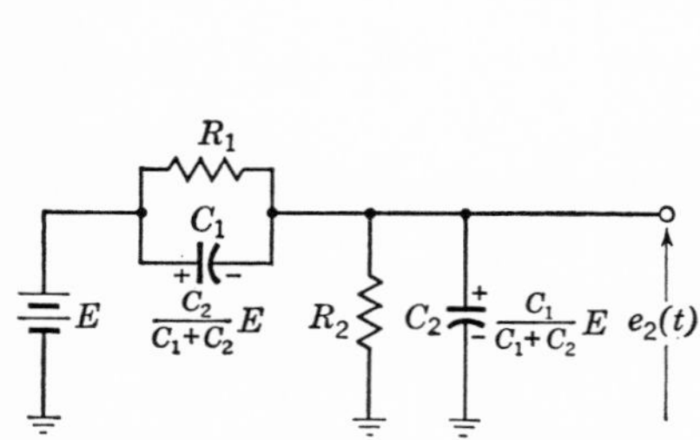

FIG. 1-18. Decay model—compensated attenuator.

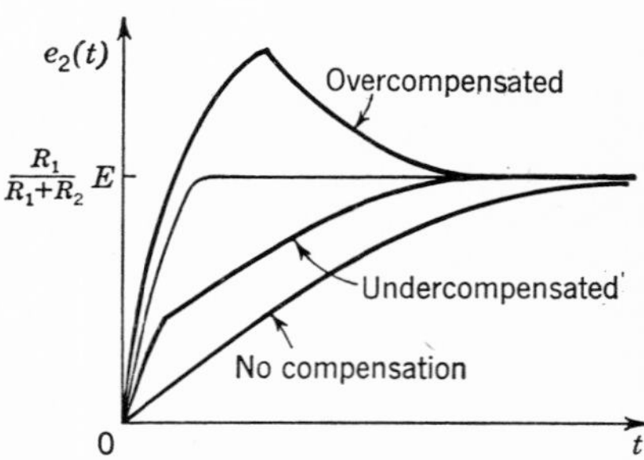

FIG. 1-19. Compensated-attenuator output (slightly exaggerated for purposes of illustration).

If the two steady-state values [Eqs. (1-35) and (1-36)] are equal, there will only be one transient, the initial rise. By equating these two voltages and solving, we arrive at the conditions for the optimum attenuator response,

$$R_1C_1 = R_2C_2 \tag{1-38}$$

Compensating the attenuator greatly improves the rise time, as shown in Fig. 1-19. When $R_1C_1 < R_2C_2$ the attenuator is overcompensated, introducing an overshoot. If we are interested in attenuation of triggers (sharp pulses), the overcompensated case is often desirable since it gives the fastest rise and the largest initial amplitude. Much to our regret, the RC-coupled amplifier cannot be compensated because r_p does not in fact exist as an entity across which a capacitor can be connected. Any external capacity added only parallels the existing strays. This simply increases the rise time, with a corresponding degeneration in the over-all response.

The initial rise time of the compensated attenuator is usually so short that it may be ignored. This leads to the assumption that the output instantaneously jumps to the point from which it starts decaying toward the final steady-state value.

Treating the same problem from the pole and zero viewpoint and neglecting the initial rise ($R_s = 0$), we see that the placing of C_1 across R_1 introduces a zero along the real axis. Proper adjustment moves it into coincidence with the pole determined by R_2C_2, annihilating that pole. Since the circuit no longer contains any poles, the response cannot be of exponential form but must be constant.

PROBLEMS

1-1. The switch in the circuit of Fig. 1-20 is closed at $t = 0$ and reopened at $t = 10$ msec.

(a) Sketch the voltage waveshape appearing across the capacitor, giving the values of all time constants and break voltages.

(b) Sketch the waveshape of the current flowing through the switch and evaluate the initial and final values of this current by using the information of part a. Do not solve the exponential-response equation in this part.

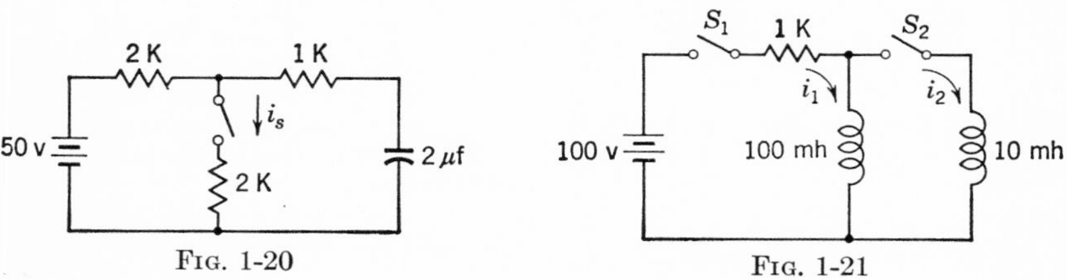

FIG. 1-20

FIG. 1-21

1-2. In Fig. 1-21, S_1 is closed at $t = 0$ and S_2 1 msec later. Evaluate and sketch on the same axis the current response of both inductances. Make whatever reasonable approximations are necessary to simplify the calculations, including changing the ideal elements to not-so-ideal elements which become ideal in the limit. Repeat if S_2 is closed 100 μsec after S_1.

1-3. The capacitor of Fig. 1-22 is initially charged to 50 volts with the polarity shown. The circuit is energized by closing S_1 at $t = 0$. When the output reaches

-10 volts, switch S_2 is closed. Draw the output voltage waveshape, indicating all time constants, and solve for the time delay between the closure of the two switches.

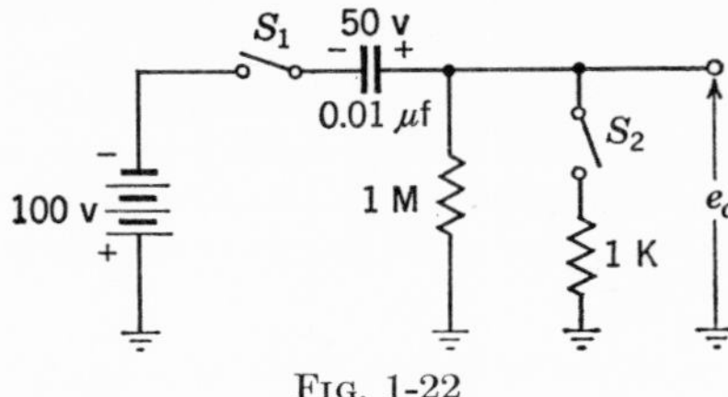

FIG. 1-22

1-4. Repeat Prob. 1-3 if the bottom of the 1-megohm resistor is returned to $+200$ volts with respect to ground instead of directly to ground. S_2 will now be closed when the output rises to zero. All other conditions remain unchanged.

1-5. A rectangular voltage wave, such as the one shown in Fig. 1-3, is the driving signal applied to a series RC circuit having a time constant of 10 msec. The 10-volt positive peak lasts for 30 msec, and the -2-volt negative peak for only 5 msec.

(a) Find the steady-state minimum and maximum voltages appearing across the capacitor.

(b) What voltage would be read on a d-c voltmeter connected across the capacitor? Explain your answer.

1-6. The excitation of a parallel RL circuit is a square wave of current having a peak-to-peak amplitude of 50 ma and a period of 200 μsec. The inductance is 1 henry, and the resistance 5 K.

(a) Sketch the steady-state node voltage and evaluate the maximum and minimum values.

(b) Find the power dissipated in the resistance.

1-7. The periodic current flowing in the series RLC circuit of Fig. 1-23 is given. What waveshape and values of excitation voltage must be applied to cause this current flow?

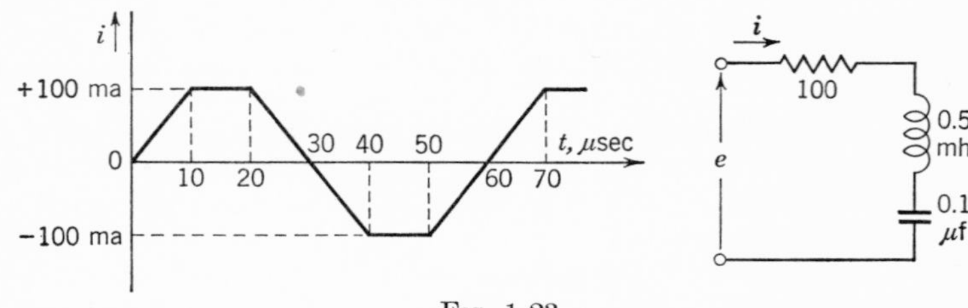

FIG. 1-23

1-8. A periodic triangular voltage of 200 volts peak to peak appears across the parallel RLC circuit shown in Fig. 1-24.

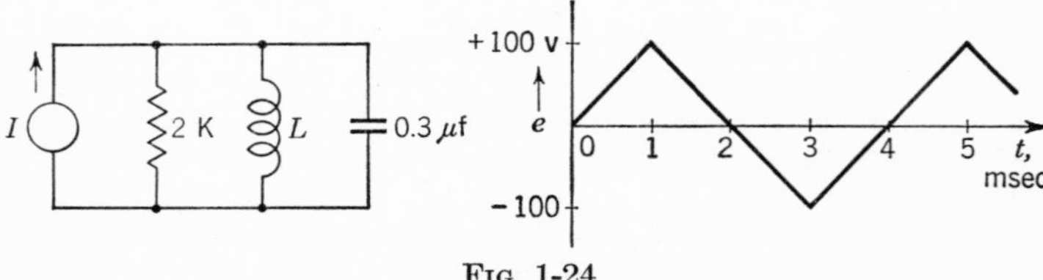

FIG. 1-24

(*a*) Calculate the inductance that will make the peak current supplied equal to 100 ma. (The d-c level of the input current is zero.)

(*b*) Sketch the current waveshape and give the values at all break points.

1-9. The nonperiodic signal shown in Fig. 1-25 is applied to a series *RC* circuit. Calculate the approximate response under the following conditions:

(*a*) The voltage across *C* when the time constant is 10 msec.

(*b*) The voltage across *R* when the time constant is 10 msec.

(*c*) The voltage across *R* when the time constant is reduced to 10 μsec.

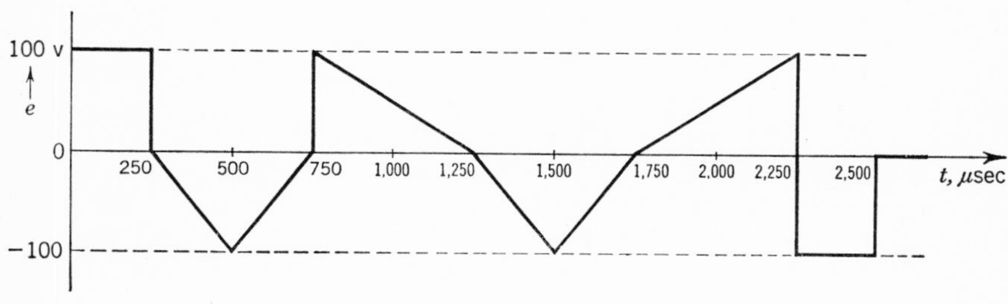

FIG. 1-25

1-10. (*a*) The triangular voltage of Fig. 1-24 is applied to an integrator circuit having a time constant of 25 msec. Sketch the steady-state voltage appearing across *C*.

(*b*) If a signal consisting of only the positive portion of the triangular wave of Fig. 1-24 were applied to this integrator, how long would it take for the output to rise to 9 volts?

1-11. (*a*) Under what conditions will one of the branch currents of a parallel *RC* circuit be proportional to the integral of the driving signal? Which branch?

(*b*) Show that a parallel *RC* circuit can also be used for current differentiation.

1-12. Repeat Prob. 1-11 with respect to a parallel *RL* circuit. Explain what further restrictions, if any, must be imposed as a result of using a nonideal inductance (winding resistance).

1-13. (*a*) A 100-volt symmetrical square wave having a period of 100 μsec is applied as the input to an integrator having a time constant of 10 msec. The output is coupled through an ideal isolation amplifier which multiplies the voltage by a factor of 50. The amplifier output is then passed through a differentiator having a time constant of 1 μsec. Sketch the ultimate output.

(*b*) The same circuits and input are again used except that the square wave is first differentiated, then integrated, and finally amplified. Sketch the output appearing in this case and explain any discrepancy between this answer and the one for part *a*.

1-14. The periodic waveshape of Fig. 1-6 is used as the input to the circuit of Fig. 1-5.

(*a*) Sketch and evaluate the output waveshape under the following conditions: $\tau = 400$ μsec, $\tau = 200$ msec.

(*b*) Drawing on the answers of part *a*, sketch, without evaluating, the output waveshape appearing when $\tau = 20$ msec. Justify your answer without finding the exact solution.

1-15. Two signals are combined in the summation circuit of Fig. 1-26. Draw the output, giving voltage values under the following conditions:

(*a*) The circuit is as shown below.

(*b*) We replace the 10-K resistor by a 0.05-μf capacitor.

(*c*) The circuit is further modified by also replacing the 500-K resistor with a 0.005-μf capacitor.

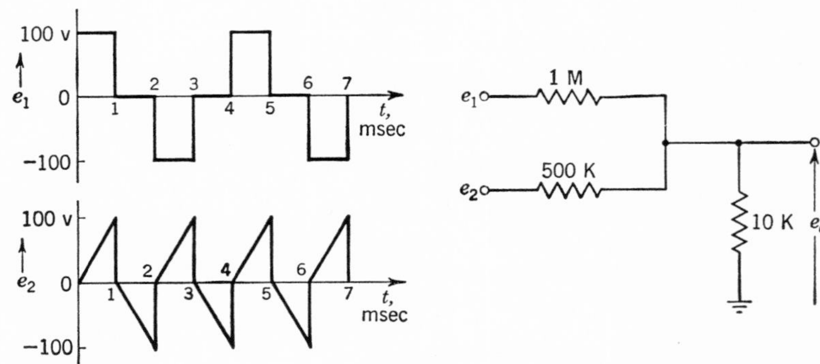

FIG. 1-26

1-16. We are interested in generating a reasonable approximation to the signal shown in Fig. 1-27. Under the conditions listed, find the circuit required and the values of components needed. Make your smallest resistor 10,000 ohms.

(*a*) The only signal available is e_2 of Fig. 1-26.

(*b*) The only signal available is a 200-volt peak-to-peak square wave of the proper period.

(*c*) Repeat parts *a* and *b* but use a series combination of circuit elements for the output branch instead of a summation-type circuit.

1-17. A single-stage amplifier having the equivalent circuit shown in Fig. 1-13 is excited by a 1-volt step at the grid. The tube and circuit components are $r_p = 10$ K, $\mu = 25$, $R_L = 20$ K, $R_g = 100$ K, $C_s = 200$ $\mu\mu$f, and $C_c = 0.01$ μf.

(*a*) Find the output response, giving all time constants and steady-state values, by the approximation method discussed in the text (time yourself).

(*b*) Solve for the exact response, using either classical or transformation methods, and compare both the time required and the accuracy of solution with those found in part *a*.

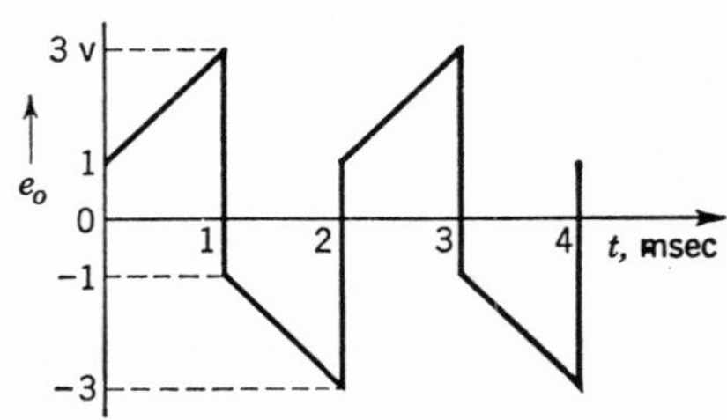

FIG. 1-27

1-18. In the circuit of Fig. 1-28, a unit step of current is applied at $t = 0$. Find i_2. Sketch your answer and give all time constants and steady-state values. Justify the approximations made in the course of your solution.

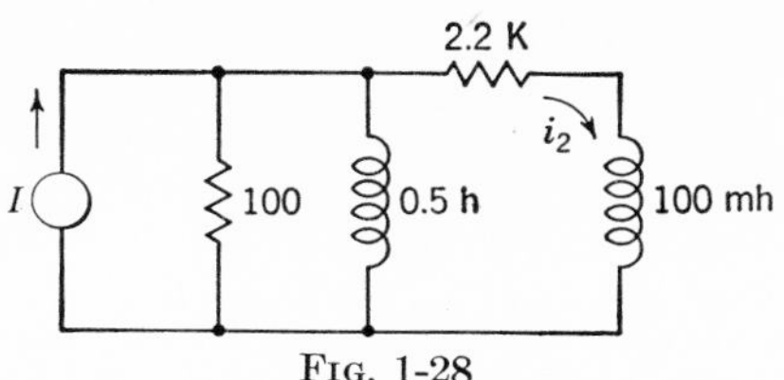

FIG. 1-28

1-19. (*a*) Derive Eqs. (1-30) and (1-33).

(*b*) Calculate the rise time of the amplifier of Prob. 1-17.

(*c*) What is the lowest-frequency square wave that would be transmitted without introducing more than 5 per cent tilt? Sketch the output if the peak-to-peak voltage is 10 volts. Give the actual voltage values.

(*d*) In order for a pulse to register its presence at some later point in the system, at least 80 per cent of it must be transmitted by the amplifier of Prob. 1-17. What is the narrowest pulse that may be used, and how will it appear after passing through the amplifier?

1-20. Find the output response of the circuit of Fig. 1-29 if the input is a 100-volt peak-to-peak square wave having a period of 200 μsec and if L_1 is (*a*) 100 mh, (*b*) 500 mh, (*c*) 400 mh. Plot the three waveshapes to scale on the same graph.

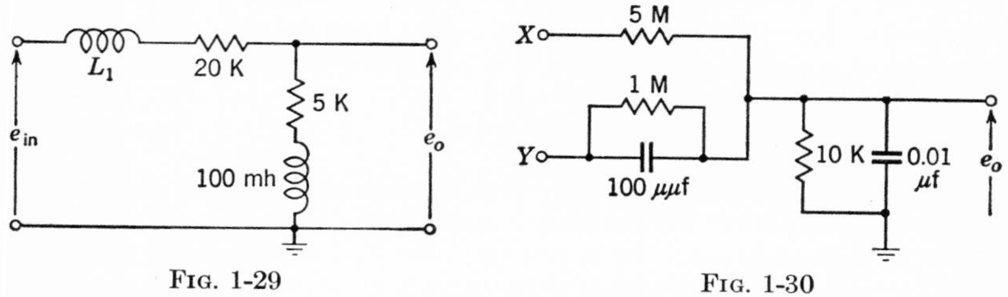

FIG. 1-29

FIG. 1-30

1-21. The two input signals of Fig. 1-26 are applied to the circuit of Fig. 1-30.

(*a*) Sketch the steady-state output, giving all voltage values when e_1 is connected to terminal X and e_2 to terminal Y.

(*b*) Repeat part *a* if a 20-$\mu\mu$f capacitor is inserted across the 5-megohm resistor.

(*c*) Repeat part *b* with the two signals interchanged.

BIBLIOGRAPHY

Brenner, E., and M. Javid: "Analysis of Electric Circuits," McGraw-Hill Book Company, Inc., New York, 1959.

Guillemin, E. A.: "Introductory Circuit Theory," John Wiley & Sons, Inc., New York, 1953.

CHAPTER 2

DIODE WAVE-SHAPING TECHNIQUES

Wave-shaping functions performed by purely linear circuits—differentiation, integration, summation, and not much else—are relatively limited. If at some point within any operation we could, at will, change the value of even one circuit component, there would result a tremendous increase in the possible shapes of the output produced. For example, if in the middle of integrating a signal, the time constant were suddenly to be greatly decreased, then the circuit would immediately become a differentiator, with a resultant total output that could not possibly be produced in a purely linear circuit. When considering periodic inputs, the component changes should be voltage- or current-controlled, e.g., a bivalued resistor—a high resistance at voltages below a threshold value and low resistance thereafter, or vice versa. Otherwise, the circuit change would not occur at the same voltage point of each cycle and a periodic output would not result from the periodic input. One method of obtaining this response is through the use of two resistors and a switch, which is thrown from one to the other and back again as the circuit voltage rises or drops past the threshold value. Of course, for fast complex waveshapes, mechanically operated switches could not possibly operate rapidly enough, and how could we throw the switch continuously?

Conveniently for us, there exist a number of voltage-controlled nonlinear devices with approximately the properties desired. One of the most common of these devices is the diode, and in this chapter we propose to examine its application to various circuits, making use of its inherent nonlinearity.

2-1. Passive-nonlinear-circuit Representation. The response of any network to a forcing function is determined by the individual characteristics of the various components comprising that network. In the analysis of so-called linear circuits, ideal elements (resistors, capacitors, inductors, and voltage and current sources) are convenient fictions introduced to simplify engineering calculations. The actual physical elements are not only slightly nonlinear, but also include various parasitics; e.g., a capacitor contains lead and winding inductance and its capacity varies somewhat with the charge storage. Analogous characteristics may be detected in all other "linear" components. These minor second-order effects will cause at most a slight correction in the calculated ideal-network response. Their inclusion in the problem will, however, obscure the phenomena under examination beneath the complexity of the additional mathematics. Thus, in the interests of simplicity, we are completely justified in treating only ideal linear elements.

Following a similar argument, we can postulate the existence of an ideal nonlinearity, which we shall call the ideal diode, to account for the response of a large class of grossly nonlinear systems. This element has as much validity as our other circuit components and will be utilized in networks in much the same manner. It has the bivalued characteristics expressed both graphically and in equation form in Table 2-1. The ideal diode is an absolute short circuit for any positive current flow and an open circuit when the polarity across its terminals is negative (back-biased). Its volt-ampere plot consists of two connected segments with the break between the two regions occurring at $e_d = 0$ (or $i_d = 0$). Thus the ideal diode is identical with the voltage-controlled switch previously discussed, the switching value being zero volts.

TABLE 2-1

Element	Symbol	Defining equations	Volt-ampere characteristic
Ideal diode.......	i_d, $+\ e_d\ -$	$e_d = 0$ or $i_d \geq 0$ and $e_d \leq 0$ or $i_d = 0$	i, 0, e
Resistor.........	i, $+\ e_R\ -$	$e_R = iR$ or $i = Ge_R$	i, Slope G, 0, e
Voltage source...	$+\ e_s\ -$ or $+\ e_s\ -$	$e_s = \text{constant} = E$ or $e_s = e(t)$	i, 0, E, e
Current source...	i_s	$i_s = \text{constant} = I$ or $i_s = i(t)$	i, I, 0, e

Table 2-1 illustrates the schematic representation of the branch elements, with which we shall be concerned, together with their defining equations and volt-ampere plots.

The combined circuit response of these elements is found directly from Kirchhoff's voltage and current laws. Any number of elements in series must have the same current flow, and thus the total terminal voltage will be the sum of the individual drops measured at this current. A parallel arrangement has an input current that is the sum of the current flow in each branch evaluated at the common terminal voltage. The diode introduces constraints dictated by its nonlinearity.

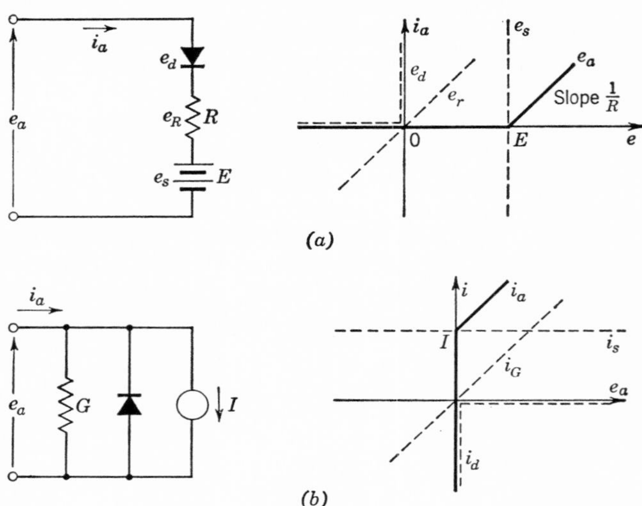

FIG. 2-1. Two biased diode circuits and their volt-ampere characteristics. (a) Series combination of elements; (b) parallel combination of elements.

Let us now consider the two examples shown below. In Fig. 2-1*a* the series diode limits the current flow to positive values, the battery shifts the break point to the right, and the resistor introduces a finite slope in the conduction region. Summing the individual equations given in Table 2-1 leads directly to the defining equations for the compound branch.

$$e_a = e_d + e_R + e_s$$

$$e_{a1} = E + i_a R \qquad \text{for } i_a \geq 0 \text{ or } e_a \geq E \tag{2-1a}$$

$$e_{a2} = e_d + E \qquad \text{for } i_a = 0 \text{ or } e_a \leq E \tag{2-1b}$$

Two equations are necessary because of the bivalued diode properties: one holds for the conduction region (2-1*a*), and the other for the back-biased zone (2-1*b*). They agree at the boundary point, which may be expressed in terms of the applied terminal voltage by setting $i = 0$ in Eq. (2-1*a*) and $e_d = 0$ in Eq. (2-1*b*). Figure 2-1*a* illustrates the graphical summation of the individual curves, i.e., the superposition of the element voltage drops. We might note that the voltage drops add normally in the positive current region but that the reverse-biased diode ($e_d < 0$) absorbs the total loop voltage.

Reversal of the diode would establish the conduction zone for negative rather than for positive currents, and reversal of the battery would shift the break point to the left instead of to the right. The diode connection determines the permissible current-flow direction, and the battery voltage only sets the break-point location.

In Fig. 2-1*b* the currents must be summed over the voltage range permitted by the diode (for negative voltages it is a short circuit forcing $e_a = 0$).

$$i_a = i_G + i_d + i_s$$

$$i_{a1} = Ge_a + I \qquad e_a \geq 0 \text{ or } i_a \geq I \tag{2-2a}$$

$$i_{a2} = i_d + I \qquad e_a = 0 \text{ or } i_a \leq I \tag{2-2b}$$

The shunt current source shifts the current coordinate of the break point to a positive value as shown in the graphical characteristic of Fig. 2-1*b*. Again, the diode restricts the region where graphical addition is necessary, in this case by introducing a short circuit upon conduction.

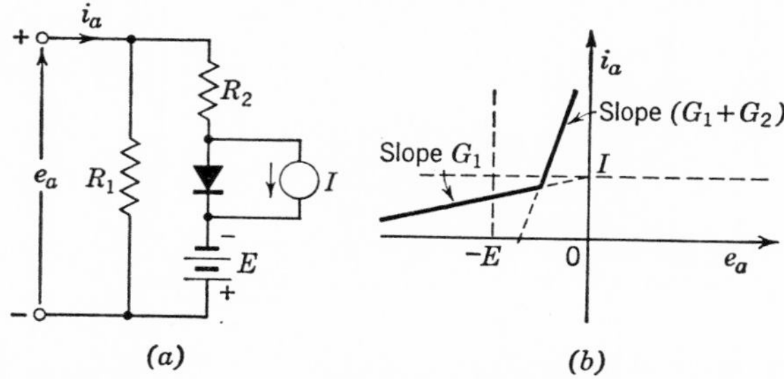

FIG. 2-2. (*a*) Combined biasing of piecewise-linear circuit; (*b*) volt-ampere characteristic.

Even if these circuits did not contain a nonlinear element, the intercepts of the series-resistance and parallel-conductance curves would still differ from zero by the value of the voltage and current biases, respectively. The addition of the diode only limits the portion of the total shifted curve which may be used.

In general, we can say that:

1. If there is no current source included across the diode, then one coordinate of the branch break point will always be the bias voltage contained in the diode branch.

2. If there is no voltage source included in a parallel arrangement of elements or branches, then one coordinate of the break point will always be the value of the current bias across the diode.

Combining parallel current and series voltage biasing with the single diode permits us to locate the break point anywhere in the volt-ampere plane. Moreover, by including both series and parallel padding resistance, the slopes in the two zones may be individually controlled (Fig. 2-2).

Suppose that we are interested in evaluating the input volt-ampere characteristic of any single diode circuit. How would we do so? We could, of course, solve the problem graphically, by summing the response of each element. For more complex circuits, such as the one shown in Fig. 2-2, this process may become somewhat tedious.

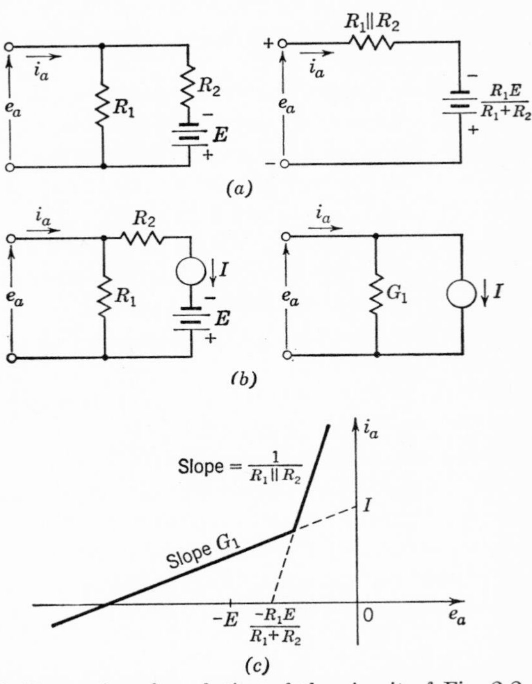

FIG. 2-3. Models illustrating the solution of the circuit of Fig. 2-2. (a) Equivalent circuit when diode conducts and the Thévenin equivalent circuit; (b) circuit when diode is back-biased and the Norton equivalent circuit; (c) composite volt-ampere characteristic.

For an algebraic solution, the simple diode circuit may be replaced by the two implicit resistive models, one of which holds when the diode conducts and the other when it is back-biased. By superposition from the model of Fig. 2-3a, where the current source is short-circuited by the conducting diode,

$$i_a = \frac{e_a}{R_1 \| R_2} + \frac{E}{R_2} \qquad i_d > 0 \tag{2-3}$$

From the second model (Fig. 2-3b), which holds for $e_d < 0$, we obtain the other defining equation,

$$i_a = \frac{e_a}{R_1} + I \tag{2-4}$$

The boundary between the regions is the intercept of the two straight lines whose equations are given by (2-3) and (2-4). This is shown graphically in Fig. 2-3c. Equating and solving for the terminal break value e_{ab} yields

$$e_{ab} = IR_2 - E$$

The current break coordinate i_{ab} can now be found by substituting e_{ab} into either defining equation.

We might observe that the break does not occur at the intersection of $i_a = I$ and $e_a = -E$. This is a direct consequence of the additional current flow through R_1 (due to E) and the additional voltage drop across R_2 (due to I). The reader might remove each resistor in sequence and observe the effect on the break-point location.

Each of the two models may be reduced to the Thévenin or Norton equivalent circuit, shown in Fig. 2-3, by algebraic manipulation. The open-circuit voltage or short-circuit current source is the value of the appropriate intercept, and the slope of the line segment is the resistance or conductance.

Since it is known that the volt-ampere curve consists of two linear contiguous segments, it follows that three pieces of information are sufficient to define these regions. Instead of writing the complete equation, we can simply solve for the coordinates of the break point and the two adjacent slopes. While doing so, attention must remain focused on the diode because its state controls the circuit behavior. Example 2-1 illustrates this technique for the circuit of Fig. 2-2.

Example 2-1. If we select the conducting state in Fig. 2-2 as our arbitrary starting point, the diode will short the current source and reduce the network to one containing two resistors and a voltage source (Fig. 2-3a). This occurs where the diode current is zero and where the current through R_2 equals I. Thus the break voltage is the total branch drop at this current flow,

$$e_{ab} = IR_2 - E$$

For $R_1 = 10$ K, $R_2 = 1$ K, $E = 25$ volts, and $I = 5$ ma,

$$e_{ab} = 1 \text{ K} \times 5 \text{ ma} - 25 \text{ volts} = -20 \text{ volts}$$

The other coordinate becomes the sum of the current through R_1, because of the applied break voltage e_{ab} and the bias current I. From Eq. (2-4),

$$i_{ab} = 5 \text{ ma} + \frac{-20}{10 \text{ K}} = 3 \text{ ma}$$

Within each region the slope is found by calculating the incremental conductance: first when the diode is conducting ($e_a > -20$), and next when it is back-biased ($e_a < -20$). These values are already indicated in Fig. 2-3c. In the forward region it is 1.1 millimhos, and in the back-biased zone it is only 0.1 millimho.

We conclude that once the nonlinear circuit is represented by a model containing a diode, we can write two sets of linear equations to describe the system response, one equation holding while the diode conducts and another when it is back-biased. These equations must coincide at the boundary point ($e_d = 0$); the continuous diode characteristic introduces no voltage or current discontinuity, and neither should the model or the equation. By using two regions to represent the nonlinear device, all theorems and techniques of the solution of linear circuits become applicable in each region. The only complexity introduced is that upon completion of a solution we must check to see that we have not left one linear region and entered another. If the circuit has done so, then the original equation, written for one region, will not hold and the answer will be incorrect. The problem must subsequently be reformulated and re-solved.

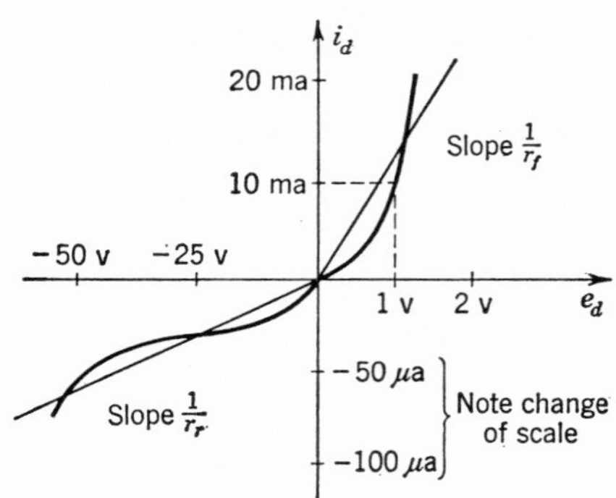

FIG. 2-4. Semiconductor diode characteristic.

2-2. Physical Diode Model. A semiconductor diode has volt-ampere characteristics of the type shown in Fig. 2-4. Note the scale change as voltage and current become negative. Vacuum-diode characteristics are similar, differing primarily in their having a much larger forward voltage drop and positive rather than negative reverse current.

Circuit analysis is greatly simplified once the actual characteristics are approximated by the two straight-line segments shown superimposed. When drawing these lines, it is convenient to start from the origin and intersect the actual characteristics at the center of the operating region. However, since this is only an approximation and the individual diode deviates rather widely from manufacturers' data, we find any reasonable set of lines acceptable for most purposes. Their slope has units of conductance. We conclude that the diode may reasonably be represented by two constant resistances, a forward resistance r_f, when $e_d > 0$, and an inverse resistance r_r, for $e_d < 0$. The change from one to the other takes place when the voltage across, and the current through, the diode drops to zero. Thus the model formulation makes use of the ideal diode

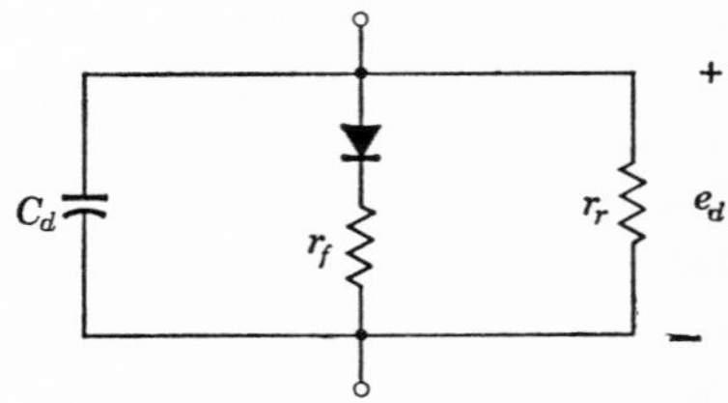

FIG. 2-5. Diode model representation.

as the switching element (Fig. 2-5); it shunts the very large r_r with the much smaller r_f upon conduction at $e_d \geq 0$. Therefore r_f and r_r in parallel are almost exactly equal to r_f. If this inequality did not happen to hold, in any particular case, we would modify the model by increasing the series resistance so that the parallel combination is the actual forward resistance of the diode. The capacitor shown in the model represents the major parasitic element present.

Forward-resistance values range from a fraction of an ohm to 250 ohms, and reverse resistance from about 25 K to 1 megohm, depending on the particular device. The lower values generally appear in power rectifiers, and the higher ones in general-purpose and switching diodes. Special-purpose diodes are available having very small forward and extremely large reverse resistances, and these very closely approximate an ideal device.

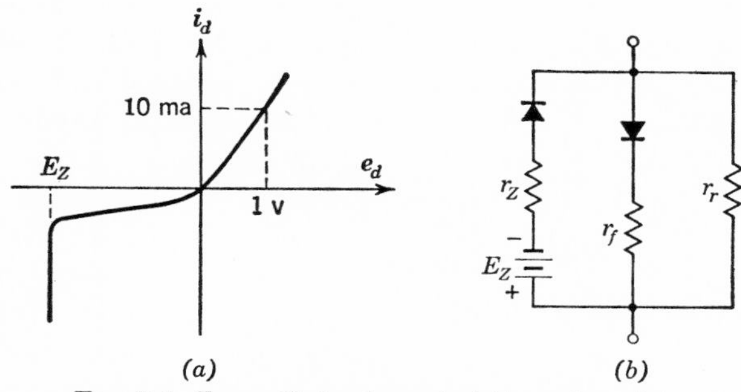

FIG. 2-6. Zener-diode characteristic and model.

Silicon diodes designed for operation into the Zener voltage region have the volt-ampere characteristics of Fig. 2-6*a*. It may be seen that three linear regions are necessary to define properly the complete curve, and therefore two ideal diodes are required in drawing its model (Fig. 2-6*b*). Generally, the small Zener-region resistance r_Z may, as a first approximation, be taken as zero.

2-3. Voltage Clipping Circuits. One of the most widely used nonlinear circuits utilizes the bivalued properties of the diode to control the signal amplitude. In the ideal shunt clipper of Fig. 2-7*a*, when the diode is back-biased, the shunt branch is opened and the input voltage is transmitted through R_1 to the output, unchanged and unaffected by the network.

On the other hand, once the rising input forces the diode into conduction, it may be replaced by a short circuit. The subsequent output is E, provided, however, that it is exceeded by the input. Thus the two zones of operation are, first, a transmission region where the output equals the input ($e_{o1} = e_{in}$) and, next, a clipped region where the output is determined solely by the bias ($e_{o2} = E$). These zones are plotted as the ideal transfer characteristic in Fig. 2-8.

Turning now to the physical diode clipper shown in Fig. 2-7*b*, the addition of r_r and r_f establish information transmission paths which are nonexistent in the ideal circuit. In each of the operating regions only one of the diode resistors need be considered and the actual output may be

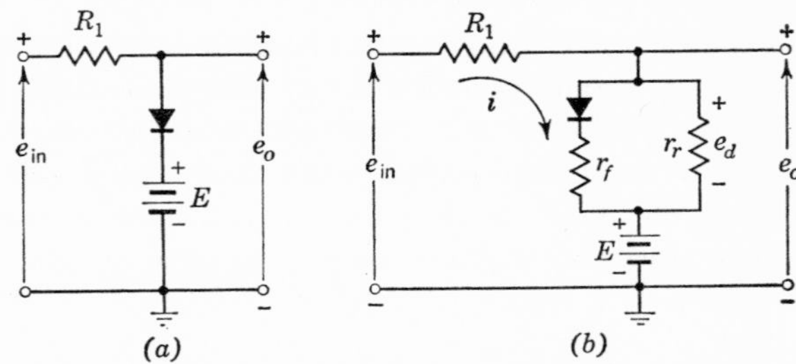

FIG. 2-7. Voltage clipping circuit (shunt diode). (*a*) Ideal model; (*b*) physical model.

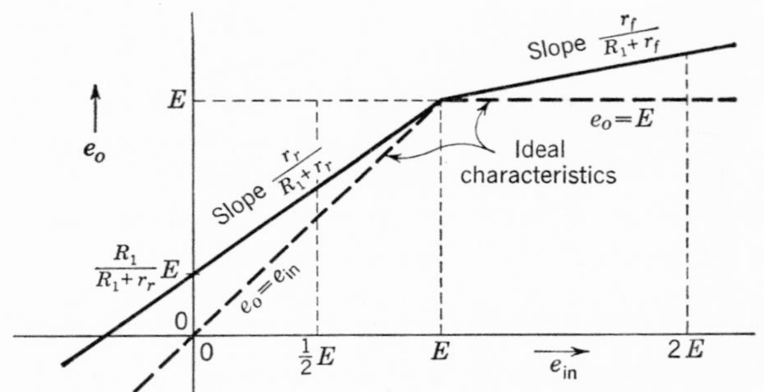

FIG. 2-8. Clipper transfer characteristics.

found by the linear superposition of the contributions from both voltage sources. When $e_{in} < E$ and the diode is back-biased,

$$e_{o1} = \frac{r_r}{R_1 + r_r} e_{in} + \frac{R_1}{R_1 + r_r} E \tag{2-5}$$

When conducting ($e_{in} > E$), the diode may be replaced by its forward resistance and the output voltage may be written

$$e_{o2} = \frac{R_1}{R_1 + r_f} E + \frac{r_f}{R_1 + r_f} e_{in} \tag{2-6}$$

Both equations, each defining the operation in an individual region, are straight lines, as shown in Fig. 2-8. At $e_{in} = E$, the break voltage, both Eqs. (2-5) and (2-6) give the output as E, proving the continuity of the transfer function.

A plot of Eqs. (2-5) and (2-6), the transfer characteristic of the clipper, appears in Fig. 2-8, with the ideal characteristic also presented for comparison. Examination of Eq. (2-5) indicates that within the transmission region, the finite diode reverse resistance results in an undesirable contribution to the output from the bias E. This contribution is the second term of the equation. In the clipping region, the second term of Eq. (2-6) represents the output contribution from the now undesired input. We are faced with the necessity of optimizing this circuit, helped in this by our knowledge of the behavior of the ideal circuit.

Freedom of choice is limited to selecting an optimum value for R_1. Rewriting Eqs. (2-5) and (2-6) in the form of (2-7) and (2-8) will aid in formulating the problem.

$$e_{o1} = \frac{r_r}{R_1 + r_r} e_{\text{in}} \left(1 + \frac{R_1}{r_r}\frac{E}{e_{\text{in}}}\right) \tag{2-7}$$

$$e_{o2} = \frac{R_1}{R_1 + r_f} E \left(1 + \frac{r_f}{R_1}\frac{e_{\text{in}}}{E}\right) \tag{2-8}$$

The term outside the parentheses in both Eqs. (2-7) and (2-8) consists of a constant multiplying the signal producing the desired output information in the several regions. We might consider the term inside the parentheses as representing the desired output (unity) plus a proportional error term. The error in both equations includes the ratio of the signal producing the undesired transmission to the signal producing the desired transmission. Equation (2-7) holds when the diode is nonconducting, and here this ratio is $E/e_{\text{in}} \geq 1$. In Eq. (2-8), defining the system response for diode conduction, the ratio of e_{in}/E is also greater than or equal to unity. Since the complete second terms of both equations represent the proportional error, they should, for optimum response, be made small compared with unity. The conditions on R_1 are contradictory: in Eq. (2-7) the optimum value becomes $R_1 = 0$, and in (2-8), $R_1 = \infty$.

We shall define the two error terms in the parentheses as

$$\epsilon_{o1} \equiv \frac{R_1}{r_r}\left(\frac{E}{e_{\text{in}}}\right)_1$$

and

$$\epsilon_{o2} \equiv \frac{r_f}{R_1}\left(\frac{e_{\text{in}}}{E}\right)_2$$

To resolve the contradiction, "a" compromise choice for R_1 will be designated the optimum value. One possibility is a resistance that results in error terms of the same magnitude in both equations when the ratio of the signal producing the undesired output to the signal producing the desired output is the same, or $\epsilon_{o1} = \epsilon_{o2}$ when

$$\left(\frac{E}{e_{\text{in}}}\right)_1 = \left(\frac{e_{\text{in}}}{E}\right)_2$$

Consequently, the compromise value becomes

$$R_1 = \sqrt{r_f r_r} \tag{2-9}$$

Substituting Eq. (2-9) back into the proportional-error terms yields

$$\epsilon_{o1} = \sqrt{\frac{r_f}{r_r}}\left(\frac{e_{\text{in}}}{E}\right)_1 \qquad \text{and} \qquad \epsilon_{o2} = \sqrt{\frac{r_f}{r_r}}\left(\frac{E}{e_{\text{in}}}\right)_2$$

We conclude that for clipping circuits a diode with the highest ratio of inverse to forward resistance represents the best choice. In any individual circuit, the series resistance used may not be the one found above; particular constraints may dictate a value closer to zero or to infinity.

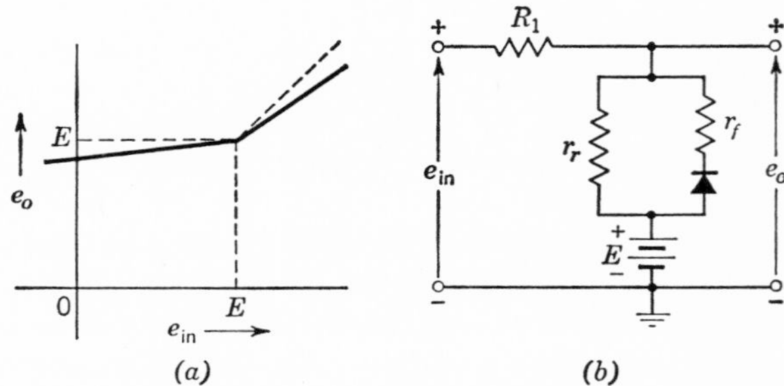

FIG. 2-9. Negative clipper transfer characteristic and circuit.

The use of the Zener region of the diode in addition to the forward-conduction region sets two clipping values instead of one. One point is located at $e_d = 0$, and the other at $e_d = E_z$, as indicated in the volt-ampere characteristics (Fig. 2-6). Biasing this diode shifts both break points in the same direction while still maintaining their original separation. It follows that one difficulty facing us is the lack of individual control over the slopes in the two conduction regions. Any series resistance added contributes equally to the Zener region and the diode forward-current region. Generally, for versatility of adjustment, two individual diodes are preferred to one Zener diode. However, the constant voltage drop in the Zener region does avoid the necessity for inserting a separate bias source.

When the diode in Fig. 2-7 is reversed, the clipping region is below the break point; the diode now conducts through its forward resistance r_f until $e_{\text{in}} \geq E$. After conduction ceases, a transmission path through the reverse resistance still exists, and the final result is the transfer characteristic given in Fig. 2-9. Here the signal is clipped below the bias voltage and transmitted above. Reversing the polarity of the bias voltage E only shifts the break point of the transfer characteristic to the third quadrant. We conclude that *the direction of the diode connection determines whether clipping will be below or above the bias value and that the bias voltage determines the actual clipping point.*

Series clipping, a possible circuit variation, gives results similar to those found for the previously discussed shunt clipping. Insertion of the diode in series with the transmission path (Fig. 2-10) allows transmission while it conducts, in this case for $e_{in} \leq E$. When back-biased, the diode introduces a high series impedance as the means of limiting the signal output. In this respect it behaves just opposite to the shunt clipper, which stops transmission upon conduction. The transfer characteristic of the circuit of Fig. 2-10 is of nearly identical shape with that of the shunt clipper of Fig. 2-7 (differing in the slopes), and the optimum value of R_1 will also be the same as that discussed above.

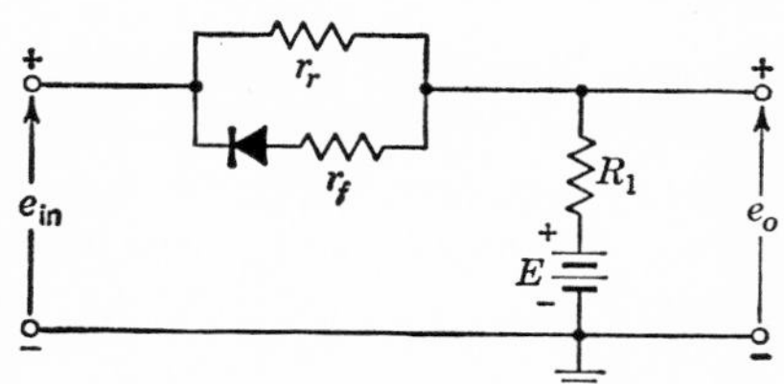

FIG. 2-10. Series clipper circuit.

2-4. Single Diode and Associated Energy-storage Element—Some General Remarks. In the solution of circuits containing both ideal diodes and energy-storage elements, notice must always be taken of the immediate past history as well as of the present excitation. The storage element should be considered as a memory which contains information stored in the past and which permits history to play a role in determining the present and future state of the circuit.

Our mode of attack follows the principle of time-zone superposition developed in Chap. 1. First the initial state of the circuit is determined; next the network is solved for the time at which the diode will change state.

Thereafter we simply treat the new circuit with the new time constant and initial conditions. The energy-storage element adds constraints to the continuity of current or voltage across the circuit and/or excitation changes and in this manner contributes to the new initial values.

Example 2-2. We shall now consider the problem posed in Fig. 2-11, where the initial voltage across the capacitor is 100 volts (its polarity is indicated in the sketch) and where the negative 50-volt 1-msec pulse is applied at $t = 0$. The capacitor charge remains constant across the instant of pulse application, and thus the output drops from -100 to -150 volts. Since the diode remains back-biased, the voltage immediately starts rising toward $+300$ volts with a time constant of $\tau_1 = 1$ msec (0.01 μf $\times$ 100 K). The defining equation becomes

$$e_{o1} = 300 - 450e^{-t/\tau_1}$$

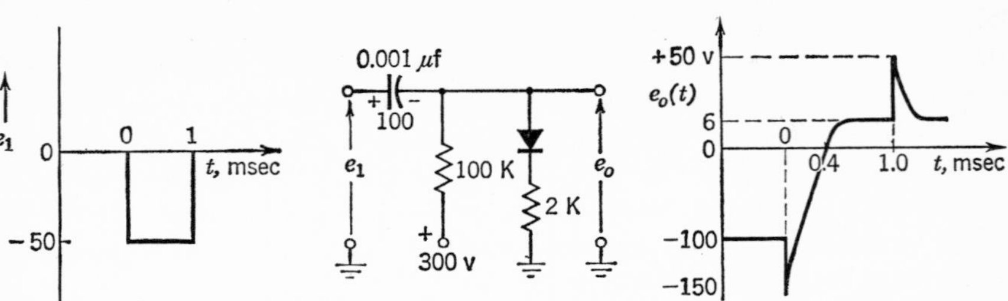

FIG. 2-11. Diode and capacitor circuit for Example 2-2, showing an input and the resultant output waveshape.

Eventually the output reaches zero, the diode conducts, and the circuit changes. Solving the above equation for the time at which $e_{o1} = 0$,

$$t_1 = \tau_1 \ln {}^{450}\!/_{300} = 0.405 \text{ msec}$$

In the new circuit the output voltage will charge toward the Thévenin equivalent value of

$$E_{Th} = \frac{2\text{ K}}{102\text{ K}} 300 \cong 6 \text{ volts}$$

with a new time constant $\tau_2 = 2$ μsec (2,000 ohms × 0.001 μf). We can assume that the circuit reaches this value in 8 μsec and that it will remain there until the excitation again changes.

At the termination of the pulse ($t = 1$ msec), the input rises by 50 volts and this same jump is coupled by C to the output. Since this does not change the diode state, the output recovers to 6 volts with the short conduction time constant of 2 μsec. The complete waveshape is shown in Fig. 2-11.

If a capacitor were placed across the diode, then the charge stored in it would maintain the diode state invariant for some time after the excitation change. An inductance in series would produce a similar effect by sustaining the current flow. We conclude that the location as well as the type of energy-storage element employed directly influences the nonlinear behavior of a single-diode system. In any analysis great care should be taken to see that the controlling factor, the diode state, is always kept in view.

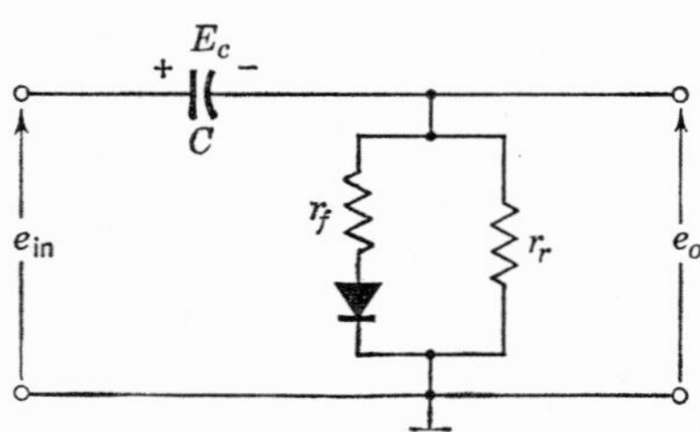

FIG. 2-12. Diode voltage clamp.

Some practical widely used circuits employing various energy-storage elements will be discussed in detail in the sections below (2-5, 2-7, and 2-9), and they will further illustrate the modes of solution.

2-5. Diode Voltage Clamps. The function of the diode clamp of Fig. 2-12 is to shift the input voltage in such a manner that the resultant maximum value of the output will be maintained at zero, without at the same time distorting the waveshape. The output voltage is then said to be clamped negatively at zero. Sketches of typical input and output waves appear in Fig. 2-13.

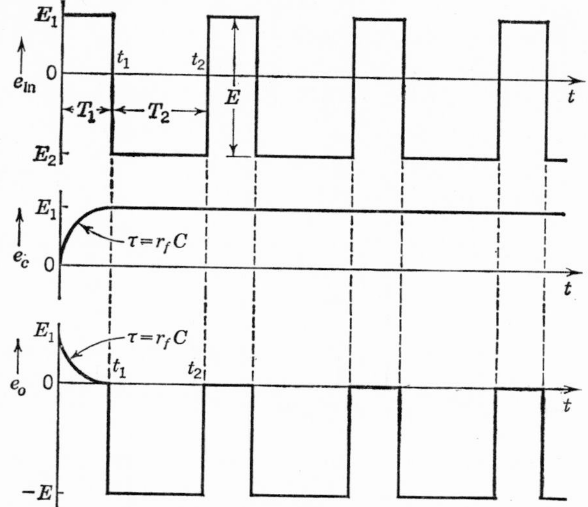

FIG. 2-13. Ideal-diode clamping waveshapes.

In the initial discussion we shall idealize the clamp at least to the extent of assuming that $r_r = \infty$. Upon application of the input signal, C charges to the peak positive value of the input with the time constant Cr_f. Provided that this time constant is sufficiently short, charging will be completed within the first cycle; otherwise it may take several cycles. Upon completion of the charging, the voltage across the diode becomes

$$e_d = e_o = e_{\text{in}} - E_c = e_{\text{in}} - E_1 \tag{2-10}$$

The conclusion drawn from Eq. (2-10) is that the output will always be less than or equal to zero since the voltage across the capacitor, E_1, is the maximum positive value of e_{in}. Diode conduction ceases once C is fully charged with the diode subsequently remaining back-biased. The output never exceeds zero, and it is said to be clamped there. For a rectangular-wave input, the clamping action is illustrated in Fig. 2-13. The diode serves first to introduce a low-resistance path for charging, and then a very-high-resistance one, preventing the discharge of C. Since the output is simply the sum of the capacitor and the input voltage, the signal-level shift in the clamp is provided through the charge accumulated in the capacitor during the initial build-up. The behavior is the same as if a battery whose voltage is dependent on the peak positive value of the input replaces the capacitor in the series transmission path.

During the interval that the diode is back-biased, C discharges slightly through the finite value of r_r with the long time constant Cr_r. The energy dissipated in r_r is supplied from the charge previously stored, and of course it must be replaced once the diode again conducts. The discharge introduces tilt over the negative portion of the cycle. Since the full change of input voltage appears across the diode (because of continuity of charge in C), the output becomes slightly positive when the input voltage rises by E at the end of each cycle. Therefore the output appears as shown in Fig. 2-14. Note that the signal has become somewhat distorted because of the cyclical charging and discharging.

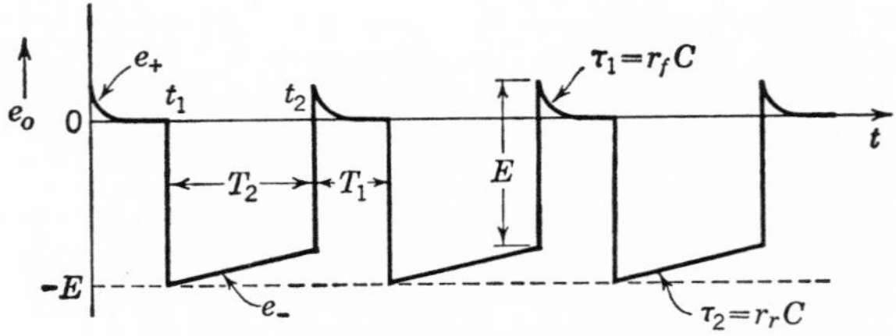

FIG. 2-14. Physical-diode clamping waveshape.

If the recharge time constant is excessively long, the circuit will not recover to zero within the recharge period. A solution for this case would follow the discussion of Sec. 1-3, with, however, different time constants used over each portion of the response.

Some general conclusions as to the circuit behavior may be drawn by realizing that for a periodic solution, the net change in the charge stored in C over any cycle must be zero. The charge flowing into the capacitor is

$$Q_+ = \int_0^{T_1} i\,dt = \int_0^{T_1} \frac{e_+}{r_f}\,dt \tag{2-11}$$

where e_+ is the time-varying voltage across the output when the diode conducts. The charge flowing out of the capacitor is

$$Q_- = \int_{t_1}^{t_2} \frac{e_-}{r_r}\,dt = \int_0^{T_2} \frac{e_-}{r_r}\,dt \tag{2-12}$$

where e_- is the voltage across the output when the diode does not conduct. Since there can be no net change in charge over the cycle,

$$Q_- = Q_+$$

Equating (2-11) and (2-12) and solving for r_f/r_r yields

$$\frac{r_f}{r_r} = \frac{\int_0^{T_1} e_+\,dt}{\int_0^{T_2} e_-\,dt} = \frac{\text{net positive area}}{\text{net negative area}} \tag{2-13}$$

Equation (2-13) leads to the conclusion that for proper clamping as well as for clipping, the diode with the maximum ratio of reverse to forward resistance performs best (least distortion). Observe that in deriving this equation the only assumption made is that the input signal is periodic. Even though the waveshape used to illustrate the clamp's behavior is rectangular, its shape appears neither explicitly nor implicitly in the charge equations (2-11) and (2-12). The final result, that the ratio of areas equals the ratio of diode resistances, must be independent of the applied waveshape.

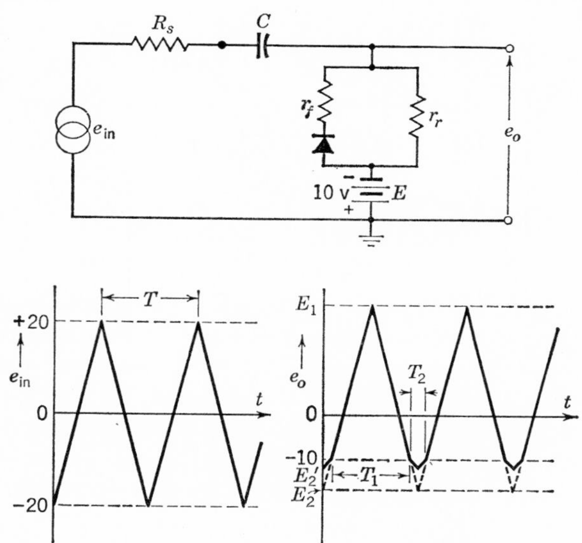

FIG. 2-15. A triangular wave clamped positively at −10 volts, illustrating distortion.

Reversing the diode clamps the input signal positively, instead of negatively, at zero volts, with the capacitor recharge showing itself as a slight negative excursion. Biasing this clamp similar to the clipping circuit sets the output voltage at any desired level, diode direction determining positive or negative clamping. Figure 2-15 shows a triangular input clamped positively at −10 volts, with the distortion exaggerated for purposes of illustration.

One necessary condition for properly biased operation is the presence of the reverse diode resistance, which establishes a path for the initial charging of C to the bias voltage. Consider the behavior when using an ideal diode ($r_r = \infty$) in the circuit of Fig. 2-15. If the negative peak of the input voltage never reaches −10 volts, the diode always remains back-biased and, since C is uncharged, the input appears at the output, unchanged and unclamped. Signals with negative peaks greater than

-10 volts forward-bias the diode on the peaks, and it provides the charging path. However, once the diode has a finite value of inverse resistance, C charges through this, and as a consequence the clamping action becomes independent of the signal amplitude.

Referring back to Eq. (2-13), we see that for optimum clamping with any given diode, the input signal should be clamped so as to minimize the net area on either side of the clamping bias voltage. When the area where the diode is back-biased is large, then the distortion area during conduction will also be large.

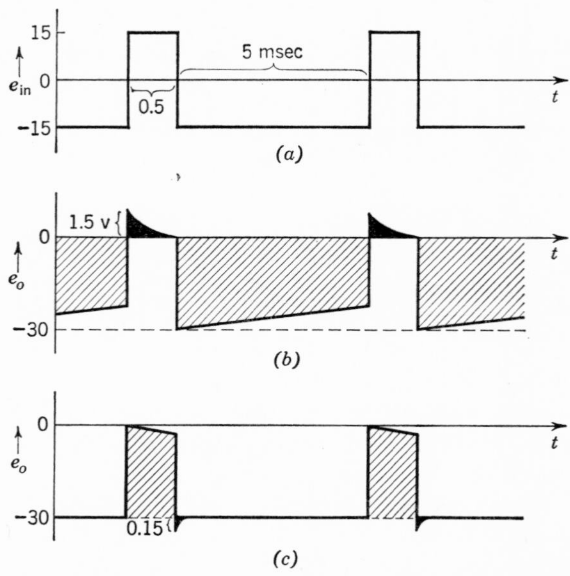

FIG. 2-16. Clamping waveshapes. (*a*) Input waveshape; (*b*) output clamped negatively at zero; (*c*) output clamped positively at -30 volts.

The waveshape of Fig. 2-16*a* must be clamped so that its maximum positive excursion is zero. It may either be clamped negatively at zero (output in Fig. 2-16*b*) or positively at -30 volts (output in Fig. 2-16*c*). The diagonally shaded areas in Fig. 2-16*b* and *c* indicate the regions where the diode is back-biased, and the solidly shaded areas, the regions of diode conduction. Since, from Eq. (2-13), the ratio of areas in the two cases is the same, clamping the longest portion of the period, rather than the shortest, is preferable. This corresponds to the case shown in Fig. 2-16*c*, which has minimum areas and hence least distortion. But if the signal amplitude varies, then no choice exists within the constraints imposed (maximum positive excursion limited to zero) and the signal must be clamped negatively at zero (Fig. 2-16*b*).

Example 2-3. Suppose that in the clamp used with the waveshapes of Fig. 2-16*a*, $r_f = 100$ ohms, $r_r = 1$ megohm, and $C = 0.1$ μf. The two time constants of interest are

$$\tau_1 = r_r C = 0.1 \text{ sec} \qquad \text{and} \qquad \tau_2 = r_f C = 10\ \mu\text{sec}$$

Since τ_1 is so very much longer than either portion of the cycle, within the back-biased region the circuit may be treated as an integrator. The output thus decays linearly toward the clamping level E.

(*a*) When the signal is clamped negatively at zero (Fig. 2-16*b*), the change in the output voltage over the 5-msec interval becomes

$$\Delta e_{o1} = \frac{30}{0.1} 5 \times 10^{-3} = 1.5 \text{ volts}$$

At the end of this period the output has risen from -30 to -28.5 volts. The input now jumps by 30 volts, driving the output to a positive peak of 1.5 volts, from which it recovers with the fast time constant τ_2.

(*b*) If the output is clamped positively at -30 volts (Fig. 2-16*c*), then, within the interval where the diode is back-biased (0.5 msec), the output decays by only

$$\Delta e_{o2} = \frac{30}{0.1} 0.5 \times 10^{-3} = 0.15 \text{ volt}$$

Thus during the recharging time the maximum excursion below the -30-volt level is 0.15 volt. The difference between these two cases is directly proportional to the duration of the nonconducting portions of the cycle, and we have verified our original argument.

Looking into a clamp, the signal source sees a different complex impedance during diode conduction than when reverse diode current flows. If the source has any internal impedance, the loading by the forward resistance of the diode introduces additional waveshape distortion. The total recharge voltage excursion divides proportionately across the source impedance and the diode forward resistance. Since the output is taken only across r_f, the voltage in this region will be smaller than expected, as seen in Fig. 2-15. During recharge, the forward voltage drop at the output, measured from the bias value, becomes

$$E_{+o} = \frac{r_f}{r_f + R_s} E_+$$

E_+ is the peak voltage drop across the total series resistance while the diode conducts.

In addition, when using Eq. (2-13), the source resistance must be added to the diode forward resistance and may even be the predominant term. We can see that this large increase in resistance decreases the ratio of areas, with correspondingly poorer clamping. When the diode is back-biased, the output is also attenuated slightly because of R_s. But if R_s were large enough to have an appreciable effect, it would so distort the conduction signal that the clamper would be unusable.

For clamped triangular and sinusoidal signals (Figs. 2-15 and 2-17), we are often interested in knowing the diode conduction period. Because the source impedance of the input generator only causes division of the recharge voltage drop, a logical first step in the calculation is to lump all forward resistors and ignore the voltage division. Furthermore, in a close-to-ideal circuit the waveshape distortion also may be neglected: the clamp is treated as a device which only shifts the output waveshape to a point where it satisfies Eq. (2-13). The two areas can now be calculated in terms of the unknown conduction angle, and their ratio equated

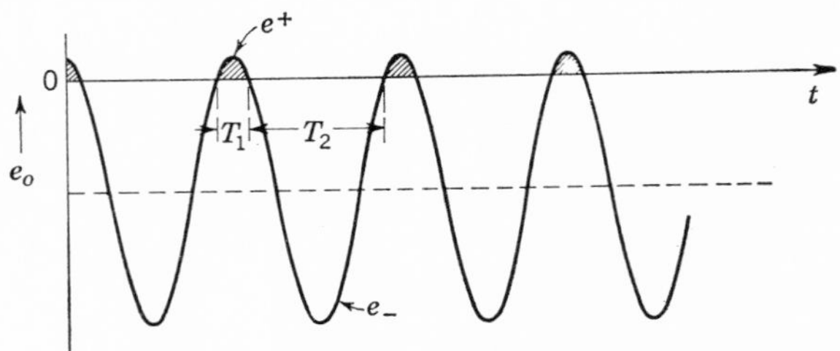

FIG. 2-17. A negatively clamped sine wave.

to the known ratio of forward to reverse resistances. For the triangular wave of Fig. 2-15, neglecting distortion, the area above the clamping voltage is

$$A_1 = \tfrac{1}{2}T_1(E_1 + 10) \tag{2-14}$$

The area below, measured from the bias voltage, becomes

$$A_2 = \tfrac{1}{2}T_2|E_2 + 10| \tag{2-15}$$

But from the input wave

$$E_1 - E_2 = 40 \qquad T_1 + T_2 = T \tag{2-16}$$

In addition, from the geometry, by setting up the ratio of similar triangles,

$$\frac{T/2}{40} = \frac{T_1/2}{E_1 + 10} \qquad \frac{T/2}{40} = \frac{T_2/2}{|E_2 + 10|} \tag{2-17}$$

Substituting first Eqs. (2-17) and then (2-16) into Eqs. (2-14) and (2-15) and equating to the ratio of resistance,

$$\frac{r_f + R_s}{r_r} = \frac{T_2^2}{T_1^2} = \frac{T_2^2}{(T - T_2)^2} \tag{2-18}$$

T_2 is the only unknown, and this equation is readily solved. We reject the negative root because it has no physical meaning. Next E_2 may be found by substituting back into Eq. (2-17). Using the resistive voltage divider of R_s and r_f and recognizing that E_2 is developed across both resistors finally gives E'_2.

Maintaining the clamping level in the face of changes of input-signal level requires fast charging of C for increasing signals and fast discharge on decreasing inputs. Both conditions are satisfied only with a small capacitor. However, too small a value allows excessive discharge during the clamp cycle with resultant waveshape distortion.

Occasionally, clamps are used in systems (such as television) where they must respond to the periodic signal but not to any noise pulse which might also be present. Since we do not wish the output to shift appreciably during the narrow noise-pulse interval, we must choose a large capacity and accept the consequences of a slow circuit response and incomplete recovery within the diode conduction region. Or, as an alternative, the reverse resistance might be reduced so that the effects of the noise pulse will be rapidly dissipated in the relatively inefficient clamp. In a practical circuit a compromise value of r_r and C would be chosen, satisfying as far as possible all requirements, weighing them in order of importance.

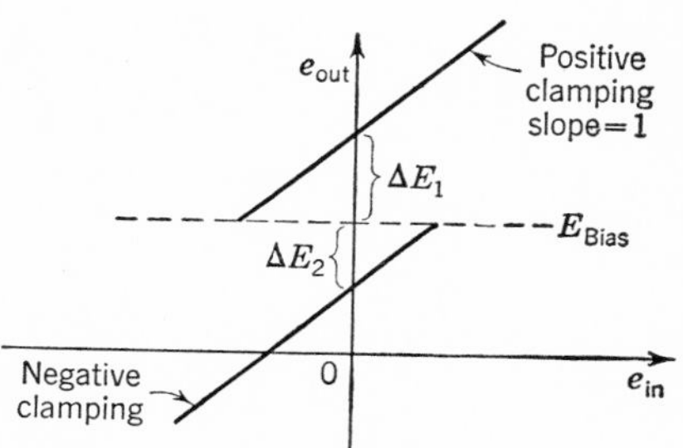

FIG. 2-18. Clamper transfer characteristics.

The transfer characteristic of a clamper is given in Fig. 2-18. Note that it is a straight line of unity slope, with the locus of the end point the bias voltage line. The y intercept depends on the input-signal amplitude. This is obvious if we consider that for positive clamping the output must always (neglecting the capacitor recharge) be equal to or greater than E_{bias}. ΔE_1 is the peak negative voltage applied to a positive clamper, and ΔE_2 is the peak positive voltage applied to a negative clamper. These transfer characteristics have no value or meaning except for periodic inputs. When presented on an oscilloscope, they do, however, show whether the clamp is operating properly.

2-6. Current Clippers. We find the concept of duality extremely helpful in developing the circuits used for current clamping and clipping. By simply taking the dual of a voltage clipper, we arrive at the circuit of a current clipper (Fig. 2-19a). Just as loop equations were ideally suited for the analysis of voltage circuits, the node equations are ideal for treating the current-activated devices. To complete the dual relationships, where previously the break point of the diode piecewise-linear model was taken at $e_d = 0$, now it might well be regarded as occurring when $i_d = 0$. Figure 2-19b shows the transfer characteristics of the current clipper. Except for the change in axis (current instead of voltage), it is identical with that given in Fig. 2-9 for the voltage clipper. Introduction of a bias current I_b sets the break point of the transfer characteristic wherever desired.

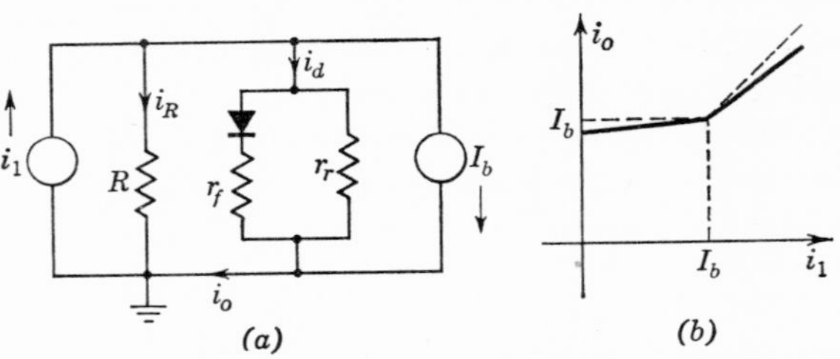

FIG. 2-19. Current clipper and transfer characteristics.

Analysis of this circuit starts with the writing of the node equation

$$i_d = i_1 - I_b - i_R \tag{2-19}$$

When $i_d \geq 0$, the diode conducts. From Eq. (2-19) we see that the conduction region corresponds to $i_1 > I_b$ and the nonconduction region to $i_1 < I_b$. The break point turns out to be, as expected, the value of the bias current. Since the regions of conduction and nonconduction are known, the two equations defining operation are, by superposition,

$$i_{o1} = \frac{r_r}{R + r_r} I_b + \frac{R}{R + r_r} i_1 \tag{2-20}$$

$$i_{o2} = \frac{R}{R + r_f} i_1 + \frac{r_f}{R + r_f} I_b \tag{2-21}$$

Equation (2-20) holds when the diode is nonconducting, and (2-21) when it conducts. The first term on the right-hand side represents the desired transmission, and the second term, the error component of load current, i.e., the transmission of undesired current to the output. These equations are analogous to the set used in describing the operation of a voltage clipper [Eqs. (2-5) and (2-6)]. Therefore identical reasoning leads to the same optimum value of the shunt resistor R as that previously found for R_1 in Sec. 2-3.

$$R = \sqrt{r_r r_f}$$

Reversing the diode changes the clipping characteristics, now allowing conduction for $i_1 \leq I_b$ and clipping when $i_1 \geq I_b$.

2-7. Current Clamps. In the treatment of voltage clamps (Sec. 2-5) we saw that the prime constituents of a clamp are an energy-storage element supplying the additional energy (previously stored) necessary in shifting the signal level, and a diode providing short storage (charge) and long decay time constants. When we must clamp current waveshapes, we logically turn to the inductance as our storage element. This circuit, the dual of the voltage clamp of Fig. 2-12, appears in Fig. 2-20. Since its basic behavior is independent of waveshape, the excitation chosen might as well be the simplest, e.g., a current square wave. For the initial discussion, assume its application at $t = 0$ as shown in Fig. 2-21.

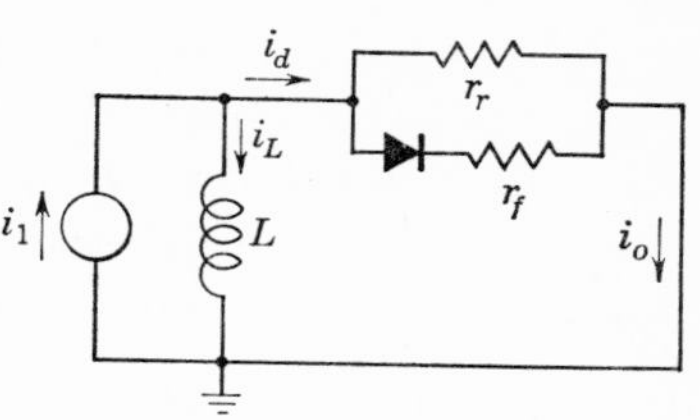

FIG. 2-20. Current clamp.

The load current may, by writing the node equation, be expressed as

$$i_o = i_d = i_1 - i_L \qquad (2\text{-}22)$$

During the first half cycle of the input square wave, the diode conducts and, assuming $r_f = 0$, the full input current flows in the output lead. However, in the second half cycle, $i_1 < 0$ and forward conduction ceases. The input current must flow somewhere. Since there was zero initial current in L, the only place left for the current to flow is through the diode's inverse resistance. Inductive current starts building up toward $-I_m$ with a corresponding decay in the reverse diode current. Build-up is rapid because of the small time constant,

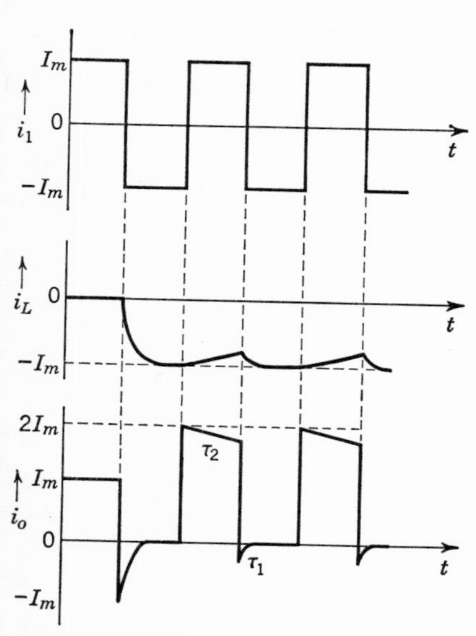

FIG. 2-21. Current-clamp waveshapes.

$$\tau_1 = \frac{L}{r_r}$$

For a sufficiently long half period compared with τ_1, that is, $T/2 \geq 4\tau_1$, charging will be completed within the half cycle, otherwise within several cycles. The input again becomes positive and, with no circuit dissipation, the inductive current remains at $-I_m$. From Eq. (2-22), the output subsequently becomes

$$i_o = i_1 - (-I_m)$$

But since i_1 takes on only one of two values, $\pm I_m$, i_o may be either zero or positive but never negative. The output current is composed of two components. On the positive peak the contribution of I_m, from the signal source, and the additional contribution of I_m, previously stored in the inductance, add. On the negative peaks these components subtract. We have thus clamped the output current positively at zero; it varies between zero and $2I_m$.

The inductance acts as the circuit's memory, remembering always the peak value of the input excitation. Once this information has been stored, the output will be shifted to satisfy the circuit conditions established by the diode.

Physically, $r_f > 0$, resulting in an inductive-current decay during diode conduction; this decay corresponds to the energy dissipated in the forward resistance. Since the decay time constant τ_2 is so very long, the load current droops only slightly.

$$\tau_2 = \frac{L}{r_f}$$

We must periodically restore the dissipated energy in the inductor's magnetic field. On alternate half cycles (negative input), recharge takes place, manifesting itself as a small negative excursion of output current. The final periodic response is sketched in Fig. 2-21. These results are exactly analogous with those obtained in Sec. 2-5 for the voltage clamps. However, whereas recharge in the voltage clamp took place during diode conduction, here it occurs when the diode is back-biased. The same condition of a large ratio of diode reverses to forward resistance is necessary for proper current clamping, and the signal will shift until the ratio of the areas equals the ratio of diode resistance.

Bias currents may be introduced, in parallel with the diode, shifting the clamp point wherever desired. As with the voltage clamp, reversing the diode reverses the direction of clamping. The nonideal inductance has associated coil resistance, which adds to the other circuit resistance and decreases both τ_1 and τ_2, having the most pronounced effect in shortening the long discharge time constant.

2-8. Arbitrary Transfer and Volt-Ampere Characteristics. Many devices and systems exhibit grossly nonlinear responses which, for analysis, we should like to approximate by an equivalent network of biased diodes and resistors. These nonlinearities may inadvertently arise from the physical properties of the device and will thus represent an undesirable characteristic. Alternatively, they may be deliberately created and inserted in the signal transmission path in order to perform various operations. In both cases generally more than two linear segments are necessary for a satisfactory piecewise-linear representation. This simply means that additional diodes must be incorporated into the network—each break point corresponds to change of state of an ideal diode—from conduction to cutoff, or vice versa. One simple example of arbitrary transfer and volt-ampere curves and the equivalent diode model appear in Fig. 2-22.

If the network contains at most two or three diodes in a relatively simple configuration, then, in solving for the break coordinates of any one diode, we can always assume the condition of the others. In Fig. 2-22, we may assume D_1 and D_2 conducting and solve for the break values of D_3. Any inconsistency arising when checking the answer (e.g., a negative current flow through a diode that was assumed conducting) means that the problem must be re-solved from the new starting point.

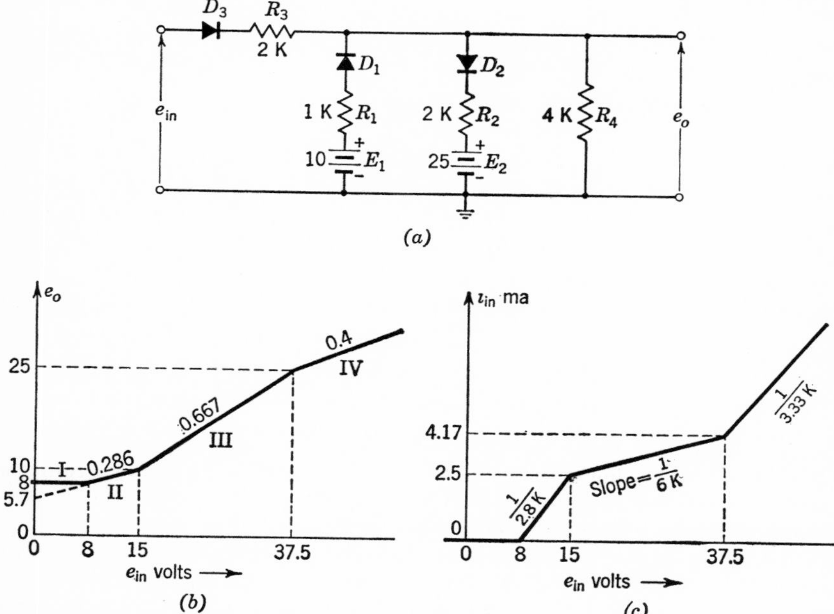

FIG. 2-22. An example of a three-diode network together with the transfer and volt-ampere characteristics. (a) Three-diode circuit; (b) transfer characteristic; (c) input volt-ampere characteristic.

Three diodes afford eight possibilities as to the circuit condition, but these would be halved by the particular diode and biasing arrangement. With more than three diodes, in other than a trivial circuit, the trial-and-error method becomes unreasonably tedious and we must seek a more organized method of solution.

Example 2-4. In the case where we can readily identify the diode states, as in the circuit of Fig. 2-22*a*, we reduce the complex circuit to a number of simpler models. Each region is defined by the resistive network obtained when all back-biased diodes are replaced by open circuits and the conducting ones by short circuits. If these regions are selected by assuming the diode states, then each model must be checked for consistency. In the circuit considered, the region limits are easily specified in terms of the output voltage: D_1 conducts when $e_o < 10$, D_2 conducts when $e_o > 25$, and D_3 is forward-biased when $e_o < e_{in}$.

Region I:

D_2 and D_3 back-biased (open circuits)
D_1 conducts (short circuit)

$$e_{o1} = \frac{R_4}{R_1 + R_4} E_1 = \frac{4\text{ K}}{1\text{ K} + 4\text{ K}} 10 = 8 \text{ volts}$$

This output remains constant at this value until D_3 conducts once $e_{\text{in}} > 8$ volts.

Region II:

D_1 and D_3 conducting ($8 \leq e_{o2} \leq 10$)
D_2 back-biased

$$e_{o2} = \frac{R_1 \parallel R_4}{R_1 \parallel R_4 + R_3} e_{\text{in}} + \frac{R_3 \parallel R_4}{R_3 \parallel R_4 + R_1} E_1 = 0.286 e_{\text{in}} + 5.7$$

Region III:

D_3 conducts ($10 \leq e_{o3} \leq 25$)
D_1 and D_2 nonconducting

$$e_{o3} = \frac{R_4}{R_3 + R_4} e_{\text{in}} = 0.667 e_{\text{in}}$$

Region IV:

D_3 and D_2 conducting ($25 \leq e_{o4}$)
D_1 back-biased

$$e_{o4} = \frac{R_2 \parallel R_4}{R_2 \parallel R_4 + R_3} e_{\text{in}} + \frac{R_3 \parallel R_4}{R_3 \parallel R_4 + R_2} E_2 = 0.4 e_{\text{in}} + 10$$

The limits of the output are inserted into the individual equations to find the limits expressed in terms of input voltage. These are indicated in Fig. 2-22*b*. Note that in each region the transfer characteristic is a straight line with a slope found from the incremental model (all battery voltages set to zero).

A further application of the type of circuit shown in Fig. 2-22*a* comes from recognition that its input volt-ampere characteristic (Fig. 2-22*c*) changes as diodes start and stop conducting. The inverse slope of these characteristics is simply the resistance seen looking into the input terminals. Therefore diode circuits are useful in developing almost any required nonlinear resistance characteristics. Piecewise approximations result in a discontinuous rather than continuous incremental input resistance, but by taking enough segments we can approximate any continuous resistance as closely as necessary.

A General Approach. Although we are developing more explicit methods of analysis and the implicit techniques of synthesis of multiple-diode circuits, we shall be forced to restrict the discussion to a single reasonably general network. This is essential if the treatment is to be kept within bounds: the model used in describing an arbitrary nonlinear characteristic is not necessarily unique, and therefore many feasible solutions exist. It is neither possible nor practicable to examine all of them.

Each branch of the general network of Fig. 2-23*a* consists of a parallel combination of biased diodes and resistors as shown in Fig. 2-23*b*. The over-all response may be determined by noting that:

1. The number of break points in the transfer or input volt-ampere characteristic equals the number of diodes contained in the two branches.
2. The piecewise-linear response is completely defined by finding the coordinates of the break points and the slopes of the two unbounded segments.
3. The maximum possible transfer slope is unity since the network is completely dissipative. (We restrict R to positive values.)

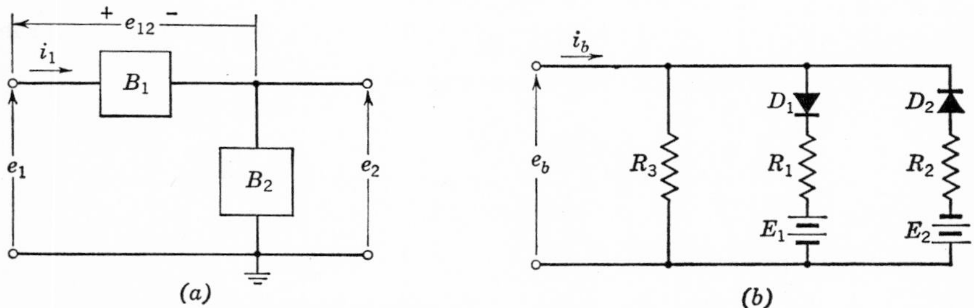

FIG. 2-23. (*a*) General two-branch network; (*b*) typical branch configuration.

In calculating these break points, each branch may be considered separately and then their individual responses combined. Under the rules developed in Sec. 2-1, the voltage break values of any branch are simply the bias voltages appearing in series with the internal diodes. Once these voltages are known, the corresponding current values are readily found by direct evaluation. It is important to determine which diodes are operative in any region, since each one that starts to conduct introduces additional shunt resistance and each one that stops conducting reduces the number of elements in the branch.

As an aid to our inconsistent memory, the behavior of each branch and the state of each diode should be tabulated as a function of the controlling terminal voltage. This not only enables us to construct the response characteristics in the most organized manner, but in itself reflects the many resistive models inherent in the diode network.

The input volt-ampere characteristic is the totality of the branch responses. Under the series arrangement shown, the current must be continuous and the voltage drops simply add. The break-point current coordinates comprise the set of those found separately for the two branches. The corresponding voltage coordinates must be found by the direct evaluation and summation of the drops at these known currents. For one branch the drop is identically the break value, and for the other it may be determined from the graph or from the equivalent resistive network.

Finally the over-all transfer characteristic is obtained by cross-plotting the output branch voltages corresponding to the input break values. In each region the slope is identical with that found from the purely resistive network holding. Voltage sources only shift the location of the segment; they cannot alter its slope. To reiterate, the complete network response is determined by the location of the break points and the incremental slopes of the line segments terminating on them. Only this information is necessary for a complete description of the network.

Example 2-5. The circuit of Fig. 2-24 utilizes series- and parallel-resistance padding of Zener diode for its series branch and two individually adjustable diodes for its

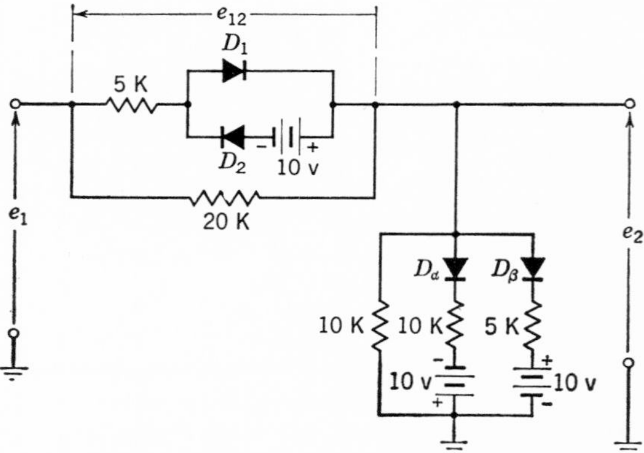

FIG. 2-24. Circuit to illustrate the method of analysis of multiple-diode networks.

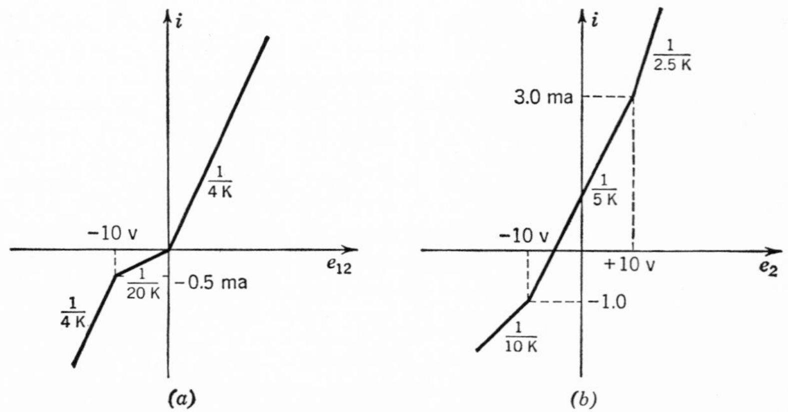

FIG. 2-25. Individual branch characteristics for the circuit of Fig. 2-24. (a) Series branch; (b) shunt branch.

shunt branch. The volt-ampere response of each branch may be tabulated with respect to decreasing terminal voltage as indicated in Tables 2-2*a* and *b*. Their characteristics are also presented graphically in Fig. 2-25*a* and *b*.

TABLE 2-2*a*. SERIES BRANCH RESPONSE

Diode states	e_{12}	i, ma	Incremental resistance* r_{12}, kilohms
D_1 on, D_2 off	$e_{12} > 0$	.....	4
D_1 turns off†	0	0	
D_1 off, D_2 off	$-10 < e_{12} < 0$	.....	20
D_2 turns on†	-10	-0.5	
D_1 off, D_2 on	$-10 > e_{12}$	.....	4

TABLE 2-2*b*. SHUNT BRANCH RESPONSE

Diode states	e_2	i, ma	Incremental resistance* r_2, kilohms
D_α on, D_β on	$e_2 > 10$	...	2.5
D_β turns off†	10	3	
D_α on, D_β off	$-10 < e_2 < 10$	...	5
D_α turns off†	-10	-1	
D_α off, D_β off	$e_2 < -10$	...	10

* The incremental resistance of each region is simply the parallel combination of all resistors inserted by the diodes conducting in that region.

† The individual branch break points, which are found first, serve as the critical points of the table. The voltage values are determined by inspection of the branch, and the current by direct evaluation.

Now that the response of each branch is known, we are in a position to find the total input volt-ampere characteristic. This can be done by direct summation of the two graphs of Fig. 2-25*a* and *b* or by considering the data presented in Table 2-2. We can construct a new table by interleaving the known break currents in descending order (Table 2-3). These represent the totality of break points and separate the linear input regions. Furthermore, the incremental resistances previously found are in series and may be directly added. The reader should compare the appropriate columns of Tables 2-2 and 2-3.

The only data still unknown are the values of the input voltage coordinates. For these we must find the voltage drops across the individual branches at the known current values. The derived voltages are given in the parentheses in columns 3 and 4 of Table 2-3. They may be found by linear interpolation from the tables of the individual branch response, from the branch graphics, or directly from the circuit.

The voltage break value may also be determined by writing and solving the equation of a straight line holding within each region. In the region defined by the bottom line of Table 2-2*a*, the segment is a straight line of slope $\frac{1}{4}K$ passing through the point (-0.5 ma, -10 volts).

TABLE 2-3. TOTAL CIRCUIT RESPONSE

Region	(1) Conducting diodes and diode changing state	(2) i, ma	(3) e_{12}*	(4) e_2*	(5) $e_1 = e_{12} + e_2$	(6) Incremental resistance, kilohms	(7) Transfer slope
I	D_1, D_α, D_β on	. . .	. . . . . .	. . . . .	$e_1 > 22$	6.5	2.5/6.5
	D_β turns off†	3	(12)	10	22		
II	D_1, D_α on	. . .	. . . . . .	. . . . .	$-5 > e_1 > 22$	9	5/9
	D_1 turns off†	0	0	(−5)	−5		
III	D_α on	. . .	. . . . . .	. . . . .	$-17.5 > e_1 > -5$	25	5/25
	D_2 turns on†	0.5	−10	(7.5)	−17.5		
IV	D_α, D_2 on	. . .	. . . . . .	. . . . .	$-22 > e_1 > -17.5$	9	5/9
	D_α turns off†	−1	(−12)	−10	−22		
V	D_2 on	. . .	. . . . . .	. . . . .	$e_1 < -22$	14	10/14

* The derived values are enclosed in parentheses.
† Circuit break points.

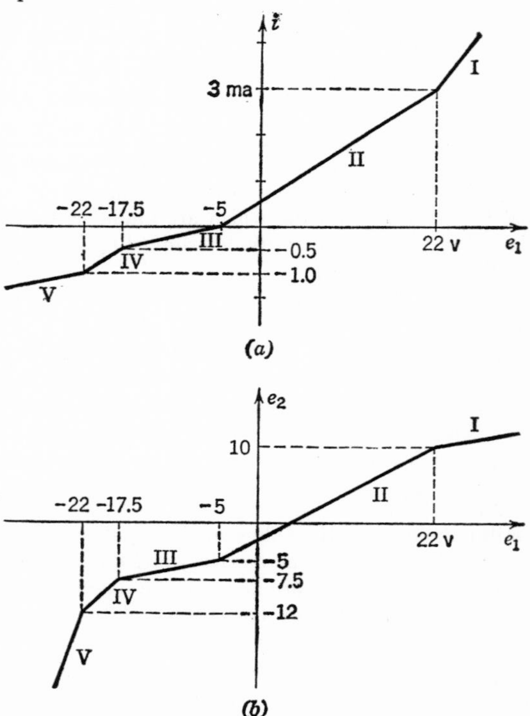

FIG. 2-26. (a) Input volt-ampere response; (b) transfer characteristics of the circuit of Fig. 2-24.

Thus

$$e_{12}(i) = -10 \text{ volts} + (i + 0.5)4 \text{ K}$$

At the known break current of -1 ma, this yields

$$e_{12}(-1) = -12 \text{ volts}$$

Similar equations may be written for the other unknown terms. Figure 2-26*a* is the plot of the complete input volt-ampere characteristics.

The transfer curve becomes immediately apparent if we recognize that the incremental transfer slope of each region is

$$\frac{\Delta e_2}{\Delta e_1} = \frac{r_2}{r_{12} + r_2}$$

where r_2 and r_{12} are the incremental resistance in the appropriate regions. Table 2-3 also includes these various slopes. Figure 2-26*b* shows the cross-plotting of the input and output voltage coordinates of the break points leading to the network transfer characteristic. The regions are those given in Table 2-3.

We can draw the following general conclusions from the above example:

1. Each time a series diode starts conducting, it reduces the net series resistance and increases the slope of the transfer characteristics. Each time a series diode stops conducting, it reduces this slope.

2. The conduction of a shunt diode reduces the branch resistance and decreases the transfer characteristic slope. As a shunt diode stops conducting, both the shunt resistance and the incremental transmission increase in value.

For reference purposes, some commonly used diode-resistor combinations and their volt-ampere responses are tabulated in Fig. 2-27. The first two diagrams illustrate a diode biased to start conducting, and then one which stops conducting, as the voltage rises above the threshold value. Figure 2-27*c* represents the response of a Zener diode, and Fig. 2-27*d* illustrates the control afforded over the break-point location by placing two Zener diodes back to back. This final branch would normally be used to insert biased break points into the series arm without having recourse to actual bias batteries.

2-9. Dead Zone and Hysteresis. Two interesting examples of diode wave shaping which are used in the analog solution of electrical, chemical, and mechanical problems are the generation of the transfer characteristics of dead zone and hysteresis. We shall first examine dead zone, which appears whenever a threshold value must be exceeded before transmission is possible. The steering system of an automobile has built-in dead zone for safety; small disturbances of the wheel are not transmitted into a turning movement. Some threshold value of steering-wheel rotation must be exceeded before the automobile responds.

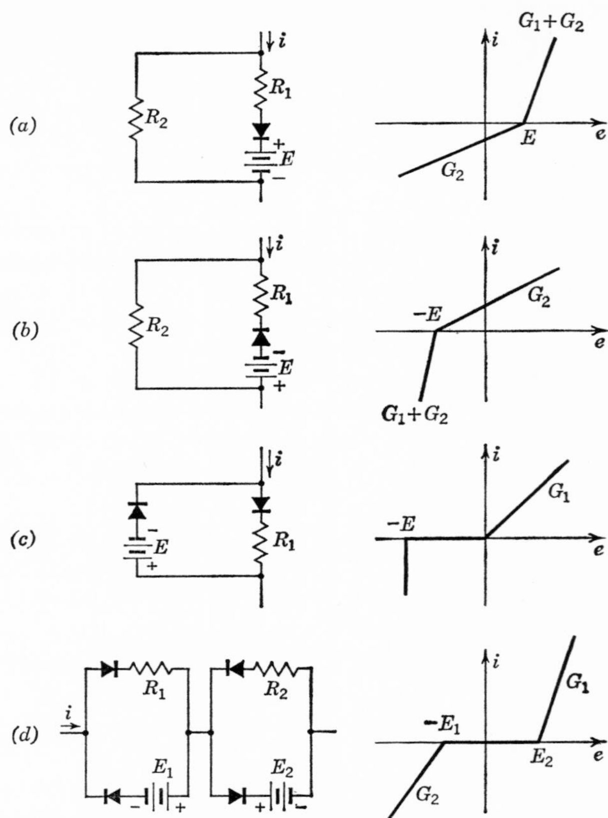

FIG. 2-27. Various diode-resistor combinations and their volt-ampere response.

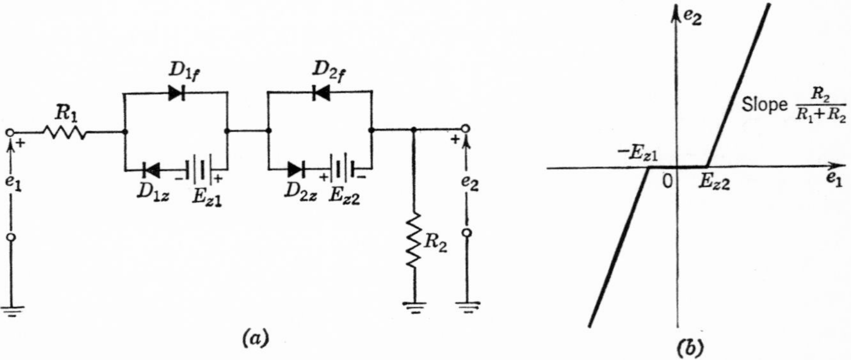

FIG. 2-28. Dead-zone circuit and transfer characteristics.

The freezing-and-melting process of pure materials presents a second example of dead zone. Here the addition of heat produces a linear temperature rise at temperatures below the critical point. But at the melting and boiling points, a finite amount of heat must be added to a constant temperature before there will be a change of state (solid to liquid, liquid to gas). In the new state, again temperature increases linearly with heat flow.

The simplest diode network which may be used to simulate a fixed-width dead zone employs, as the series branch, two Zener diodes connected back to back (Fig. 2-28*a*). Their constant voltage drop in the Zener region avoids the addition of any series bias source (a difficult problem since this voltage must be isolated from ground).

We shall consider the response of the nonlinear series branch first. On positive voltages conduction eventually becomes possible through the forward diode of D_1 (D_{1f}) and the Zener region of D_2 (D_{2z}). However, this will not occur until the branch voltage exceeds E_{z2}. The coordinates of the break point are

$$e_1 = E_{z2} \qquad i = 0 \tag{2-23}$$

At zero current there will be no drop in R_2 and the input break coordinates are identical with those given in Eq. (2-23).

By symmetry, we can see that the other break point occurs at

$$e_1 = -E_{z1} \qquad i = 0 \tag{2-24}$$

Consequently, within the limits

$$-E_{z1} < e_1 < E_{z2}$$

only the extremely limited transmission through the high inverse resistance of a physical diode is possible. Outside these limits the incremental transfer slope is determined by the voltage divider composed of R_1 and R_2.

$$S = \frac{R_2}{R_1 + R_2} \tag{2-25}$$

In the transfer characteristic of Fig. 2-28*b* we note that the width of the dead zone is a function of the individual Zener diode break voltages and that the transmission slope is controlled by the series padding resistor. The dead zone may be shifted to any output voltage by suitably biasing the output resistor.

Hysteresis arises in many physical properties of materials, such as the magnetization curve of iron and the stress-strain relationship. If the forcing function is increased from zero to some final value and then removed, the forced system parameter will remain fixed at a value other than zero. But this is simply the object's memory which shows up as the magnetic flux still present after the removal of the magnetizing current or as the residual stress in a steel rod after the stretching force is released. Of course, limits are imposed by the physical nature of the materials. Only so much flux can be supported regardless of the magnitude of the magnetization current; this value is called the saturation flux. In a stressed bar, excessive force will cause fracture.

To return a system (one which may be saturated but not fractured) to its original state requires the application of a forcing function in the opposite direction, usually of somewhat smaller magnitude than the original signal. If the new input is too large, it will simply leave the system in an excited state of the opposite magnetic polarity or with the strain acting in the opposite direction (Fig. 2-29*b*).

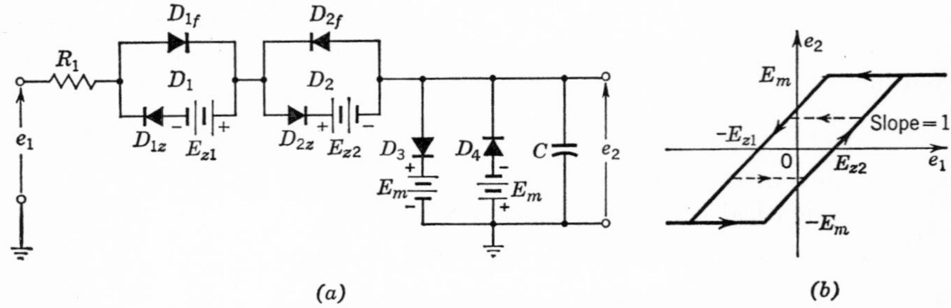

FIG. 2-29. Hysteresis circuit and characteristics.

A smaller amplitude excitation will generate smaller area loops with regard to both the displacement from the origin and the maximum output amplitude. These are extremely difficult to simulate, and therefore we shall concentrate our attention on the circuit of Fig. 2-29*a*, which gives the response shown in Fig. 2-29*b*. The two diodes D_3 and D_4 limit the maximum output excursion to $\pm E_m$ and establish the saturation values so necessary in many hysteresis systems. (Fracture may be simulated by fuses.)

Operation is similar to that of the dead-zone circuit. On a rising input, the forward diode D_{1f} and the Zener diode D_{2Z} eventually conduct, providing an output across C. Capacitor voltage then follows the input to a maximum value determined by the clipping diode D_3. As the input falls, the charge on the capacitor (the memory of previous maximum excitation) back-biases the formerly conducting diodes and, since no discharge path exists, the output remains at the maximum value previously reached. Eventually the falling input brings D_{1Z} and D_{2f} into conduction, establishing a discharge path, and again the output follows the input. The transfer characteristic now traces the left-hand portion of the curve. If the input continues falling and then rises, the cycle repeats, with the roles of the series diodes interchanged.

There is no necessity to drive the output into saturation. For generation of hysteresis or backlash curves, smaller inputs generate the minor loops indicated by the dashed lines of Fig. 2-29*b*.

The slowest input signal for proper response is determined by the leakage of the capacitor charge through the diode inverse resistance, and the fastest signal by the charging time constant

$$\tau_c = CR_1$$

We choose C for reasonable response to the expected time range of the input signals.

2-10. Summary. Many nonlinear systems whose externally measured characteristics are available may be treated from the viewpoint of their piecewise-linear representation. The nonlinear system, difficult to treat in all its complexity, is reduced to a sequence of linear problems, each with its own response and limits of operation. Simple mathematical tools already at our disposal from studies of linear systems are sufficient to reach acceptable engineering answers in those cases amenable to this treatment. We can always handle circuits involving only dissipative elements, no matter how nonlinear their characteristics may be. When energy-storage elements are also contained in the nonlinear system, the problem becomes much more difficult.

If in each region the boundary conditions are independent (able to be calculated only from the model and the boundaries of the region), we can solve the system in a straightforward manner. If the constraints involve past history, as in the hysteresis circuit, then when only a single energy-storage element is present, we are able to complete the analysis. And if multiple modes of energy storage existed, the circuit would not have yielded so readily to simple methods. Except in very special cases, the problem faced is extremely difficult and beyond the scope of this text.

The first step in any analysis is the construction of the appropriate models together with the clear delineation of their boundaries. Generally, boundaries are determined by the energy-storage elements and points of conduction. Secondly, conditions of continuity across the region's boundaries must be considered. These arise primarily from the original characteristics and the type of energy-storage elements involved, with, however, the energy-storage elements often determining the diode conditions. And finally we are ready to proceed to the solution.

The same techniques are used in solving many chemical, thermal, and mechanical systems, where, for example, an ideal mechanical "diode" might be postulated rather than an electrical one. A velocity-operated clutch which engages or disengages at present shaft speeds is one mechanical example. Its slip on engagement is analogous with the diode forward resistance, while its imperfect disengagement represents reverse resistance. In fluid flow, on-off pressure valves behave similarly, with their pressure loss and leakage modifying the ideal valve in much the same way as resistance modified the ideal diode. A metal plate, polished on one side and black on the other, allows radiant heat to flow more readily in one direction than in the other; it may be used as our thermal diode under the applicable conditions.

In many cases where it is difficult to formulate proper models, making the grossest approximations leads to a circuit which can be solved. The answer, admittedly incorrect, often gives some insight. This enables us to refine the analysis later, eventually coming within an acceptable engineering solution.

PROBLEMS

2-1. (*a*) By direct graphical construction evaluate the input volt-ampere characteristics of Fig. 2-30. Specify the individual slopes and the coordinates of the single break point.

(*b*) Convert the circuit holding for each diode state into both Thévenin and Norton equivalent circuits and find the break point from the two defining equations.

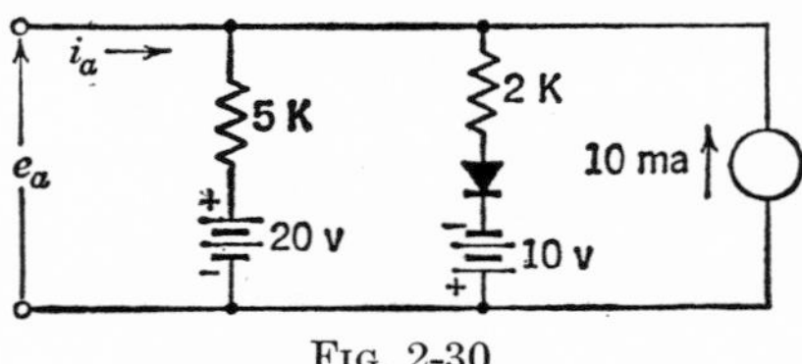

FIG. 2-30

2-2. Show how the transfer characteristics of Fig. 2-8 may be derived by a graphical construction. (The volt-ampere characteristics of the input and of the shunt diode branch must first be evaluated.)

2-3. A diode clipper such as the one shown in Fig. 2-7 is used in a system where the input may vary from zero to a value that will never exceed four times the clipping level. What series resistor should be chosen, expressed in terms of r_f and r_r, so that the maximum error voltage on both sides of the clipping value will be equal?

2-4. A triangular wave such as the one shown in Fig. 2-15 (40 volts peak to peak) is the input to the series clipper of Fig. 2-10. The bias battery is +5 volts, and the diode parameters are $r_r = 100$ K and $r_f = 40$ ohms. Sketch the transfer characteristics and draw the input and output waveshapes to scale when R_1 equals (*a*) 25 K, (*b*) 4 K, and (*c*) 1 K. In all cases calculate the peak values of the output signal.

2-5. Repeat Prob. 2-4*b* for the circuit of Fig. 2-9 where the +5-volt bias is derived from a tap on a 10,000-ohm bleeder connected across a 50-volt power supply.

2-6. We wish to clip the positive peaks of a signal at +10 volts by using a shunt clipper similar to that shown in Fig. 2-7. The available diode has a forward resistance of 100 ohms and an inverse resistance of 0.5 megohm, and in addition it has a Zener break point at −25 volts.

(*a*) Calculate the optimum series resistance and draw the circuit.

(*b*) Sketch the transfer characteristics, indicating the values of slopes and the coordinates of all break points.

(*c*) Draw the output waveshape when the driving voltage is a 100-volt peak-to-peak sinusoidal signal.

(*d*) Under the conditions of part *c*, what angular percentage of the sine wave would be transmitted relatively unaffected by the clipping circuit?

2-7. The single pulse shown excites the circuit of Fig. 2-31 at $t = 0$. If the initial charge on C is -20 volts (polarity shown), evaluate the complete output response. Specify all voltage and time-constant values. Make all reasonable approximations.

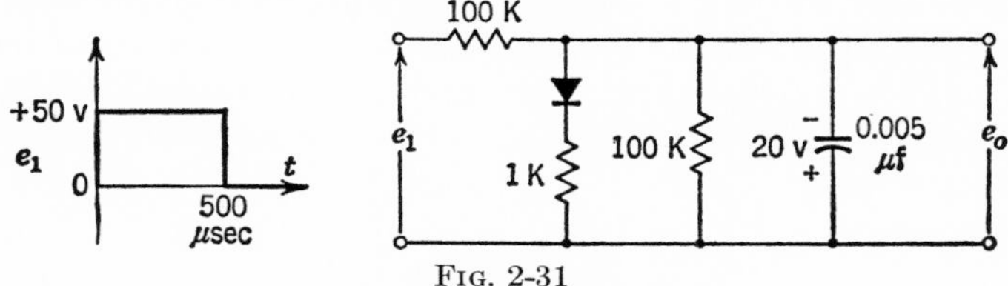

FIG. 2-31

2-8. A 30-volt peak-to-peak 100-μsec-period square wave is clamped negatively at +5 volts. The diode has a forward resistance of 50 ohms and an inverse resistance of 100 K. We want to use the smallest possible capacitor so that this clamp will have a fast response to changes in the input-signal level, but we are absolutely restricted in that the output must never exceed the clamping level by more than 2 per cent of the peak-to-peak input signal.

(*a*) What is the smallest-size capacitor which we may use? Round off your answer to the larger even value, for example, $0.00228 \cong 0.0025$. Explain why you would use a larger value.

(*b*) How much energy must be restored in the capacitor over each cycle? (Make any reasonable approximations to simplify your calculations.)

(*c*) If the peak-to-peak signal is suddenly increased to 50 volts, how many periods of the input signal will the circuit take to recover its clamping action?

(*d*) Repeat part *c* if the signal is decreased to 10 volts. (HINT: Consider the superposition of the square-wave input and the initial voltage across C. Find the time at which the diode again conducts.)

2-9. The signal of Fig. 2-32 is the input to a clamp having $r_r = 1$ megohm, $r_f = 50$ ohms, and $C = 0.005$ μf.

(*a*) Sketch the output if this signal is clamped positively at zero and indicate all important voltage values and time constants.

(*b*) Sketch the output if this signal is clamped negatively at zero.

(*c*) Under the conditions of part *b*, how long after the termination of the large pulse before the clamp capacitor is again charged? (See hint given in Prob. 2-8*d*.)

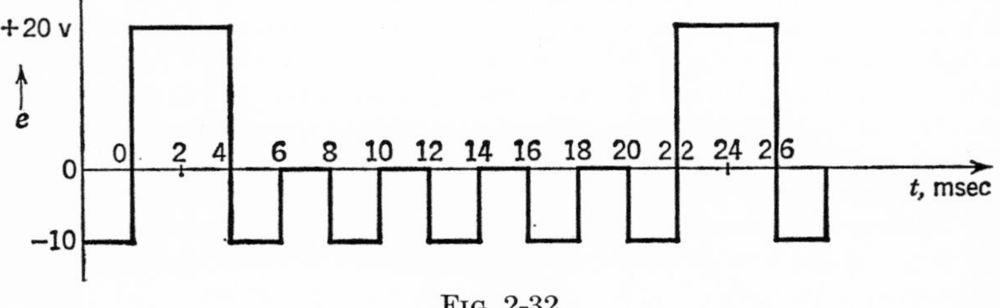

FIG. 2-32

2-10. Solve the circuit of Fig. 2-15 for E_1, E_2', T_1, and T_2 where $r_f = 10$ ohms, $r_r = 200$ K, $R_s = 1$ K, where the triangular wave period is 10 msec. Assume that C is very large.

2-11. Consider the response of the circuit of Fig. 2-33 to the signal given. The input has been at 200 volts for a very long time before the negative pulse appeared. Draw the output waveshape, indicating all time constants and voltage values.

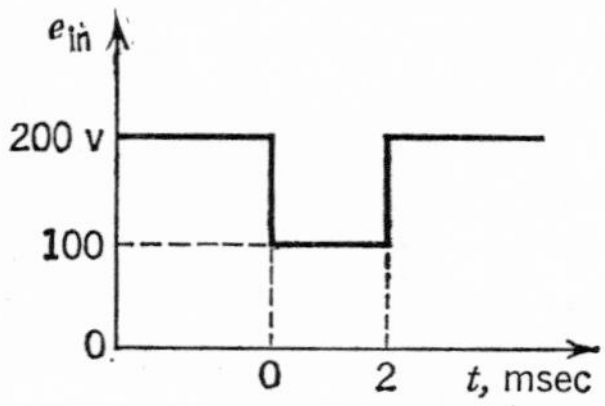

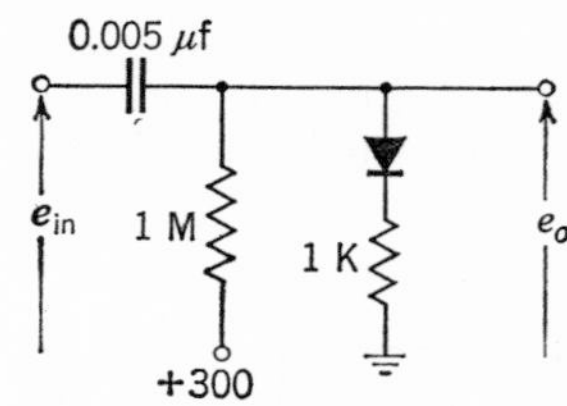

FIG. 2-33

2-12. Draw a circuit that will clip the positive peak of a 100-ma peak-to-peak triangular driving current at the 20-ma point. Use a diode having a forward resistance of 50 ohms and $r_r = 100$ K and specify the optimum shunt resistance. Sketch the output current, giving all important waveshapes. Explain how an other-than-zero load resistance would affect the clipping action.

2-13. The current waveshape of Fig. 2-34 is to be clamped negatively at -5 ma. The diode available has a forward resistance of 500 ohms and an inverse resistance of 1 megohm. The coil approximates an ideal inductance in that its resistance is only 10 ohms and its inductance is 50 mh.

(*a*) Draw the circuit used, showing where the bias current would be injected.

(*b*) Sketch the output current, indicating all important values and time constants.

(*c*) To what should the spacing between the pulses be changed so that the output overshoot will just equal 1 per cent of the peak-to-peak current?

(*d*) Repeat part *b* if a 500-mh coil is used in place of the one specified above.

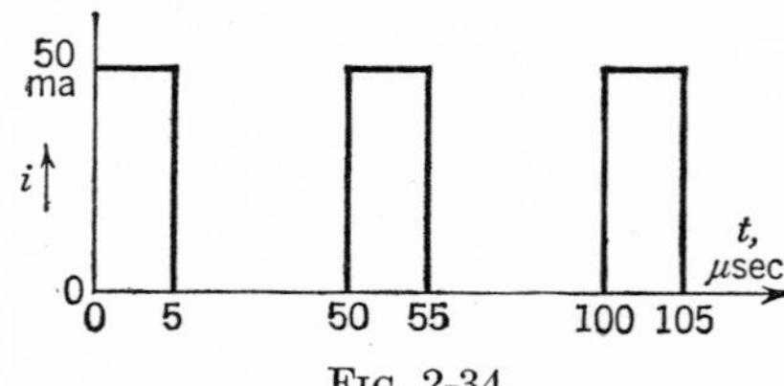

FIG. 2-34

2-14. What effect would the coil resistance R_L of a nonideal inductance have on the current clamping action? Consider clamping a square wave of current at zero to simplify your analysis.

2-15. Prove that the output waveshape of a current clamp will shift until the ratio of areas is equal to the ratio of diode resistances.

2-16. A 20-volt peak-to-peak 1-msec square wave is the input to the clamp of Fig. 2-12. The diode has a forward resistance of 20 ohms and an inverse resistance of 100 K; $C = 0.01$ μf.

(*a*) Sketch the output waveshape for the first two cycles if the square wave is initially applied when it is zero, going positive.

(*b*) Repeat part *a* if a 0.001-μf capacitor is shunting the diode. Make all reasonable approximations.

2-17. Given a d-c vacuum-tube voltmeter with a 10-megohm input impedance, our problem is to construct an a-c voltmeter. The d-c unit reads correctly in conjunction with a 1-megohm probe. Two different a-c probes are under consideration (Fig. 2-35*a* and *b*). In each case they will be connected directly to the voltmeter, i.e., not through the d-c probe.

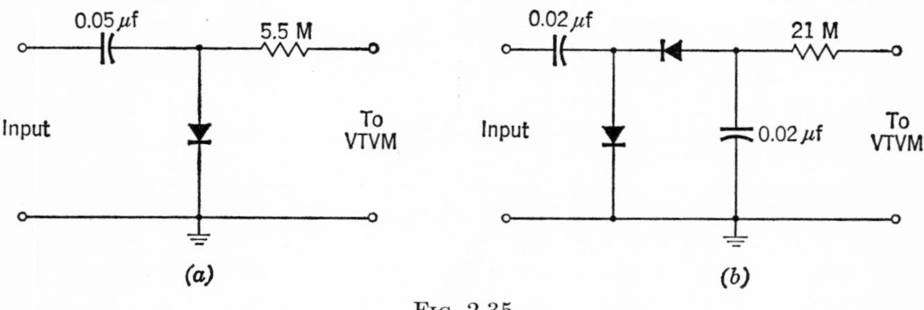

Fig. 2-35

Calculate the VTVM reading for each probe for the various inputs listed below. In each case relate the reading to some parameter of the input signal (rms, peak, or average).

(*a*) 10-volt-peak 1,000-cps sine wave.
(*b*) 10-volt-peak 1,000-cps square wave.
(*c*) 20-volt peak-to-peak 1,000-cps triangular wave having +10-volt average value.
(*d*) Signal same as in part *c* except that it has a −10-volt average value.
(*e*) 10-volt 10-μsec-wide positive pulses with a period of 100 μsec.
(*f*) Repeat part *e* for negative pulses.

2-18. Plot the transfer and input volt-ampere characteristics of the circuit given in Fig. 2-36. Sketch the output voltage if $e_{in} = 100 \sin \omega t$, giving all important values (assume ideal diodes).

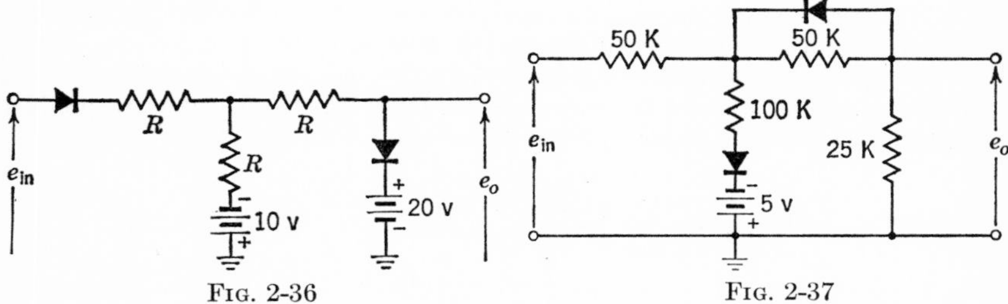

Fig. 2-36

Fig. 2-37

2-19. Draw the input volt-ampere and the transfer characteristics of the circuit of Fig. 2-37 and sketch the output when a 50-volt peak-to-peak triangular wave is impressed at the input.

2-20. (*a*) Set up the equations representing each region of operation given in Table 2-3 (Sec. 2-8) and verify the values of all break points.

(*b*) Show the purely resistive model (Thévenin or Norton equivalent) implicit within each region and specify the various component values. By direct solution of the intersection of the models found, evaluate the break points bounding these regions.

2-21. Design a circuit which will have the transfer characteristics given in Fig. 2-38. Specify all batteries and resistors, taking the smallest resistor as 10 K.

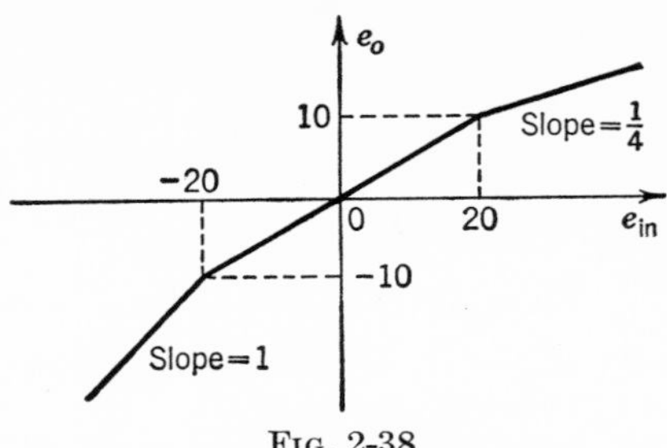

FIG. 2-38

2-22. In the circuit of Fig. 2-39, the input voltage is a symmetrical triangular wave having a period of 16 sec, a peak-to-peak amplitude of 80 volts, and an average value of zero.

(*a*) Plot the output voltage as a function of time and label all break points with their time and voltage values.

(*b*) The output signal is to be a rough approximation of a sine wave, with only the break points agreeing exactly with the sinusoidal signal. What is the peak amplitude of the sine wave we are approximating, and to what angles do the break points correspond?

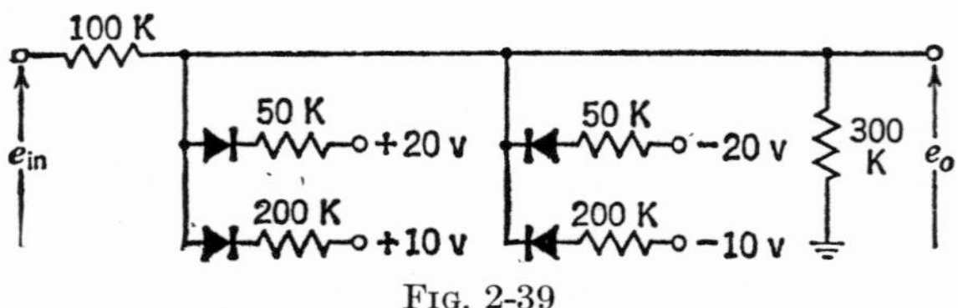

FIG. 2-39

2-23. One method of multiplying two voltages together is to convert each voltage signal into a current proportional to its logarithm (to the base 10) and then to add the two currents in an arrangement similar to the summer of Chap. 1. If the output voltage is kept small compared with the input, then we might employ a circuit whose volt-ampere characteristics are logarithmic to reconvert $\log A + \log B$ to the product AB. This basic circuit is shown in block-diagram form in Fig. 2-40.

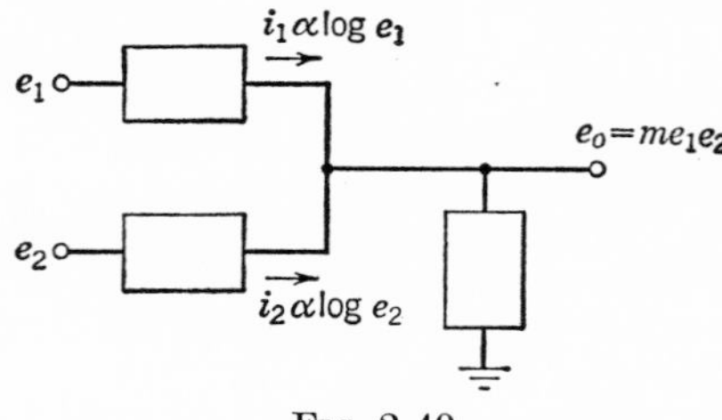

FIG. 2-40

(*a*) As the first step, design a diode circuit which will approximate the logarithmic volt-ampere response for positive input signals. Except for a scale factor, the input current should exactly agree with $\log e_{in}$ at the following integer voltages: 10, 20, 40, 70, and 100 volts. Use 100 K as your smallest resistance value and specify all resistors and bias sources.

(*b*) If we use tables to reconvert the sum of the logs found from the two circuits of part *a*, what error is introduced when multiplying the following numbers: 20 × 65, 20 × 50, 12 × 30?

(*c*) If we use a circuit identical with that developed in part *a* (except that the smallest resistor is now 1,000 ohms) for reconversion of the sum of the logs to the product of the input voltages, then

$$e_o = me_1e_2$$

What is the circuit constant m? To what values would the errors of the products of part *b* increase as a result of this additional circuit?

2-24. (*a*) Discuss the effects on the transfer characteristic of the circuit of Fig. 2-28 when we return the bottom of R_2 to a variable bias instead of directly to ground.

(*b*) A 100-volt peak-to-peak sinusoidal signal is applied at the input of this circuit. Sketch the input and output to scale and determine the transmission angle if the following circuit components are used:

$$|E_{z1}| = |E_{z2}| = 20 \text{ volts} \qquad R_1 = 10 \text{ K} \qquad R_2 = 100 \text{ K}$$

2-25. Prove that the circuit of Fig. 2-41 also simulates a dead zone. Calculate the transfer characteristic and specify all break points and slopes. What would happen to the transfer characteristics if diode D_1 is transferred from point A to point B?

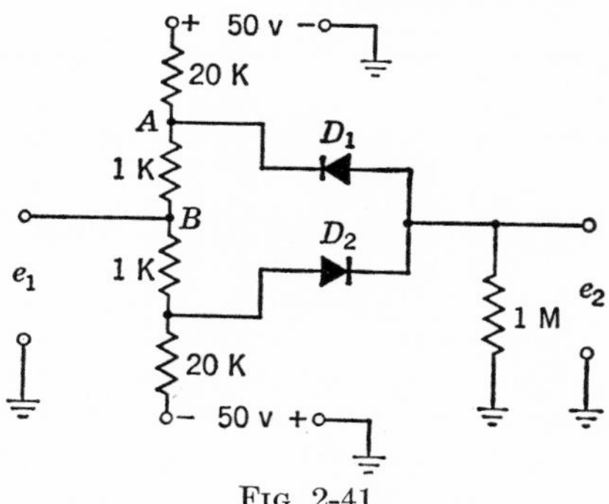

FIG. 2-41

2-26. An 80-volt peak-to-peak symmetrical triangular wave is impressed at the input of the hysteresis circuit of Fig. 2-29. The dead zone is symmetrically located about the origin and has a width of ±10 volts. Sketch the input and output to scale if the circuit saturates at ±30 volts. R_1 is very small, and C is very large.

2-27. The circuit of Fig. 2-29 may also be employed as a memory, as may any device exhibiting hysteresis. If the saturation region crosses the vertical axis, then once the input drives the output into saturation, the output will remain there even after the removal of the input pulse. Only by injecting a pulse of the opposite polarity can the circuit be reset to the other saturation value.

(*a*) Design a circuit which will saturate at ±10 volts and which will cross the $e_1 = 0$ line at this value. The only two available voltages are ±45 volts. Specify all resistors and draw the transfer characteristic.

(*b*) Explain the disadvantages of setting the crossover point on the sloping side of the transfer characteristic instead of in the center or near the center of the saturation region.

(*c*) Sketch the output waveshape if the input pulses are those shown in Fig. 2-42.

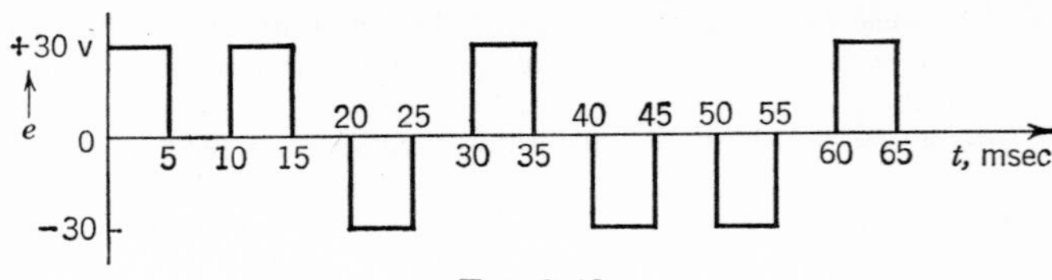

FIG. 2-42

2-28. The temperature-vs.-heat-content curve of many pure substances exhibits one or more dead zones. These occur where heat of fusion or heat of vaporization must be added to cause a change of state: solid to liquid or liquid to gaseous. For example, the temperature of ice increases linearly with heat content from −20 to 0°C and then remains there until sufficient heat has been added to melt all the ice. Temperature again increases with the addition of heat, but at a new rate to the boiling point.

(*a*) We are interested in developing a circuit to represent this action where the input voltage would correspond to the heat content (each volt to 2 cal) and with the output voltage corresponding to the temperature (5°C/volt). Choose water at 0°C as the origin of the axis and calculate the slopes, intercepts, and voltages needed to represent a temperature range from −20 to 90°C. Design the diode circuit which will give the required transfer characteristic. Try to use the minimum number of components.

(*b*) Repeat part *a* for a temperature range from −20 to 110°C. Choose a new calorie-temperature conversion ratio.

BIBLIOGRAPHY

Angelo, E. J., Jr.: "Electronic Circuits," McGraw-Hill Book Company, Inc., New York, 1958.

Millman, J., and H. Taub: "Pulse and Digital Circuits," McGraw-Hill Book Company, Inc., New York, 1956.

Stern, T. E.: Piecewise-linear Network Theory, *MIT Research Lab. Electronics Tech. Rept.* 315, June 15, 1956.

Zimmermann, H. J., and S. J. Mason: "Electronic Circuit Theory," John Wiley & Sons, Inc., New York, 1959.

CHAPTER 3

DIODE GATES

In contrast to Chap. 2, which treated diode networks excited at a single terminal, this chapter will discuss circuits designed for operation with multiple inputs. Where previously the complete circuit response was characterized by the transmission and volt-ampere curves, this simple representation now becomes quite inadequate. The multiplicity of inputs interact, and consequently the state of any particular diode, at any particular time, cannot be defined in terms of one input but rather depends on the relative effects of the several sources. It is completely possible for a signal applied at one set of terminals to control the transmission path between another terminal and the output. Since it is impossible to solve this problem in completely general terms, we shall at least try to answer the following three questions in the course of the analysis of specific circuits:

1. Does a transmission path exist from any one terminal to the output?
2. What conditions must be satisfied elsewhere in the network to establish (or to interrupt) this path?
3. How does the circuit behave in the two regions separated by the transmission threshold?

3-1. Application. Gates are circuits which make use of the bistate diode properties for switching purposes. Defined, not in the narrow sense of turning something on and off, even though this is included, but as the establishment of information transmission paths upon the application of a proper stimulus, diode gates find wide application in digital computers, control and measuring instruments, and stimulation systems. In computers the gate output amplitude is usually of little or no importance provided that it at least exceeds a preset threshold value. We consider the output's presence as representing a "yes," or 1, answer, with its absence as a "no," or 0, answer. Almost any desired information for computing or control can be conveyed and operated upon by passing a coded time sequence of pulses through various combinations of gates, each pulse carrying one item of information.

In special-purpose instruments, an external control signal, or proper sequence of signals, opens and closes the gate, thus allowing or preventing transmission of the information signal. Here the amplitude response becomes important because this information may later be used for control purposes.

Diode gates are classified, according to their performance, into three groups: the OR gate, which has an output when any one *or* all inputs are present; the AND gate, which allows an output only when *all* inputs are applied; the controlled gate, where a controlling signal turns on the gate, allowing transmission upon satisfaction of its other requirements.

Gate inputs are often short pulses. Consequently, to avoid introducing reading errors, the gate should open fast to transmit the individual pulse and close fast upon its removal to prevent false information from appearing at the output. Any delay in opening and closing creates an ambiguity in performance; therefore our investigation of the particular circuits must be concerned with both their amplitude and time response.

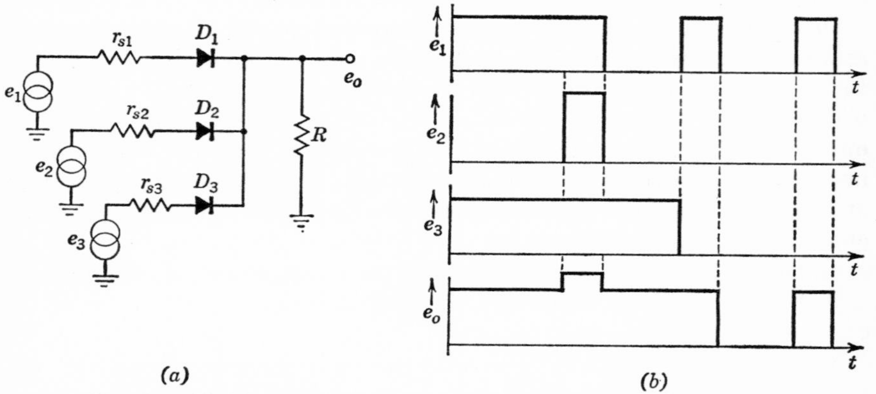

FIG. 3-1. (a) Three-diode OR gate; (b) input-output relationships.

3-2. OR Gate. The circuit of a simple OR gate designed for operation with positive input pulses appears in Fig. 3-1*a*. For negative inputs all diodes are reversed. The time relationship of the various inputs to the output is illustrated in Fig. 3-1*b*, ideal gate operation assumed.

For the initial discussion assume that the circuit is ideal; i.e., all source impedances (r_{s1}, r_{s2}, and r_{s3}) are zero and all diodes switch between open and short circuits. Suppose that at some instant $e_1 > 0$ and $e_2 = e_3 = 0$, the single diode D_1 associated with e_1 conducts, establishing the transmission path between input and output. The output, now equal to e_1, is larger than e_2 and e_3, back-biasing their associated diodes. Only the single source e_1 supplies power; it sees the load R. All other signal sources work into the open circuits of nonconducting diodes.

When all inputs are greater than zero, the output is equal to the largest. To prove this, apply the signals $e_1 > e_2 > e_3 > 0$ and assume that initially D_3 conducts. The resultant output e_3 is less than e_1 and e_2, forward-biasing their diodes. Thus there appears to be a transmission path for each of the inputs. However, this argument is fallacious: once D_1 conducts, the output reaches e_1, the highest voltage of all applied signals, back-biasing the diodes D_2 and D_3. Since we can only maintain the single transmission path through D_1, *the output of the* OR *gate automatically becomes equal to the largest input signal at each instant of time.*

The OR gate may be considered analogous to a group of normally open parallel relays or switches connected from various signal sources to the common output. Closing any one provides an output regardless of the state of any of the others. A mechanical system of several power sources coupled through clutches to the same drive shaft behaves similarly. The engagement of any single clutch furnishes rotational power, and if ratchet or slip clutches are used, only the one connected to the fastest-rotating power source transmits power. All others slip (back-biased).

Often a number of instrument or telemeter outputs whose source impedance may be too large to be ignored are the signals driving the gate. Before we can begin calculating the corrected amplitude response, we would like to know each diode's state so that it can be replaced by either an open or a short circuit. If only one input is applied, this problem is trivial. But suppose that all inputs are simultaneously excited by voltages of the same order of magnitude; how do we now find each diode's state? We might, as a first attempt, guess that they all conduct. Then, by superposition from the model found by replacing all diodes by short circuits ($r_s \gg r_f$), the output is

$$e_o = \frac{R \parallel r_{s2} \parallel r_{s3}}{r_{s1} + R \parallel r_{s2} \parallel r_{s3}} e_1 + \frac{R \parallel r_{s1} \parallel r_{s3}}{r_{s2} + R \parallel r_{s1} \parallel r_{s3}} e_2 + \frac{R \parallel r_{s1} \parallel r_{s2}}{r_{s3} + R \parallel r_{s1} \parallel r_{s2}} e_3 \tag{3-1}$$

The next step is to compare e_o found above with each input (e_1, e_2, e_3). If it is larger than one or more, then the diodes connecting the smaller-amplitude generators are back-biased and those particular inputs cannot contribute to the output. For example, when $e_o < e_1$, $e_o < e_2$ but $e_o > e_3$, we must modify Eq. (3-1) by opening the transmission path from e_3 to the output. The output now becomes

$$e_o' = \frac{R \parallel r_{s2}}{r_{s1} + R \parallel r_{s2}} e_1 + \frac{R \parallel r_{s1}}{r_{s2} + R \parallel r_{s1}} e_2 \tag{3-2}$$

Under the circuit conditions leading to Eq. (3-2), signal sources e_1 and e_2 are loaded by both R and each other; e_3 isolated by its back-biased diode need not be considered. The signal power requirements are determined by the current each source must supply. This depends upon the difference between the open-circuit terminal voltage and the output voltage, and thus upon the contributions from all other signals. For example, the current flow from e_1 is

$$i_1 = \frac{e_1 - e_o}{r_{s1}}$$

If the OR gate contains more than the three sources shown, the additional ones are treated similarly, contributing to the output only when their particular diode conducts.

Transient Response. Our investigation of the transient response of the OR gate will initially concern itself, for simplicity, with the two-diode gate shown in Fig. 3-2. High source impedance degenerates the pulse waveshape by increasing the circuit time constants; if we are interested in fast response, the gate must be driven from such low-impedance sources as cathode followers or transformers.

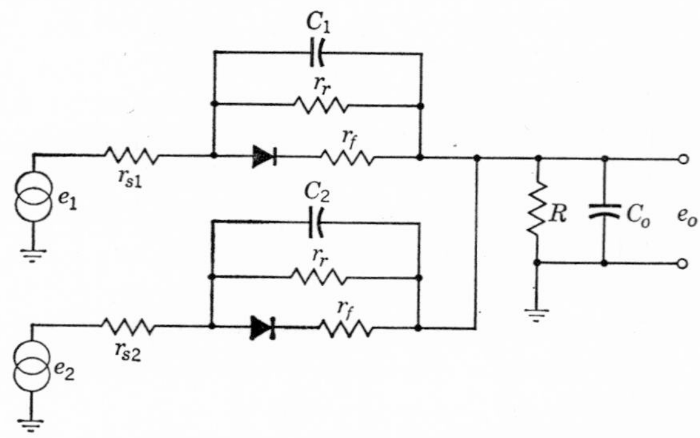

FIG. 3-2. Two-diode OR gate—piecewise-linear circuit.

In the above circuit the diode shunt capacity, only about 1 or 2 $\mu\mu$f, is obviously much less than the total stray output capacity (10 to 50 $\mu\mu$f). By neglecting the small term, we avoid the necessity of calculating the response of a circuit containing two independent energy-storage elements, the series combination of r_{s2} and C_2 in parallel with R and C_o. Furthermore, a gate should not attenuate the input pulse excessively while transmitting it. This requires that $(r_r \parallel R) \gg (r_f + r_{s1})$. Under these conditions the output's peak value will be almost the same as that of the single input, rising toward this peak with a time constant τ_1, which is found from inspection of the simplified model.

$$\tau_1 = [(r_{s1} + r_f) \parallel R \parallel r_r]C_o \cong (r_{s1} + r_f)C_o \tag{3-3}$$

After the input pulse disappears, the output decays toward zero with the much longer time constant

$$\tau_2 \cong \left(R \parallel \frac{r_r}{2}\right) C_o \tag{3-4}$$

Figure 3-3 shows the applied input and the resultant output pulse. We might observe that for an extremely narrow input pulse, e_o might never reach the final value and might not even pass the arbitrarily designated threshold before the input drops to zero. In addition, the long decay time constant smears the trailing edge, causing the output to persist for some time after the input's removal, a false indication that the input is still present. We see that the gate's resolution is severely limited by its time constants; it cannot distinguish extremely narrow pulses.

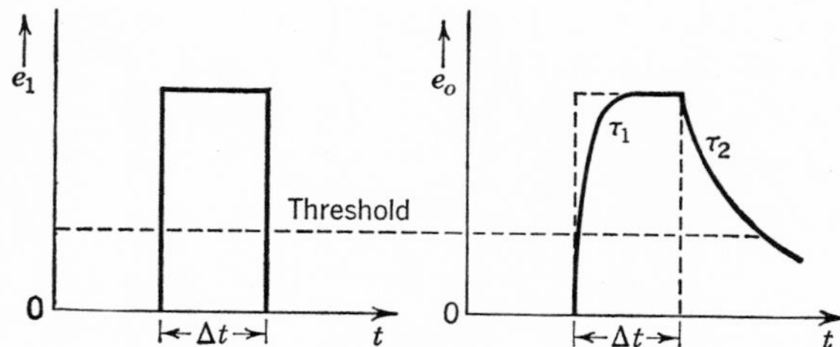

FIG. 3-3. OR-gate input and resultant output pulse.

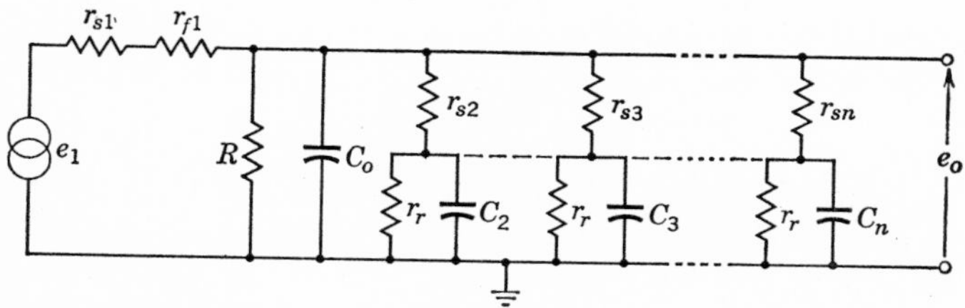

FIG. 3-4. n-diode-gate equivalent circuit—single-diode excitation.

Computer OR gates, receiving information pulses from many sources, usually contain appreciably more than the two diodes shown in Fig. 3-2. We suspect, even before we begin calculating the response, that the additional ones will affect the pulse waveshape through the increased resistive and capacitive loading introduced. In any OR gate, when only one diode is excited, all the others are back-biased and in parallel. This is indicated in the equivalent circuit of an n-diode OR gate (Fig. 3-4). Furthermore, it might reasonably be expected that, in any one system, the inputs would be supplied from similar sources to nearly identical diodes. Since all the back-biased diode branches are identical, the same voltage must be developed across each branch element, thus allowing us to connect equivalent elements together (the dashed line of Fig. 3-4).

By doing this we parallel all source impedance ($r_{s1}, r_{s2}, \ldots, r_{sn}$); and as n increases, this combination decreases proportionally, approaching zero as a lower limit. Even though it is difficult to justify the omission of a single source impedance, it is relatively easy to justify the neglect of the very-low-resistance parallel combination. The reduced circuit places all capacity in parallel, becoming a single-energy-storage-element system. Furthermore, $R \parallel [r_r/(n-1)] \gg (r_{s1} + r_f)$, preventing excessive pulse attenuation by the gate. As a consequence,

$$\tau_1 \cong (r_{s1} + r_f)[C_0 + C_d(n-1)] \qquad (3\text{-}5)$$

where C_d is the shunt capacity of the individual diode. The increase in time constant, completely due to the diode capacity loading, slows the initial rate of pulse rise. Therefore, if narrow pulses are to be transmitted, we must limit the number of diodes in any one gate.

After the termination of the pulse, the energy stored in the output capacity back-biases all diodes and the output decays with the slow time constant

$$\tau_2 \cong R \parallel \frac{r_r}{n} (C_0 + nC_d) \qquad (3\text{-}6)$$

For n sufficiently large, the circuit resistance during decay is primarily determined by the reverse resistance of the parallel diode. It follows that Eq. (3-6) may be rewritten

$$\tau_2 \cong C_0 \frac{r_r}{n} + C_d r_r \qquad (3\text{-}7)$$

The first term of Eq. (3-7) is obviously much less than the two-diode decay time constant [Eq. (3-4)], and it further decreases with an increasing number of inputs. The second term is the very small recovery time constant of the individual diode. We come to the surprising conclusion that the additional diodes may even improve recovery through reduction of the circuit time constant. This is the direct consequence of the circuit resistance decreasing faster than the capacity increases. However, the greater loading of signal source has the adverse effect of increasing both the attenuation of the pulse and the source power requirements.

3-3. AND Gate. The AND gate determines coincidence, presenting an output when, and only when, all inputs are simultaneously excited. Its operation may be compared to a parallel combination of normally closed switches shorting the output to ground; only after opening all switches will the output be other than zero. In hydraulics, the analogous circuit is a series of check valves, all of which must be opened before any fluid flows from the source to the sink.

A simple diode AND gate operating on positive pulses appears in Fig. 3-5*a*, with the input-output time relationships shown in 3-5*b*. Since transmission of negative pulses is possible without coincidence of inputs, we include at the output a diode D_o whose function is to prevent negative excursions. For operation with negative inputs, all diodes and bias voltages are reversed.

When e_1 and/or e_2 are zero, at least one diode conducts, shorting the output to ground. (Ideal diodes and zero source impedance, as shown in Fig. 3-5*a*, are assumed for this initial discussion.) However, if signals

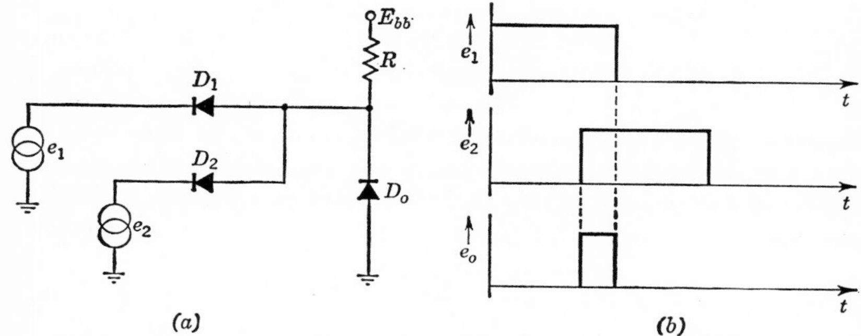

FIG. 3-5. (*a*) Ideal AND gate; (*b*) AND-gate input-output relationships.

are applied so that $E_{bb} > e_1 > e_2 > 0$, only diode D_2 conducts, and it connects the output terminal directly to the source e_2. Diode D_1 is back-biased, removing e_1 from the circuit. The output, consequently, will *always equal the smaller of the inputs.* A second possibility arises where both input signals are greater than E_{bb}, back-biasing both diodes. In this case the output rises to E_{bb}, its maximum possible value.

Transient Response. Having established the basic behavior of the AND gate, we are ready to proceed to the quantitative analysis of the possible modes of operation defined above, using, for this, the complete model of Fig. 3-6.

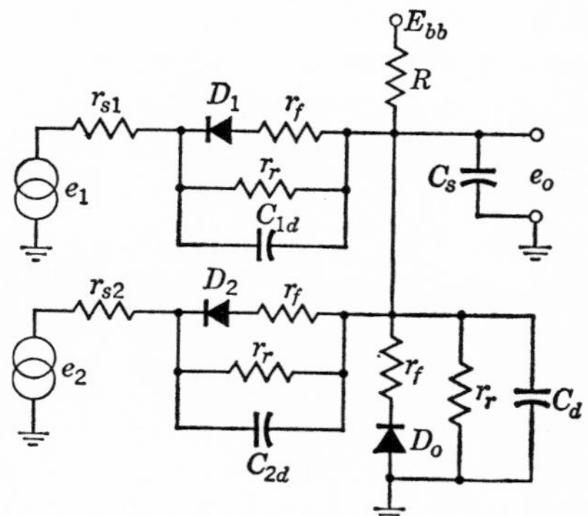

FIG. 3-6. Model of an AND gate showing parasitic capacity and resistance.

Case 1: $E_{bb} > e_1 > e_2 > 0$

Here the output rises to approximately e_2 from an initial voltage slightly above zero (due to the drop across $r_s + r_f$). Exact initial and final values are easily found by drawing and solving the resistive models holding. Before the pulses are applied, both diodes are conducting, but after reaching steady state, only D_2 conducts. Even a superficial examination convinces us that the condition necessary to minimize the small initial value and simultaneously to maximize the final value is

$$r_{s2} + r_f \ll R \ll \frac{r_r}{3} \tag{3-8}$$

Since the stray capacity prevents any instantaneous change at the output, upon injecting the input pulses all diodes are immediately driven off. The output rises toward E_{bb} with the time constant

$$\tau_1 = \left(R \parallel \frac{r_r}{3}\right)(C_s + 3C_d) \tag{3-9}$$

However, it will never reach E_{bb}; before it can do so the output will equal the smaller of the two inputs, e_2. D_2 is again forward-biased, and it limits the rise. At this point the charging suddenly ceases. The time required for the complete rise is given by

$$t_1 = \tau_1 \ln \frac{E_{bb}}{E_{bb} - e_2} \tag{3-10}$$

When the smallest pulse is 30 per cent less than E_{bb}, this time is only $1.2\tau_1$. Limiting e_2 to an even smaller percentage of E_{bb} will further reduce the circuit response time: with a pulse of $0.5E_{bb}$, the rise time is appreciably less than one time constant; it is only $0.69\tau_1$.

As soon as a single input returns to zero, the connecting diode again conducts and, using the inequality of Eq. (3-8), the output decays with the time constant

$$\tau_2 = (r_{s2} + r_f)(C_s + 2C_d) \tag{3-11}$$

Obviously, the decay through the on diode is much faster than the initial rise.

Case 2: $$e_1 > e_2 > E_{bb}$$

Under these circumstances the output will always be less than the amplitude of the applied excitation. The coupling diodes are initially driven off and remain in this state until the input pulses disappear. There will be no shortening of the output rise, which, within approximately $4\tau_1$, reaches E_{bb}. Even if the rise time is defined as in Eq. (1-32) (the time for the output to rise from 10 to 90 per cent of E_{bb}), it will still take $t_2 = 2.2\tau_1$ sec to reach an acceptable final value.

The decay in this case is identical with that found for case 1.

A graphical comparison of these cases, where the value of E_{bb} is adjusted so that both outputs are of the same amplitude, appears in Fig. 3-7. We conclude, from this sketch and from the relative rise times calculated above, that case 1 is the preferred class of operation, especially if we can set E_{bb} well above the pulse amplitude. It also offers other advantages in that the output pulse is not clipped during transmission and that it is available at low impedance (through the conducting diode) for direct application at the input of the next gate.

Additional input diodes change the gate response primarily by increasing the stray capacity and reducing the effective reverse resistance during the initial pulse rise. Arguments similar to those used with the OR gate lead to the same general conclusion: when extremely narrow pulses are the gating signals, the number of diodes in the gate must be limited; otherwise the gate will distort the pulse beyond all recognition.

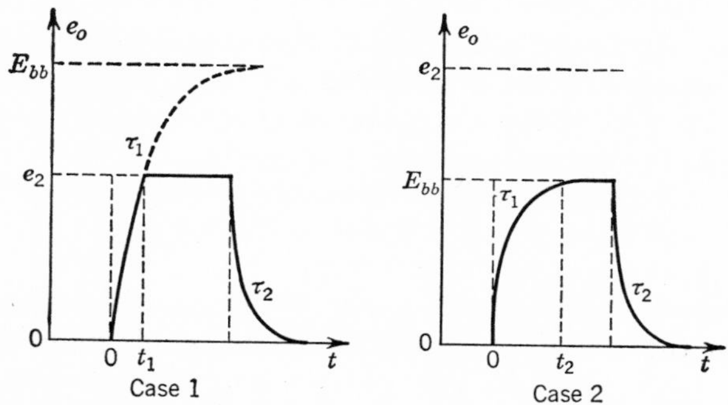

FIG. 3-7. Comparison of the output pulses under the two modes of AND-gate operation.

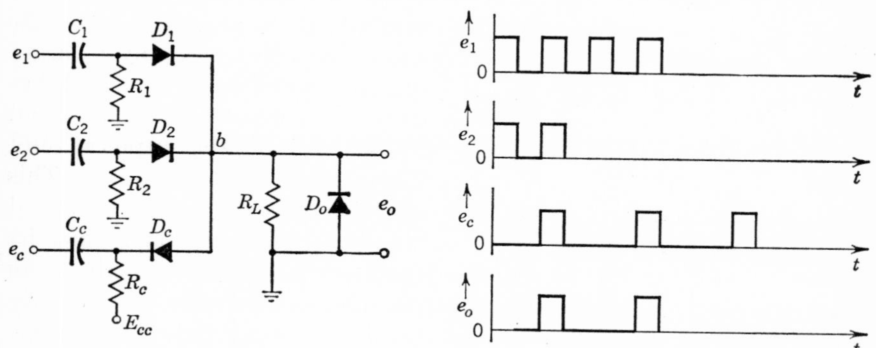

FIG. 3-8. Controlled gate, AND-OR, and the applied inputs and resultant output.

3-4. Controlled Gates. Almost any method of either shifting the d-c operating point of the gate or applying the control voltage in such a manner that it prevents transmission converts an ordinary AND or OR gate into a controlled one. An extremely simple change results in the circuit of Fig. 3-8, where the pulses are a-c-coupled rather than d-c-coupled as previously. Changing the input circuits back to the direct coupling used in Secs. 3-2 and 3-3 will not change the basic operation; it only changes the required driving signal.

The two input diodes constitute a simple OR gate transmitting to point b any positive pulses applied at e_1 and/or e_2. However, if D_o is kept conducting, the output pulse will have to be developed across its very low forward resistance. Consequently, the output remains close to zero regardless of the signals e_1 and e_2. The additional control diode D_c and its very negative bias voltage E_{cc} serve to maintain this condition by establishing a large forward-current flow. Diode D_o also performs the second function of preventing negative excursions at the output. A large positive control pulse applied at e_c back-biases the previously conducting control diode and keeps it back-biased until C_c can recharge through R_c. This pulse effectively disconnects the bias voltage from the output, allowing transmission of any positive pulses now applied at e_1 and/or e_2. We see, therefore, that the condition for opening this gate is the simultaneous excitation *at* e_c *and* e_1 *or* e_2.

Unless the input-circuit time constants are very long in comparison with the pulse duration, they will distort the applied signals, leading to a correspondingly poor output waveshape.

Returning the control diode of Fig. 3-8 to a positive bias voltage E_{bb}, rather than the negative one shown, changes this gate into a NOT-OR circuit. The positive voltage normally back-biases D_c so that it plays no role when pulses are applied at e_1 and/or e_2. But if simultaneously we apply a larger negative pulse at e_c, it establishes a conduction path through D_o and D_c, maintaining the output at zero, independent of e_1 and e_2. This negative pulse is sometimes referred to as an inhibiting signal since its function is to prevent the gate from opening. A similar modification of an AND gate produces an equivalent NOT-AND circuit.

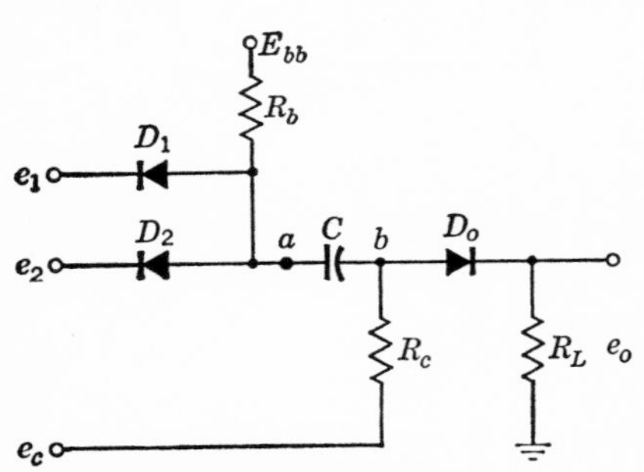

FIG. 3-9. Threshold gate.

Another type of controlled gate appears in Fig. 3-9, where we can recognize the two input diodes as an AND gate. D_1 and D_2 normally conduct, maintaining the voltage of point a at zero, provided that at least one input remains zero. C charges to the negative control voltage e_c. To prevent this negative voltage also appearing at the output, we decouple through the diode D_o.

After opening the AND gate (large positive pulses at all inputs), whatever signal appears at point a must be transmitted by C to point b. If e_c is a slightly negative d-c bias, D_o will now be forward-biased, allowing the output to rise to the difference between the minimum applied input pulse and the control voltage. When e_1 is that particular pulse, the output becomes

$$e_o = e_1 - e_c > 0 \tag{3-12}$$

where e_c, the initial charge on the coupling capacitor, may be considered as the transmission threshold. Coincidences of input signals of greater amplitude are transmitted, while those of lesser amplitude cannot establish a transmission path and will not produce any output [Eq. (3-12)]. If the threshold is set slightly above the noise level, then the random noise pulses will not be transmitted and will not register falsely at the output.

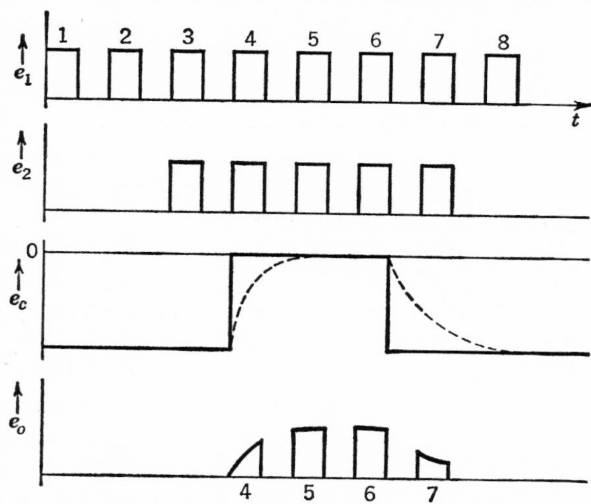

FIG. 3-10. Controlled-gate input-output pulses.

An alternative mode of gate operation occurs when we initially set e_c negative enough to prevent transmission for all possible amplitude input pulses. Only after a positive control signal e_c charges the capacitor to a voltage close to zero will satisfaction of the AND gate produce an output. This switching action is similar to that discussed for the first controlled gate considered. But where the first gate was primed immediately upon the injection of the control pulse, this gate is not ready for transmission until considerably later, until C charges. Even though one of the input diodes always conducts, the charge and discharge time constants R_cC are quite long. In the pulse-time relationships (Fig. 3-10), note that the direct consequence of this is very poor transmission of pulse 4, good transmission of pulse 5, proper transmission of pulse 6, and false transmission of pulse 7. Obviously, use of this gate must be limited to pulse trains having wide separation. Replacing R_c with a diode connected for fast charging of C during the positive control pulse improves the turn-on time, but not the gate's final recovery time.

3-5. Diode Arrays. One problem which arises quite often when information must be transmitted along several channels is how to select the proper one out of a number of possibilities. But the problem may be even more complicated; the same input may have to be transferred between various paths in a controlled time sequence. We can do this by using a number of independent diode gates. One input to each gate is used for the information to be transmitted while the other inputs are used for the control signals, i.e., the pulses that open and close the gate at the appropriate times.

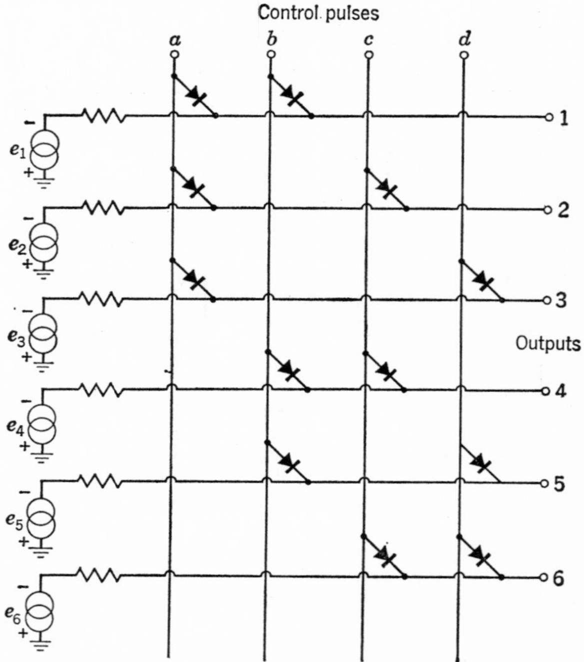

FIG. 3-11. AND array used for transmission selection.

When these gates are combined into one matrix, we refer to the resultant circuit as a diode array. Figure 3-11 illustrates one such array where the excitation of two out of four control channels opens an information path for negative signals. The diodes connected to any one of the information channels (1 to 6) constitute an AND gate. As they are normally conducting through the control-pulse generator, they establish a low-impedance path, shunting the signal to ground. However, if large negative pulses are simultaneously applied to two out of the four control channels (a, b, c, and d), the associated pair of diodes are back-biased, the gate is opened, and transmission along one path becomes possible.

For example, the excitation of a and b opens path 1, the excitation of a and c opens path 2, etc.

The statement of the particular two-out-of-four coding used for the selection of one out of six channels may be presented in a tabular form, called a truth table. We indicate by the symbol 1 that a pulse must be present in a particular control channel and by the symbol 0 that it may be absent. The array of Fig. 3-11 satisfies the following statement:

Channel	Pulse inputs			
	a	*b*	*c*	*d*
1	1	1	0	0
2	1	0	1	0
3	1	0	0	1
4	0	1	1	0
5	0	1	0	1
6	0	0	1	1

If all signal sources in the various channels (1, 2, . . . , 6) are identical, e.g., a constant negative voltage E_{cc}, then upon the application of the appropriate control signals, an output pulse will appear in a single channel. Thus the array translates the two pulses ab to mean number 1, as shown in the truth table. The simultaneous excitation of two out of four inputs steers the output to one point out of the six possibilities.

More complex logic situations may be satisfied by adding additional diodes in a larger matrix. These may appear as ORS as well as ANDS, and if both positive and negative control pulses are available, NOT diodes can also be included.

3-6. Diode Bridge—Steady-state Response. Under circumstances where the amplitude of the output contains important information, the gate requirements become extremely critical. Neither of the circuits examined in Sec. 3-4 is satisfactory for amplitude gating; in both the output voltage not only varies as a function of the control signal, but also contains some percentage of the control signal, even when all inputs are zero. For example, in the gate of Fig. 3-8 a small negative voltage is developed across the forward resistance of the output diode as a direct consequence of the current flow to E_{cc}.

One convenient method of avoiding these errors is by using a balanced system driven by two equal signals of opposite polarity. The error voltage produced by each signal will be equal and opposite, canceling out. Since we know that in linear circuits almost complete voltage cancellation takes place in a balanced bridge, we might well consider the application of a diode bridge for amplitude gating (Fig. 3-12). For the output to be completely free of the control signal, i.e., not contain any component directly contributed by this signal, the bridge must remain balanced under all conditions. Or rather, we must limit circuit operation to the conditions that will not unbalance the bridge.

Two balance conditions are obvious, the first when all diodes conduct:

$$\frac{r_{f1}}{r_{f2}} = \frac{r_{f3}}{r_{f4}} \tag{3-13}$$

and the second when all are back-biased:

$$\frac{r_{r1}}{r_{r2}} = \frac{r_{r3}}{r_{r4}} \tag{3-14}$$

To satisfy both Eqs. (3-13) and (3-14), the same type of diode is not only used for each arm of the bridge but is even individually selected and matched so that all will have identical forward and reverse resistance. Sometimes to further improve the balance, additional series and shunt resistors are added to each diode.

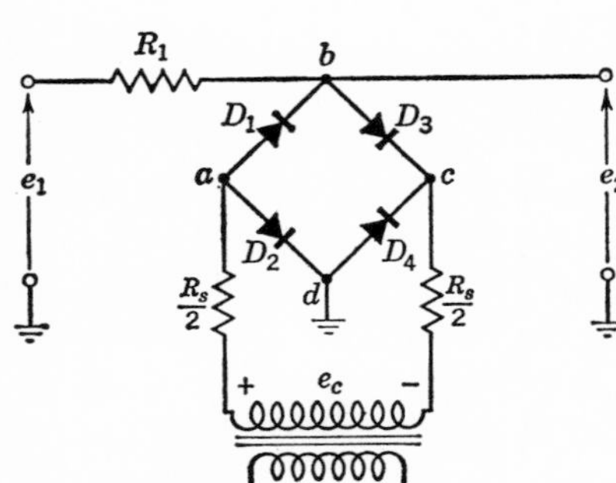

FIG. 3-12. Diode bridge.

Other conditions of bridge balance are also possible, for example, D_1 and D_2 on and D_3 and D_4 off or vice versa. We shall see below that this represents an impossible mode of bridge behavior and need not be considered. The remaining possible combinations of diode states occur when one set of diagonal diodes, D_1 and D_4, conducts and the other set, D_2 and D_3, is back-biased. But this leaves us with an unbalanced bridge, an undesirable situation which must be avoided.

From the above discussion, we conclude that the sole function of the control or gating signal is the closing and opening of the gate, i.e., bringing the diodes into and out of conduction. Any large enough signal will cause switching, but to guarantee definitive diode states the signal should switch them smartly. For this reason we choose a symmetrical square wave, having a peak-to-peak amplitude of $2E$ for our gating voltage. If this signal is supplied from a source unbalanced with respect to the balance point of the bridge (in this case ground), then all diodes will not be equally excited, and with a very unbalanced drive some diodes may remain completely unexcited. We must therefore either use a balanced generator output or drive the bridge through a transformer. For the polarity indicated in Fig. 3-12, all diodes are conducting, and on reversed polarity, all become back-biased. However, this statement implicitly assumes that the contribution from e_1, which will be examined below, is not large enough to turn off a conducting diode or to turn on a nonconducting one.

When e_c forces all diodes into their active region, they present a very low resistance from the output to ground. By replacing them with their forward resistance, we see that across either diagonal ac or bd (Fig. 3-12), the resistance is the same as that of a single diode r_f. Secondly, when the bridge is properly balanced, the voltage from b to d, due to e_c, must be zero; it depends only on e_1. Likewise, the voltage developed from a to c depends only on e_c.

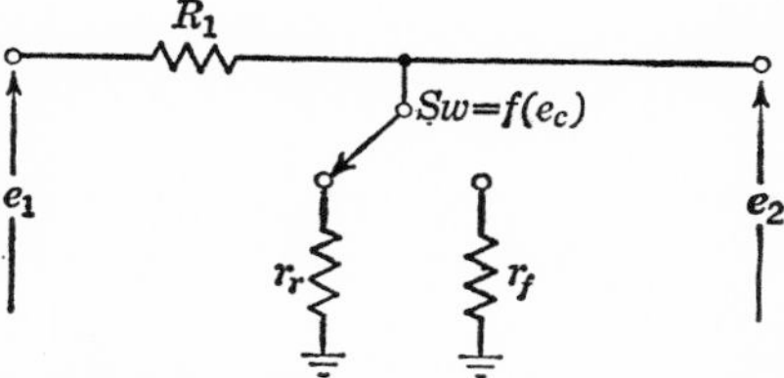

FIG. 3-13. Equivalent bridge circuit—the switch position is a function of the control signal.

The reversal of the control signal back-biases all diodes, allowing us to replace them by their reverse resistance. The resistance from output to ground, bd, now becomes r_r, and if the bridge is still properly balanced, again e_c will not contribute to the output.

Thus the gating signal causes sequential shunting of the output, first by r_f and then by r_r. The circuit related to e_1 appears similar to the shunt clipper of Chap. 2 where the clipping diode shunted the output by its forward resistance to prevent undesired transmission and by its reverse resistance to allow desired signal transmission. This leads us to interpret bridge operation as controlled clipping with its information transmission path a function of the control signal period (and voltage) rather than input signal amplitude. Since the two circuit states shown in Fig. 3-13 are the same as those existing in the clipper, the problem posed in solving for the optimum value of R_1 must lead to the identical value found in Chap. 2 [Eq. (2-9)]:

$$R_1 = \sqrt{r_r r_f}$$

We shall now direct our attention to the input signal and examine the circumstances under which it could unbalance the bridge by changing the state of one or more diodes. A straightforward and convenient approach is to first calculate, and then compare, the two current components in the individual diode, one produced by the gating source and the other by the input signal. When the total diode current changes sign, the diode changes state. The individual diode current component maintaining the bridge closed (diodes conducting) is supplied by the gating signal.

Solving the model of Fig. 3-14 yields

$$I_{co} = \frac{E}{2(R_s + r_f)} \tag{3-15}$$

The maximum contribution from e_1 occurs at the peak of the input voltage.

$$I_{1o} = \frac{E_{1m}}{2(R_1 + r_f)} \tag{3-16}$$

The total current supplied by each signal is twice the current flow in the individual diode due to that source.

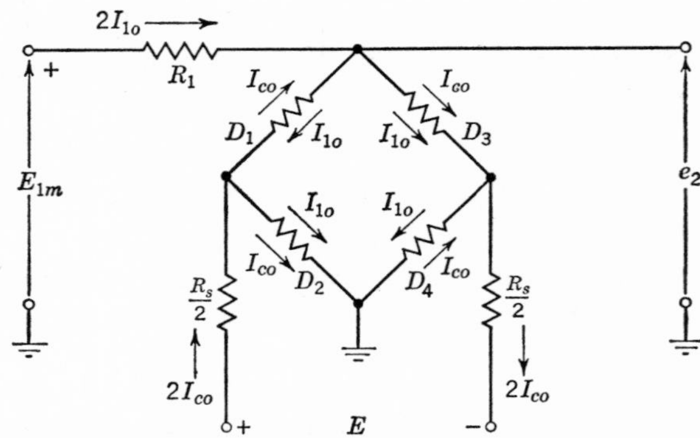

FIG. 3-14. Bridge current flow during conduction (all bridge resistors are r_f).

In Fig. 3-14 the direction of the individual current components is indicated by the arrows. Note that the two components subtract in D_1 and D_4 but add in D_2 and D_3. The former diode pair is in danger of being forced out of conduction on the positive input peaks, and the latter on the negative peaks. To prevent this, the contribution from the gating signal [Eq. (3-15)] must always be greater than the current supplied by the signal source [Eq. (3-16)]. By writing the required inequality, we arrive at one relationship between the three remaining unknowns E, E_{1m}, and R_s:

$$\frac{E}{R_s} \geq \frac{E_{1m}}{R_1} \tag{3-17}$$

Equation (3-17) takes the form given since both R_1 and R_s are much greater than r_f.

For a second relationship, we naturally turn to the second bridge state, the open gate (all diodes back-biased). The individual diode current supplied by the gating voltage flows in the direction opposite to the previously found I_{co}, and its amplitude is

$$I_{cn} = \frac{-E}{2(R_s + r_r)} \tag{3-18}$$

The current furnished from the signal source still can flow in the same direction as I_{1o}, but its value changes to

$$I_{1n} = \frac{E_{1m}}{2(R_1 + r_r)} \tag{3-19}$$

Under these circumstances the direction of current flow is such that on the positive inputs the two components add in D_1 and D_4 and subtract in D_2 and D_3. Conditions established may drive one pair of diagonal diodes into conduction on the positive peak and the other pair on the negative peak of the input signal. Of course, this would again seriously unbalance the bridge, and to prevent this, we must also satisfy the second inequality

$$\frac{E_{1m}}{R_1 + r_r} < \frac{E}{R_s + r_r}$$

But since $R_s \ll r_r$ and $R_1 \ll r_r$, this simply reduces to

$$E_{1m} < E \tag{3-20}$$

An additional complication arises because a diode's resistance is not constant in each region as depicted by the piecewise-linear model, but varies rather widely with its current. By taking the slope of the curve (Fig. 3-15), we see that the forward incremental resistance decreases from a relatively high value at small currents to a very low nearly constant resistance for large forward-current flow. The inverse incremental resistance increases with increasing reverse-current flow to some maximum, and then begins decreasing.

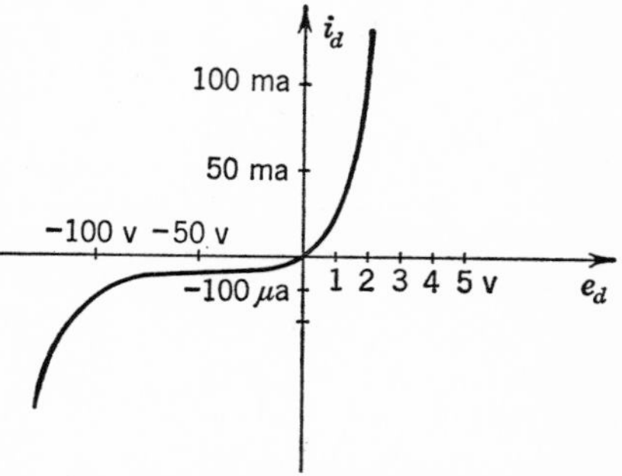

FIG. 3-15. Diode characteristic.

Whether the bridge is open or closed, the additional current contribution from the signal source increases current flow in one and decreases it in the opposing diagonal diode pair, thus decreasing the resistance of the first and increasing that of the second set of diodes. These opposing changes just compound the unbalancing of the bridge. We can minimize this second-order effect through setting the quiescent point at the center of the forward linear region of the diode and permitting only small current excursions about this point. Since $E/2$ appears across each back-biased diode ($R_s \ll r_r$), this voltage should place the diode in the center of its reverse linear region for optimum bridge performance.

Examination of Eqs. (3-15), (3-16), (3-18), and (3-19) indicates that in both regions, e_c may be considered as setting the quiescent current and e_1 as causing the incremental current variations about this point. And as in all piecewise-linear circuits, when the peak incremental current exceeds the quiescent value, the circuit limits. We conclude from Eq. (3-15) that with any given peak driving signal E, we should choose R_s to supply sufficient forward current to set the conducting bridge in its linear region. In addition, in order to maintain small-signal performance, E_{1m} must be limited to some small fraction of E [Eq. (3-20)]. The exact

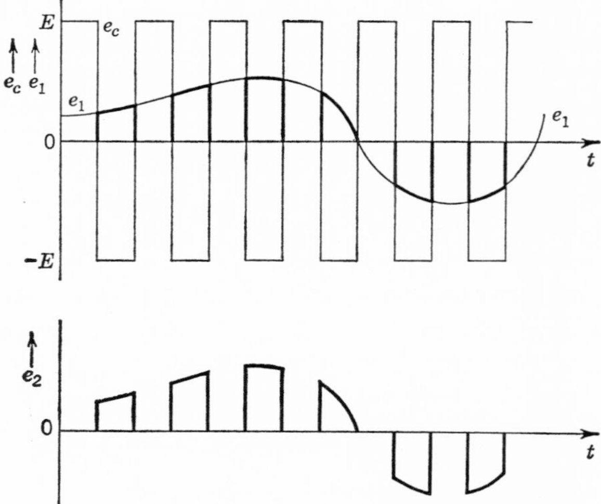

FIG. 3-16. Bridge input-output signal relationships.

percentage depends on the second-order variation of diode resistance and, of course, will vary with diode type. Generally, satisfactory results have been obtained on limiting the signal to 10 to 50 per cent of E.

Waveshapes of the input (square-wave control signal superimposed) and the resultant gate output, illustrating the gate's operation, are shown in Fig. 3-16. Note that the output appears only during the negative half period of the gating signal when the bridge is nonconducting. The gating signal chops the input into a train of equally spaced varying-amplitude pulses. For this reason the bridge gate is often referred to as a chopper, or a bridge modulator.

Many alternative circuit configurations are practicable, each solving a particular amplitude gating problem. The bridge can be interposed in series with the transmission path rather than in shunt. It can be used in a push-pull system or the single-ended one previously discussed, driven by direct current pulses, or even sinusoidal signals. The bridge might be used for bilateral as well as unilateral transmission, since its resistance is independent of signal direction. One feasible circuit, illustrating many versatile attributes of the diode bridge, is shown here in Fig. 3-17. The bilateral transmission path (e_1 to e_2 and vice versa) is instituted by forward-biasing the diodes and interrupted by back-biasing them.

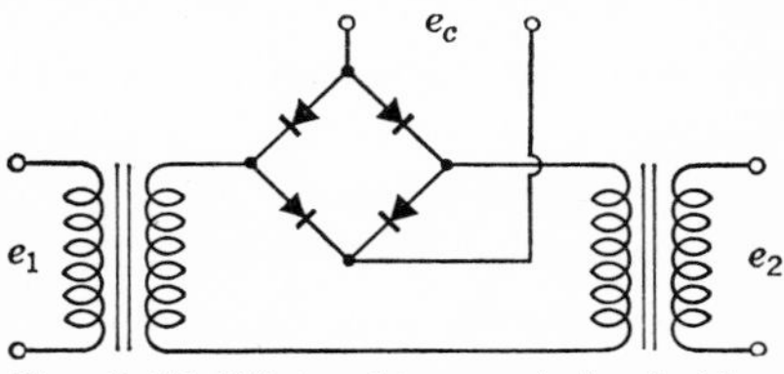

FIG. 3-17. Bilateral transmission bridge.

3-7. Diode Bridge—Transient Response. The response of the diode bridge to the leading and trailing edges of the control signal determines the switching time and, consequently, the output waveshape. Moreover, because of the interaction within the gate, the input signal will likewise play a role in determining the response of the bridge to the gating signal. An exact analysis of the total problem becomes unreasonably tedious, but the approximate response, sufficient to delineate the limitations of the bridge, is not difficult to calculate. We divide the problem into two parts: first, we find the time required to turn the bridge on and off with the signal set at zero; second, we calculate the response of the bridge output with respect to the input, while the bridge alternately conducts and opens.

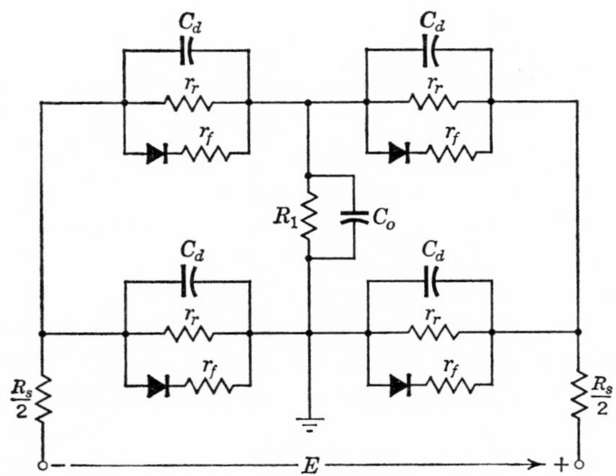

FIG. 3-18. Bridge model for the calculation of turn-on, turn-off times.

For calculation of the turn-on, turn-off time, we can use the model of Fig. 3-18 and, if the bridge is perfectly balanced, the parallel combination of R_1 and C_o will not influence its response. Assume that the bridge is open (diodes off), on the verge of switching closed. Since

$R_s \ll r_r$, the initial charge on each diode capacitor is $-E/2$, maintaining the diode cut off.

At $t = 0$, e_c changes polarity. Each capacitor starts charging toward the new steady-state voltage of $+E/2$ with a time constant found from the series-parallel diode branches,

$$\tau_1 = (r_r \parallel R_s)C_d \cong R_s C_d \tag{3-21}$$

In calculating Eq. (3-21) we might note that, in terms of the effective resistance and capacity, the four diodes in the balanced bridge look like a single diode. Thus the exponential response of the voltage across a single diode becomes

$$e_d = \tfrac{1}{2}E - Ee^{-t/\tau_1} \tag{3-22}$$

Eventually this voltage reaches zero and the diodes change state—they begin conducting. Equation (3-22), evaluated at $e_d = 0$, gives the bridge turn-off time as

$$t_1 = \tau_1 \ln 2 \tag{3-23}$$

The now-active diodes reduce the circuit time constant to the almost insignificant τ_2.

$$\tau_2 \cong C_d r_f$$

C_d continues charging, but toward a new steady-state value E_2, found by taking the Thévenin equivalent voltage across each diode in the model holding for this region.

$$E_2 = \frac{r_f}{r_f + R_s}\frac{E}{2} \cong \frac{r_f}{2R_s}E$$

When the control signal again changes polarity, the energy stored in the shunting capacity maintains conduction for some short time. Instead of initially charging toward $-E/2$, each diode charges toward

$$E_3 \cong -\frac{r_f}{2R_s}E$$

with the time constant τ_2.

The bridge turn-on time (diodes cut off) becomes

$$t_2 = \tau_2 \ln 2 \tag{3-24}$$

which is the same fraction of the appropriate time constant τ_2 as the turn-on time was of τ_1 [compare Eqs. (3-23) and (3-24)]. On reaching zero after this very short time, the diode turns off and its capacity recharges to $-E/2$, with the reverse time constant τ_1. Recovery is virtually complete within four time constants. Figure 3-19 illustrates the behavior of a single diode, showing both its turn-on and turn-off times.

When the gating period is sufficiently long, these switching times become insignificant. They do, however, set a definite lower limit to the usable square-wave period. In addition, any capacitive unbalance causes unequal diode turn-on and turn-off times, unbalancing the bridge and producing sharp exponential pulses at the output. Sometimes additional trimmer capacitors are placed across each diode and adjusted for proper capacitive balance. This, of course, increases C_d, and consequently the time required to switch the diodes from on to off, and vice versa.

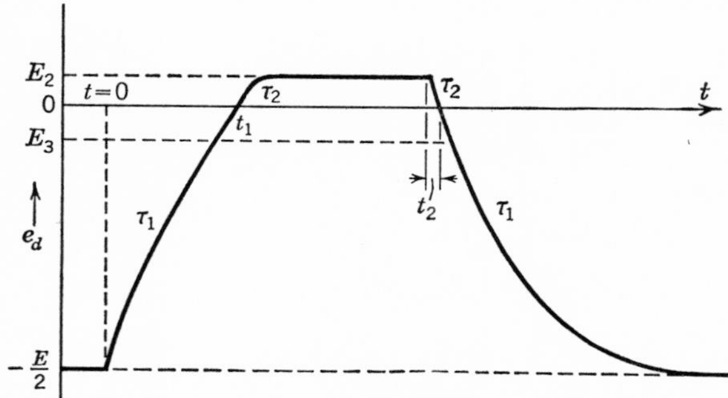

FIG. 3-19. Single-diode voltage waveshape produced by e_c.

The solution of the second part of the response problem, i.e., calculation of the output waveshape with respect to the input itself, becomes almost trivial once we draw the proper model. Since the bridge behaves as a controlled clipper, it might well be represented as two resistors and a switch controlled by e_c, alternately connecting one and then the other (Fig. 3-20a). The circuit has two time constants: a long one for the rise τ_3 and a short one for the decay τ_4.

$$\tau_3 \cong R_1(C_o + C_d) \qquad \tau_4 \cong r_f(C_o + C_d) \tag{3-25}$$

We can expect τ_3 to be much longer than the bridge turn-off time constant τ_1 [Eq. (3-21)], as a consequence of the extra stray capacity at the output, and it will determine the fastest allowable gating signal.

If we now attempt to find the actual bridge response by combining the response of each signal taken individually, we find ourselves facing a rather difficult problem. The calculation of turn-on and turn-off times had ignored the presence of the input signal, which will, during the turn-off interval, contribute additional current to one diagonal pair and reduce that flowing in the other pair. A rising voltage appears across the diodes because of the gating signal (Fig. 3-19); therefore Eq. (3-20) will not remain satisfied until the gate is completely off. The two diagonal diodes D_2 and D_3 conduct first, unbalancing the bridge. A similar effect appears during the turn-on time; one pair of diagonal diodes cut off before the other pair, again causing bridge unbalance.

Because of this unbalancing, exponential overshoots contributed by the gating signal are evidenced at the output (Fig. 3-20*c*). By reconsidering the previous simplified discussion, the method of minimizing then becomes apparent. When the time constants τ_1 and τ_2 are small, the bridge recovers fast, remaining unbalanced for the smallest possible time and producing only narrow overshoots. Excessive output capacity may also slow circuit response, preventing the rapid rise shown below.

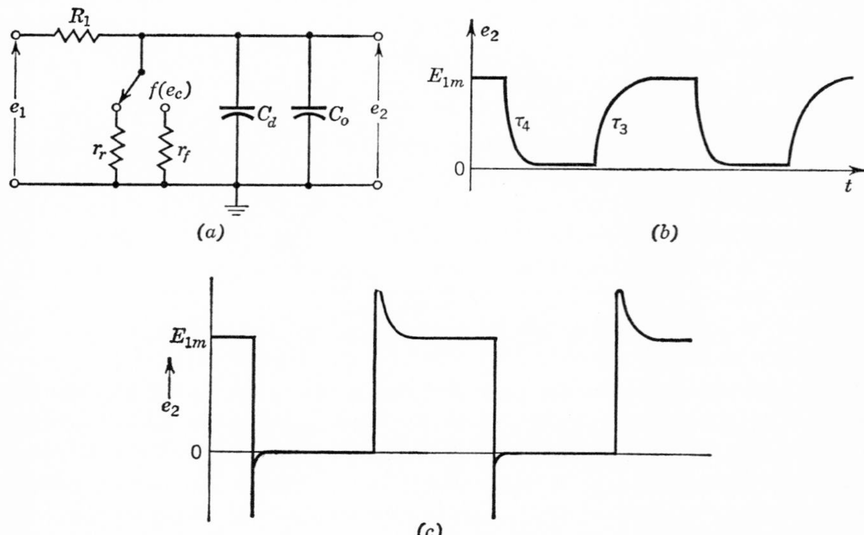

FIG. 3-20. (*a*) Bridge input-output equivalent model; (*b*) ideal output waveshape (constant input voltage); (*c*) actual output response.

However, these overshoots do improve the time response of the bridge, and if they are sufficiently narrow they may not disturb us at all.

3-8. Concluding Remarks on Diode Gates. Most gates may be broken down into combinations of the various types discussed in this chapter. The methods of analysis used are applicable to all since the problems faced are similar: rise and decay times, steady-state response, and the time required to open and close the gate.

Our discussion of the AND and OR gates purposely omitted the last point in order to simplify the first look at the subject. The student may now go back and with the material from Sec. 3-7 reexamine the earlier gates. In those gates the energy-storage elements across the diodes also prevent the immediate change of state; they maintain the previous condition in the face of circuit or excitation changes until they charge or discharge, as the case may be.

In the first sections of this chapter, the time constants given are those which affect the response after the diode has changed state. With diodes in common use, the opening and closure times are too small to be significant except when we try gating extremely narrow pulses. Of course, any additional stray capacity will change the circuit behavior and increase the significance of the switching delay.

Semiconductor diodes introduce additional delays in that they themselves do not immediately switch from on to off and back again upon pulse excitation. As a consequence of their physical structure, they have three inherent delays:

1. Turn-on time
2. Turn-off time
3. Storage time

Turn-on and turn-off times correspond to the very short time required to inject and sweep out the majority charge carriers in the diode materials. They depend on the physical structure, diode material, junction area, and mean electrical path. Generally, these times are relatively insignificant in determining total response, as they are much less than the storage time.

Some majority carriers are transported across the diode junction into the other material, where they become minority carriers; i.e., the current flow carries holes from the p to the n material and electrons from the n to the p material. Upon suddenly back-biasing the diode, forward current keeps flowing until recombination of the minority carriers is virtually completed. This again depends on the physical structure of the diode and even upon its crystal lattice configuration. The storage time varies widely with diode type, from a few microseconds to several millimicroseconds. Data available from the manufacturer aid in selecting the proper diodes for the various waveshapes employed; obviously, fast pulses cannot be transmitted by a diode which does not respond until after the pulse has disappeared.

At this point we shall briefly summarize our mode of attack on the nonlinear circuits analyzed in this chapter. A developmental procedure was followed, starting with the simplest possible circuit configuration and, step by step, increasing the complexity. In the first stage, we attempted to gain perspective by evaluating the steady-state operation and completely ignoring the transition from the initial to the final conditions. Knowledge of the starting point and of the end point aids in mapping the proper path between them. Our second consideration was the effects of the external energy-storage elements on the system response to the drive signals. At this time simplification, even drastic simplification, of the circuit avoids the necessity of concurrently treating more than a single independent energy-storage element.

Our third step concerned itself with the external capacity affecting the switching response of the nonlinear circuit element. Again we calculated the response as if this were an independent problem and used the results primarily to establish inherent circuit limitations. Finally, we had to consider any additional complexity introduced by the circuit-element response: diode on, off, and storage time; possible resistor and capacity nonlinearity; and any other phenomena which might affect the response in even minor ways.

PROBLEMS

3-1. In the OR gate of Fig. 3-1*a* the three signal sources have relatively high impedance (2 K each) and therefore, by comparison, the diodes may be assumed to be ideal elements. The inputs are shown in Fig. 3-21.

(*a*) What is the minimum load resistor which will ensure only one conducting diode at $t = 0.3$ sec?

(*b*) If $R = 10$ K, at what time will D_3 begin conducting? At what time will D_1 cease conduction?

(*c*) What is the effective load (e/i) on each of the three signal sources at a time midway between the two answers of part *b*?

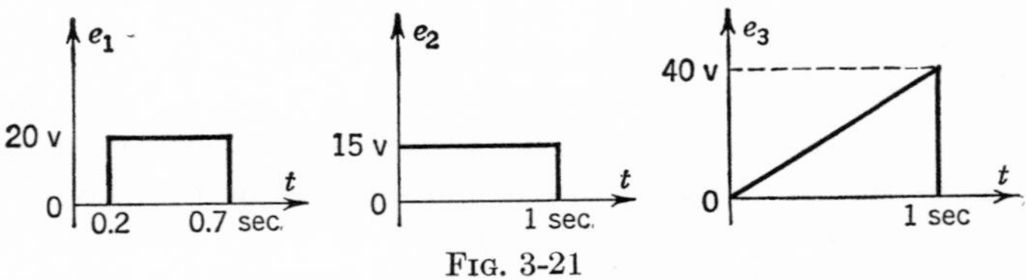

FIG. 3-21

3-2. The inputs of the OR gate of Fig. 3-2 are each excited by a positive pulse: e_1 is a 4-μsec-wide 20-volt pulse injected at $t = 0$ and e_2 is a 30-volt 5-μsec pulse applied 1 μsec later. Draw the output waveshape, labeling all important voltage values and time constants. The circuit parameters are given below. (Make all reasonable approximations.)

$$r_{s1} = r_{s2} = 500 \text{ ohms} \qquad R = 20 \text{ K}$$
$$C_1 = C_2 = 10\ \mu\mu\text{f} \qquad C_o = 0.001\ \mu\text{f}$$
$$r_f = 10 \text{ ohms} \qquad r_r = 100 \text{ K}$$

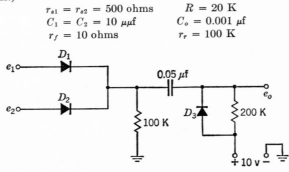

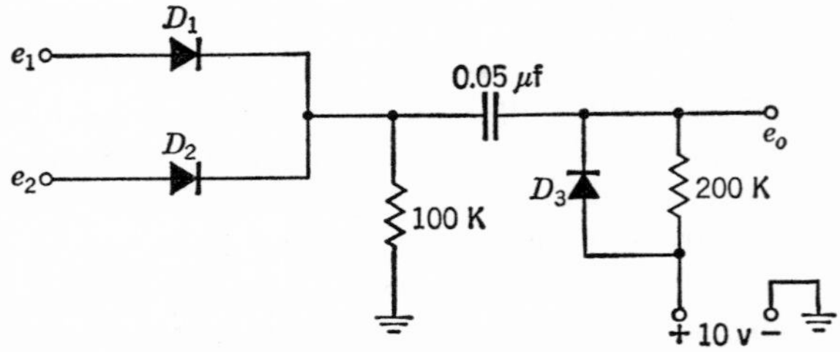

FIG. 3-22

3-3. Assume that the diodes in the gate of Fig. 3-22 are ideal and that they are excited from low-impedance sources.

(*a*) Sketch the output, giving all voltages and time constants if at $t = 0$ a 1-msec 15-volt positive pulse is applied at e_1 and a 2-msec 5-volt pulse at e_2.

(*b*) Repeat part *a* if D_3 is reversed.

3-4. (*a*) Sketch the output waveshape of the circuit of Fig. 3-23 if the diodes may be considered ideal.

(*b*) Show that the time constant of the input coupling circuit must be long compared with the rise time of the gate and the pulse width for optimum circuit response (nonideal diode).

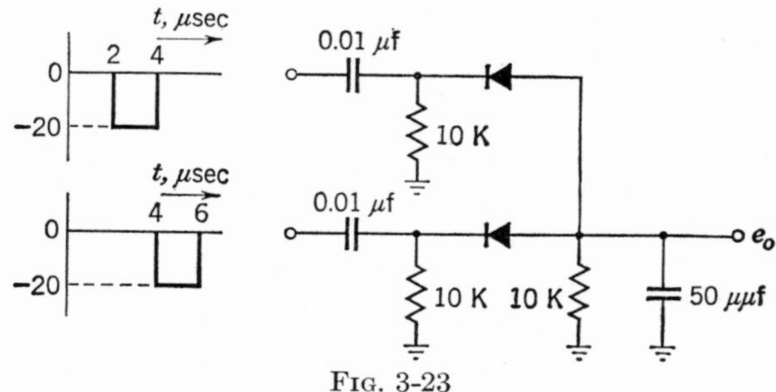

FIG. 3-23

3-5. (*a*) Draw the output waveshape of the AND gate of Fig. 3-24 if both inputs are simultaneously excited by 50-μsec pulses of −20 volts amplitude. Repeat if one pulse is reduced to −10 volts and the other remains at −20 volts.

(*b*) Repeat part *a* for the circuit resulting when D_o is removed.

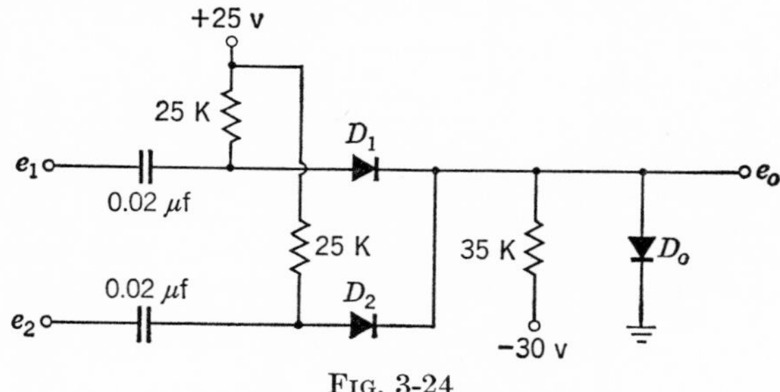

FIG. 3-24

3-6. The AND gate of Fig. 3-6 is excited by a unit step of 30 volts at e_1 and a staircase voltage which increases in steps of 10 volts every 5 μsec at e_2. A short time after the 40-volt step is reached, both inputs simultaneously drop to zero. The diode and circuit parameters are

$$r_f = 200 \text{ ohms} \qquad C_s = 250\ \mu\mu\text{f}$$
$$r_r = 500 \text{ K} \qquad R = 20 \text{ K}$$
$$C_d = 0 \qquad E = 25 \text{ volts}$$
$$r_s = 500 \text{ ohms}$$

Sketch the approximate output, indicating all time constants and important voltage values.

3-7. (*a*) If $E_{bb} > e_1 > e_2 > 0$ in an AND gate and if the signal source impedance is very small, show that the gate's excitation will result in a small jump in the output waveshape, after which it will rise exponentially to its final value. Calculate the value of this jump in terms of the circuit parameters. (HINT: Treat this gate as a compensated attenuator at $t = 0$.)

(*b*) Will such a jump appear in the OR gate? If it will, how large is it? Explain your answer.

3-8. The gate of Fig. 3-25 is connected as shown to two inputs, a pulse of 10 volts and 10 msec duration and a unit step of 100 volts.

(*a*) Find and sketch e_o, labeling the waveshape with respect to important voltages and times.

(*b*) If a 1,000-ohm relay coil which will operate when the current reaches 1 ma is inserted in series with D_2, at what time will the relay be energized? When will it be deenergized?

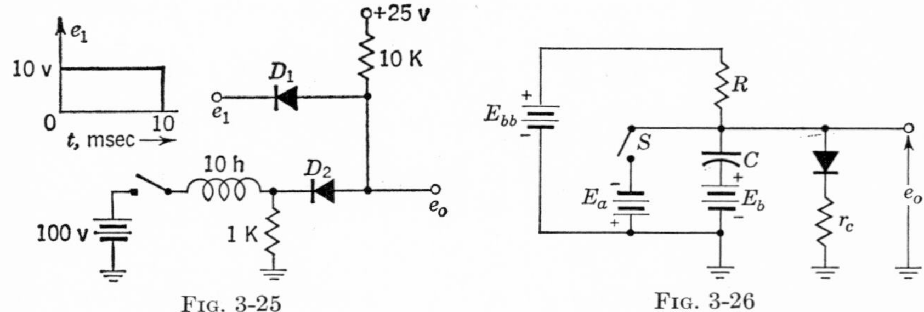

FIG. 3-25

FIG. 3-26

3-9. Figure 3-26 simulates the action of a single diode in a gate slowly recovering from a back-biased toward a conduction region. The switch is opened at $t = 0$, and the various circuit parameters are $r_c = 500$ ohms, $R = 20$ K, $C = 0.01$ μf, $E_{bb} = 50$ volts, $E_a = 10$ volts, and $E_b = 5$ volts.

(*a*) Plot the time response of this circuit.

(*b*) Evaluate the slopes of the two exponential segments at the point where they meet.

(*c*) Prove, in general terms, that in a circuit such as the one shown, the slopes of the two exponential segments are always equal at the point of intersection ($r_c \ll R$).

(*d*) Would the statement of part *c* be applicable if the diode was biased so as to conduct at a value other than zero?

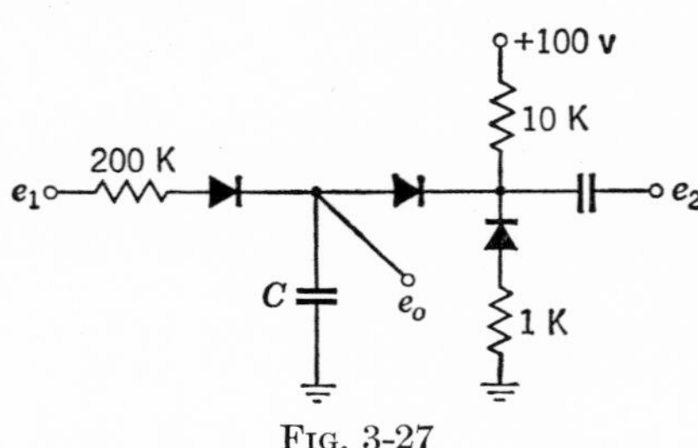

FIG. 3-27

3-10. (*a*) Show that the counting circuit of Fig. 3-27 will have an output proportional to the number of applied input pulses (e_1) provided that they are of equal amplitude and duration. Also discuss the possibility of erasing this stored information upon the injection of a sufficiently large negative pulse at e_2.

(*b*) If the amplitude of each pulse is 100 volts and its duration is only 2 μsec, what size capacitor must we use so that the output will rise by approximately 1 volt/pulse for up to 10 pulses? Sketch the output waveshape.

(*c*) Under the conditions of part *b*, how many pulses have been applied if the output reads slightly less than 25 volts?

3-11. In the controlled gate shown in Fig. 3-28 the controlling pulse is a 1,000-μsec 20-volt pulse which raises the normally negative control voltage from −20 volts to zero.

(*a*) A train of 10-volt 20-μsec positive pulses, spaced 100 μsec apart (from the end of one pulse to the beginning of the next one is 100 μsec) is the input to e_1. Sketch the output waveshape from slightly before the control pulse is applied until slightly after.

(*b*) Repeat part *a* if we simultaneously apply a 25-volt positive pulse train of the same duration and period at e_2.

(*c*) Does this gate offer any advantage over a similar operating version of the one shown in Fig. 3-9?

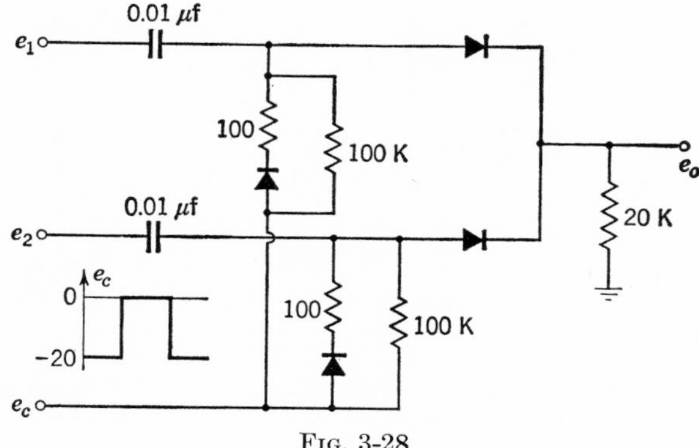

FIG. 3-28

3-12. (*a*) Draw the circuit of a direct-coupled controlled AND-NOT gate designed to operate on positive pulses (similar to the AND-OR gate of Fig. 3-8 except that it should be direct-coupled to all signal sources).

(*b*) Designate the relative amplitudes of the pulses which should be used.

(*c*) Sketch the input and output waveshapes and compare the results with that obtained for the gate of Fig. 3-8. Does this circuit offer any advantages?

3-13. In an automatic milling machine, the work must be properly positioned on the bed before the machine can be permitted to operate. The proper position is indicated when the states of three separate single-pole double-throw (SPDT) switches are changed by the pressure of the work. The center point of each switch is connected to a constant voltage (positive), and the other terminals are available for connection to various diode gates.

(*a*) Sketch a circuit which will indicate when the machine can start functioning.

(*b*) Sketch a circuit which can be used at the same time as the gate of part *a* and which will keep the positioning mechanism in operation until the work is properly seated.

(*c*) Show how you would modify the gate of part *b* so that the output decreases by equal increments as each switch is activated in any sequence.

(*d*) If you used diodes in the above parts, redraw the circuits so that they do not require any diodes. If you did not use diodes, repeat using them as elements in the various gates.

3-14. Figure 3-29 illustrates a simple controlled amplitude gate which will operate for positive or negative input signals.

(*a*) If e_1 is a 20-volt peak-to-peak sinusoidal signal, how large must we make the peak-to-peak square-wave control signal so that the diodes will not change state as a function of e_1 but only as a function of e_c? Specify your answer in terms of the circuit and diode parameters r_r, r_f, R_1, and R_s ($r_r \gg R_1 \gg r_f$, $r_r \gg R_s \gg r_f$).

(*b*) Specify the optimum value of R_1 for the maximum ratio of desired to undesired output, when the peak-to-peak control signal is 100 volts ($r_f = 10$ ohms, $r_r = 100$ K, and $R_1 = R_s$).

(*c*) Sketch the input and output waveshapes to scale, under the conditions of part *b*, if the period of the control signal is 5 per cent of the sine-wave period.

(*d*) Repeat part *c* when the input signal is zero.

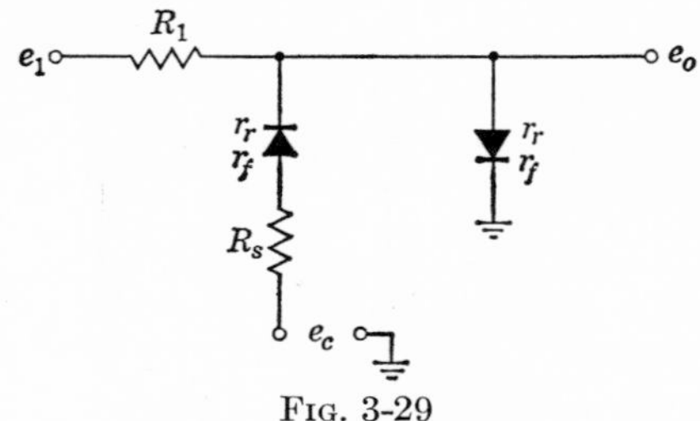

FIG. 3-29

3-15. Show the circuit of a diode array that will satisfy the following three conditions:

1. Select the proper 1 out of 10 channels upon the simultaneous application of pulses in 3 out of 5 channels.
2. Reject all odd outputs upon the application of an inhibit pulse.
3. Reject all even outputs upon the application of a second inhibit pulse.

3-16. Construct a diode array satisfying the following truth table. All channels marked with an asterisk are statements of an OR gate; all others are AND gates. Under which conditions are there multiple outputs?

Channel	*a*	*b*	*c*	*d*	*e*
1	0	0	1	1	1
2	0	1	0	1	1
3	1	1	0	1	0
4*	1	1	1	0	0
5	1	1	1	0	0
6*	1	1	0	0	1
7	1	1	0	1	1
8*	1	0	0	0	1

3-17. Evaluate the percentage of the control signal appearing at the output of a diode bridge if one diode, D_1, differs by 5 per cent from the other diodes. Its parameters are $r'_r = 1.05r_r$ and $r'_f = 0.95r_f$ expressed in terms of their nominal values.

Three cases should be considered:

(a) $R_s = 0.2\sqrt{r_r r_f}$.

(b) $R_s = \sqrt{r_r r_f}$.

(c) $R_s = 5\sqrt{r_r r_f}$.

In all cases R_1 remains fixed at $\sqrt{r_r r_f}$. Can you draw any general conclusions as to the best choice of R_s in the face of the expected small variations in diode parameters? (Let r_f = 10 ohms and r_r = 100 K in your calculations.)

3-18. (a) Find the optimum reflected impedance through each transformer to the common bridge circuit for the maximum ratio of desired to undesired signal-voltage transmission (Fig. 3-17). What attenuation factor does the bridge introduce under these circumstances?

(b) Further show that the conditions found in part *a* will also apply to a shunt connection. (The bridge is connected across the two transformer windings, which are in parallel.)

3-19. Diodes having the characteristics of Fig. 3-15 are used in the bridge of Fig. 3-12. The maximum reverse diode voltage is 100 volts, and for safety's sake we limit our driving signal to 75 per cent of the absolute maximum. We desire that the diode should be biased at 1.5 volts when it is in its active region. Furthermore, the peak input signal will never exceed 20 volts, thus ensuring that the bridge remains balanced at all times. Find the values of R_s and R_1 for optimum operation under the above conditions.

3-20. A diode bridge having the parameters listed below is to be controlled by a square wave, and a total of not more than 5 per cent of the period can be devoted to the turn-on and turn-off transients. What is the fastest allowable gating signal?

$$r_f = 100 \text{ ohms} \qquad R_1 = \sqrt{r_r r_f}$$
$$r_r = 250 \text{ K} \qquad R_s = 50 \text{ K}$$
$$C_d = 10\ \mu\mu\text{f} \qquad C_o = 250\ \mu\mu\text{f}$$

3-21. In a diode bridge circuit any capacitive unbalance will cause large spikes to appear at the output. If R_s is small, calculate the time constant and relative amplitude of these spikes if C_{d1} is (a) twice all other diode capacity; (b) one-half all other diode capacity. Take C_o as zero in this problem. (Hint: Treat in the same manner as the compensated attenuator of Chap. 1 and use a constant input signal.)

BIBLIOGRAPHY

Brown, D. R., and N. Rochester: Rectifier Networks for Multiposition Switching, *Proc. IRE*, vol. 37, no. 2, pp. 139–147, 1949.

Chen, T. C.: Digital Computer Coincidence and Mixing Circuits, *Proc. IRE*, vol. 38, no. 5, pp. 511–514, 1950.

Hussey, L. W.: Semiconductor Diode Gates, *Bell System Tech. J.*, vol. 32, pp. 1137–1154, September, 1953.

Millman, J., and T. H. Puckett: Accurate Linear Bidirectional Diode Gates, *Proc. IRE*, vol. 43, no. 1, pp. 27–37, 1955.

——— and H. Taub: "Pulse and Digital Circuits," McGraw-Hill Book Company, Inc., New York, 1956.

Richards, R. K.: "Digital Computer Components and Circuits," D. Van Nostrand Company, Inc., Princeton, N.J., 1957.

CHAPTER 4

SIMPLE TRIODE, TRANSISTOR, AND PENTODE MODELS AND CIRCUITS

An active element such as a triode, pentode, or transistor, with its unidirectional transmission path, its internal amplification, and related conversion of energy from the power source to the signal output, adds a third dimension to our capabilities for wave generation and shaping. Where previously we had only linear and nonlinear elements at our disposal, in this chapter we shall discuss some simple uses for a controlled energy source which can be incorporated within, instead of remaining external to, the wave-forming network.

4-1. Triode Models. Consider, for example, the terminal characteristics of a typical average triode, expressed by the two experimentally determined families of curves shown in Fig. 4-1. One set represents the input grid characteristics, and the other, the plate volt-ampere (output-terminal) response. Any specific tube of the same type may be expected to deviate by up to ± 30 per cent or even more from the average characteristics given by the manufacturer, as a consequence of the manufacturing tolerances. Thus we should expect a macroscopic model to represent reasonably well, but not necessarily exactly, the conditions expressed in Fig. 4-1.

For the simplest analysis of the subsequent circuits, the model should be a piecewise-linear one, allowing us to write a separate linear defining equation for each region of operation. In formulating the model, we first observe that the plate voltage has no effect on the grid characteristics in the negative grid region and but small effect when the grid voltage becomes slightly positive. If this second-order phenomenon is ignored by using the average of the curves shown to define the complete grid response (Fig. 4-1*a*), then the approximate characteristic is identical with that given for a diode (Chap. 2) and we can represent the grid-cathode behavior by an equivalent diode (Fig. 4-3). This diode's forward resistance r_c depends on the particular tube type and will generally lie between 300 and 2,500 ohms; for the tube shown, it is approximately 1,400 ohms. The inverse resistance is so very large that it is almost always assumed to be infinite.

Turning now to Fig. 4-1b, the location of any individual plate characteristic, which happens to be of the same basic shape as the diode volt-ampere curve, is a function of the particular value of the applied grid-to-cathode voltage. All these curves are quite similar, one to the other, roughly parallel, and approximately equally spaced for equal grid-voltage

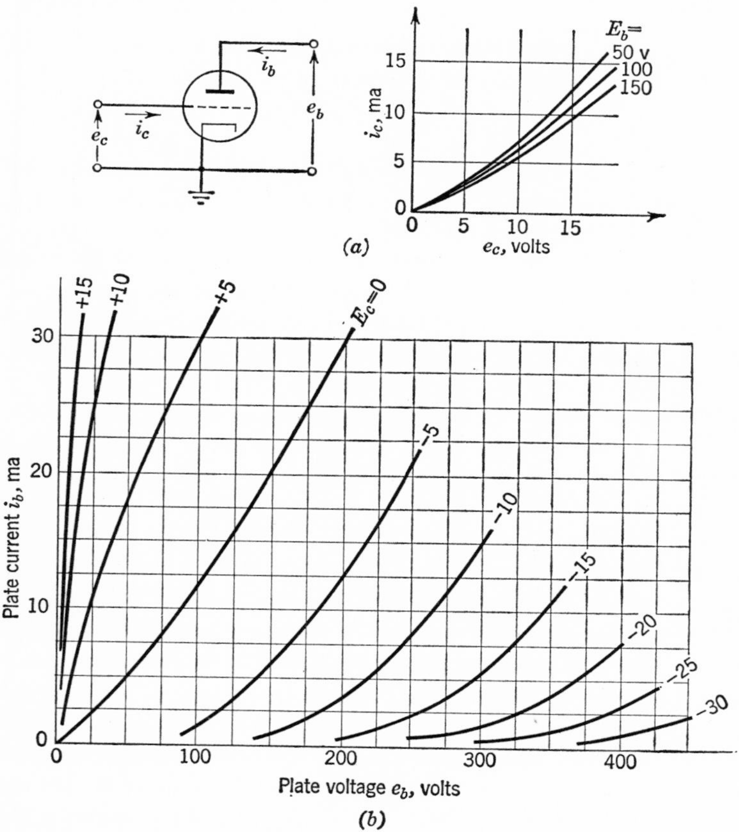

Fig. 4-1. Typical triode characteristics of a 12AU7. (a) Grid volt-ampere terminal response; (b) plate volt-ampere characteristic.

increments. We shall therefore extend the piecewise-linear concept as previously applied to the diode and approximate the totality of plate characteristics by a family of parallel, equally spaced straight lines (Fig. 4-2). The slope of these lines should be chosen for the best match to the original characteristics and will be roughly the reciprocal of the plate resistance averaged over the entire plane, $1/r_p$. Since at any constant value of plate current the ratio of the change in plate voltage to the change in grid voltage is

$$\mu = -\frac{\Delta e_b}{\Delta e_c}\bigg|_{i_b = \text{constant}} \tag{4-1}$$

the separation between the adjacent plate curves will be $-\mu\,\Delta e_c$.

From Fig. 4-2 we can see that a reasonable representation of a 12AU7 requires an average $\mu \cong 18$ and $r_p \cong 8$ K. With some other triodes the μ may vary from 10 to 100 and the r_p from 1 to 100 K. Usually the low values of r_p are associated with the low-μ tubes.

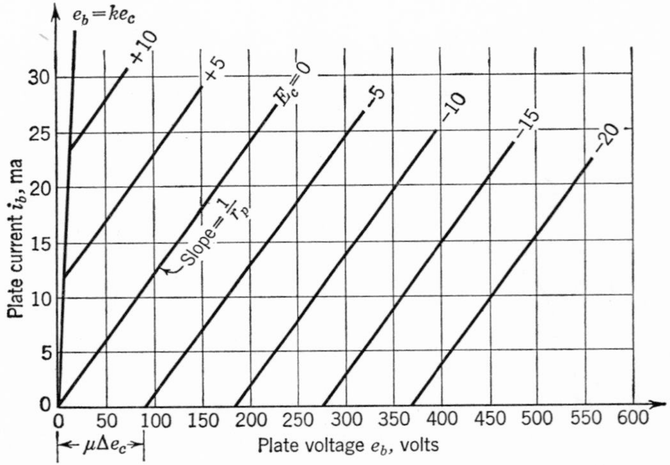

FIG. 4-2. Piecewise-linear approximation of the plate volt-ampere characteristics for type 12AU7 triode.

In the interests of clarity, the derived linear characteristics are presented in a separate diagram (Fig. 4-2) rather than superimposed on the actual curves. However, in order to find the piecewise-linear parameters used to classify the particular tube type (μ, r_p, r_c), we would have to refer to the manufacturer's characteristics, draw the family of straight lines, and then calculate these parameters. After this has been done once, there is no need to repeat the process whenever we must solve a new problem using the same tube. Even when the piecewise-linear characteristics are carefully approximated by eye, the deviation between the actual and the linear curves will usually be less than 10 per cent over the major portion of the region we are attempting to define, i.e., the first quadrant. As expected, the largest errors occur at low plate current where the curvature becomes rather severe.

Once the curvilinear representation is decided, we can derive a mathematical expression for the simplified curves drawn. The parametric equation describing the family of straight lines of Fig. 4-2 becomes

$$e_b = -\mu e_c + r_p i_b \qquad i_b \geq 0,\ e_b \geq 0 \tag{4-2}$$

where $-\mu e_c$ is the plate-voltage intercept. Equation (4-2) may be interpreted as representing the volt-ampere characteristics of a voltage generator $-\mu e_c$ having an internal impedance of r_p (Fig. 4-3). As the control voltage changes by any increment, the open-circuited output changes proportionately and the linear curve moves to a new position parallel to itself.

An additional limitation must also be imposed to restrict further the region defined by Eq. (4-2):

$$e_b \geq k e_c \tag{4-3}$$

when $e_c > 0$. Unless the tube's operation is so restricted, the excessive grid current flow, with the consequent lowering of the value of r_c, which occurs at low values of plate voltage and high grid voltage, may destroy the tube; the flimsy grid structure is not designed to dissipate the heat produced. In Eq. (4-3), the constant is a function of the interelectrode spacing and the physical construction of the tube and takes on a relatively small range of values; k usually lies between 0.5 and 2.5. If the tube is designed to operate under these conditions, then a new model is necessary to represent adequately the behavior at high positive grid voltages. The construction of such a model will be deferred until needed in Chap. 12.

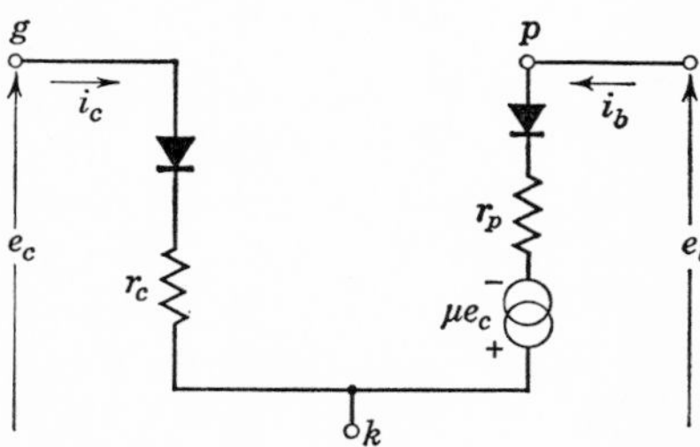

FIG. 4-3. Triode piecewise-linear model.

It follows, from the previous discussion, that the macroscopic piecewise-linear model of the triode is the one shown in Fig. 4-3. The two diodes serve to limit operation to the proper quadrants. The grid diode permits grid current flow only when the grid voltage is positive and the plate diode prevents reverse plate current flow.

When constructing the model of Fig. 4-3, we found it necessary to introduce a new element, a controlled source, in order to account for the influence of grid voltage over the plate current. The particular signal source chosen, μe_c, is a voltage generator whose amplitude is a linear function of the grid-to-cathode controlling voltage. It reflects the input signal into the output loop and thus represents the voltage amplification inherent in the tube.

Under the normal operating conditions the grid diode remains back-biased while the plate diode conducts. We say that the tube "saturates" when the grid diode changes stage and conducts at $e_{gk} = e_c = 0$. Cutoff corresponds to back-biasing the plate diode ($i_b = 0$), and by writing the voltage across this diode, the necessary condition becomes

$$E_{co} = E_{\text{cutoff}} \leq -\frac{E_{bk}}{\mu} \tag{4-4}$$

where E_{bk} is the voltage appearing from plate to cathode when $i_b = 0$.

If instead we choose to replace the plate circuit by its dual representation (Norton equivalent), the voltage-controlled voltage source becomes a voltage-controlled current generator. This transformation follows directly from Eq. (4-2), which is rewritten so that the plate current is the dependent rather than the independent variable. The new defining equation is

$$i_b = g_m e_c + \frac{e_b}{r_p} \tag{4-5}$$

where $g_m = \mu/r_p$ is called the transconductance. Even though the output-controlled source is now a current generator ($g_m e_c$), its value is still a function of the grid voltage. Furthermore, the transformation converted the series resistance into a shunt conductance (Fig. 4-4). The two diodes used in the model reflect the physical limitations of the tube, and therefore they will remain invariant across the change in modular representation.

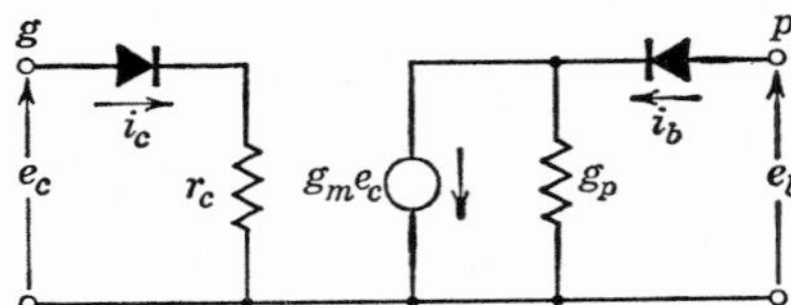

FIG. 4-4. Alternative triode model.

Triode Amplifier. As an example of how the piecewise-linear model is applied in the solution of specific circuits, we shall concern ourselves with the single-tube amplifier of Fig. 4-5*a*, which employs the tube whose characteristics are given in Figs. 4-1 and 4-2. The assumption is made that the driving signal is of a high enough frequency so that the cathode remains completely bypassed with respect to all signal components. Two problems require solution: first, the circuit's quiescent conditions and, second, the input-output transfer characteristic.

At the quiescent point the tube is biased within its grid base, i.e., between cutoff and zero, and the grid is nonconducting. The grid-to-cathode voltage is determined by the current flow through the cathode resistor.

$$E_{cq} = -E_K = -I_{bq}R_3 \tag{4-6}$$

As shown in Fig. 4-5*b*, the substitution of the value of E_{cq}, given by Eq. (4-6), into the model yields a generator whose terminal voltage is proportional to the current flow through it. But since such a response is the same as the voltage drop appearing across a resistor due to its current flow, this particular voltage source can be replaced by an equivalent 18-K resistor, μR_3. The reduced quiescent circuit consists of the power supply in series with various resistors; therefore

$$I_{bq} = \frac{E_{bb}}{R_2 + r_p + (\mu + 1)R_3} = \frac{300}{20\text{ K} + 8\text{ K} + (19)1\text{ K}} \cong 6.4\text{ ma} \tag{4-7}$$

From the circuit we see that the other quiescent conditions are

$$\begin{aligned} E_K &= I_{bq}R_3 = 6.4\text{ volts} \\ E_{2q} &= E_{bb} - I_{bq}R_2 = 172\text{ volts} \end{aligned} \tag{4-8}$$

where I_{bq} is as given in Eq. (4-7).

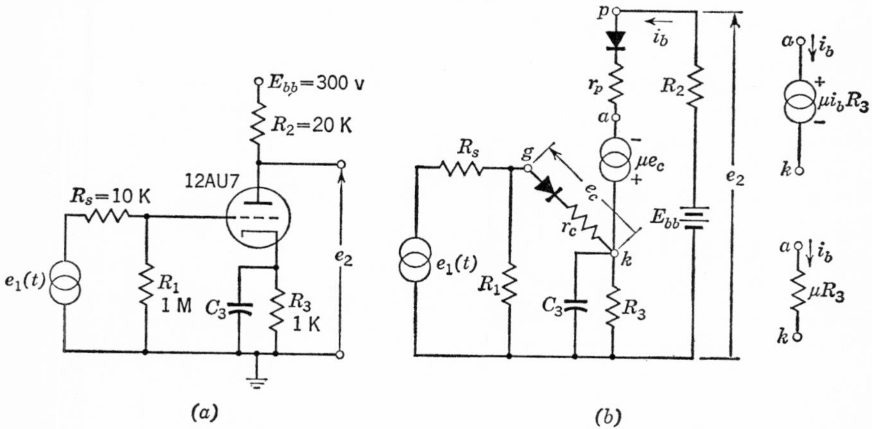

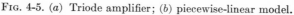

FIG. 4-5. (a) Triode amplifier; (b) piecewise-linear model.

Before beginning the evaluation of the transfer characteristic, we might observe that the linearization of the tube characteristics results in three linear regions of operation. Furthermore, the segments of the transfer curve for each region are contiguous, permitting their solution by zone superposition, i.e., the calculation of the transfer slope within each region and the location of the boundary-point coordinates. These individual segments can then be superimposed on the input-output plane with respect to the quiescent point to obtain the over-all response.

Since only the slope is needed, it is only necessary to define an operating region and to consider the incremental output response with respect to some variation of the input signal falling within the defined zone. In this way the complete output variation is contributed by the controlled source and the effects of the power supplies may be ignored. The three operating regions are:

1. The large positive peaks of the input signal force the tube into grid conduction over some function of the cycle (saturation).

2. The tube operates within its normal grid base.
3. The negative peaks of the input signal are large enough to drive the tube into cutoff.

Incremental models, which hold for each of these regions, may be derived from the piecewise-linear model of Fig. 4-5*b* by shorting all batteries and conducting diodes and opening any branches containing back-biased diodes. The three models appear in Fig. 4-6*a* to *c*. When considering the bounds of these regions, we would have to refer back

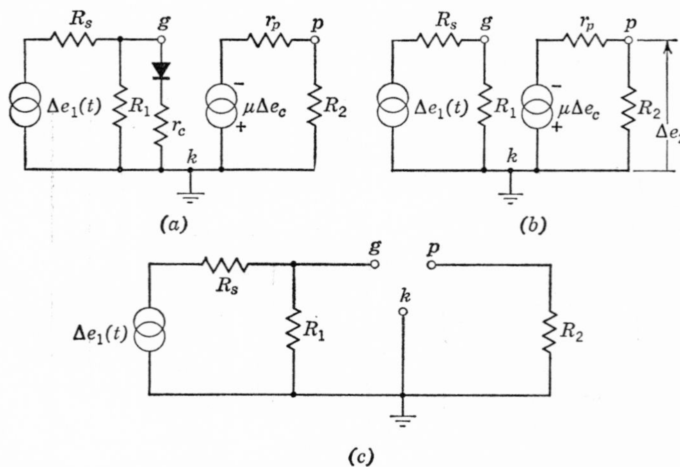

FIG. 4-6. Incremental models for the circuit of Fig. 4-5. (*a*) Saturation region; (*b*) active region; (*c*) cutoff region.

to the complete model of Fig. 4-5*b*, where the complete bypassing of R_3, afforded by C_3, permits its replacement by the constant voltage E_K [Eqs. (4-8)].

Region 1: $e_1(t) \geq E_K$ (saturation)

In this region, since $R_1 \gg r_c$,

$$\Delta e_c = \frac{r_c}{r_c + R_s} \Delta e_1 \cong \frac{1.4}{11.4} \Delta e_1 = 0.123 \Delta e_1$$

and from the incremental model of Fig. 4-6*a*,

$$\Delta e_2 = -\frac{\mu R_2}{r_p + R_2} \Delta e_c = 0.123A \Delta e_1 \tag{4-9}$$

where the grid-to-plate amplification is

$$A = \frac{\Delta e_2}{\Delta e_c} = -\frac{\mu R_2}{r_p + R_2} = -\frac{18 \times 20 \text{ K}}{8 \text{ K} + 20 \text{ K}} = -12.9$$

Note that the conducting grid introduces an additional attenuation factor due to its loading of the signal-source impedance. The output voltage corresponding to the boundary value of the input may be found from Fig. 4-5*b* by setting $e_c = 0$ and replacing R_3 by the battery E_K. The controlled source disappears at this point, and the simple resistive network of Fig. 4-7*a* yields

$$E_{2s} = E_K + I_{bs}r_p = E_K + \frac{E_{bb} - E_K}{r_p + R_2} r_p \cong 90 \text{ volts} \qquad (4\text{-}10)$$

where I_{bs} is the saturation value of plate current.

Region 2: $\quad E_K \geq e_1(t) \geq E_K - \dfrac{E_{bb} - E_K}{\mu} \quad$ (active)

The grid now operates within its normal base, it is nonconducting, and it does not load the signal source. Thus, when $R_1 \gg R_s$, $\Delta e_{c1} = \Delta e_1$, and

$$\Delta e_2 = -\frac{\mu R_2}{r_p + R_2} \Delta e_c = A\,\Delta e_1 \qquad (4\text{-}11)$$

As the negative portion of the signal cuts off the tube, the circuit enters the third region of operation, and by again substituting the battery E_K for R_3 in the model of Fig. 4-5*b*, we find the cutoff value of $e_1(t)$. The resultant simplified circuit appears in Fig. 4-7*b*. Using Eq. (4-4), E_{co} and the equivalent input voltage become

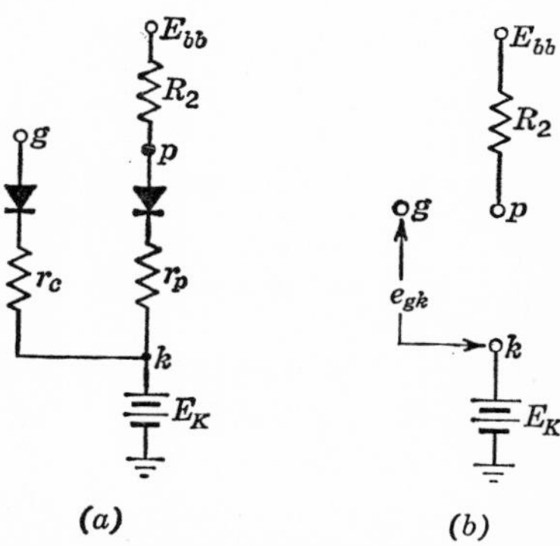

FIG. 4-7. Limiting models for the amplifier of Fig. 4-5*a*. (*a*) Tube under saturation conditions; (*b*) tube cut off.

$$\begin{aligned} E_{co} &= e_{1o}(t) - E_K \leq -\frac{E_{bb} - E_K}{\mu} = -16.3 \text{ volts} \\ e_{1o}(t) &\leq +E_K - \frac{E_{bb} - E_K}{\mu} = -9.9 \text{ volts} \end{aligned} \qquad (4\text{-}12)$$

The plate voltage at cutoff is simply E_{bb}.

Region 3: $\quad e_1(t) \leq +E_K - \dfrac{E_{bb} - E_K}{\mu} \quad$ (i.e., below cutoff)

Since the cutoff tube opens the transmission path for the input signal, the output will remain constant at E_{bb} and, in this region, the slope of the transfer characteristic is identically zero.

The conclusion which may be drawn from the above calculations is that it is much easier to locate the circuit's break points than it is to find the quiescent operating condition. In the triode, one coordinate of each of these limits is already known; in one case it is where the plate current drops to zero, and in the other it is where the grid-to-cathode voltage rises to zero. We can always simplify the piecewise-linear models at these two boundaries by eliminating the unessentials: the controlled source is shorted at $e_c = 0$, and the complete plate loop is opened at $i_b = 0$. Finally, the remaining extremely simple network is solved for the single unknown coordinate.

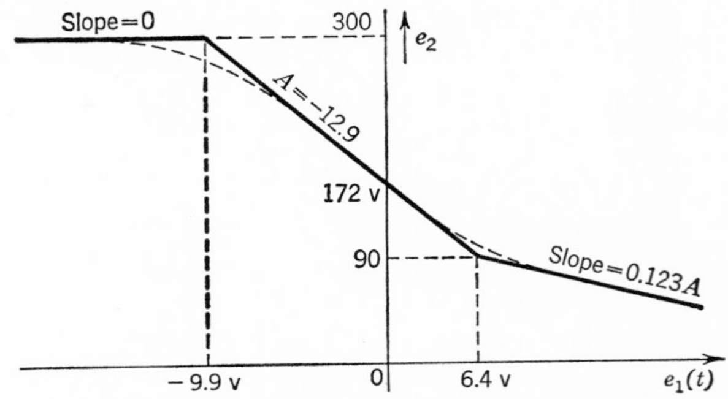

FIG. 4-8. Transfer characteristic of the one-tube amplifier of Fig. 4-5.

Figure 4-8 illustrates the complete piecewise-linear transfer relationship, and as a summary of the previous discussion, all slopes and intercepts are labeled. The superimposed curve (dashed lines) is the transfer characteristic as might be evaluated point by point from the manufacturer's tube characteristics. Agreement between the two curves is generally satisfactory, except in the vicinity of the break points, where the pronounced curvature of the actual plate characteristics results in wide divergence from the model representation. The slope of Fig. 4-8 is the value of the incremental gain at that particular value of drive voltage. If we are interested in linear amplification, the drive must be restricted to keep the operating locus in the active region. Furthermore, for the largest possible dynamic range, the Q point should be placed halfway between grid conduction and cutoff.

The limitations as well as the advantages of the piecewise-linear analysis become apparent once we consider how to obtain the actual operating path of the single-stage amplifier of Fig. 4-5.

In the graphical construction of this locus we must first locate the Q point, which lies along the d-c load line

$$e_b = E_{bb} - i_b(R_2 + R_3) \tag{4-13}$$

The line defined by Eq. (4-13) appears superimposed on the triode characteristics in Fig. 4-9. Secondly, the actual bias point is also determined by a graphical construction. The bias equation (4-6) is cross-plotted on the plate characteristics, and its intersection with the d-c load line located. Finally, the locus of the time-varying output, the so-called a-c load line having the slope $-1/R_2$, is drawn through the Q point.

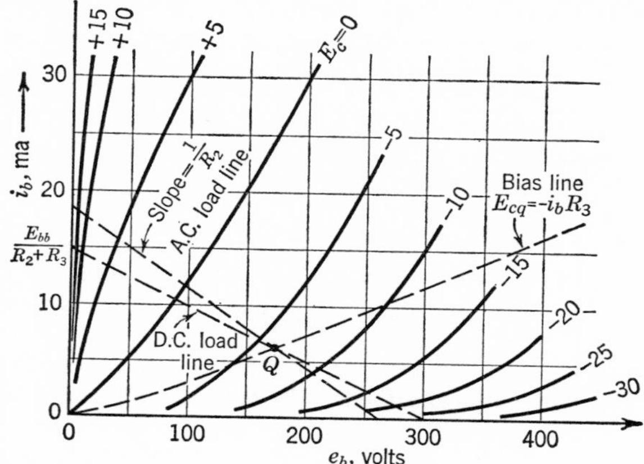

FIG. 4-9. Graphical solution of the single-tube triode amplifier (the position of the a-c load line is exaggerated for the purposes of the illustration; it does not correspond to the circuit of Fig. 4-5).

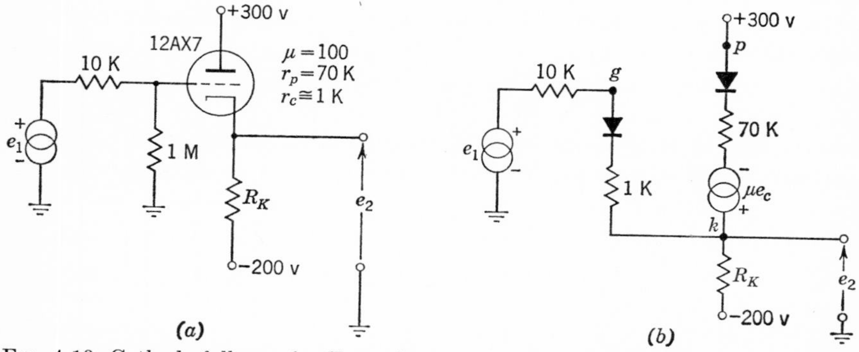

FIG. 4-10. Cathode follower for Example 4-1. (a) Circuit; (b) equivalent piecewise-linear model.

For simple circuits, a graphical construction is almost as easy as the analytical solution. In more complex circuits this is no longer true. Even in the single-tube amplifier, once the grid becomes positive we would have to solve two sets of graphically presented characteristics: first, those of the grid to find the actual value of e_c and, next, those of the plate circuit to find the corresponding output voltage.

Example 4-1. This example will consider the cathode follower of Fig. 4-10. We shall solve for the cathode resistor R_K that places the quiescent point exactly in the center of the active region.

Solution. In the cutoff region the full supply voltage appears across the tube. Thus the grid-to-cathode voltage at the boundary is given by

$$E_{cko} = \frac{-500}{\mu} = -5 \text{ volts}$$

Since the net current flow is zero, the output voltage is $E_{2o} = -200$ volts, and the corresponding value of the input becomes

$$E_{1o} = E_{cko} - E_{2o} = -205 \text{ volts}$$

The saturation limits may be determined by setting $e_c = 0$ in the model of Fig. 4-10*b*. By doing so, the controlled source is eliminated and

$$I_{bs} = \frac{500}{r_p + R_K}$$

The output voltage, which is now equal to the input, is given by

$$E_{1s} = E_{2s} = I_{bs}R_K - 200 \qquad \text{volts}$$

To obtain a second equation involving R_K and I_b, we consider the quiescent conditions. When $E_1 = 0$, the grid-to-cathode voltage may be expressed as

$$E_{ckq} = -E_{2q} = 200 - R_K I_{bq}$$

Substitution of this equation into the network of Fig. 4-10*b*, by way of the controlled source, requires the multiplication of each term by μ. At the Q point the controlled source may be replaced by an equivalent resistor of R_K in series with a voltage source of $-(\mu + 1)E_{cc}$ volts. The tube's current, found from the single loop remaining after the substitution, is

$$I_{bq} = \frac{E_{bb} - (\mu + 1)E_{cc}}{r_p + (\mu + 1)R_K} \cong -\frac{E_{cc}}{R_K}$$

where the approximation holds for a high-μ tube [$E_{bb} \ll -E_{cc}(\mu + 1)$ and $R_K(\mu + 1) \gg r_p$]. In order for the quiescent point to lie in the center of the active region $I_{bq} = I_{bs}/2$.

$$-\frac{E_{cc}}{R_K} = \frac{1}{2}\frac{E_{bb}}{r_p + R_K}$$

Substituting values and solving results in $R_K = 280$ K. The previously unknown values can now be evaluated.

$$\begin{aligned} I_{bq} &= 0.715 \text{ ma} \\ E_{2q} &= -2.5 \text{ volts} \qquad \text{(from the more exact solution for } I_{bq}) \\ E_{1s} &= E_{2s} = 200 \text{ volts} \end{aligned}$$

The piecewise-linear model has not only freed us, in our calculations of the tube quiescent point of operation, from any dependency on graphical construction, but also has contained within the model a diagrammatic representation of the complete range of tube behavior. All incremental models were directly derived from the single piecewise-linear model, and the particular constraints imposed on the regional models also explicitly appear. If, in any region of operation, a more exact calculation as to the incremental behavior is needed, we can always return to the actual tube characteristics and calculate the incremental values of r_p and μ for the microscopic portion of the volt-ampere plane under review. This is particularly necessary when operating at low plate currents where the low slopes of the actual characteristics indicate a large increase in r_p. In this same region, adjacent curves begin crowding together, with a consequent decrease in the incremental μ (Fig. 4-1*b*).

The piecewise-linear model cannot account for these variations in tube parameters since the basis of its construction was the linearization of the tube characteristics. Over most of the plane, the values of μ and r_p are not much different from the constant values assumed in the linear curves of Fig. 4-2. We may conclude that the macroscopic model is generally valid for large-signal applications, that it is reasonably valid for small-signal analysis over much of the operating region, and that it represents a convenient first-order approximation over the remainder of the plane.

4-2. Triode Clipping and Clamping Circuits. From a study of the transfer characteristic of Fig. 4-8 we conclude that, besides functioning as a linear amplifier within its active region, the nonlinearity of the triode may also be utilized as a double-ended clipper. Each break point corresponds to a change in state of one of the diodes used in the piecewise-linear representation (Fig. 4-3); the clipping of the positive input peak occurs as the grid is driven into conduction, and the negative peak is clipped in the plate circuit as the controlled source cuts off the tube. We generally reflect the cutoff action back to the grid and speak of the spacing between the two break points, in terms of the grid-to-cathode voltage, as the grid base of the particular tube. Control over the width of the transmission region is rather awkwardly effected; either the cutoff point must be changed by adjusting the plate supply voltage or we must replace the tube with one which will operate within a smaller or a larger grid base (i.e., a different value of μ).

In spite of this limitation, the triode is widely used as a clipper because advantage may be taken of its internal amplification to develop a large clipped output from a relatively small driving signal. For example, if a sinusoid having a peak-to-peak amplitude much larger than the grid base is chosen as the input, then the clipped output will be a fair approximation of a square wave. Even better squaring results when a second stage is cascaded for further clipping and amplification. Simple differentiation converts the square wave into a pulse train which might be applied to other circuits for synchronization or control.

The undesirable information transmission occurring in the saturation region may be minimized by inserting a very large resistor in series with the control grid. But since the input capacity of a triode is quite large, 50 to 300 $\mu\mu$f, the resultant long input time constant adversely affects the rise time of the stage. For this reason, clipping is usually limited to the cutoff region and a compound circuit, such as the cathode-coupled amplifier shown in Fig. 4-11, would be used instead for double-ended operation. Here each clipping region corresponds to one of the tubes being driven into cutoff, and therefore no special provision need be made for operation in the saturation region.

Qualitatively, this circuit operates in the following manner: tube T_1 is a cathode-follower input stage, injecting the input signal into the cathode circuit of T_2. The negative bias E_{cc} serves to set the proper quiescent conditions. At very large positive values of e_1, the positive common-cathode voltage cuts off tube T_2, and through doing so destroys the transmission path from the input to the output. In this region the slope of the transfer characteristic becomes zero. As the input signal falls, T_2 enters its active region and the circuit functions as a cathode-coupled amplifier. Linear amplification ceases when the falling signal voltage finally cuts off T_1, again interrupting the transmission path and again making the transfer slope zero.

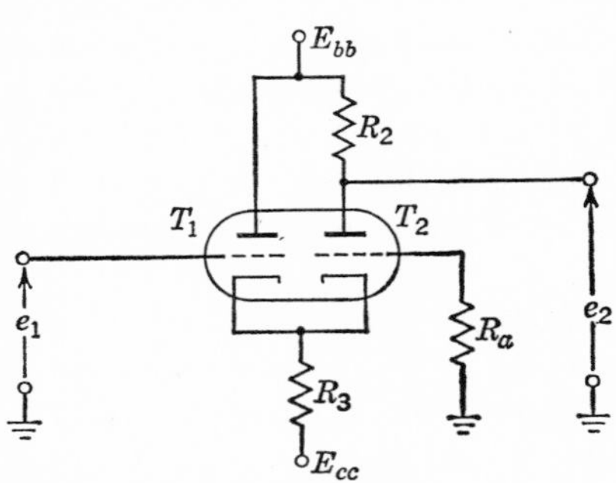

FIG. 4-11. Double-triode clipping circuit—cathode-coupled amplifier.

When the input is large enough to cut T_2 off, the model of Fig. 4-12a holds and will be used to calculate one of the boundary values. We must first write the following grid-circuit defining equation:

$$e_{c1} = e_1 - i_{b1}R_3 - E_{cc} \tag{4-14}$$

Substitution of Eq. (4-14) into the model of Fig. 4-12a results in the replacement of the controlled source μe_{c1} by two voltage sources $-\mu E_{cc}$ and μe_1 and an equivalent resistor μR_3. Thus the effect of the driving signal is brought to the fore and the plate current becomes

$$i_{b1} = \frac{E_{bb} - (\mu + 1)E_{cc} + \mu e_1}{r_p + (\mu + 1)R_3}$$

But in order to ensure that T_2 is off and that our argument as to the circuit operation is valid, the grid-to-cathode voltage of T_2 must be equal to or below cutoff. By taking the external loop voltages, from the grid to the cathode, we obtain

$$e_{c2} = -E_{cc} - E_3 \leq -\frac{E_{bb} - E_{cc} - E_3}{\mu} \tag{4-15}$$

where $E_3 = i_{b1}R_3$ and the plate-to-cathode voltage of T_2 is $E_{bb} - E_{cc} - E_3$. Solving Eq. (4-15) for E_3 and equating to $i_{b1}R_3$ yields

$$E_3 = \frac{E_{bb} - (\mu + 1)E_{cc}}{\mu + 1} = \frac{E_{bb} + \mu E_{11} - (\mu + 1)E_{cc}}{r_p + (\mu + 1)R_3} R_3$$

The upper bounding value of the drive signal E_{11} is readily found by solving the above equation.

The location of the other break point would be found in a similar manner by directing our attention to the model of Fig. 4-12*b*. Again the additional information needed for a complete solution is furnished by the cutoff equation of the nonconducting tube T_1. The two equations involving E_3 are

$$E_3 = i_{b2}R_3 = \frac{E_{bb} - (\mu + 1)E_{cc}}{r_p + R_2 + (\mu + 1)R_3} R_3$$

$$e_{c1} = E_{12} - E_{cc} - E_3 \leq - \frac{E_{bb} - E_{cc} - E_3}{\mu}$$

The simultaneous solution of these equations for E_{12}, the minimum value of the input which can be tolerated before T_1 is driven into cutoff, completes the solution of this problem.

Triode-grid-circuit Clamping. A further circuit application of the triode, with its two-diode representation (Fig. 4-3), is as a clamp. Both the grid and plate circuits will individually clamp an external signal in exactly the same manner as the diode clamps of Chap. 2, but because the equivalent diodes used in the triode model are irreversible, only negative clamping is permitted.

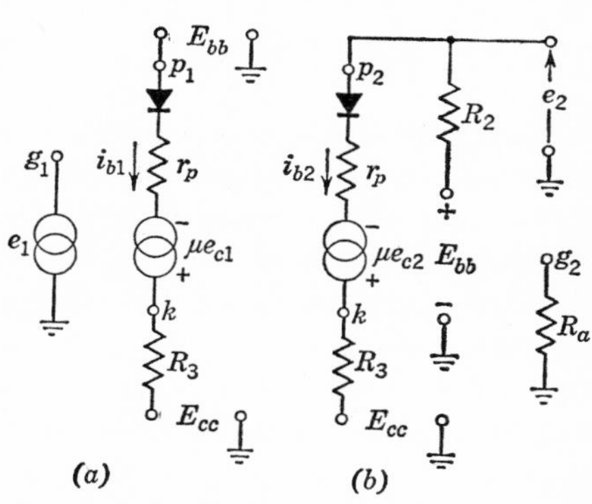

FIG. 4-12. Piecewise models of the circuit of Fig. 4-11. (*a*) T_1 on and T_2 cut off; (*b*) T_2 on and T_1 cut off. (NOTE: $E_{cc} < 0$.)

By properly adjusting the cathode bias resistor, the grid-circuit clamp level may be varied from zero to a positive value equal in magnitude to the tube's cutoff voltage. Since the triode grid has an almost infinite reverse resistance, this circuit would require a resistor, shunted from grid to cathode, in order to ensure the proper charging of the clamp capacitor (Sec. 2-5).

This same clamping action is widely employed as a means of establishing the grid bias of the tube. In Fig. 4-13, the grid conduction on the positive peaks of the applied signal results in a current which charges C to the positive peak of the input voltage. Except for the short interval when the dissipated energy is restored in the capacitor, the circuit automatically adjusts itself so as to avoid operating in the positive grid region. The negative grid clamping is reflected, through the controlled source, into effective positive plate-circuit clamping as illustrated by the waveshapes of Fig. 4-13. Note that operation over the complete grid base is guaranteed before the tube cuts off. Of course, a small amount of distortion appears as a consequence of the small grid conduction angle, but if this can be tolerated, then this circuit represents an extremely simple way to self-bias a tube and still ensure the maximum possible voltage swing.

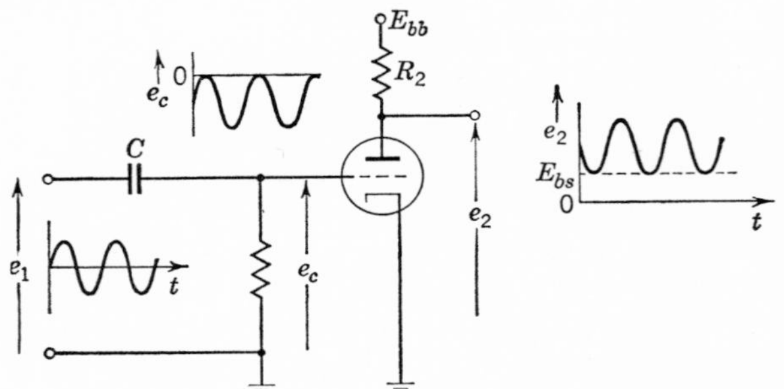

FIG. 4-13. Grid-circuit clamping and resultant waveshapes.

We might further observe that any capacitor-coupled amplifier will exhibit a measure of grid-clamping action when the input signal overdrives the grid, i.e., when the positive peak of the input is greater than the cathode bias voltage. The additional bias component produced shifts the operating point away from the positive grid region, and provided that the tube is not driven into cutoff, the actual distortion will always be less than expected on the basis of a simplified analysis.

4-3. Triode Gates. Almost any configuration of triodes, coupled together by a common load resistor in either their cathode or their plate circuit, will serve as an AND or an OR gate (Figs. 4-14 and 4-16). Since the individual tubes are essentially in parallel, the basic consideration for proper functioning as an OR gate is that each input pulse should be able to make its presence known at the output. If the tubes are normally biased below cutoff, then the conduction of any one tube, brought about by an input pulse, will operate the gate and produce a change in the circuit state.

On the other hand, in an AND gate the effects of a single excitation pulse must be swamped out by the normal conditions of the other parallel tubes. In biasing them in their saturation regions the aggregate effect of the load current contributed by all the tubes would not be seriously disturbed if, upon the injection of a negative pulse, a single tube switches from saturation to cutoff. The major change of circuit state will occur only when all the tubes are driven off.

Triode OR *Gate.* We now propose to examine the operation of the common-cathode OR gate of Fig. 4-14*a*. Besides calculating the steady-state response from the piecewise-linear model, we are also interested in finding the rise and decay time constants of the output waveshapes. All tubes are normally maintained completely cut off by returning the grid resistors to a large negative bias ($E_{cc} \ll 0$). The input pulse is applied through the R_1C_1 time constant, which may be assumed long

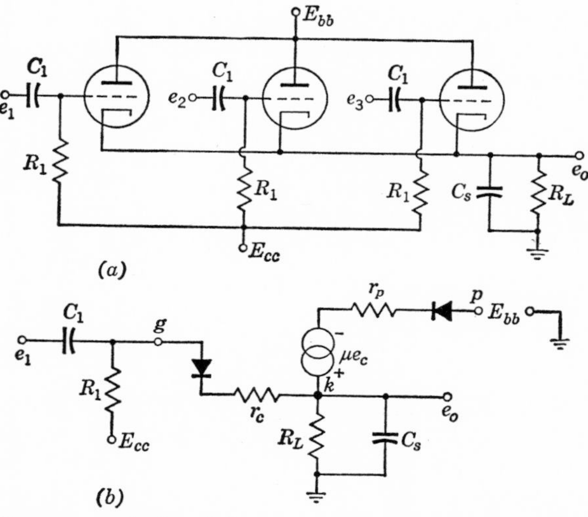

FIG. 4-14. (*a*) Common-cathode triode OR gate; (*b*) piecewise-linear model of a single on tube.

enough, with respect to the duration of the driving signal, so as not to introduce any additional shaping. We shall further assume, purely for the ease of calculation, that the single pulse applied to any grid will drive that tube to the verge of saturation.

The grid-to-ground voltage corresponding to saturation may be found by setting $e_c = 0$ in the piecewise-linear model of Fig. 4-14*b*. Solving the reduced network for the equivalent input and output voltages leads to

$$E_{cs} = E_{ks} = \frac{R_L}{r_p + R_L} E_{bb} \tag{4-16}$$

However, the grid was initially at E_{cc}, and since we wish to raise it to the value given in Eq. (4-16), the input pulse height would have to be

$$E_{1m} = E_{ks} - E_{cc}$$

The output due to smaller or larger inputs could be calculated, quite easily, once values are assigned to the circuit parameters.

The output rises toward this steady-state value with a time constant determined by the output load and the internal impedance of the tube. Since, in the circuit configuration shown, the controlled source includes the output voltage as one of its components, the value of the output impedance is not immediately obvious upon inspection of the model. By proceeding from the basic definition, i.e., the output impedance is equal to the ratio of open-circuit terminal voltage and the short-circuit current, its evaluation is straightforward. Furthermore, the d-c sources may be ignored since they only set the quiescent operating point.

By removing the external load $R_L \parallel C_s$, the open-circuit output voltage of Fig. 4-14*b* is given by

$$e_o = \mu e_c = \mu(e_1 - e_o) \tag{4-17}$$

In finding the short-circuit current, we return the cathode directly to ground, thus removing the dependency of the controlled source upon any voltage appearing in the output loop. Therefore

$$i_{sc} = \frac{\mu e_1}{r_p} \tag{4-18}$$

Solving Eq. (4-17) for e_o and dividing the result by Eq. (4-18) yields

$$Z_o = \frac{e_o}{i_{sc}} = \frac{r_p}{\mu + 1} \cong \frac{1}{g_m} \tag{4-19}$$

The above approximation holds for a high-μ tube (i.e., where $\mu + 1 \cong \mu$). The single tube considered to be in its active region is operating as a cathode follower, and Eq. (4-19) expresses its very small output impedance, on the order of 400 to 700 ohms. Consequently, the rise time constant is quite small:

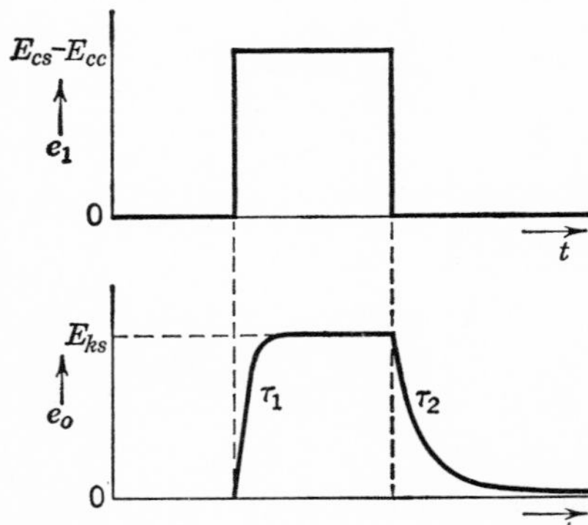

FIG. 4-15. Input and output pulse appearing in the common-cathode OR gate of Fig. 4-14*a*.

$$\tau_1 = \left(R_L \parallel \frac{r_p}{\mu + 1}\right) C_s$$

where C_s represents the total stray capacity appearing across the output.

Upon removal of the excitation, the tube cuts off and the output decays back toward zero with the new, much longer time constant

$$\tau_2 = R_L C_s$$

which is simply that of the external load. The input and output waveshapes sketched in Fig. 4-15 illustrate the pulse distortion introduced by this gate. Usually R_L is kept small so that the trailing edge will not be smeared excessively and therefore falsely indicate the presence of a gating signal after its removal.

The particular gate of Fig. 4-14 was designed for positive pulse excitation; for gating negative pulses we would turn to a common plate connection and apply the negative input pulses in the cathodes of the individual tubes. Under these circumstances, the triode would amplify the input pulse, but with its larger output impedance it would also introduce a greater degree of distortion in the initial rise of the output pulse.

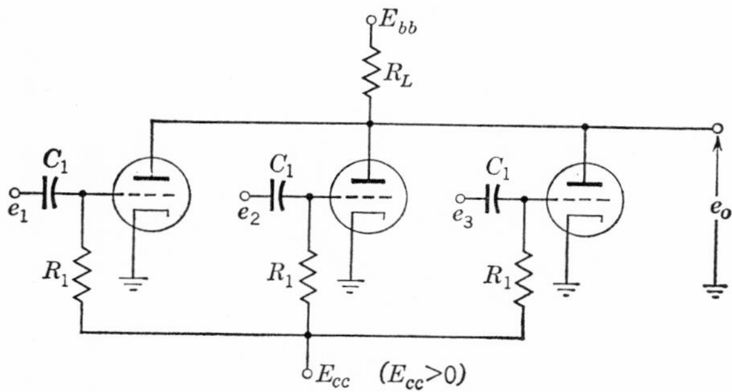

FIG. 4-16. Common plate connection—AND gate.

Triode AND *Gate.* An alternative mode of gate operation is typified by the AND gate of Fig. 4-16. The grids, returned to the positive bias E_{cc} through R_1, are normally maintained in their saturation region, with, however, their self-clipping action limiting the maximum positive grid excursion to

$$E_{cs} = \frac{r_c}{R_1 + r_c} E_{cc} \cong \frac{r_c}{R_1} E_{cc} \cong 0 \tag{4-20}$$

where $R_1 \gg r_c$.

Upon the excitation of any one grid, by a negative pulse, that particular tube will cease conduction, and since its plate current no longer flows through R_L, the composite plate voltage rises slightly. Provided, however, that $R_L \gg r_p$, this change in voltage will be almost negligible. Only after every tube is simultaneously cut off does the plate voltage change by an appreciable amount. It rises from its initially low saturation value of

$$E_{bs} \cong \frac{r_p/n}{R_L + r_p/n} E_{bb} \tag{4-21}$$

which is found from the piecewise-linear model holding when n tubes are saturated—to the final value of E_{bb}.

One obvious peculiarity of this AND gate is that it produces a positive output upon excitation by negative input pulses, and if we wish to drive a second, similar gate, a buffer amplifier must be inserted to invert the pulse. If the circuit is modified so that positive driving pulses are injected into each cathode, the gate output will be an amplified pulse of the same polarity as the input.

Amplitude Gates. Triode amplitude gating is predicated on the control signal (normally injected at the cathode) shifting the operating point of the cutoff tube into its active region. At this time the amplification from grid to plate permits the transmittal of the information signal. The basic gating behavior is illustrated by the simplified circuit of Fig. 4-17*a*. But to avoid loading the control-signal generator by the low output impedance seen in the cathode circuit, the control signal might well be

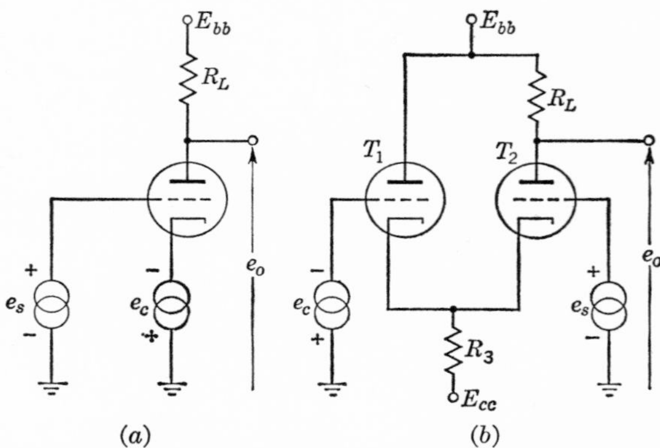

FIG. 4-17. (*a*) Basic amplitude gate; (*b*) cathode-coupled controlled gate.

coupled through a cathode follower. The resultant circuit (Fig. 4-17*b*) is of the identical configuration with the cathode-coupled clipper of Fig. 4-11, with, however, signals applied to both grids.

Under normal conditions, the positive d-c level of the control signal raises the common-cathode voltage to a value that is high enough to ensure biasing T_2 well below cutoff. For optimum performance, the response of this gate should be independent of the control-signal amplitude; to this end, the gating signal simply drives T_1 into its cutoff region, allowing T_2 to function as a normal amplifier. If the above conditions are satisfied, the calculation of the output voltage, with respect to the gated signal e_s, may be carried out without reference to T_1.

The control pulse still makes its presence felt at the output, although somewhat indirectly. As seen in the waveshapes of Fig. 4-18, the abrupt change of state of T_2, which takes place when the tube enters into its active region, effectively superimposes the gated output on a pedestal having the same duration as the gating pulse. Under many circumstances such an additional term would be intolerable. It follows that in order to eliminate the output pedestal, we must maintain the current flow through the output load invariant with respect to the state of T_2. We accomplish this by adding a third triode (T_3 of Fig. 4-19) which is gated off at the same time T_2 is gated on. Since T_3 normally conducts and since it time-shares the output load, we can adjust its plate current, by varying R_4, so that the output voltage remains constant across the change of circuit state. The application of a negative gating pulse drives both T_1 and T_3 into cutoff. These tubes are effectively removed from the circuit, and the transmission path, now established through T_2, is unaffected by any other triode. As the waveshapes testify, the output voltage no longer changes abruptly; the pedestal is now missing.

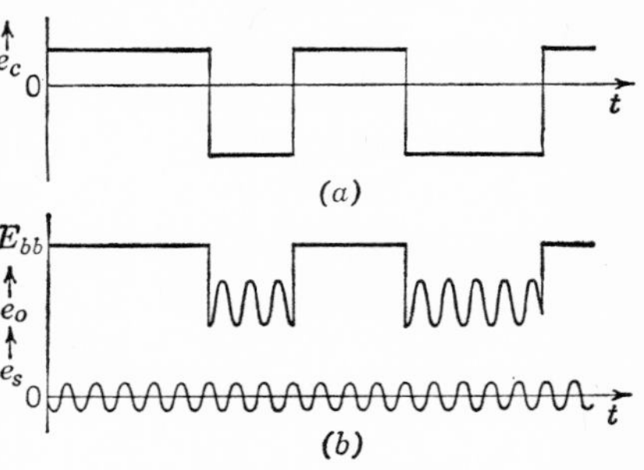

FIG. 4-18. Cathode-coupled gate waveshapes. (a) Control signal; (b) input signal and gate output.

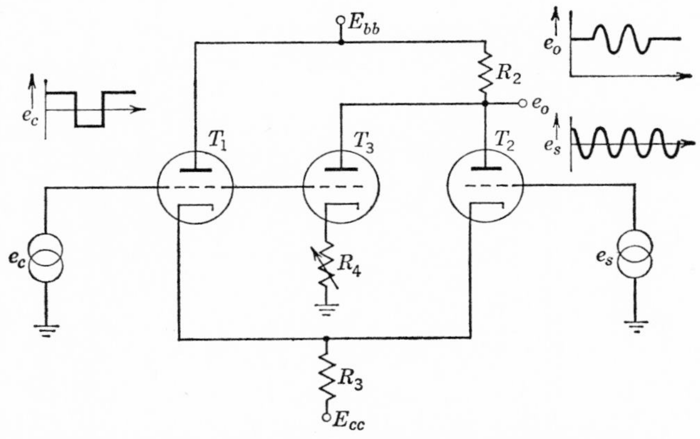

FIG. 4-19. Circuit for elimination of the output pedestal.

In concluding this summary of triode gates, we might note that the controlled source, which is inherent within the triode, affords a much greater degree of isolation between the input and the output than was possible with diode gates. Moreover, this isolation greatly reduces or eliminates completely any interaction between the various driving signal sources.

4-4. Transistor Models. An *n-p-n* transistor consists of two junctions of *n* material, either silicon or germanium, to which *n*-type impurities have been added. These are formed on each side of the thin layer of *p* material constituting the base of the transistor. One junction is normally forward-biased with respect to the base structure, in this case by making its polarity negative ($v_{eb} < 0$), and it serves as the emitter. We might observe that structurally the emitter-base junction forms a forward-conducting diode. The remaining junction becomes the collector, and for proper transistor operation, it should be back-biased (positive with respect to the base). Furthermore, the collector junction current is approximately equal in magnitude to the emitter current (Fig. 4-20*c*), but its voltage drop will be much larger. Since most of the transistor power is dissipated at the collector, its junction must be commensurate in size. However, special transistors have been designed for bidirectional transmission, and in these the particular junction which would function as the emitter would be determined solely by the voltages present in the circuit. At any instant whichever junction happens to be forward-biased becomes the emitter, and if the other is back-biased, it becomes the collector.

A transistor's characteristics are determined by the particular material used, i.e., germanium or silicon, and by the nature of the junction formed. The major differences in the volt-ampere curves appear at low collector voltages. These variations are relatively minor, and therefore the models which shall be derived below are adequate representations of all types of transistors.

Figure 4-20*a*, the schematic representation of the *n-p-n* transistor, is presented in order to define the circuit polarities which we shall employ in the remainder of the text. The ready availability of complementary units, i.e., both *n-p-n* and *p-n-p* transistors, creates some confusion when a current direction is arbitrarily assigned. In an effort to avoid any ambiguity, we shall choose the emitter arrow as the reference and assume all current flows in the direction it points. If the emitter current flows out (as shown in Fig. 4-20*a* for the *n-p-n* unit), then the base and collector currents flow into the device. Alternatively, in the *p-n-p* transistor the emitter arrow is pointed in the opposite direction, into the transistor, and all voltages and currents would be reversed. Thus the transistor may be considered as a simple node where

$$i_e = i_b + i_c \tag{4-22}$$

Before attempting construction of a piecewise-linear model for the transistor, we must satisfy ourselves as to the suitability of such a representation. Following much the same procedure used in deriving the triode model, our starting point will be the examination of the empirically determined transistor characteristics, which are either furnished by the manufacturer or obtained by measurement in the laboratory. Even though gross approximations may be acceptable in replacing the actual characteristics by a family of straight lines, the linearized curves should

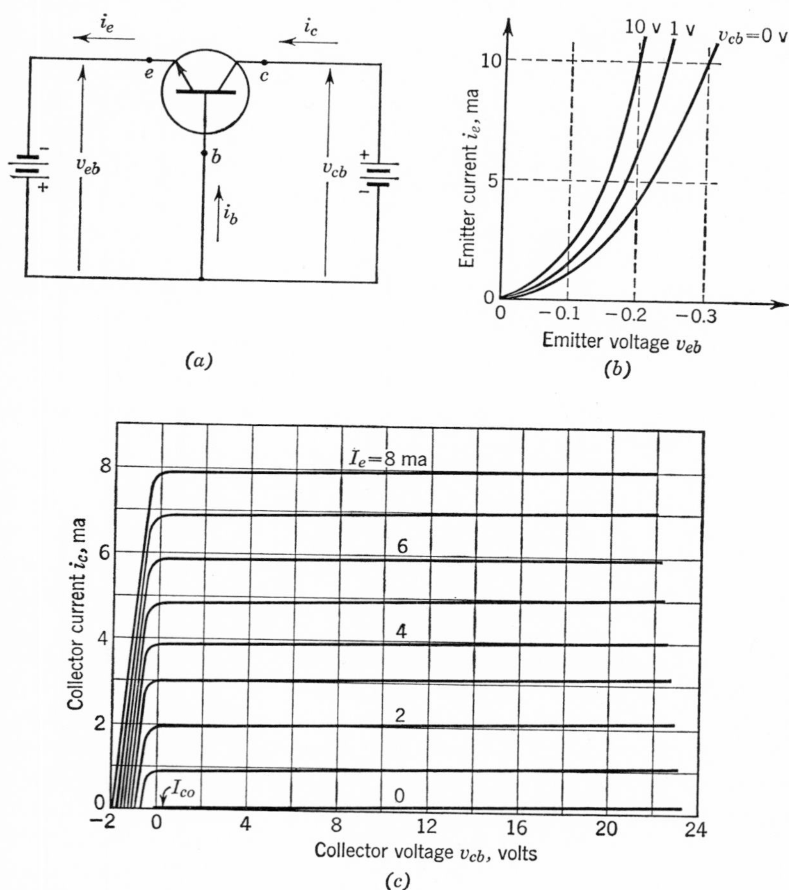

FIG. 4-20. Typical common-base characteristics—junction *n-p-n* transistor. (*a*) Schematic showing current flow and polarity; (*b*) input volt-ampere characteristic; (*c*) collector characteristics.

still lead to results consistent with the transistor's physical behavior; that is to say, the actual curves must be readily representable by straight-line segments and the equal increments of the controlling variable should produce roughly equal changes in the controlled term.

The most superficial glance at the volt-ampere characteristics of the typical *n-p-n* junction transistor (Fig. 4-20) convinces us that the device itself behaves in an almost piecewise-linear manner. Therefore we expect that the model representation will bear a closer correlation to the actual characteristics than it was possible to achieve with the triode. On the other hand, since the difficulties encountered in the manufacture of transistors manifest themselves in a wider divergence of characteristics, their actual response in a circuit would probably differ, by a comparable amount, from the ideal. By again directing our attention to Fig. 4-20, we would draw the following additional conclusions. First, the transistor exhibits current-controlled behavior in contrast to the voltage-controlled response of the triode. Secondly, we see that the collector curves are almost constant-current lines, with the particular operating path determined by the emitter current. Finally, from a

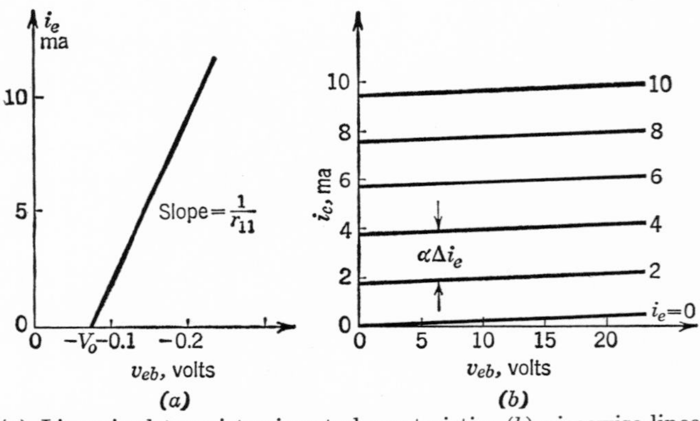

FIG. 4-21. (a) Linearized transistor input characteristic; (b) piecewise-linear collector characteristics.

macroscopic viewpoint, the effect of the collector current on the input response is not very pronounced; for the initial discussion the feedback rom the output to the input may be ignored.

Common-base Model. In finally replacing the actual characteristics by the linear segments needed for the large-signal model, we shall approximate the set of input volt-ampere curves (Fig. 4-20*b*) by the single line of Fig. 4-21*a*. Its equation is

$$v_{eb} = -(V_0 + i_e r_{11}) \qquad i_e \geq 0 \tag{4-23}$$

Equation (4-23) corresponds to a biased diode having a forward resistance of r_{11}. Often this term is referred to as the large-signal input resistance (grounded-base connection).

The collector characteristics are replaced by a family of parallel straight lines having a spacing determined by the emitter current. Their parametric equation, which we write in terms of the variable of interest, becomes

$$i_c = f(v_{eb}, i_e) = g_c v_{cb} + \alpha i_e \qquad i_e \geq 0 \text{ and } v_{cb} \geq 0 \tag{4-24}$$

The above defining equation (4-24), representing the response of the output circuit, is analogous to that written for the triode plate circuit [Eq. (4-2)]. The roles of current and voltage are simply interchanged, and we shall see that this leads to the dual-model representation. With respect to the original characteristics of Fig. 4-20*c*, the linear slope is g_c (the open-circuit collector admittance) and the current intercept is αi_e. Moreover, the forward-current amplification factor

$$\alpha = \left.\frac{\Delta i_c}{\Delta i_e}\right|_{\Delta v_{cb}=0} \tag{4-25}$$

fulfills a similar role to that performed by μ in the vacuum tube. Both coefficients may be found by measuring the collector current, first, with an applied collector voltage and the emitter open-circuited (g_c), and second, with an applied emitter current and the collector short-circuited (α).

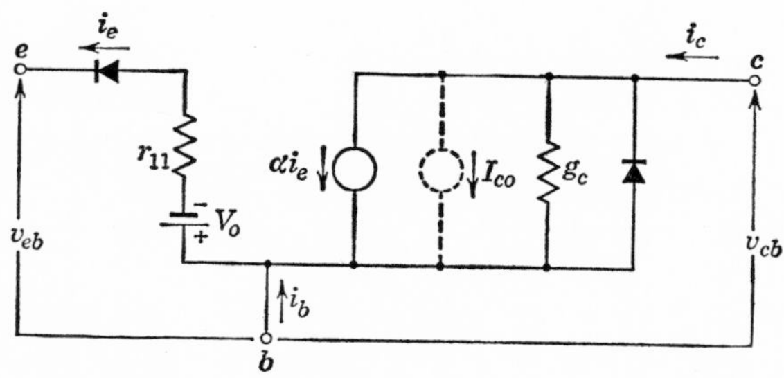

FIG. 4-22. Piecewise-linear model—*n-p-n* junction transistor.

We can construct the piecewise-linear model shown in Fig. 4-22 from the above defining equations. The forward-current transmission appears in the output circuit as the current generator αi_e. Diodes are inserted to restrict operation to the appropriate regions as well as to represent the transistor's behavior under saturation and cutoff conditions. We consider that the transistor is cut off when the input diode is back-biased and that it is saturated once the collector diode conducts. These conditions lead to the following limits for the active region:

$$v_{eb} \leq -V_0 \qquad v_{cb} \geq 0 \tag{4-26}$$

When the external emitter supply voltage is relatively large, the error in subsequent calculations due to omitting the small constant emitter drop will be insignificant. Moreover, the treatment of the input circuit as a constant resistance will greatly simplify any analysis. Except when using low supply voltages, the small drop will be ignored and the emitter will be assumed to conduct at zero volts. The values of the parameters of the junction transistor normally lie within the following bounds:

$$
\begin{aligned}
r_{11} &= h_{ib} \cong 10 \text{ to } 100 \text{ ohms} \\
V_o &\cong 0.05 \text{ to } 0.4 \text{ volt} \\
g_c &= h_{ob} = \frac{1}{r_c} \cong 10^{-5} \text{ to } 10^{-7} \text{ mho} \\
\alpha &= h_{fb} \cong 0.95 \text{ to } 0.99
\end{aligned}
$$

The h parameters tabulated above are those normally given by the manufacturer; the first subscript indicates the terminal under consideration (i for the input and o for the output), and the second subscript, the common grounded terminal (b for the base and e for the emitter).

If we refer back to the collector characteristics, we shall observe some small collector-base current flow even when $i_e = 0$. This term is I_{c0}, a temperature-dependent current which is due to the minority charge carriers present in the transistor material and which might be equated to the reverse current flow of a semiconductor diode. At room temperatures I_{c0} would be only a few microamperes, but since it roughly doubles for every 10°C rise in the ambient temperature, it would become important at elevated temperatures. Its equivalent-circuit representation would be an additional current generator in parallel with the controlled source shown. In the interests of simplicity, I_{c0} will be omitted from the following discussion; the reader can always include this term where necessary.

Common-emitter Model. Many transistor circuits exist where the input current is injected into the base and where the emitter replaces the base as the reference terminal. Consequently, it would be of interest to construct an alternative large-signal model in which the base current is the controlling term.

This transformation follows directly from the model of Fig. 4-22. We might first note that

$$i_b = i_e - i_c = (1 - \alpha)i_e \tag{4-27}$$

Solving Eq. (4-27) for i_e and multiplying the result by α yields

$$\alpha i_e = \frac{\alpha}{1 - \alpha} i_b = \beta i_b \tag{4-28}$$

where β is identified as the base-to-collector current-amplification factor. Since α is close to unity, taking on the values given above, β normally ranges between 20 and 100.

To complete the transformation from the emitter-controlled circuit of Fig. 4-22 to the base-controlled model of Fig. 4-23, we must ensure that all the remaining terminal characteristics of the two models are identical. In both, the emitter-to-base voltage drop must be the same for a given emitter current. For the grounded-base circuit,

$$v_{eb} = -(V_0 + i_e r_{11})$$

In the grounded-emitter configuration

$$v_{be} = -v_{eb} = +V_0 + i_b r'_{11} \tag{4-29}$$

Substituting the value of i_b given in Eq. (4-27) into Eq. (4-29),

$$v_{be} = V_0 + (1 - \alpha)r'_{11}i_e$$

Thus, by comparing appropriate terms,

$$r'_{11} = \frac{r_{11}}{1 - \alpha} = (1 + \beta)r_{11} \tag{4-30}$$

Under saturation conditions (conduction of the collector diode) the controlled source is shorted, β is removed from the circuit, and r'_{11} reduces to r_{11}.

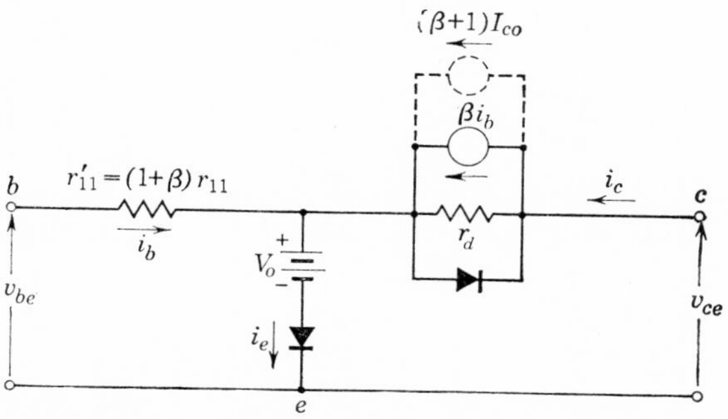

FIG. 4-23. Large-signal transistor model—common-emitter equivalent circuit.

The single remaining unknown term in the new model is the relative value of the output conductance r_d. Once we set $i_e = 0$, in the circuit of Fig. 4-22, we can then write the simple equation

$$v_{cb} = i_c r_c = \frac{i_c}{g_c} \tag{4-31}$$

where the small constant term V_0 is neglected. From Fig. 4-23, under the same conditions of an open-circuited emitter,

$$i_b = -i_c$$

But the current source in the output loop is controlled by the base current flow, which in this case is $-i_c$. Substitution into the model of

Fig. 4-23 results in the following output equation:

$$v_{ce} = i_c(1 + \beta)r_d \tag{4-32}$$

Since the emitter-to-base voltage is extremely small, $v_{cb} \cong v_{ce}$. By equating Eq. (4-31) to (4-32), we can find the internal impedance of the base-controlled current source. It becomes

$$r_d = (1 - \alpha)r_c = \frac{r_c}{\beta + 1} \tag{4-33}$$

and r_d is only one-tenth to one one-hundredth part of r_c.

The reverse collector current I_{c0} also flows through the base circuit and with no input

$$i_b = -I_{c0}$$

This term will also be multiplied by the base amplification factor β. For consistency of current flow, the controlled source must be shunted by an equivalent current generator of $(1 + \beta)I_{c0}$. The parallel combination of these two generators adds up to the actual current flow I_{c0}.

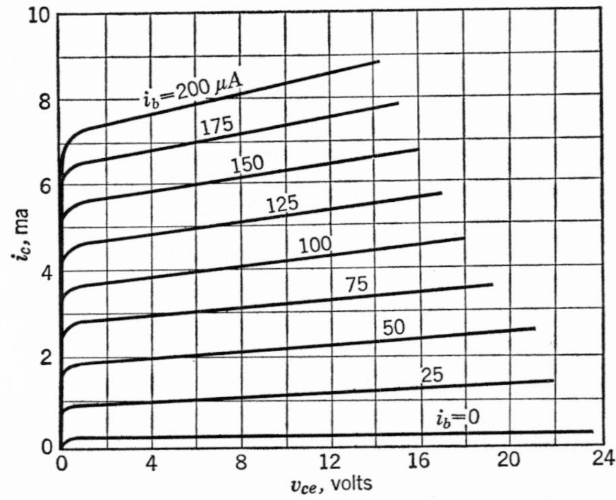

FIG. 4-24. Transistor-collector volt-ampere characteristics—common-emitter configuration.

The nonlinear attributes of the model must remain invariant under the circuit transformation, and therefore the two diodes remain in the emitter and in the collector arms. This is consistent with physical behavior since the emitter-base and the collector-base circuit each superficially constitute a diode, one forward-biased and the other back-biased.

If we started the construction of the transistor models from the volt-ampere characteristics which are measured for the common-emitter configuration (Fig. 4-24), the model resulting would be identical with

Fig. 4-23. We note that the slope of the collector curve is much steeper than that of the common-base circuit, thus verifying the result of Eq. (4-33). Moreover, as we anticipated in Eq. (4-28), the change in collector current with respect to changes in base current is much larger than with respect to the former controlling changes in the emitter current.

The comparative h parameters for the terms in the model of Fig. 4-23, together with their range of values, are

$$r'_{11} = h_{ie} = 100 \text{ to } 1{,}000 \text{ ohms}$$
$$g_d = \frac{1}{r_d} = H_{oe} = 2 \text{ to } 100\ \mu\text{mhos}$$
$$\beta = h_{fe} = 20 \text{ to } 100$$

Incremental Models. When dealing with small signals it is occasionally necessary to account for the effects on the input circuit of the changing collector voltage. In the large-signal model this factor was neglected, leading to the simple input circuit of Fig. 4-22. To take it into account in the incremental model, we can insert a voltage-controlled source as shown in Fig. 4-25. The reverse-voltage amplification h_{rb} is very small, on the order of 10^{-5} to 10^{-3}. For a more accurate representation, the other parameters (α, r_c, and r_{11}) may be reevaluated at the operating point.

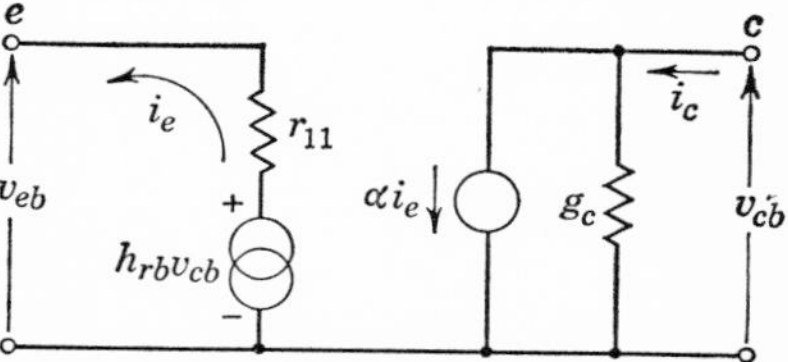

FIG. 4-25. Hybrid transistor model—common-base connection.

For the model of Fig. 4-25, the two defining equations are

$$v_{eb} = -r_{11}i_e + h_{rb}v_{cb} \tag{4-34a}$$
$$i_c = \alpha i_e + g_c v_{cb} \tag{4-34b}$$

where the voltage and current terms represent incremental variations about the operating point. From Eq. (4-34a) we see that the small reverse-voltage transmission is defined as

$$h_{rb} = \left.\frac{\Delta v_{eb}}{\Delta v_{cb}}\right|_{\Delta i_e = 0} \tag{4-35}$$

Inspection of Fig. 4-20b would indicate that h_{rb} increases with decreasing collector voltage and decreases with decreasing emitter current. In any calculations, it must be evaluated at the known operating point.

If the two-source hybrid model of Fig. 4-25 is replaced by the equivalent T network of Fig. 4-26, one of the controlled sources will be eliminated. Yet its effect is still present, represented instead by the common-base resistor r_b. The equivalents of the two models are found by solving the terminal response under identical operating conditions.

For a short-circuited output, the input equation of the hybrid model [Eq. (4-34a)] reduces to

$$v_{eb} = -r_{11}i_e$$

The equivalent equation found from Fig. 4-26 is

$$v_{eb} = -[r_e + (1 - \alpha)r_b]i_e \tag{4-36}$$

where r'_c is very large compared with r_b and may be neglected. Thus

$$r_e + (1 - \alpha)r_b = r_{11}$$

and for α very close to unity, r_e very closely approximates r_{11}.

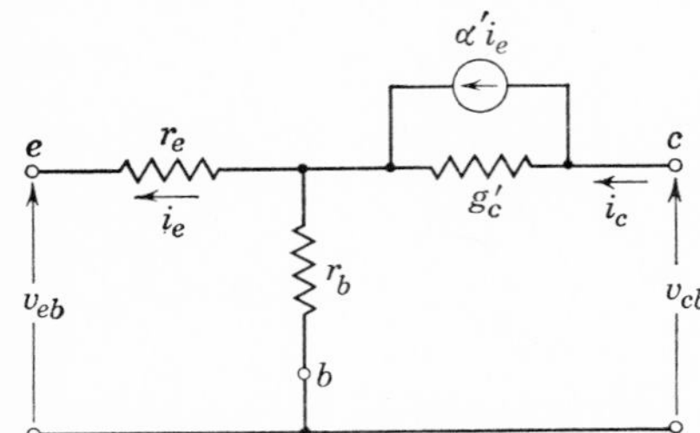

FIG. 4-26. Incremental T model—common-base connection.

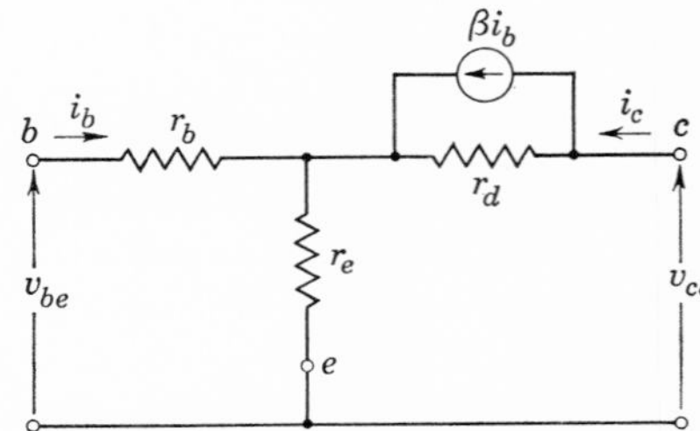

FIG. 4-27. Incremental T model—common-emitter connection.

By solving for v_{cb} from the models of Figs. 4-25 and 4-26 at $i_e = 0$,

$$h_{rb} = \frac{r_b}{r_b + r'_c} \cong \frac{r_b}{r'_c} \tag{4-37}$$

Following the same procedure with respect to the collector-to-base terminal response and remembering that $r'_c \gg r_b$, the remaining equivalents are

$$r'_c \cong r_c \qquad \text{and} \qquad \alpha' = \alpha \tag{4-38}$$

The values of the two new parameters generally lie within the range

r_b, from 100 to 400 ohms
r_e, from 10 to 50 ohms

and in much the same manner as h_{rb}, r_b varies widely with emitter current and collector voltage. It may decrease by a factor of 2 to 10 as we drive the transistor from close to cutoff to close to saturation.

The common-emitter T model (Fig. 4-27) will be almost identical with the common-collector model, with the major difference appearing in the collector branch. As in the equivalent hybrid model, r_d replaces

r_c and β replaces α. Furthermore

$$r'_{11} \cong r_b + (1 + \beta)r_e$$

Large-signal T Models. As an alternative to developing the incremental model from the large-signal representation, we can begin by examining a small section of the volt-ampere plane and, as we expand the area under review, modify the incremental circuit toward a large-signal model. Our starting point might be one of the T circuits of Fig. 4-26 or 4-27, and two limiting diodes would be added to restrict the permissible operating region. If necessary, a bias battery V_0 can also be inserted in the emitter circuit. Since a model is, at best, a reasonable approximation of the actual response, if average values are chosen for the T parameters, the circuits of Fig. 4-28 will be as serviceable as the hybrid models of Figs. 4-22 and 4-23.

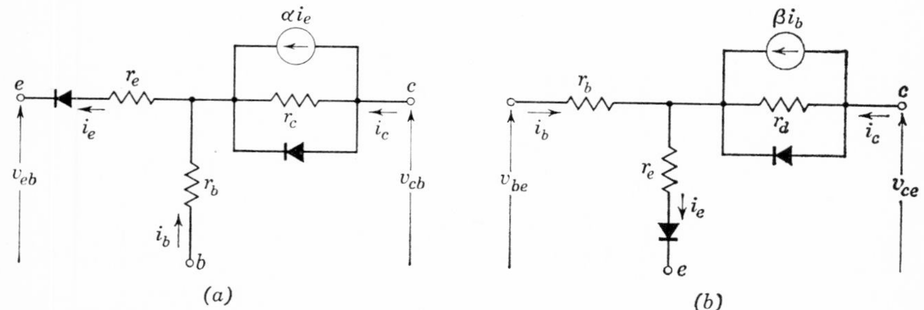

FIG. 4-28. Piecewise-linear T models. (*a*) Common-base connection; (*b*) common-emitter connection (V_0 and I_{c0} terms omitted).

4-5. Simple Transistor Circuits. The transistor, even more so than the triode, is readily adaptable for clamping and clipping applications. Since structurally it may be likened to a pair of diodes back to back, we might use either one independently in any of the circuits of Chap. 2. As a single diode is more economical, this is at best a dubious choice. But if advantage is taken of the current source shunting the collector diode to establish the location of the clamping level or the clipping point, as in Fig. 2-19, then the necessity of introducing an external bias generator will be avoided. Furthermore, since complementary transistors exist, *n-p-n* and *p-n-p*, we are no longer restricted, as we were with the triode, to unidirectional operation.

It is of interest to calculate the over-all transfer characteristics and, in the process, to delineate the various regions of transistor behavior. At the same time an attempt will be made to simplify the two-loop models of Figs. 4-22, 4-23, and 4-28 to the point where they become almost ridiculously simple. Of course, the approximations made must be kept in mind because many transistor circuits may not lend themselves to this treatment. The many others that do, including most of the circuits which will be treated in later chapters, justify our spending some little time on this topic.

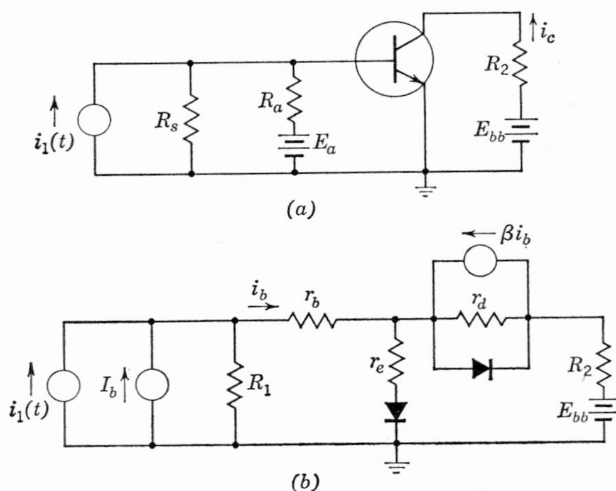

FIG. 4-29. (a) Transistor amplifier circuit; (b) piecewise-linear model.

Consider, for example, the transistor amplifier circuit of Fig. 4-29a. In drawing the T piecewise-linear model (Fig. 4-29b), we also converted the circuit, external to the base, to its Norton equivalent, where

$$R_1 = R_s \parallel R_a \qquad \text{and} \qquad I_b = \frac{E_a}{R_s + R_a}$$

Before beginning the analysis, we might note that the percentage of the driving current which actually flows into the base depends on the relative magnitudes of the transistor base input impedance Z_b and the external base load R_1.

$$i_b = \frac{Z_b}{R_1 + Z_b} i_1(t) \tag{4-39}$$

It thus seems logical to evaluate the over-all transmission in two steps: first, the direct transmission from the base terminal to the output and, second, the transmission factor relating the driving source and the base current. The over-all forward transmission is the product of these two terms. Moreover, since the bias current I_b only shifts the transfer characteristics with respect to the zero point, it might be just as easy initially to ignore I_b and, after the solution is complete, then consider the shift in axis introduced by this constant-current term.

The first operating region with which we shall be concerned is the cut-off zone, characterized by the back-biasing of the emitter diode. Figure 4-30a presents the reduced model holding in this region. The input-circuit defining equation will enable us to locate the boundary.

$$\begin{aligned} v_{be} &= i_b r_b + (\beta + 1) i_b r_d + R_2 i_b + E_{bb} \\ &= i_b[r_b + (\beta + 1) r_d + R_2] + E_{bb} \end{aligned} \tag{4-40}$$

But the reader may verify from Eq. (4-33) that $(\beta + 1)r_d = r_c$. It now seems reasonable to neglect the small voltage drop appearing across r_b

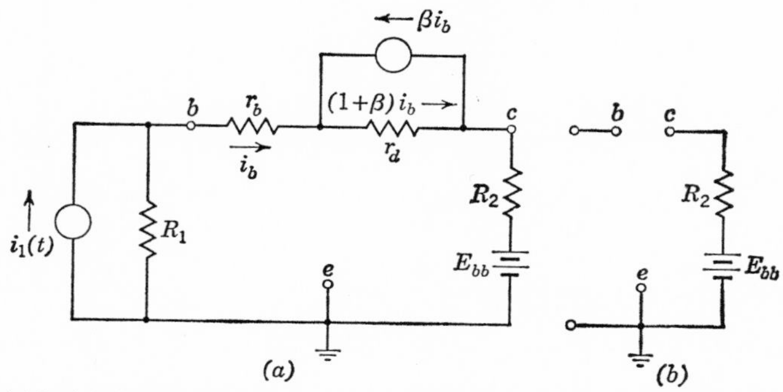

FIG. 4-30. (a) Model defining cutoff region; (b) approximate representation.

while considering the bounds of this region ($r_c \gg r_b$). For the emitter to be back-biased $v_{be} \leq 0$; solving Eq. (4-40) establishes the cutoff region, in terms of i_b, as

$$i_b \leq \frac{-E_{bb}}{r_c + R_2} \cong 0 \tag{4-41}$$

The current flowing in the base under cutoff conditions is simply the reverse current through the back-biased collector-to-base diode.

The input impedance of the transistor is the coefficient of i_b in Eq. (4-40). Since the predominant term is r_c, which is usually very much larger than any external load appearing at either the collector or the base, practically all the signal source current will be shunted through R_1. Transmission from the input to the output is completely negligible, and for simplicity, this path may be replaced by an open circuit. The model of Fig. 4-30b results, and we have seen that it represents, quite adequately, the transistor's behavior under cutoff conditions.

Next, in considering the active region of transistor operation (Fig. 4-31a), we note that for maximum load current, the external load should be very small compared with the internal impedance, that is, $R_2 \ll r_d$. Under this condition the current through R_2 will be βi_b. Along with neglecting the current flow through r_d, the resistance itself will be removed from the equivalent circuit. A current of $i_b(1 + \beta)$ flows through r_e, and the input equation for this region becomes

$$\begin{aligned} v_{be} &= i_b r_b + (1 + \beta) r_e i_b \\ &= i_b[r_b + (1 + \beta) r_e] \end{aligned} \tag{4-42}$$

The interpretation given to Eq. (4-42) is that any resistance in series

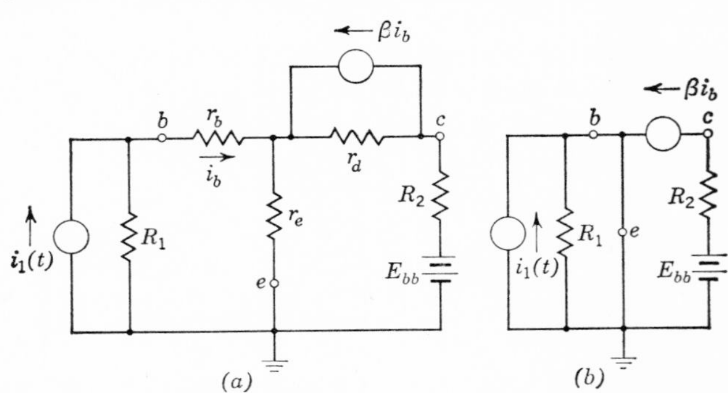

FIG. 4-31. (*a*) Model defining active region; (*b*) approximate representation.

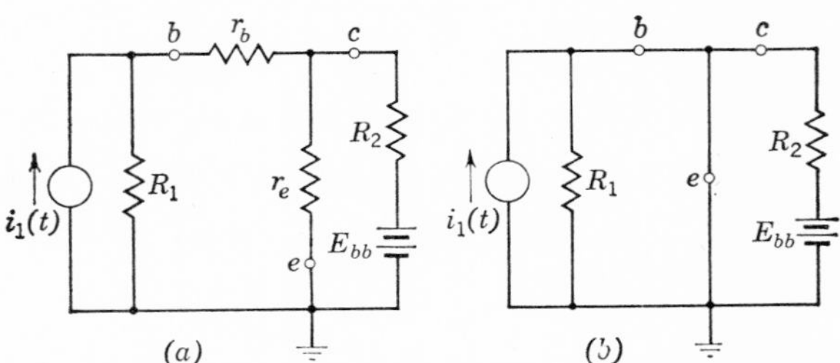

FIG. 4-32. (*a*) Model defining saturation region; (*b*) approximate representation.

with the emitter is multiplied by $(1 + \beta)$ as it is reflected into the base input circuit. From Eq. (4-39),

$$i_b = \frac{R_1}{r_b + (1 + \beta) r_e + R_1} i_1(t)$$

and

$$i_c = \beta i_b = \beta \frac{R_1}{r_b + (1 + \beta) r_e + R_1} i_1(t) \tag{4-43}$$

For the maximum possible current gain, $R_1 \gg r_b + (1 + \beta) r_e$. Upon satisfaction of this necessary inequality, both the base and emitter resistors are replaced by short circuits and the trivial model of Fig. 4-31*b* results.

The upper bound of the active region occurs when the collector voltage drops to zero. From the simplified model of Fig. 4-31*b*,

$$v_{ce} = E_{bb} - \beta i_b R_2 \geq 0$$

Thus the limits of the active region are

$$0 \leq i_b \leq \frac{E_{bb}}{\beta R_2} \tag{4-44}$$

As $i_1(t)$ continues to increase, the circuit enters upon its saturation region. The collector diode conducts, and, using the approximations previously made, the model of Fig. 4-32*a* may be reduced to the simple representation of Fig. 4-32*b*. We might observe that since there is no longer any transmission from the input to the output, the slope of the transfer characteristics will be zero.

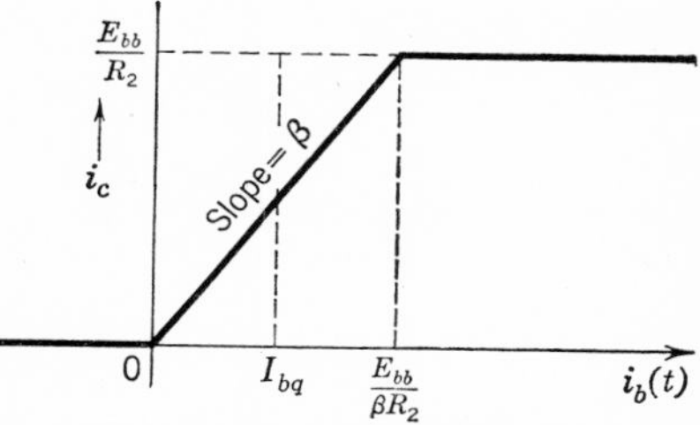

FIG. 4-33. Transfer characteristics of the circuit of Fig. 4-29.

Figure 4-33 shows the input-output transfer characteristics. In addition, the shift in axis produced by the bias current I_{bq} is also accounted for by the second ordinate (dashed line).

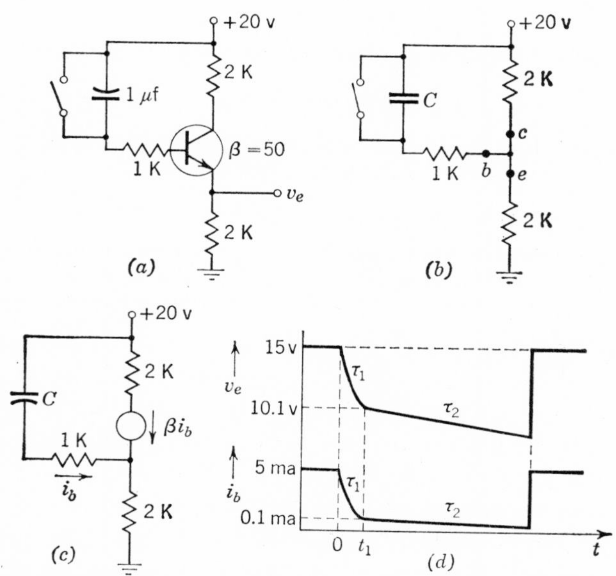

FIG. 4-34. Circuit, models, and waveshapes for Example 4-2.

Example 4-2. The model techniques are also quite useful in evaluating the time response of active circuits containing energy-storage elements. To illustrate the methods employed, we shall solve the simple circuit of Fig. 4-34*a*. The switch, which is initially closed, will be opened at $t = 0$ and closed after steady state is reached.

Before the switch is opened the large base current flow saturates the transistor. This statement can be verified by assuming that it is true and calculating the current flow. The model of interest reduces to that shown in Fig. 4-34*b*. By taking the Thévenin equivalent of the circuit seen looking into the transistor,

$$i_b(0^-) = \frac{10}{2{,}000} = 5.0 \text{ ma}$$

From the active-region model of Fig. 4-34*c*, the conditions for saturation are given by

$$\beta i_{bs} \times 2 \text{ K} + (\beta + 1)i_{bs} \times 2 \text{ K} = 20 \text{ volts}$$

or

$$i_{bs} = 100 \ \mu\text{a}$$

and this current is greatly exceeded.

Solving the circuit of Fig. 4-34*b*, the voltage at the emitter is

$$v_e(0^-) = \frac{2 \text{ K}}{2 \text{ K} + 1 \text{ K} \parallel 2 \text{ K}} 20 = 15 \text{ volts}$$

After the switch is opened, the emitter starts decaying toward 10 volts, with the time constant

$$\tau_1 = 1 \ \mu\text{f} \times 2 \text{ K} = 2 \text{ msec}$$

But the base current also decreases as C charges. When it falls to 100 μa or when $v_{es} = 10.1$ volts, the transistor becomes active. The elapsed time will be found from the exponential charging equation

$$v_e = 10 + 5e^{-t/\tau_1}$$

by substituting in the final value. Virtually the complete exponential is used, and thus

$$t_1 \cong 4\tau_1 = 8 \text{ msec}$$

After the circuit becomes active, the increase in input impedance to $(\beta + 1)2$ K [from Eq. (4-42)] increases the charging time constant to

$$\tau_2 = 1 \ \mu\text{f}(51 \times 2 \text{ K} + 1 \text{ K}) = 103 \text{ msec}$$

The discharge continues toward zero with this very long time constant. Finally the switch is closed and the transistor switches back into saturation.

The waveshapes of the base current and the emitter voltage are shown in Fig. 4-34*d*.

4-6. Transistor Gates. If we reexamine the basic premise from which we constructed the various circuit configurations used as gates, i.e., the opening or closing of a transmission path upon signal excitation, it would seem that perhaps a series arrangement of active elements would serve as well as the parallel gates of Sec. 4-3. With triodes, the high plate supply voltage necessary for their proper operation would have made any such discussion academic. However, at this point we have at our disposal the transistor, an active element requiring very low operating voltages, and we may therefore contemplate this alternative configuration. Of course this does not prevent the use of transistor parallel gates.

The series gate fulfills its function as the individual transistors switch from the almost direct short they present under saturation to an open circuit when cut off. Since the opening of a series transmission path anywhere along its length is equally effective, for an OR gate (Fig. 4-35) the individual transistors would normally be biased full-on. As any one changes state into cutoff, the output path opens and the gate indicates the presence of the input pulse. Conversely, in an AND circuit (Fig. 4-36), all the transistors would be biased below cutoff, with the output terminal remaining above ground potential until the simultaneous excitation at all

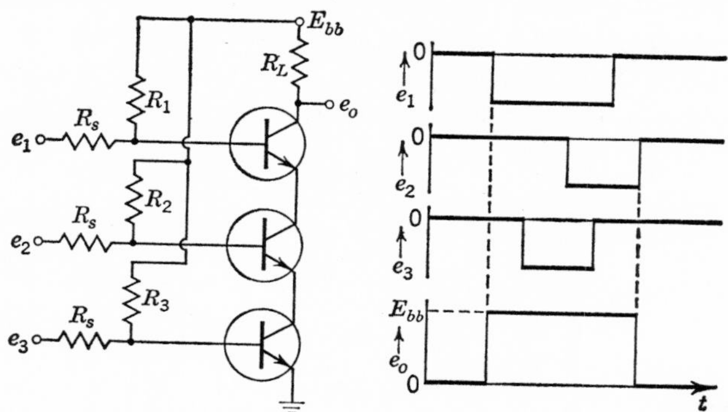

FIG. 4-35. Series OR gate and waveshapes.

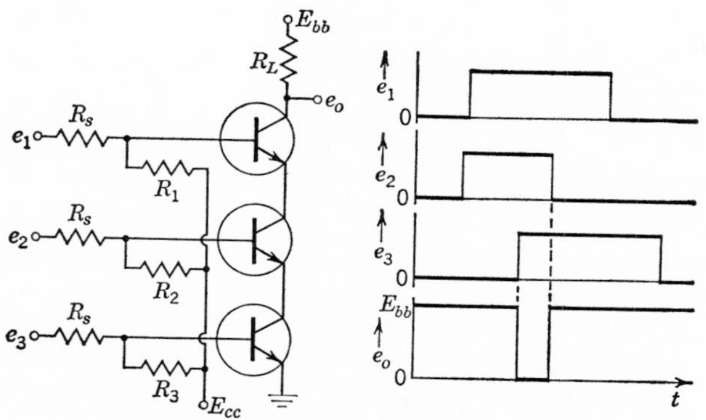

FIG. 4-36. Series AND gate and waveshapes.

inputs closes the gate. An important contrast between these two gates is that the OR gate, being biased on, requires heavy saturation current flow under stand-by conditions, whereas the series AND gate only conducts when its logic situation is satisfied.

One of the major problems facing the designer of logical systems, such as digital computers and control equipment, is the power requirements imposed by the large number of active elements employed. Besides the expense involved in supplying the current drain at the regulated voltages needed, the heat produced by the dissipated power must be conducted away from the equipment. Otherwise the ambient temperature of the enclosed components may rise to a point where some elements will be seriously damaged or even destroyed. To this end, the engineer seeks circuits operating with little or no stand-by power. Furthermore, since a single triode requires approximately 1 watt of filament heating power, transistors have almost completely superseded tubes in many critical applications.

The two transistor gates which best satisfy the above specifications are the parallel-connected OR gate and the series-connected AND gate. Each is normally biased below cutoff. Combinations of these two find wide application in the development of systems of binary logic employed

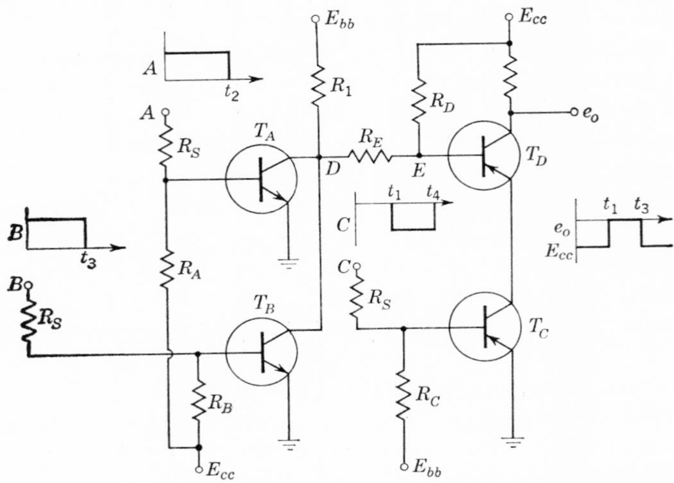

FIG. 4-37. Direct-coupled complementary transistor gate producing an output upon satisfaction of *A or B and C*.

in digitally operated equipment. Moreover, complementary design, i.e., use of alternating *p-n-p* and *n-p-n* gates, permits the output of one gate to be directly coupled as the input to the next gate.

Consider, for example, the circuit of Fig. 4-37, where all the transistors are normally cut off: T_A, T_B, and T_C by having their bases returned to the appropriate polarity bias voltage and T_D by adjusting the network of R_1, R_D, and R_E so that the voltage from point E to ground will be above zero. Satisfaction of the parallel OR gate, upon the positive excitation of either A or B, will force the related transistor into conduction, with the voltage at point D now dropping to zero. The base of T_D becomes negative, as a consequence of returning the coupling resistor R_E to ground through T_A or T_B, and the series AND gate is now primed for conduction. As soon as a negative pulse appears at point C the gate opens, allowing the output to rise from E_{cc} to zero. If instead a negative output pulse is desired, the load could be shifted to the emitter-ground circuit of T_C, with the output now dropping from zero to E_{cc} upon the gate's closure.

We see that if the transistor is allowed to switch between cutoff and saturation, then its simplified model representation is an open circuit followed by a short circuit. Only in so far as the saturation value of base current depends on the transistor parameters will the circuit's operation be affected by the particular type of transistor chosen. Provided that the threshold value is exceeded for the lowest value of β expected, the switching performance becomes completely independent of the particular active element and would not deteriorate upon the substitution of an entirely different transistor.

4-7. Pentodes. Both the transistor and the triode are three-terminal devices, and therefore only two equations, involving four variables, were necessary to define their complete operation. Moreover, the approximations made in linearizing their characteristics were not so extreme as to be incompatible with the actual physical functioning of the device. If we attempt to extend this concept to the pentode, we find ourselves in some difficulty. We are now forced to consider the related response of four terminals instead of two (all voltages are specified with respect to the cathode, the reference terminal). Each defining equation will involve the terminal characteristics of the remaining three tube elements. As a specific example, the equation of plate current must include its own voltage as well as terms reflecting the effects of the suppressor, screen, and control-grid voltages on the plate current flow. These latter terms appear as controlled sources in any model drawn.

$$i_b = f(e_b, e_{c1}, e_{c2}, e_{c3}) \tag{4-45}$$

Analogous equations could be written for the other pentode elements.

First of all, in order to expand Eq. (4-45) into a form amenable to expression as a piecewise-linear model, we would have to examine the curves of plate current and voltage drawn with each of the three grid voltages as a parameter. From these families of characteristics we might be able to estimate the relative error introduced by linearization. After replacing the actual curves by straight lines, the coefficients of the linear equation are evaluated from the various slopes and intercepts. Since the manufacturer does not usually make such data available, the engineer would have to perform his own measurements. As the final step, one or more biased diodes would be inserted to restrict the range of operation at the plate.

Assuming that reasonably satisfactory linear operation is possible, Eq. (4-45) may be expanded so that it leads to a current-source representation.

$$i_b = g_p e_b + g_{1b} e_1 + g_{2b} e_2 + g_{3b} e_c \tag{4-46}$$

The numerical subscripts indicate the particular grid under consideration. Each of the coefficients represents the transfer admittance from the appropriate grid to the plate. If we restrict operation to the first quadrant, the model representation of the plate circuit is as shown in Fig. 4-38.

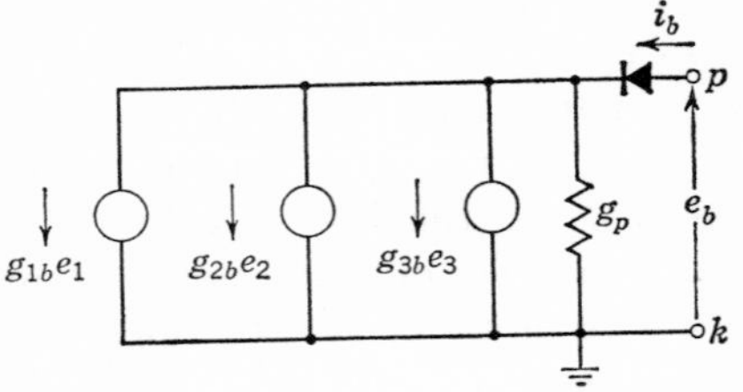

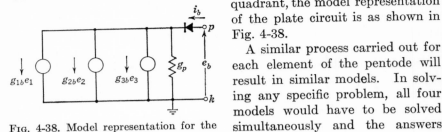

FIG. 4-38. Model representation for the plate circuit of a pentode.

A similar process carried out for each element of the pentode will result in similar models. In solving any specific problem, all four models would have to be solved simultaneously and the answers individually checked to ensure that none of the boundary values are exceeded.

It appears that the desire for generality in this case has greatly increased the complexity, even to the point of allowing the model to obscure the actual physical processes. Therefore we might best deal directly with the characteristics rather than bother to construct a model.

In many specific circuits, however, the tube voltages are so restricted that simpler models may be drawn. The suppressor primarily serves to determine the division of the cathode current between the plate and the screen grid, while the total cathode current depends on the screen-grid voltage. If both of these are held constant, then the plate volt-ampere characteristics are almost constant-current curves, with the particular value of current determined solely by the control-grid voltage (Fig. 4-39). The model for the plate-circuit operation would be reduced by combining the two constant terms of Fig. 4-38, $g_{2b}e_2$ and $g_{3b}e_3$, into a constant-current generator I_o equal to the current intercept of the zero grid-voltage line.

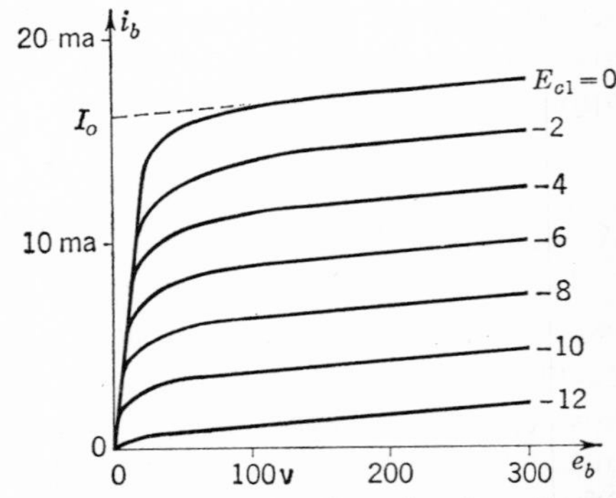

FIG. 4-39. Pentode-plate-circuit volt-ampere characteristics—constant screen and suppressor voltage.

Each of the pentode's grids has sufficient control over the plate current flow so that if any one or all are made highly negative, the tube is completely cut off. We can thus utilize any individual grid as a gate input, and for special gating functions we may employ various combinations of the three grids. They function in series as valves. Changing any one from the on to the off state gives us the OR gate. If all elements are normally biased off, they must all be turned on before plate current will flow (AND gate). Another commonly used pentode circuit is the controlled gate of Fig. 4-40. Here the suppressor will maintain the plate cutoff until the application of a control pulse. Once current flows, the tube operates in a normal manner, amplifying and transmitting the control-grid signal to the plate circuit.

We note that advantage is taken of the control characteristics in much the same manner as the series arrangement of transistors. Each control element, reflected as a controlled source, has the ability to turn the device on and off, and by acting in unison, they create the logical situation sought.

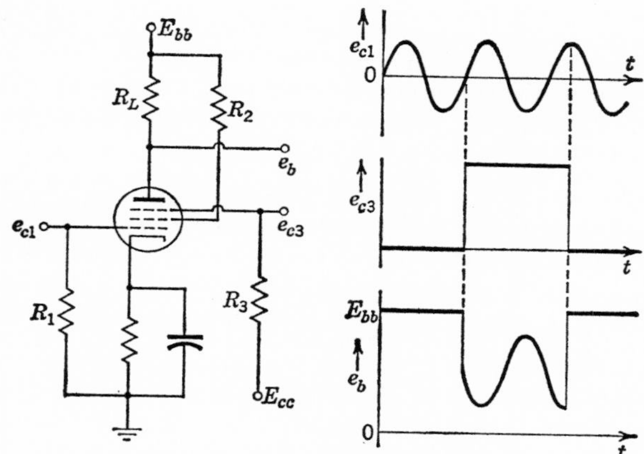

FIG. 4-40. Pentode-controlled gate.

4-8. Summary. The importance of the model concept in freeing the engineering viewpoint from the conformity imposed by the rigor of graphically presented data cannot be overstressed. It is extremely difficult to give the imagination free reign when the active element, the heart of electronics circuit design, must be treated in a manner different from its associated circuit components. Constant referral back and forth from the tube or transistor graphics to the circuit equations involving the passive elements denies the grasp of the basic nature of the system behavior; it leads to the treatment of each circuit as a separate entity.

In direct contrast to this approach, the very nature of the simplifying approximations made when drawing a model must lead to a simpler presentation of the phenomena under examination. Furthermore, the essential unity of circuits and systems immediately becomes clear from the similarity of their models. Regardless of the type of control, be it voltage, current, pressure, velocity, or temperature, an equivalent controlled-source representation places the controlling element in the forefront. After the piecewise-linear model of the nonlinear element is drawn and the remaining circuit components are placed in their proper relationship, then, within each region, analysis proceeds as in a linear circuit. All linear-circuit theory becomes applicable, and many methods that would not normally be applied give power to the engineer.

PROBLEMS

4-1. (*a*) Construct a piecewise-linear model to represent the 12AU7 which will agree exactly with the tube characteristics at $E_c = -10$ and $I_b = 15$ ma. Give all parameter values.

(*b*) Superimpose your model on the tube characteristics of Fig. 4-1 and delineate the regions where the agreement is within 20 per cent of the actual current.

(*c*) Construct an alternative model which will hold for currents less than 5 ma. How does it differ from the one found in part *a*?

4-2. (*a*) Drawing on the answers of Prob. 4-1, construct a model which will represent the plate characteristics by two contiguous segments. In this manner we can obtain closer agreement with the measured curves.

(*b*) For this model repeat part *b* of Prob. 4-1.

4-3. The 12AU7 is used as a simple plate-loaded cathode bias amplifier with $R_L =$ 12 K and $E_{bb} = 250$ volts. Calculate the incremental gain as found from the piecewise model and from the actual characteristics at the following bias voltages: +5, 0, −5, −10, and −15 volts. Express the deviation from the value found from the model as a percentage. (Assume that $r_c = 1{,}000$ ohms in the positive grid region and that the signal source impedance is 2,000 ohms.)

4-4. If we restrict operation to $e_b \geq ke_c$ (as shown in Fig. 4-2), show that the approximate plate-circuit model for $e_b \leq ke_c$ is simply a resistor of $kr_p/(\mu + k)$.

4-5. Calculate and plot the transfer characteristic for the circuit of Fig. 4-5*a* when the cathode bypass capacitor is removed. The tube parameters are $r_p = 70$ K, $\mu = 100$, and $r_c = 1$ K, and we choose a load resistor of 200 K with $E_{bb} = 250$ volts. What value must we specify for R_3 if the quiescent current is to be 0.5 ma?

Sketch the output if the input is a triangular wave of 50 volts peak to peak.

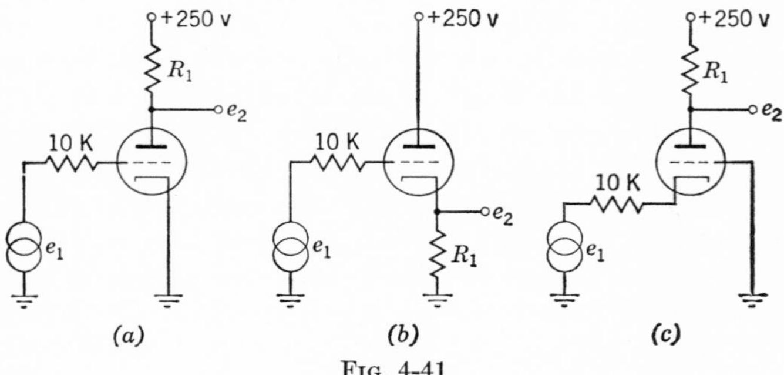

FIG. 4-41

4-6. The three circuits of Fig. 4-41 illustrate the most common amplifiers. The same tube and load resistor are used in each case ($r_p = 25$ K, $\mu = 50$, $R_1 = 50$ K, and $r_c = 1$ K).

(a) Draw the complete transfer characteristics of all three circuits on the same axis.

(b) Specify the output impedance of each amplifier in each of the three regions of operation.

(c) Specify the input impedance of each circuit in each region.

(d) Can you draw any conclusions as to the applicability of these amplifiers?

4-7. (a) Calculate and plot e_o versus time for the circuit of Fig. 4-42 when $C = 200\ \mu\mu f$ and $R = 25$ K. The input signal is periodic.

(b) Repeat part *a* with $C = 2{,}000\ \mu\mu f$ and $R = 250$ K.

(c) Repeat part *b* when R is connected between the grid of T_2 and 300 volts instead of being returned to ground.

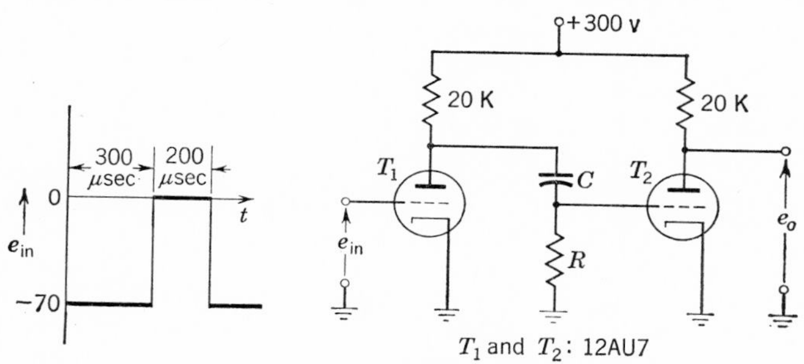

FIG. 4-42

4-8. At what time after the switch is opened will the tube in Fig. 4-43 start conducting and how much later will the grid conduct? ($\mu = 20$, $r_p = 10$ K, and $r_c = 1$ K.) Sketch and label the waveshapes appearing at the plate and grid.

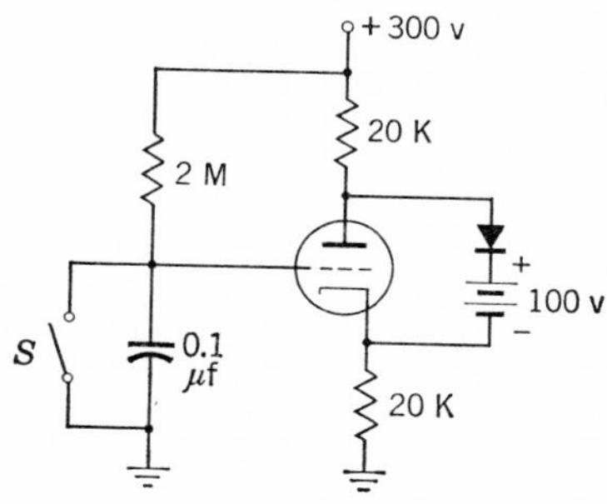

FIG. 4-43

4-9. Repeat Prob. 4-8 when the *RC* combination in the grid circuit is replaced by a 10-K resistor and a 100-mh inductance, respectively.

4-10. In the circuit of Fig. 4-11, $\mu = 70$, $r_p = 50$ K, $E_{bb} = 300$ volts, $R_2 = 100$ K, and $E_{cc} = -150$ volts. Find the value of R_3 that will ensure symmetrical clipping of the input signal. Plot and label the transfer characteristics.

4-11. Consider the cathode-coupled clipper of Fig. 4-11 having the following parameters:

$r_p = 70$ K	$R_2 = 100$ K	$E_{bb} = 300$ volts
$\mu = 100$	$R_3 = ?$	$E_{cc} = -150$ volts

(a) Calculate the value of R_3 that will result in a quiescent current of 0.6 ma through T_2. (HINT: Since the common-cathode voltage is approximately zero, the drop across R_2 and T_2 is almost exactly equal to E_{bb}.)

(b) Calculate the two clipping levels with respect to the input.

(c) Sketch and label the transfer characteristic.

4-12. In the circuit of Fig. 4-41a (Prob. 4-6) a triangular wave is coupled through a 0.01-μf capacitor rather than the 10-K resistor. What is the largest possible peak-to-peak input signal before the circuit begins to clip the input? Sketch the output when the input is twice as large as found above.

4-13. (a) A cascode amplifier, such as shown in Fig. 4-44, is widely employed in television sets where the noise must be kept within bounds. If both of the triodes shown are 12AU7's, calculate the quiescent operating point and the transfer characteristics. Draw the simplified models holding at each break point.

(b) Explain the steps which must be taken in order to find the quiescent point by a graphical construction. Check the answer to part a by this means.

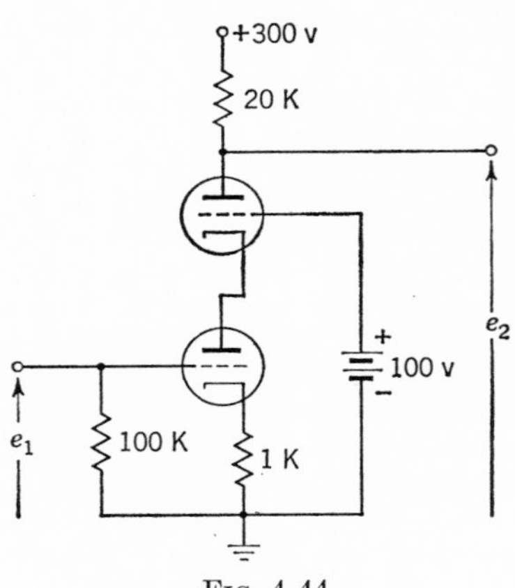

FIG. 4-44

4-14. (a) Calculate the value of R_1 that will set the quiescent output of the circuit of Fig. 4-45 at zero ($E_2 = E_{cc} = -150$ volts).

(b) What kind of gate is this? What is the minimum input amplitude that will produce the maximum output amplitude?

4-15. In the circuit of Fig. 4-45, E_2 is set equal to E_{bb}. The load resistor R_1 is 50 K, and it is shunted by 150 $\mu\mu$f stray capacity.

(a) Sketch the output if we apply −100-volt 20-msec pulses to e_1 at $t = 0$; to e_2, 5 msec later; and to e_3 at $t = 10$ msec.

(b) Repeat part a if the inputs are changed to 20-volt positive pulses.

(c) Can you see any way to improve the operation of this gate?

4-16. Repeat Prob. 4-15 when the load resistor is transferred to the plate circuit making the AND gate of Fig. 4-16. The cathodes are returned to ground.

4-17. We wish to eliminate the pedestal present in the controlled gate of Fig. 4-17. The tube and circuit parameters are $r_p = 100$ K, $\mu = 100$, $R_L = 200$ K, and $E_{bb} = 300$ volts. The gating tube T_2 is normally maintained cut off by the 12-volt d-c level of the gating signal applied at the grid of T_1; superimposed 10-volt negative pulses turn T_2 on.

Use a tube with the same parameters and calculate the value of the cathode resistor necessary to completely eliminate the pedestal. Assume that the control pulses are coupled into its grid through a large capacitor. Specify the amplitude and polarity of the signal which must be simultaneously applied to this additional triode.

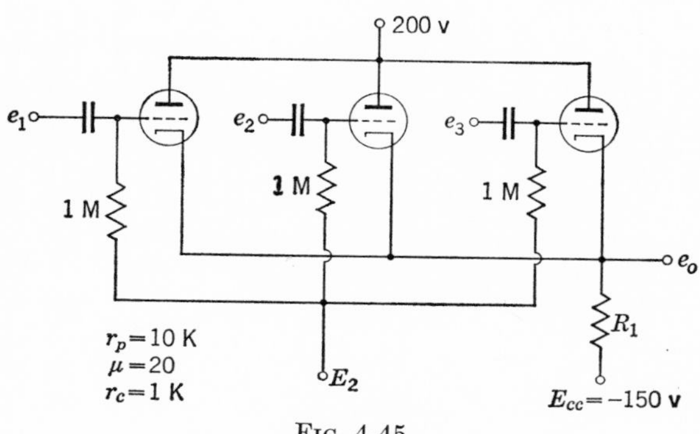

Fig. 4-45

4-18. There are four possible models which may be used to represent the four variables i_b, v_{be}, i_c, v_{ce} in the grounded-emitter configuration. Draw these models and show where diodes must be inserted to restrict the operation to the proper quadrant. Give the meaning of the various circuit parameters in terms of those given in the model of Fig. 4-27.

4-19. The circuit of Fig. 4-46*a* is used as a current-voltage converter.

(*a*) Plot the transfer characteristics (e_2 versus i_1), taking all terms into account, and compare it with the plot found from the appropriate approximate models.

(*b*) Calculate the input admittance and output impedance in each of the three operating regions.

(*c*) Plot the output if $i_1 = 50 \sin \omega t$ ma.

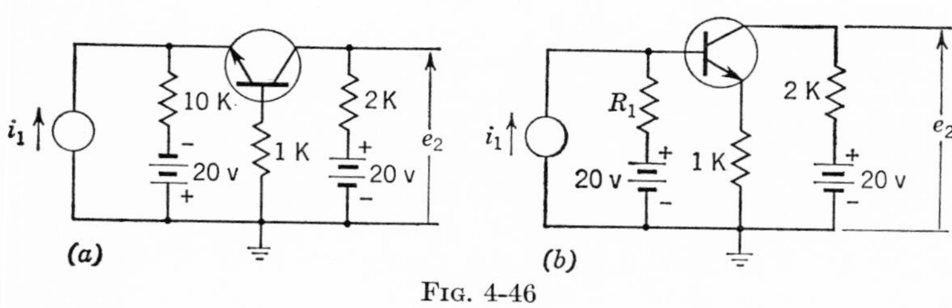

Fig. 4-46

4-20. We wish to choose R_1, in the circuit of Fig. 4-46*b*, so as to achieve symmetrical clipping. Under these circumstances repeat Prob. 4-19.

4-21. The transistor used in Fig. 4-46 has an I_{c0} of 10 μa at room temperature, and it doubles for every 10°C rise. If the value of R_1 in Fig. 4-46*b* is 100 K, by how much will the Q point shift with a 20°C rise in ambient temperature? Repeat this calculation for the circuit of Fig. 4-46*a* and express both shifts as a ratio of the Q point calculated when I_{c0} is assumed zero.

4-22. The circuit of Fig. 4-47 employs transistors having $r_e = 30$, $r_b = 300$, and $\beta = 20$. Sketch to scale the input e_2 and the output e_3 when the excitation shown is applied. Two cases should be considered:

(*a*) When $C = 1$ μf.

(*b*) When $C = 0.001$ μf.

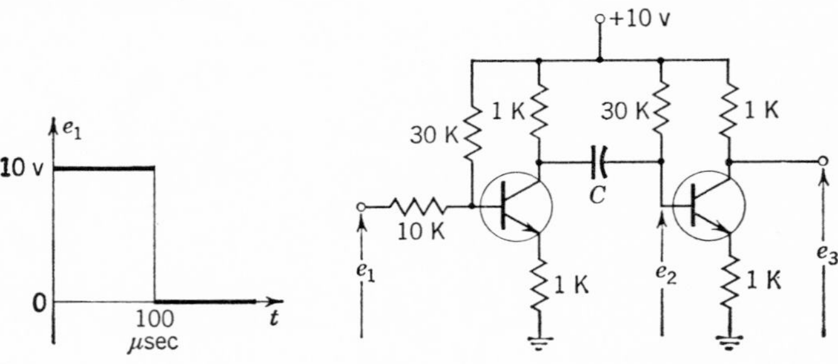

FIG. 4-47

4-23. Sketch and label the collector voltage in the circuit of Fig. 4-48 if the switch is opened at $t = 0$ and closed after the transistor is forced as far into saturation as possible. Make all reasonable approximations and indicate the times at which the transistor changes state.

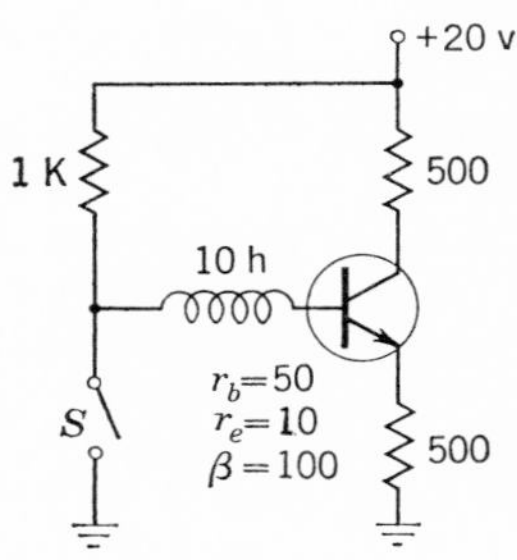

FIG. 4-48

4-24. As the reverse bias of a transistor drops to zero, the current gain of the transistor also decreases. Figure 4-49 shows a semiquantitative view of this decrease for the G.E. 2N-123 *p-n-p* transistor.

(*a*) Using Fig. 4-49 and given the data that $r_e = 28$ ohms and $r_b = 80$ ohms, find the input impedance of the transistor when it is biased such that $e_o \cong 0$.

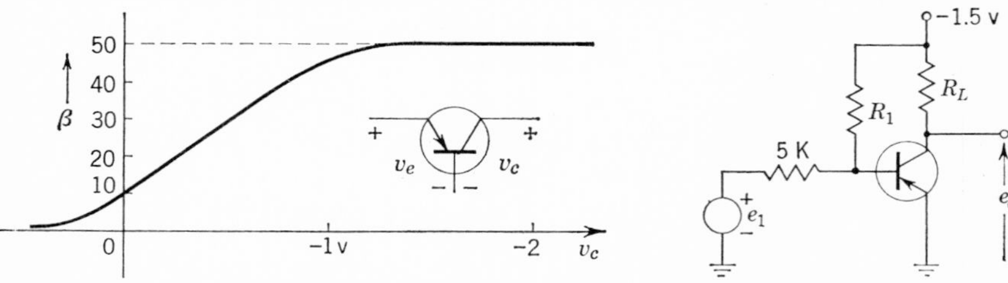

FIG. 4-49. The transistor parameters are $r_b = 200$, $r_e = 20$, $r_c = 2$ megohms, and $\alpha = 0.95$.

(b) The maximum emitter current is to be 1 ma. What values of R_1 and R_L will just meet this requirement?

(c) What value of e_1 is necessary to just cut off the transistor?

4-25. The circuit of Fig. 4-46a is modified by connecting a 1-henry choke from the emitter to ground. The input is a 10-kc current sine wave of adjustable amplitude. If the signal distortion due to the periodic charge and discharge of the coil is neglected, what is the peak input amplitude before the output appears clipped?

4-26. A parallel combination of transistors is connected as an AND gate similar to the one shown for the triodes in Fig. 4-16. Their collectors are connected together, and the output load resistor inserted in this circuit. We desire to drive this gate with negative pulses at the base.

(a) If we have both n-p-n and p-n-p transistors, a 2,000-ohm load resistor, and two 20-volt batteries at our disposal, what circuit would be used?

(b) How large must the input switching pulses be for the maximum output swing? The voltage pulses are applied through 20-K resistors directly into the base. Any bias resistors selected must furnish a base current of five times the saturation value.

(c) Repeat this problem if the pulses are injected into the base and the output load is connected from the common emitter to ground. Transistor parameters are

$$r_b = 150 \text{ ohms} \qquad r_e = 30 \text{ ohms}$$
$$\alpha = 0.98 \qquad r_c = 2 \text{ megohms}$$

Make all reasonable approximations to simplify your calculations.

4-27. Using either n-p-n or p-n-p transistors having the parameters given in Prob. 4-26, we desire to construct a parallel OR gate. It should operate on positive signals injected at each emitter and should furnish an output across a 2,000-ohm resistor in the common-base circuit as well as across a 1,000-ohm resistor in the common-collector circuit.

(a) Draw a three-transistor circuit when two 25-volt batteries are available for power.

(b) If the bias resistors are 2 K, what is the impedance seen by the driving signal source?

(c) The input signal at one emitter is 10 per cent above the value necessary to drive the transistor into saturation. Specify this signal and draw both outputs to scale.

4-28. In the gates of Figs. 4-35 and 4-36 the transistors used are those given in Prob. 4-26. In both cases $R_L = 2$ K, $R_1 = R_2 = R_3 = 20$ K, $E_{bb} = 20$ volts, and $E_{cc} = -20$ volts.

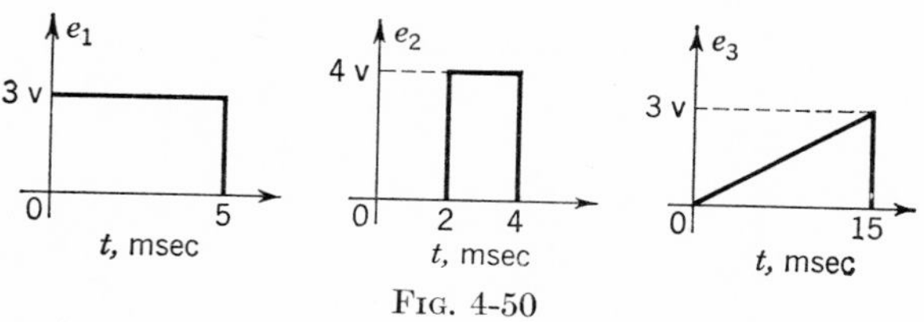

FIG. 4-50

(a) We apply the signals given in Fig. 4-50 to these inputs through a 2,000-ohm source impedance. Sketch to scale the resultant outputs. (Assume that the signal polarity is inverted for the OR gate and make all reasonable approximations in your calculations.)

(*b*) Calculate the input impedance seen at e_2, in both gates, under each condition of operation.

4-29. Figure 4-51 shows an *n-p-n* gate directly coupled to a *p-n-p* gate. When no pulse is applied to the first gate, both gates are "on," that is, $v_c = 0$. When, however, a negative pulse appears at the input of T_1, both gates are cut off.

(*a*) What is the approximate input impedance of each transistor?

(*b*) When $e_1 = 1.5$ volts both transistors are just cut off, and when $e_1 = 0$ both are just saturated. What values of R_1, R_2, R_3, and R_4 are necessary to produce this effect? Make all necessary valid assumptions to simplify the analysis.

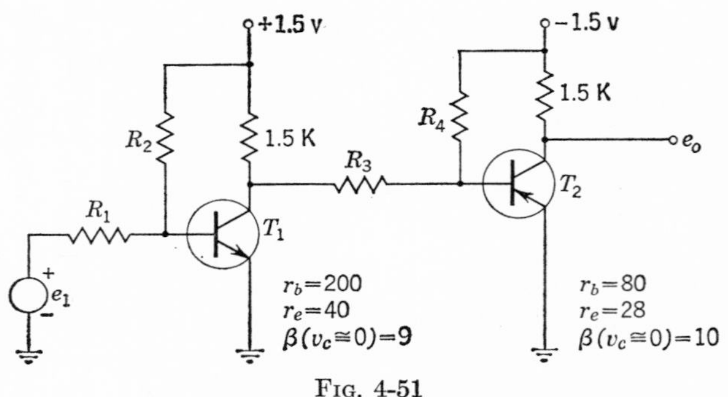

FIG. 4-51

4-30. The circuit of Fig. 4-52 is adjusted so that each transistor is normally biased cut off. Sketch the output waveshapes at all three terminals in proper time sequence, specifying all voltage values.

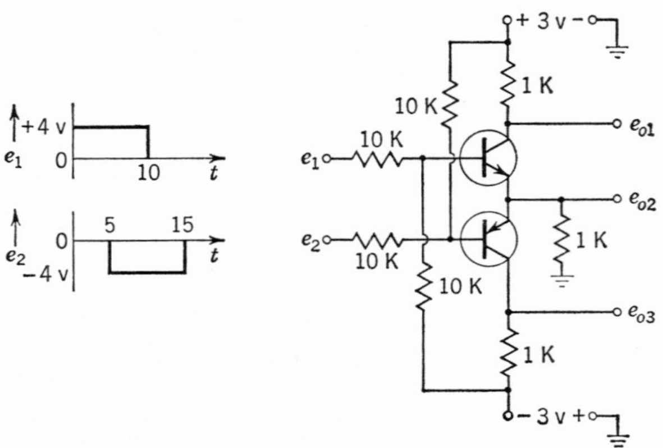

FIG. 4-52

4-31. The two transistors in the gate of Fig. 4-53 are characterized by the two curves shown. They hold when the collector is back-biased, but when it is forward-biased, we can take $v_{ce} = 0$.

(a) If the excitations are as specified, sketch the outputs at e_1 and e_2 to scale, giving all values.

(b) Repeat part a if the collector supply voltage is changed to −3 volts.

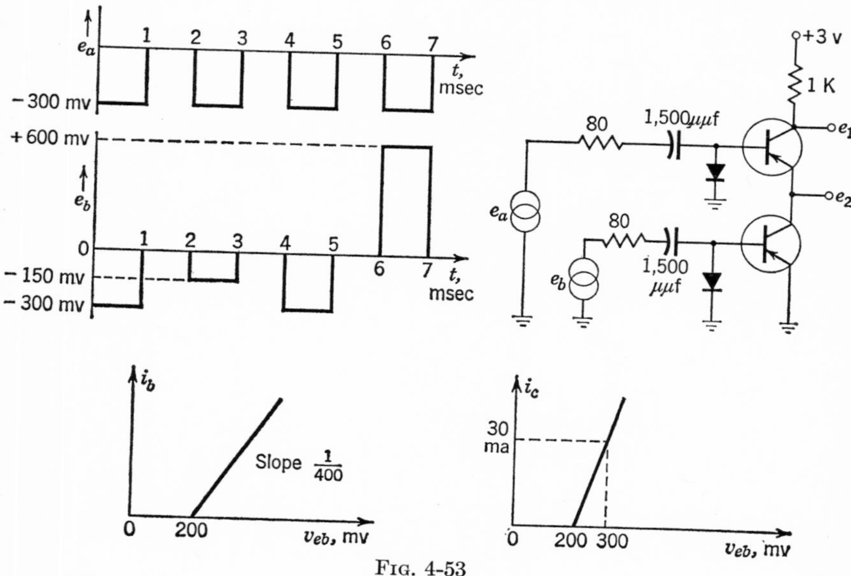

FIG. 4-53

4-32. Design a pentode AND circuit such that there will be an output if two inputs are positive and there will be no output if either of the two inputs or both inputs are zero. Draw waveforms showing all these possibilities. Specify the inputs and outputs. Numerical answers are not required, but the relative values should be stated, i.e., which voltages are negative and which are positive and whether one voltage should be much higher than another for proper operation.

BIBLIOGRAPHY

Angelo, E. J., Jr.: "Electronic Circuits," McGraw-Hill Book Company, Inc., New York, 1958.

Clarke, K. K., and M. V. Joyce: "Transistor Circuit Analysis," Addison-Wesley Publishing Company, Reading, Mass., in press.

Ebers, J. J., and J. L. Moll: Large Signal Behavior of Junction Transistor, *Proc. IRE*, vol. 42, no. 12, pp. 1761–1772, 1954.

Lo, A. W., et al.: "Transistor Electronics," Prentice-Hall, Inc., Englewood Cliffs, N.J., 1955.

Middlebrook, R. D.: "An Introduction to Junction Transistor Theory," John Wiley & Sons, Inc., New York, 1957.

Shea, R. F.: "Transistor Circuit Engineering," John Wiley & Sons, Inc., New York, 1957.

Zimmermann, H. J., and S. J. Mason: "Electronic Circuit Theory," John Wiley & Sons, Inc., New York, 1959.

PART 2

TIMING

CHAPTER 5

SIMPLE VOLTAGE SWEEPS, LINEARITY, AND SYNCHRONIZATION

The preceding chapters were concerned with the shaping of voltage and current signals by various configurations of linear and nonlinear elements, e.g., differentiation, integration, amplification, clamping, clipping, and gating. No consideration was given to the origin of the signals applied, but as we now begin this study, we should realize that many of the analytic techniques previously developed are applicable to our paramount problem, the generation of simple waveshapes.

In this chapter we shall concentrate our attention on some characteristics of one particular waveshape, the linear voltage sweep. Ideally, the output voltage increases linearly with time until it reaches a predetermined final value, instantaneously returns to zero, and immediately starts increasing again as the cycle repeats. This waveshape finds widespread application: in the horizontal deflection circuit of an oscilloscope so that time-varying signals may be displayed against a linear time scale; in radar systems, for measuring the time required for the return of the echo signal; in television transmitters and receivers as a means of generating the raster; and in various control systems where it is used to time preprogrammed functions.

5-1. Basic Voltage Sweep. All linear-voltage-sweep circuits, regardless of individual variations, have a common basic mode of operation: some form of exponential charging; an automatic change of circuit which introduces a discharge path at the proper point of the cycle; and then reestablishment of the charge path. Differences in sweeps usually concern the active elements controlling the points at which discharge commences and ceases. But to approximate more closely the ideal sweep, we are sometimes also forced to modify the charge and discharge paths. Thus the basic voltage sweep might well be characterized by the circuit shown in Fig. 5-1*a*, which generates the waveshape of Fig. 5-1*b*. The capacitor charges through R_1 toward E_{bb}. When its voltage reaches some preset final value E_f, we throw the switch to position 2, discharging C through R_2. Upon decaying to its initial value E_i, the switch is returned to position 1 and the cycle repeats.

Before turning to practical sweep circuits, we can reach some conclusions as to their general requirements from a closer examination of Fig. 5-1*a* and *b*. Of prime importance is the recognition that we are generating, not a linear sweep, but an exponential charging curve, and only through restricting operation to a relatively small portion of the total possible curve will the capacitor voltage even approximate a linear rise. Thus E_{bb} must be made much higher than the desired output swing E_f-E_i to ensure reasonable linearity. Secondly, we note that the retrace time, a direct function of R_2, becomes insignificant only when the discharge time constant is very small. Making R_2 zero obviously reduces the discharge time to zero, but other circuit considerations may negate this choice. Therefore R_2 should be chosen as small as possible, consistent with any limitations imposed.

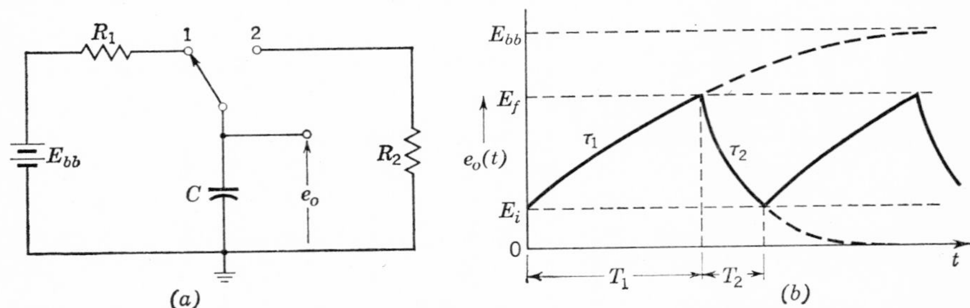

FIG. 5-1. (*a*) Basic voltage sweep circuit; (*b*) output sweep voltage.

Finally, we can write the equation of the capacitor voltage during either portion of the cycle and, by substituting the known final value E_f, solve for the sweep duration. During the voltage rise, when $\tau_1 = R_1C$,

$$e_o(t) = E_{bb} - (E_{bb} - E_i)e^{-t/\tau_1}$$

Thus

$$T_1 = \tau_1 \ln \frac{E_{bb} - E_i}{E_{bb} - E_f} \tag{5-1}$$

The capacitor discharges from E_f toward zero with a time constant $\tau_2 = R_2C$, and consequently the sweep recovery time, the time required to fall to E_i, becomes

$$T_2 = \tau_2 \ln \frac{E_f}{E_i} \tag{5-2}$$

The only remaining unknown is the mechanism of circuit switching, which must be evaluated in terms of the physical characteristics of the particular device employed.

5-2. Gas-tube Sweep. An extremely simple sweep-voltage generator (Fig. 5-2*b*) makes use of the double-valued characteristics of a cold-cathode gas tube to periodically discharge the sweep capacitor. As long as the anode voltage remains below the ignition potential, E_f of Fig. 5-2*a*, it supports only a very limited leakage current flow; for all practical purposes the tube is an open circuit. However, once the voltage rises to E_f and the tube fires, the terminal voltage drops to a lower, almost constant value E_o. Both E_f and E_o depend on the particular gas used. The tube current is now primarily limited by the external circuit and C begins discharging through the path established by the ionized gas.

The discharge path will be maintained only as long as the current flow is sufficient to sustain ionization. As C discharges, the tube current drops, tracing the dashed path of Fig. 5-2*a* instead of retracing the original curve. Because we are interested in generating a repetitive waveshape, we must ensure the existence of circuit conditions that will extinguish the tube, preferably rapidly.

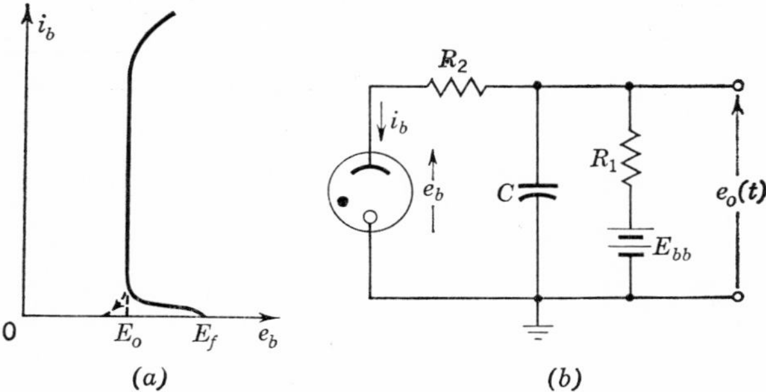

FIG. 5-2. (*a*) Gas-tube volt-ampere characteristics; (*b*) gas-tube sweep circuit.

The mechanism of the gas-discharge extinction, the recombination of ions previously produced by the large forward-current flow, requires some small finite time. It is impossible to state the deionization time in simple terms, since it depends on the past history of the tube, i.e., on the peak current on ignition and on the time rate of current change during the capacitor discharge. This time varies from tube type to tube type and even changes in any given tube during its life; it usually ranges between 0.5 and 2 μsec.

In order to simplify the calculations, we find it convenient to assume that the tube voltage remains unchanged during the whole discharge interval. Additionally, a fictitious extinction current I_{bx} might well be postulated as a means of representing the complete, complex extinction phenomena. Thus the following statement suffices: when the tube current drops below I_{bx}, the tube goes out. I_{bx} depends on the tube type in much the same manner as does the extinction time, with its value generally falling between 25 and 250 μa.

During capacitor charging, the nonconducting tube can be omitted, leaving an equivalent circuit identical with that of Fig. 5-1*a* (switch in position 1). Therefore the rise time is identically given by Eq. (5-1). However, evaluation of this equation is contingent on finding the still unknown initial value E_i. Referring to the output waveshape (Fig. 5-3b), we see that the initial value of the rise corresponds to the final value of the decay, i.e., to the point at which the tube extinguishes.

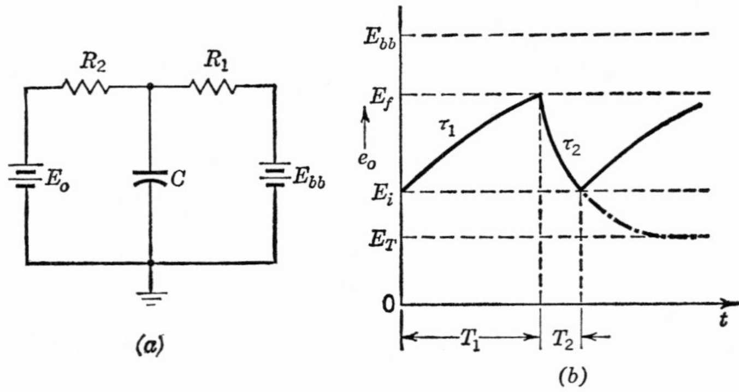

FIG. 5-3. (a) Discharge circuit of gas-tube sweep; (b) gas-tube sweep waveshape.

The circuit enters the region of operation defined by Fig. 5-3a with the capacitor voltage at E_f and leaves it when the output drops to E_i. Immediately upon the tube's firing, C starts discharging toward the Thévenin equivalent voltage across its terminals.

$$E_T = \frac{R_1}{R_1 + R_2} E_o + \frac{R_2}{R_2 + R_1} E_{bb} \tag{5-3}$$

Extinction occurs when the tube current falls to I_{bx}, which corresponds to a capacitor voltage of

$$e_c(T_2) = E_i = E_o + I_{bx}R_2 \tag{5-4}$$

Since we now know the initial, final, and steady-state voltages in this region, the decay time becomes

$$T_2 = \tau_2 \ln \frac{E_T - E_f}{E_T - (E_o + I_{bx}R_2)} \tag{5-5}$$

where $\tau_2 = (R_1 \parallel R_2)C \cong R_2C$

Normally, R_2 serves to limit the maximum tube current to a safe value and is very much smaller than R_1. Reexamination of Eq. (5-3) indicates that under these circumstances the Thévenin equivalent voltage will be only slightly larger than E_o. The second term of Eq. (5-4), defining the initial voltage E_i, will generally be almost negligible compared with the first term as a consequence of the small values of both I_{bx} and R_2. E_o may vary from 10 to 50 or 100 volts, depending on the tube type, but

$I_{bx}R_2$ is usually somewhere between 25 and 250 mv. The steady-state discharge voltage, the initial voltage, and the tube's extinction voltage are so close together that we might as well approximate them by the single value E_o. We conclude that the discharge curve will constitute virtually the complete exponential, requiring roughly four time constants for completion.

$$T_2 \cong 4R_2C \tag{5-6}$$

Occasionally, the deionization time may be longer than the time given by Eq. (5-6), and if it is, it will predominate.

A glance at Fig. 5-3*a* discloses that during ignition part of the tube current is contributed by E_{bb}. If this component is greater than I_{bx}, the tube will never extinguish. To prevent continuous ignition, the inequality of Eq. (5-7) must be satisfied.

$$I_b = \frac{E_{bb} - E_o}{R_1 + R_2} < I_{bx} \tag{5-7}$$

Equation (5-7) sets the lower limit of R_1 necessary for guaranteed repetitive sweep generation. Since $R_1 \gg R_2$,

$$R_1 > \frac{E_{bb} - E_o}{I_{bx}} \tag{5-8}$$

In practice, the circuit may operate properly when R_1 is from one-half to one-quarter of the limiting value given by Eq. (5-8). This apparent inconsistency arises because I_{bx} is only a convenient fiction approximating the whole discharge phenomenon and a steady-state current several times as large may still allow extinction.

Limits must also be imposed on R_2: if too large, the discharge time becomes excessive, and if too small, the peak current on ignition may exceed the tube's rating. Therefore it must satisfy

$$R_2 \geq \frac{E_f - E_o}{I_{b,\max}} \tag{5-9}$$

where $I_{b,\max}$ is the maximum allowable tube current.

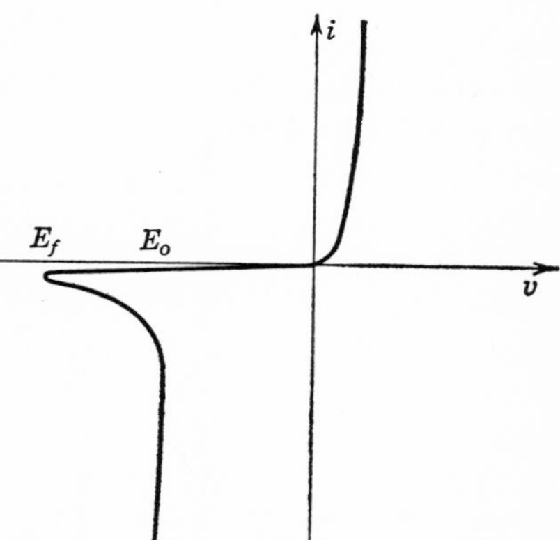

FIG. 5-4. Avalanche diode characteristic.

Several semiconductor devices have two-terminal volt-ampere characteristics quite similar to that of the gas tube. Among these are the avalanche diode, the unijunction diode, and the *p-n-p-n* transistor. One typical characteristic is shown in Fig. 5-4, and it should be compared with Fig. 5-2*a*. A somewhat more detailed discussion of these devices will be deferred until Chap. 11, at which point some simple sweeps will again be treated, but from a different viewpoint from that expressed here. However, it is important to note that similar volt-ampere characteristics mean similar circuit behavior and therefore these semiconductor devices may be used to replace the gas tube in the sweep of Fig. 5-2*b*, especially in low-voltage applications.

5-3. Thyratron Sweep Circuits. The sweep of Sec. 5-2 has many inherent disadvantages: among them, that its sweep amplitude is small in comparison with the ignition potential and depends solely on the noncontrollable firing point and sustaining voltages; that synchronization cannot be effected through injection of external signals; and finally that the relatively long recovery time precludes use for generation of short-duration sweeps. All but the last of these drawbacks are overcome in one practical sweep (Fig. 5-5) by employing a thyratron in place of the

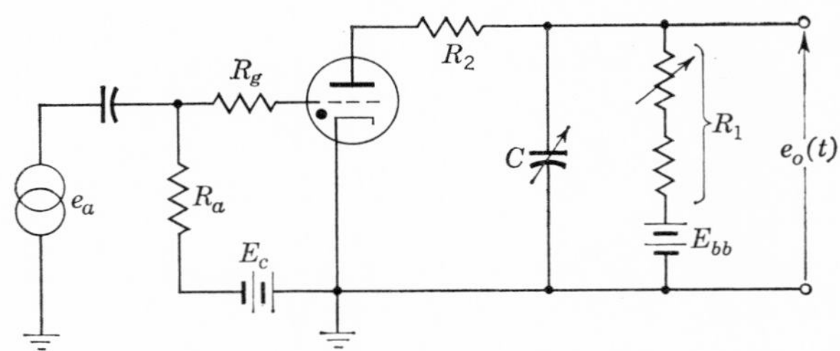

FIG. 5-5. Thyratron sweep circuit.

cold-cathode gas tube. Except for the control afforded by the grid, this circuit performs identically with the sweeps discussed in Secs. 5-1 and 5-2, and consequently all equations previously derived are applicable.

Where one curve sufficed to define completely the operation of the cold-cathode gas tube, two are required for the thyratron because of its additional control element: one expressing the grid-voltage–firing-point relationship (Fig. 5-6*a*), and the other, the plate volt-ampere characteristic (Fig. 5-6*b*). The thyratron grid is a massive structure, physically situated so that it almost completely shields the cathode from the influence of plate voltage. A negative grid voltage establishes a potential barrier, preventing electron travel from the cathode to the plate, cutting off the tube. As the plate voltage increases, its influence on the potential distribution in the interelectrode space between grid and cathode increases proportionately. Eventually the potential barrier is lowered enough to allow high-energy electrons into the grid-plate region, where they collide with gas molecules, ionizing them. This value of plate voltage is called the firing point of the tube. Referring to Fig. 5-6*a*, we see that the more negative the grid, the higher the plate voltage necessary for ignition.

Upon firing, the plate voltage drops to E_o, and as in the cold-cathode gas tube, the current increases until limited by the external circuit. Since the drop across the thyratron is relatively small (10 to 25 volts) in comparison with the firing voltage, it generates a large-amplitude sweep.

Once the tube ignites, the positive ions are attracted by the most negative element in the tube, the grid. They form a sheath on the grid structure, effectively insulating it from the tube and preventing further control. The grid current that now flows is limited to a safe value by choice of the external resistor R_g. Breaking the plate connection or reducing the tube current below I_{bx} extinguishes the tube, with the grid now regaining control.

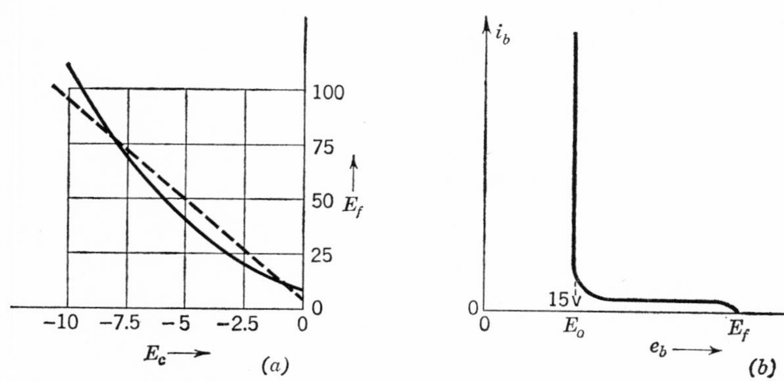

FIG. 5-6. (a) Thyratron firing and (b) thyratron plate characteristics.

Direct algebraic solution of thyratron circuits necessitates the algebraic expression of the plate firing-point characteristics. The simplest representation is the dashed line shown in Fig. 5-6a. Its equation is

$$E_f = mE_c + E_1 \cong -9E_c + 5 \tag{5-10}$$

where $E_c < 0$ and $E_f > E_o$. In this equation m is the slope and E_1 the intercept. Substituting Eq. (5-10) into Eq. (5-1), the sweep time becomes

$$T_1 = \tau_1 \ln \frac{E_{bb} - E_o}{E_{bb} - (mE_c + E_1)} \tag{5-11}$$

With a supply of 250 volts and a bias of −10 volts, the sweep lasts for

$$T_1 = \tau_1 \ln \frac{250 - 15}{250 - 95} = 0.415\tau_1 \qquad \text{sec}$$

Under the above conditions, the total sweep amplitude is 80 volts ($E_f - E_i$) out of a maximum possible swing of 235 volts. Even over this large fraction of the charging curve, the sweep approximates a straight line reasonably well.

The sweep period, a linear function of the time constant R_1C, is varied by changing C in steps for coarse control and by changing R_1 continuously as a fine adjustment. In each range the minimum resistance must satisfy Eq. (5-8), and therefore R_1 usually consists of a fixed resistor of the minimum value in series with a potentiometer.

Minor modification of the free-running sweep of Fig. 5-5 converts it into a single-shot generator (Fig. 5-7), which produces a single sweep upon each application of an input trigger. In its normal state the plate voltage is limited to E_b by the plate catching diode D_1. E_c sets the firing voltage well above this value. The injection of a positive trigger at the grid momentarily lowers the ignition potential below E_b, and the tube immediately fires. C now discharges, the tube extinguishes, and C

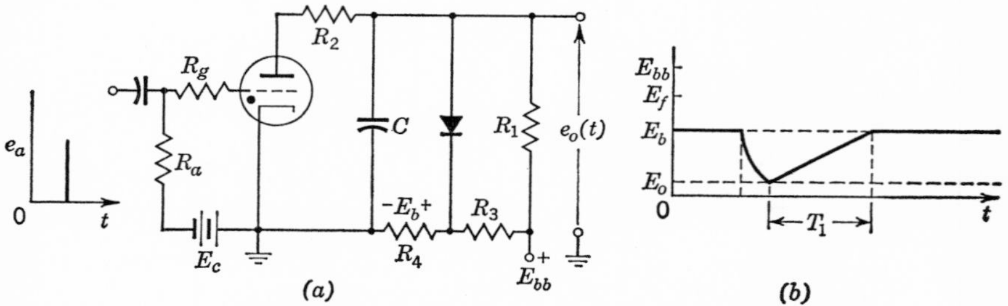

FIG. 5-7. Single-shot sweep generator and output waveshape.

starts recharging, only now generating the single sweep shown. Because sweep starts after the discharge is complete, unless the delay introduced is small, a portion of the signal we wish to observe may not appear on the oscilloscope.

5-4. Sweep Linearity. Since our announced objective is the generation of a linear sweep, we should have a means of expressing the linearity, or departure from linearity, as a measure of the sweep quality. This entails making a comparison between an ideal and the actual sweep, with any divergence representing the nonlinearity. Three possible choices are presented in Fig. 5-8. The first is a straight line drawn tangent to the sweep at the origin (Fig. 5-8*a*); the second is a compromise, intersecting the sweep at the point that results in equal deviation above and below the line (Fig. 5-8*b*); the third line connects the end points of the sweep (Fig. 5-8*c*).

Depending on the particular application of the sweep, any one of the three will be eminently satisfactory as a basis for comparison. Whenever the sweep time duration becomes important, the sweep is usually synchronized by an external reference signal which constrains its end points (Sec. 5-5). Under these conditions it seems reasonable to calculate the amplitude deviation from an ideal sweep connecting the two restricted ends. Referring to Fig. 5-8c, the deviation is

$$\delta(t) = e_c(t) - e_l(t) \tag{5-12}$$

The ratio of maximum deviation to sweep amplitude, expressed as a percentage, is defined as the sweep nonlinearity.

$$\mathrm{NL} \equiv \frac{\delta_{\max}}{E_s} 100\% \tag{5-13}$$

where $E_s = E_f - E_i$.

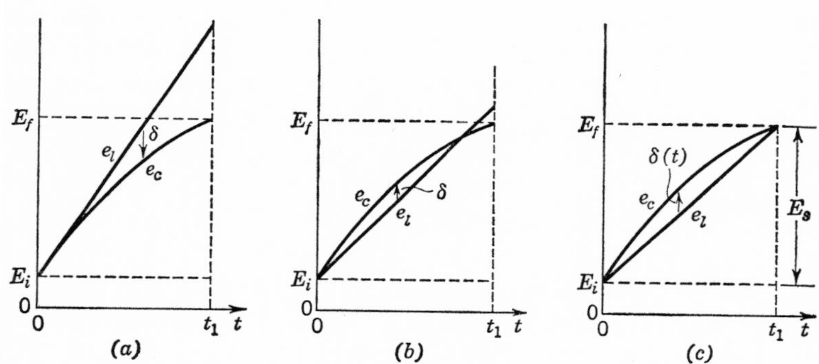

FIG. 5-8. Various methods of defining sweep nonlinearity.

By shifting the axis and writing all equations with respect to E_i, the equation of the linear sweep becomes

$$e_l(t) = kt = \frac{E_s}{t_1} t \tag{5-14}$$

and that of the exponential sweep

$$e_c(t) = (E_{bb} - E_i)(1 - e^{-t/\tau_1}) \tag{5-15}$$

When the limits of E_s and t_1 are substituted into Eq. (5-15), the coefficient can be expressed in terms of the known sweep quantities.

$$E_{bb} - E_i = \frac{E_s}{1 - e^{-t_1/\tau_1}} \tag{5-16}$$

The first two terms of the power-series expansion of the exponential [Eq. (5-17)] represent its linear approximation, and the remaining higher-order terms, the deviation from linearity. Because we are interested in an almost linear sweep, the contribution of the higher-order terms must be kept to a minimum, though using only a small portion of the total exponential curve. Therefore t/τ_1 will always be much less than unity and we can assume that the complete nonlinearity is due to the square term of Eq. (5-17).

$$e^{-t/\tau_1} = 1 - \frac{t}{\tau_1} + \frac{1}{2!}\left(\frac{t}{\tau_1}\right)^2 - \frac{1}{3!}\left(\frac{t}{\tau_1}\right)^3 + \cdots \tag{5-17}$$

Substituting Eq. (5-16) into (5-15) and using the first three terms of the expansion in both numerator and denominator, the equation of the exponential sweep becomes

$$e_c(t) \cong \frac{\tau_1 E_s}{t_1(1 - t_1/2\tau_1)}\left[\frac{t}{\tau_1} - \frac{1}{2}\left(\frac{t}{\tau_1}\right)^2\right]$$

and since $t_1/\tau_1 \ll 1$,

$$e_c(t) \cong \frac{\tau_1}{t_1} E_s\left(1 + \frac{t_1}{2\tau_1}\right)\left[\frac{t}{\tau_1} - \frac{1}{2}\left(\frac{t}{\tau_1}\right)^2\right] \tag{5-18}$$

The one missing piece of information, the time location of $\delta_{\max}$, will be found from geometric considerations. Any curve having only slight curvature, such as the exponential sweep of Fig. 5-8*c*, may be approximated by the arc of some circle with large radius. The linear sweep becomes a chord of this circle, and the maximum distance from a chord to the arc, measured at any fixed angle, occurs at the center of the chord, at the point corresponding to $t_1/2$. We evaluate Eqs. (5-14) and (5-18) at this time and substitute the answers into Eq. (5-12), with the result

$$\delta_{\max} = \delta\left(\frac{t_1}{2}\right) = \left[\frac{t_1}{8\tau_1} - \frac{1}{16}\left(\frac{t_1}{\tau_1}\right)^2\right] E_s$$

$$\cong \frac{t_1}{8\tau_1} E_s \tag{5-19}$$

Consequently, the percentage nonlinearity becomes

$$\text{NL} = \frac{t_1}{8\tau_1} 100 \qquad \% \tag{5-20}$$

Substitution of the exact period, expressed in terms of the circuit voltages [Eq. (5-1)], provides us with an alternative form for the nonlinearity, one which brings to the forefront the dependency on the voltage limits imposed.

$$\text{NL} = \frac{100\%}{8} \ln \frac{E_{bb} - E_i}{E_{bb} - E_f} \tag{5-21}$$

A third expression for the nonlinearity is possible when the sweep starts close to zero and constitutes only a small fraction of the total exponential. If $E_{bb} \gg E_i$ and $E_{bb} \gg E_f$, then by expanding Eq. (5-21) into a series and taking only the first term,

$$\text{NL} \cong 12.5\% \frac{E_s}{E_{bb}} \tag{5-22}$$

Equations (5-20) to (5-22) verify our previous contention that good sweep linearity can be realized only by operating over a small portion of the total exponential. For less than 1 per cent nonlinearity, the sweep time must be restricted to 8 per cent of the time constant and its amplitude to 8 per cent of possible charging voltage.

Since the other possibilities presented in Fig. 5-8 referred to the same sweep, with the same amplitude, end points, and time constant, any nonlinearity defined in their terms will differ from Eq. (5-20) or (5-21) only by a constant multiplier.

5-5. Synchronization. The period of a sweep depends on many factors: on the circuit time constant, on the voltage at which the capacitor discharge commences and at which it terminates, and finally, on the steady-state supply voltage. These parameters are never completely constant but vary slightly because of ambient-temperature change, line-voltage variation, aging of tubes and components, noise, etc. As a direct consequence of the random circuit changes, sequential sweep cycles will not have identical duration but will jitter about some average time. When this sweep is used for oscilloscope display, a corresponding jitter appears in the pattern seen on the screen. If used for timing, there will be uncertainty as to its exact time duration. However, by injecting an external control signal, the sweep time can be locked to some multiple of the synchronizing signal period, and when this input is derived from the display signal, the oscilloscope pattern will remain stationary.

Synchronization of the sweep is accomplished by forcing the free-running sweep period t_1 to some integral multiple of the signal period t_s, that is, by changing t_1 to nt_s. In effecting the change of period, the sweep amplitude may also be affected, but as the amplitude can always be adjusted elsewhere in the system, this is relatively unimportant.

The sweep period is controlled by varying either the initial voltage or the discharge point. For example, in the thyratron sweep of Fig. 5-5, the sync signal is injected at the grid, with its fluctuation about the quiescent grid point changing the instantaneous firing voltage. Since the slope of the plate firing characteristic [Eq. (5-10)] represents the "gain" of the gas tube, the effective variation at the plate will be m times as large as the applied grid signal. Figure 5-9 indicates the firing voltage in the presence of a sinusoidal sync signal. We observe that, because of the assumed linearity of the grid-plate transfer characteristics, the grid waveshape is simply multiplied, reflected into the plate, and plotted about the quiescent firing line. The sweep ends earlier because it intersects the firing curve at a lower voltage value. As a consequence it fires at the same point of each cycle, whereas the free-running sweep (dashed line of Fig. 5-9) terminates randomly with respect to the applied sinusoidal signal.

If we use an ideal free-running sweep instead of an actual thyratron sweep, the quantitative treatment below will be greatly simplified. In addition, the lack of identification with any particular circuit increases

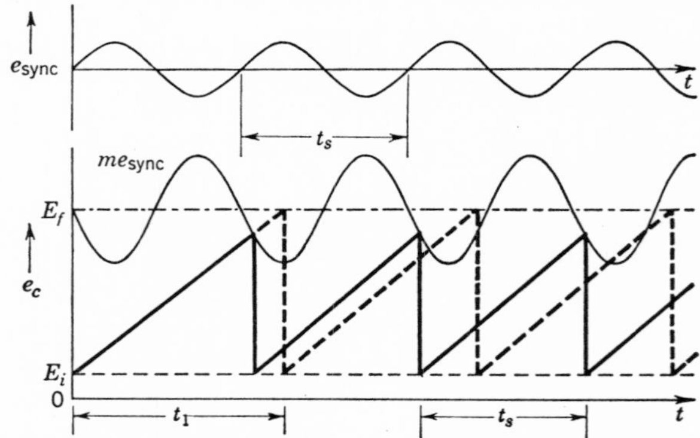

FIG. 5-9. Applied synchronizing signal and its effect on sweep duration.

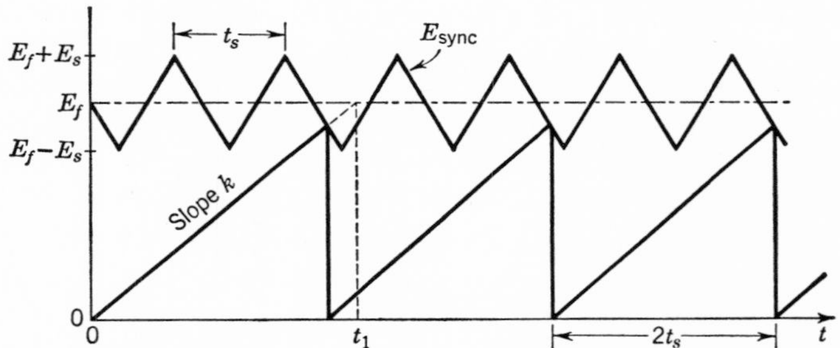

FIG. 5-10. Ideal sweep synchronized by a triangular wave.

the generality of our discussion. This perfectly linear sweep starts rising from zero at a rate of k volts/sec, ending at the firing voltage t_1 sec later.

The introduction of a sync signal of proper amplitude and period pulls the sweep into synchronization as shown in Fig. 5-10. This build-up may take one or several cycles, but eventually the sweep will start and end at the same point of the sync cycle.

One obvious question facing us is, Why does synchronization increase the stability of the sweep with respect to random circuit changes? Our argument might begin with the observation that these changes result in sweep time instability, and since the effect produced is the same, any circuit variation may be represented as an equivalent small perturbation of firing voltage. In Fig. 5-11*a*, the slight increase of E_f by ΔE_f increases a single free-running sweep period by Δt. The subsequent cycles are back to the normal time, but each is delayed by Δt sec. However, once the sweep is synchronized by terminating it at a point on the sync signal that has a slope of opposite sign to the sweep slope (in this case, on a point of negative slope), then the time perturbation rapidly damps out. Figure 5-11*b* shows how the sweep returns to its original firing point within several cycles of the original disturbance.

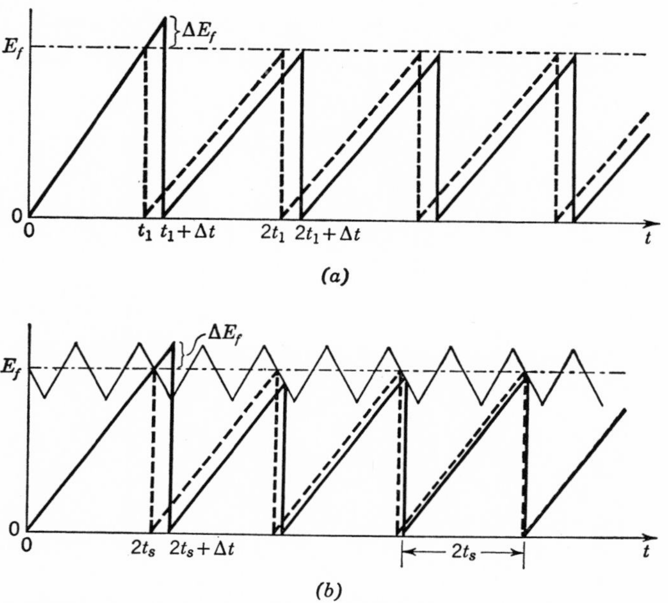

FIG. 5-11. (*a*) Sweep perturbation—no sync signal; (*b*) sweep perturbation—sync signal present.

The reason for the rapid damping can easily be seen when we expand two adjacent cycles of the sweep for a closer look at the end point (Fig. 5-12). At the first firing point, the voltage jitter ΔE_f produces an increase in the sweep period of Δt. Thus the second cycle starts Δt later, but because of the geometry at the intersection of the two straight lines, this cycle ends only $\Delta t'$ later. The time variation is reduced by a factor δ, at the instant of firing, where

$$\delta = \frac{\Delta t'}{\Delta t} \tag{5-23}$$

When the two intersecting curves have slopes of opposite sign as in Fig. 5-12, δ will always be less than unity. The third sweep starts

$\Delta t'$ later, and at the instant of firing, this is also reduced by the factor δ. After n sweeps, the total time displacement from the normal time will be $\delta^n \Delta t$ and

$$\lim_{n \to \text{large}} \delta^n \Delta t = 0$$

Thus the sweep eventually returns to its original firing point with respect to the sync signal. We see from Fig. 5-12 that the steeper the slope of the synchronizing signal at the point of sweep intersection, the smaller the value of δ and the fewer the number of cycles required for sweep recovery time. We further conclude that the optimum point to effect synchronization (with any input signal) is where the slope is the steepest,

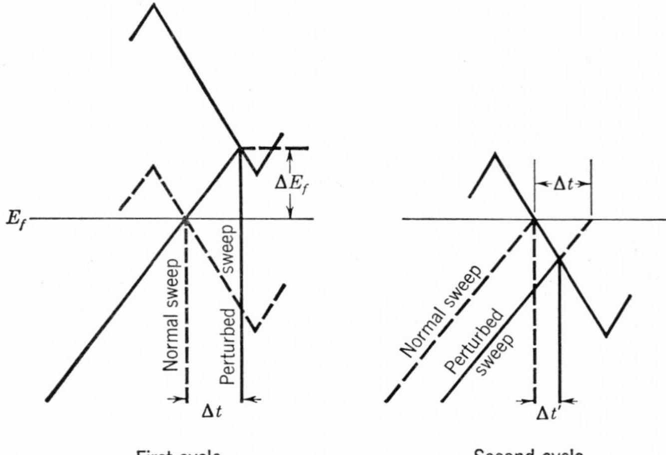

FIG. 5-12. Expanded sweep firing point showing stability.

such as the crossover point of a sine wave. If a choice presents itself, the optimum sync signal would be a square wave or pulse train where the sweep can terminate on a point of infinite slope.

Suppose that the sweep intersects the sync signal at a point that has the same sign of slope; i.e., both are positive (Fig. 5-13). Under these circumstances any slight time perturbation Δt increases at the point of firing by the factor δ' to $\Delta t''$.

$$\delta' = \frac{\Delta t''}{\Delta t} > 1 \tag{5-24}$$

Instead of damping out, the change in sweep time now builds up geometrically as $(\delta')^n$ over n cycles. Eventually, as the sweep shifts its relative position, it intersects the sync voltage at a point of negative slope. If the sync signal has the proper time and amplitude relationship, with respect to the sweep, synchronization will now be effected.

5-6. Regions of Synchronization. Synchronization is not automatically guaranteed upon the injection of just any external signal. The sweep will not be pulled in unless the sync amplitude and period happen to fall within regions well-defined in terms of the sweep constants; regions, which we shall see below, are also a function of the sync signal waveshape. As an initial example, refer to Fig. 5-14, where a symmetrical square wave of variable amplitude is used as the control signal.

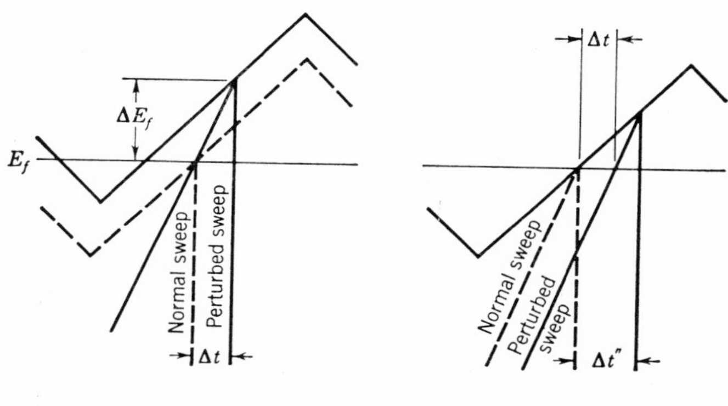

FIG. 5-13. Unstable sweep synchronization—expanded firing region.

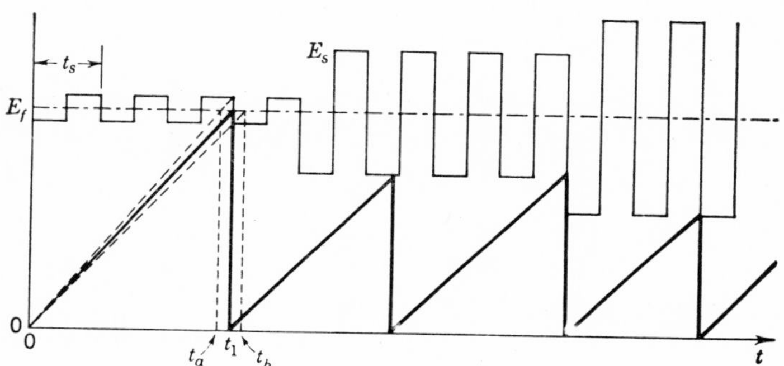

FIG. 5-14. Square-wave synchronization.

The first sweep fires when it terminates on the square wave at $3t_s$, and if the input remains unchanged, the sweep will continue to fire once every 3 cycles. However, the increased square wave causes the second and third sweeps to end at nonintegral multiples of the sync signal period, and therefore they are unsynchronized. The fourth cycle is again synchronized, this time at the next smaller integral multiple of the sync period, at $2t_s$. We might also note that any free-running sweep bounded by the dashed lines shown in the first sweep cycle, that is, $t_a < t_1 < t_b$, intersects the changed firing voltage along the same portion of the square wave and also fires at $3t_s$.

Let us now assume that the control signal is a square wave having a constant amplitude of E_s volts peak value. Then if its period falls anywhere within the two extremes given in Fig. 5-15*a* and *b*, the fixed free-running sweep will fire over the same integral number of sync cycles, over n cycles. At the one limit shown in Fig. 5-15*a*, the sweep period becomes foreshortened because a portion of the sync signal extends below the original firing line. Figure 5-15*b* illustrates the possible lengthening of the sweep as a consequence of the effective increase in the firing voltage.

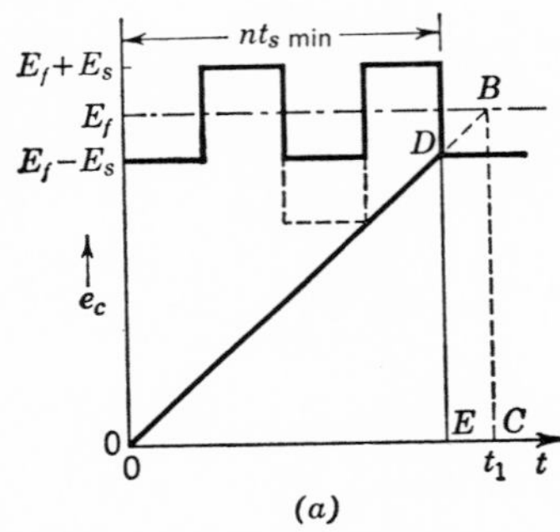

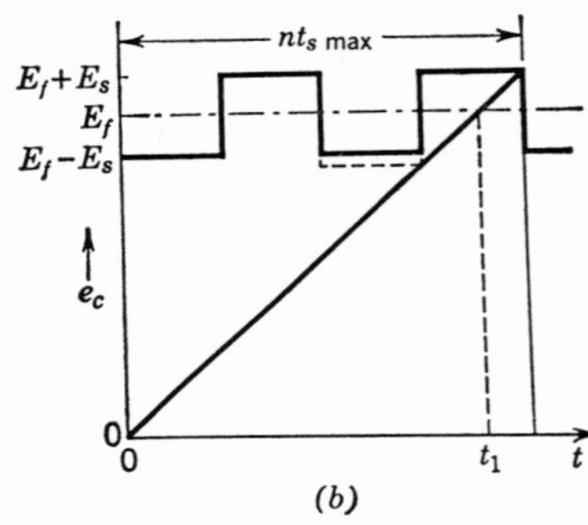

FIG. 5-15. (*a*) Minimum sync period producing synchronization; (*b*) maximum sync period producing synchronization.

We shall first concern ourselves with expressing the lower usable limit of the sync period (Fig. 5-15*a*). Since the two sweep triangles OBC and ODE are similar, the ratios of their equivalent sides must be equal.

$$\frac{OE}{OC} = \frac{DE}{BC} \qquad \frac{nt_{s,\min}}{t_1} = \frac{E_f - E_s}{E_f}$$

Hence one limit becomes

$$\frac{t_{s,\min}}{t_1} = \frac{1}{n}\left(1 - \frac{E_s}{E_f}\right) \tag{5-25}$$

The solution of Fig. 5-15*b*, also by similar triangles, yields a second limit,

$$\frac{t_{s,\max}}{t_1} = \frac{1}{n}\left(1 + \frac{E_s}{E_f}\right) \tag{5-26}$$

If the sync amplitude is now increased, the sweep will stay in synchronization until the corner of the preceding half cycle intersects the rising sweep, causing premature firing. This condition is indicated, for both cases, by the dashed lines of Fig. 5-15. Consequently, for any value of nt_s, the following condition on the maximum allowable sync amplitude may be written

$$\frac{nt_s - \frac{1}{2}t_s}{t_1} = \frac{E_f - E_{s,\max}}{E_f}$$

or

$$\frac{E_{s,\max}}{E_f} = 1 - \frac{2n - 1}{2}\frac{t_s}{t_1} \tag{5-27}$$

Equations (5-25) to (5-27) are all straight lines in terms of the normalized coordinates t_s/t_1 and E_s/E_f. Each delineates one set of the boundary

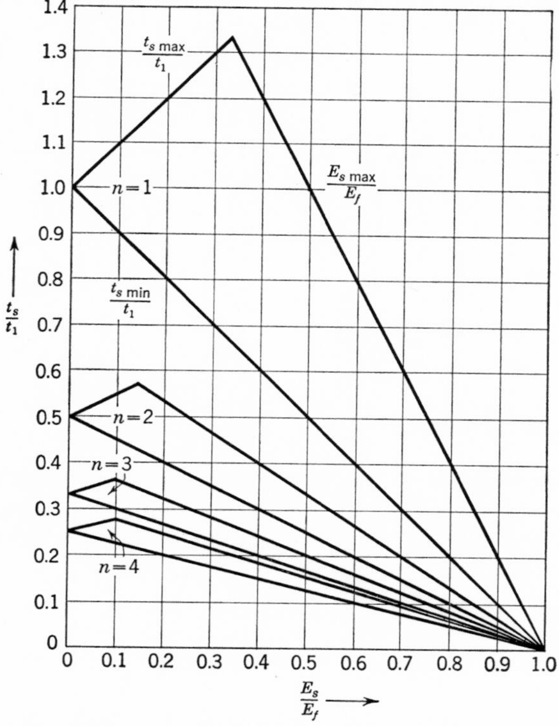

FIG. 5-16. Regions of synchronization—square-wave input signal.

values which limit possible synchronization. By plotting these equations with n as a parameter, we define the regions of synchronization for a square-wave input (Fig. 5-16). Any combination of periods and voltages lying within a region ensures proper synchronization over n cycles of the square wave. And to allow for possible fluctuation of sync and sweep voltage amplitude, and sweep period, the best combination of parameters lies at the center of any one region. Furthermore, the area of each region decreases extremely rapidly as n increases, with the consequence that it becomes very difficult to ensure synchronization over ratios greater than 4 or 5. The expected component variations would easily shift the operating point out of the small synchronization regions holding for large n.

All sync signals that effectively increase and decrease the firing voltage by equal amounts, e.g., sine waves, triangles, sawtooths, etc., will have two limits of their synchronization regions defined by Eqs. (5-25) and (5-26). Equivalent limits for nonsymmetrical signals may be calculated quite easily from their geometry.

For example, if the square wave used above is differentiated and the train of equal-amplitude positive and negative pulses is applied, then only the negative pulse will influence the timing. The sweep cannot be lengthened since it will always terminate on the negative pulse or along the original firing line, as in Fig. 5-17. In this case Eq. (5-26) reduces to

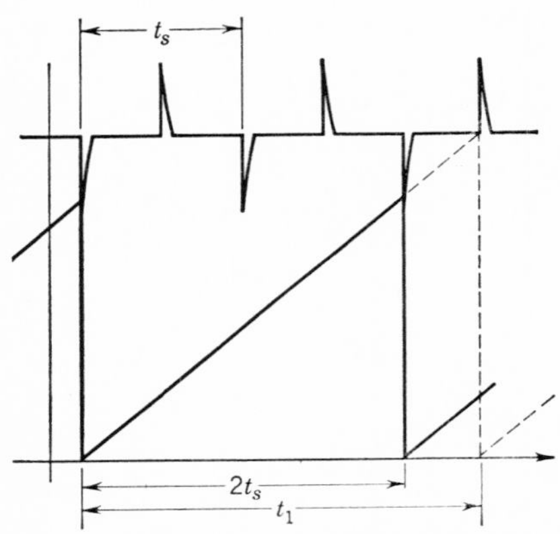

FIG. 5-17. Synchronization with pulses.

$$\frac{t_{s,\min}}{t_1} = \frac{1}{n}$$

Equation (5-25) will still hold as a second limit. A new equation must be found to delineate the third boundary (Prob. 5-14).

Equations (5-25) and (5-26) may also be applied to nonsymmetrical waves by properly interpreting the various voltage terms they contain. We rewrite these equations

$$\frac{t_{s,\min}}{t_1} = \frac{1}{n}\left(1 - \frac{E_{sn}}{E_f}\right) \tag{5-28}$$

$$\frac{t_{s,\max}}{t_1} = \frac{1}{n}\left(1 + \frac{E_{sp}}{E_f}\right) \tag{5-29}$$

where E_{sn} is the negative peak of the sync signal and E_{sp} is the effective positive peak, both measured from the original firing line. Of course, as with the pulse, the sweep must be able to terminate at these voltage values.

The difficult problem in finding the regions of synchronization is the evaluation of the third boundary.

$$\frac{E_{s,\max}}{E_f} = f\left(\frac{t_s}{t_1}\right)$$

For signals having simple geometric waveshapes, it is possible to find an explicit analytic solution, but for more complex signals we would have to turn to a tedious graphical construction.

We can appreciate the increase in complexity by treating the case of triangular-wave synchronization (Fig. 5-10). Two limits are known [Eqs. (5-25) and (5-26)], and the third will be found from Fig. 5-18, which illustrates the conditions existing at the maximum possible value of the sync signal. If we assume that the sweep is still properly synchronized but on the verge of limiting,

$$\frac{nt_s}{t_1} = \frac{E_f + KE_{s,\max}}{E_f} \tag{5-30}$$

where K is a positive or negative constant relating the point of intersection to the peak value of the triangular wave. The sweep starts

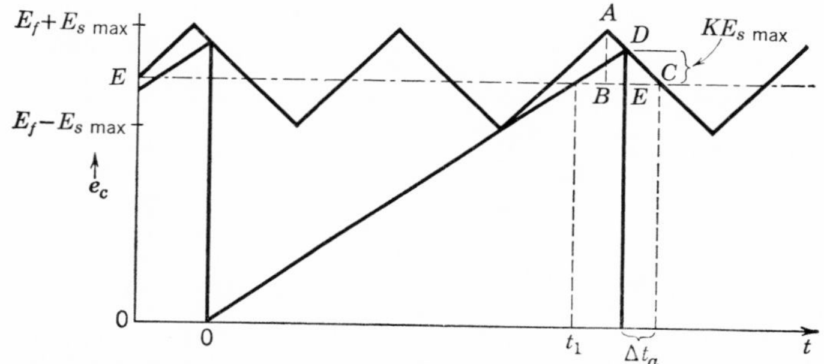

FIG. 5-18. Triangular-wave synchronization—maximum value of sync signal.

and ends when it intersects the sync wave Δt_a sec before the triangular wave crosses the quiescent firing line. From the similar triangles ABC and DEC,

$$\Delta t_a = \frac{Kt_s}{4} \tag{5-31}$$

When the sync voltage becomes infinitesimally larger than the value assumed for Eq. (5-30), the sweep no longer clears the negative peak. It now fires prematurely upon intersecting the sync signal $3t_s/4 - \Delta t_a$ sec before the original firing point. Thus the following ratio now holds:

$$\frac{nt_s - (3t_s/4 - \Delta t_a)}{t_1} = \frac{E_f - E_{s,\max}}{E_f} \tag{5-32}$$

Substitution of Eq. (5-31) into (5-32) provides us with a second equation relating t_s/t_1 and $E_{s,\max}/E_f$, one which, however, also includes the third variable K. The simultaneous solution of Eqs. (5-30) and (5-32), eliminating K, completes the solution, with the final answer given in Eq. (5-33).

$$ny^2 - y + (4n - 3)xy - 4x + 4x^2 = 0 \qquad (5\text{-}33)$$

where
$$x = \frac{E_{s,\max}}{E_f} \qquad y = \frac{t_s}{t_1}$$

Equation (5-33), the equation of a conic section, defines the third boundary of the synchronization regions which are plotted in Fig. 5-19.

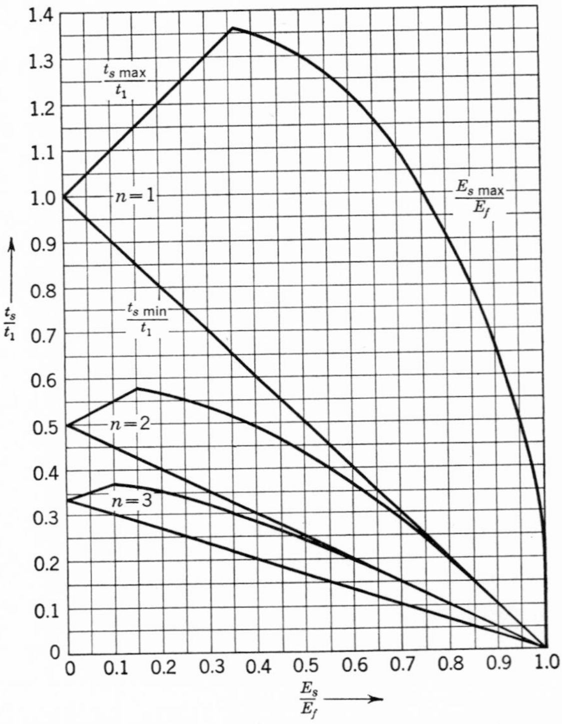

FIG. 5-19. Synchronization regions—triangular-wave input signal.

The larger areas indicate that synchronization will be maintained in face of wider-latitude parameter variations than can be tolerated for the square wave (compare Figs. 5-16 and 5-19). However, a square wave or pulse is vastly preferable because of the fast recovery from sweep perturbations.

The two waveshapes above were presented primarily in an effort to establish graphically the interlocking conditions which must be evaluated and satisfied for precise and accurate output control. We made no pretense of covering the multitudinous possible sync signals, such as pulses, sine waves, etc. When order of magnitude or approximate boundaries will serve our purposes, the replacement, for calculation, of complex waveshapes by simpler ones suffices. For example, a sinusoidal signal might be approximated by a truncated triangular wave, leading to regions slightly smaller than those of the triangle and slightly larger than those of the square wave. If we are interested in only one parameter's variation, then evaluation from a sketch gives the allowable limits directly.

Synchronization is employed in many circuits other than the thyratron sweep. In complex systems, often all waveform generators are controlled by one master, which is made extremely stable with respect to time changes. The process of synchronization imparts this same stability to the remaining circuits. Each free-running generator, oscillator, multivibrator, phantastron, etc., has its own mode of synchronization contingent on its individual control characteristics. Consequently, the individual regions will be well defined but will differ from one circuit to the other. When needed, they may be calculated by application of the methods discussed in this chapter, modified as necessary to suit the particular problem.

Example 5-1. A signal having a highly complex structure with many jagged peaks must be used to synchronize a sweep over a ratio of 2:1. In its original form, the input is not suitable for synchronization, but by amplifying and clipping, it can be converted into a square wave. And, if needed, we can differentiate it to obtain pulses or integrate it to obtain a triangular wave. The questions of interest are:

(*a*) Which signal is best for synchronization?

(*b*) At what point should synchronization be effected?

Solution. For optimum operation the sweep should be synchronized so that the nominal operating point is in the center of the appropriate region. By this we mean that it should be located as far as possible from the boundaries, allowing the time and voltage to vary over the widest possible limits before the sweep becomes erratic. In general, the operating point which permits the greatest variation in the time ratio will not be the optimum one with respect to voltage changes. However, from Figs. 5-16 and 5-19 we see that the time bounds are much narrower, and therefore we shall usually design the circuit for the best response with respect to time variations.

1. For square-wave synchronization, the plot of Fig. 5-16 indicates that the widest changes in t_s/t_1 occur along a line through the apex of the region $n = 2$. The bounds are

$$0.425 \le \frac{t_s}{t_1} \le 0.575$$

and the nominal free-running sweep should be set at the center, i.e., at $t_s = 0.5t_1$. Assuming a constant sweep time, the sync signal can increase from $0.15E_f$ to $0.25E_f$ or can decrease to zero before the sweep becomes unstable.

2. With the triangular-wave input, the maximum permissible change in t_1 does not occur along a line through the apex. In Fig. 5-19 we see that at $E_s/E_f = 0.3$,

$$0.35 \le \frac{t_s}{t_1} \le 0.53$$

The free-running sweep should be adjusted to the center value $t_1 = 2.27t_s$. This establishes the following nominal limits on the sync amplitude from the operating point given above:

$$0.12E_f \leq E_s \leq 0.5E_f$$

3. The regions which might be drawn for pulse synchronization (Prob. 5-14) would indicate that the optimum operating point should lie at

$$t_1 = \frac{t_s}{0.375} \qquad E_s = 0.5E_f$$

Permissible time and voltage variations are between the limits

$$0.25 \leq \frac{t_s}{t_1} \leq 0.5 \qquad 0.25 \leq \frac{E_s}{E_f} \leq 0.625$$

To summarize, the percentage variations of free-running sweep time and sync voltage, as related to the nominal value of t_1 and E_f, are:

	Percentage variation		
	Square	Triangle	Pulse
$\frac{\Delta t}{t_1}$	± 15	± 20	± 33
$\frac{\Delta E_s}{E_f}$	$-15, +10$	$-18, +20$	$-25, +12.5$

We conclude that pulses are best for synchronization purposes. Besides allowing the widest tolerances in time, their steep edges force recovery of any perturbation within one, or at most two, cycles. The triangular wave does permit wider latitude to the sync amplitude, but the difficulties involved in its generation as well as the longer recovery time would usually preclude its use; pulses or even the square wave is to be preferred.

PROBLEMS

5-1. We have at our disposal a cold-cathode gas tube with the following characteristics. The tube fires at 90 volts and maintains a constant drop of 50 volts while ionized. It requires at least 50 μa to sustain conduction and would be damaged by a current in excess of 200 ma. Using a power supply of 200 volts, compute the minimum values of R_1 and R_2 that may be employed. Adding a safety factor of 20 per cent to the resistor values found, compute the value of C necessary to give a 100-cps sweep.

5-2. The circuit of Fig. 5-20 is a schematic representation of a basic current sweep. The switch stays in position 1, while the coil current rises from its initial value toward I_{ss}. At the firing-current value I_f, the switch is thrown to position 2, discharging the coil. Once the current falls to its initial value, the switch is returned to position 1 and the cycle repeats.

(*a*) Draw the current waveshape i_L, indicating all time constants.

(*b*) If $I_{ss} = 200$ ma, $I_i = 80$ ma, and $G_1 = 0.001$ mho, what values must be chosen for I_f and R_2 if we wish to produce a triangular waveshape?

(*c*) When the inductance is 1 henry, to what must G_1 and R_2 be changed if the triangular sweep period is to be 2 msec?

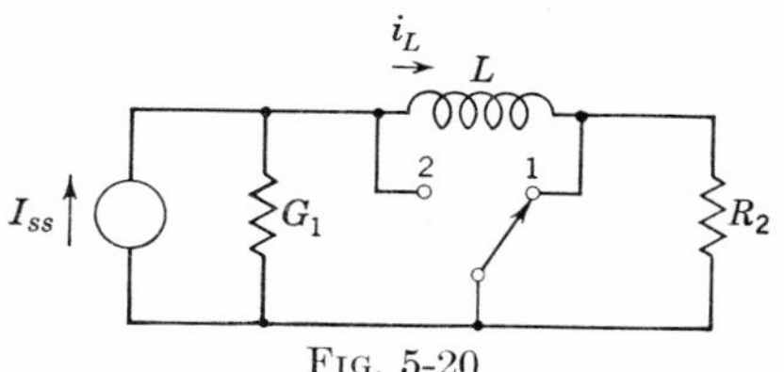

FIG. 5-20

5-3. We have a thyratron with the following characteristics: $I_{max} = 1$ amp, $I_{bx} = 100\ \mu a$, $E_f = 10 - 5e_c$, and $E_o = 10$ volts. This tube is used in a circuit similar to Fig. 5-5, where $E_{bb} = 300$ volts, $R_1 = 3$ megohms, $E_c = -20$ volts, $C = 0.001\ \mu f$.

(*a*) What is the sweep frequency of this circuit?

(*b*) For the optimum sweep response, what value should be assigned to R_2?

(*c*) With R_2 as given in part *b*, what is the sweep recovery time?

5-4. A 884 thyratron has a firing characteristic which may be approximated by $E_f = 16 - 10e_c$. Its maintaining voltage E_o is 16 volts, and I_{bx} is 200 μa. Design a free-running sweep of 100 μsec duration that will be not more than 5 per cent nonlinear. Use a power supply of 250 volts and the minimum value of sweep resistance. In the interests of simplicity, assume that the discharge time is insignificant. Specify all circuit values and all sweep voltages.

5-5. We wish to use the thyratron of Prob. 5-4 in a circuit that will generate an approximately triangular waveshape. (The rise and fall times are identical.) The free-running peak-to-peak output amplitude should be 50 volts.

(*a*) If the available power supply is 300 volts, and if $R_1 = R_2$, calculate the initial and the firing voltage for this sweep.

(*b*) Express the period as a function of the time constants and voltage values.

5-6. Design a driven sweep which makes use of the thyratron of Prob. 5-3. The sweep is to have a duration of 300 μsec and an amplitude of 50 volts and is to be triggered by a positive pulse 1 volt greater than the minimum amplitude. Use a power supply of 300 volts and a capacitor of 10^{-9} farad in your sweep.

(*a*) Find suitable values for E_c, R_1, R_2, R_3, and R_4 in Fig. 5-7. Express R_3 and R_4 as a ratio rather than as actual resistance values.

(*b*) Calculate the minimum pulse amplitude for triggering.

(*c*) How long after the pulse is applied will the sweep start?

5-7. The circuit shown in Fig. 5-21 is a triggered sweep operated by the 20-volt positive input triggers. It uses an 884 thyratron whose characteristics are given in Prob. 5-4.

(*a*) What is the minimum spacing of the trigger pulses t_1 so that each trigger will initiate one complete sweep?

(*b*) How long after the trigger is applied will the sweep start?

(*c*) Sketch the output waveshape, giving all values and times.

5-8. Assume that the input impedance appearing from grid to cathode of the sweep circuit shown in Fig. 5-21 is 50 $\mu\mu f$ in parallel with 1 megohm before firing. What is the narrowest pulse that would institute a sweep? Sketch the voltage appearing from grid to cathode if, after firing, the grid-to-cathode resistance falls to 2,000 ohms.

5-9. (*a*) Calculate the output sweep period and amount of nonlinearity for the circuit of Fig. 5-22. The initial value of the sweep is 20 volts, and the thyratron fires when the capacitor voltage reaches 100 volts.

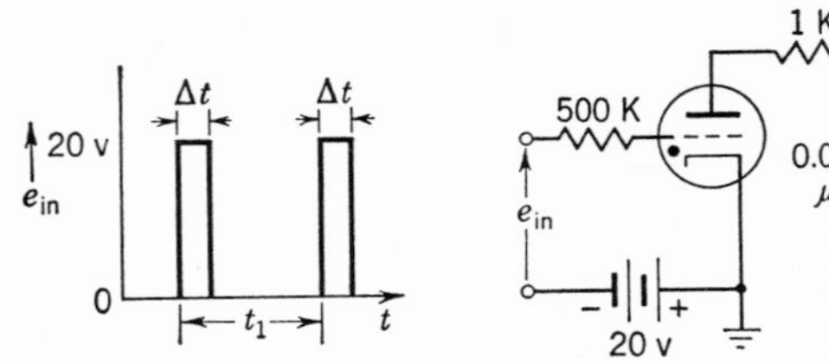

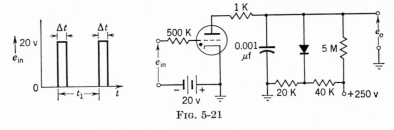

FIG. 5-21

(*b*) Replace the triode by a resistor that will give the same sweep time and amplitude. Recalculate the linearity and compare with the results obtained in part *a*.

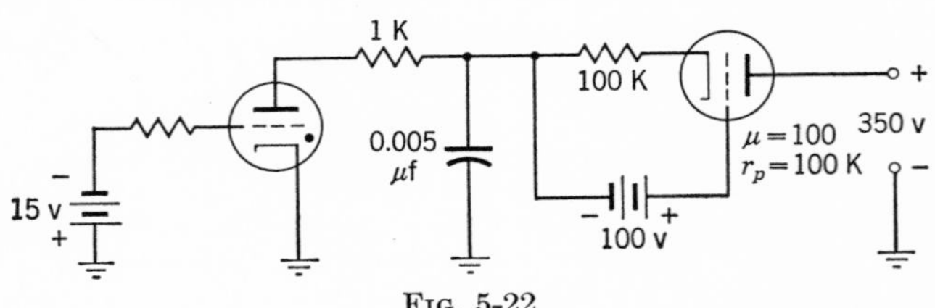

FIG. 5-22

5-10. A simple thyratron sweep starts charging from $E_i = 20$ volts toward 250 volts, and the tube fires at $E_f = 100$ volts.

(*a*) Calculate the sweep NL.

(*b*) Considering the following parameters, one at a time, find the percentage change in m, E_1, E_f, E_c, and E_{bb} which will result in a 1 per cent increase in sweep nonlinearity. (HINT: In each case expand the natural logarithm into a series.)

(*c*) List these parameters in the order that they affect the sweep quality. Assign the value of 1 to the term having the most pronounced effect and give proportional values to each of the other terms.

5-11. (*a*) Repeat Prob. 5-10 with respect to the sweep duration; i.e., calculate the permissible changes in the various parameters, taken one at a time, which will cause a 1 per cent change in the sweep duration.

(*b*) By reference to other texts on gas tubes, discuss the effect of temperature variation on the sweep duration. Is there any way to minimize this problem within the expected range of 30°C change in ambient temperature?

5-12. Derive an expression for the percentage nonlinearity of the sweep, starting from the straight-line representation of Fig. 5-8*a*. Express your answer in terms of the sweep period and the time constant and also in terms of the critical voltages.

5-13. Verify Eq. (5-22).

5-14. Plot the regions of synchronization for a train of equally spaced positive and negative pulses. Assume that the pulses are extremely narrow. Explain your answer.

5-15. A 3-volt peak-to-peak square wave is injected at the grid of a thyratron sweep. The tube is biased to fire at a nominal value of 100 volts, and the drop across the conducting tube is constant at 25 volts. We can express the firing characteristic as $E_f = 20 - 10e_c$.

(*a*) If the free-running sweep period is 500 μsec, what range of sync frequencies will cause the sweep to lock in over a ratio of 2:1? How does the amplitude of the sweep extremes compare with the nominal free-running values?

(*b*) When the square-wave period is 400 μsec, what range of the sync voltage will effect synchronization? Calculate the bounds by means of a graphical construction and then check the results against Fig. 5-16.

5-16. A perfectly linear sweep has a normal period of 1.0 msec. This can be expected to vary by as much as ± 10 per cent because of the variations in the firing voltage. In the absence of synchronization, the sweep starts at zero volts and terminates at the nominal value of $E_f = 100$ volts. The retrace time is zero. It is required that the sweep be synchronized so that its period is exactly 1.0 msec despite the instability in amplitude.

Three synchronization waveshapes are shown in Fig. 5-23 plotted at the firing line of sweep. In each, t_s is 1.0 msec or some integral submultiple.

(*a*) Which among these will provide the desired synchronization?

(*b*) When the sweep is synchronized under the conditions specified, what is the possible number of cycles of the synchronizing wave over which synchronization can take place?

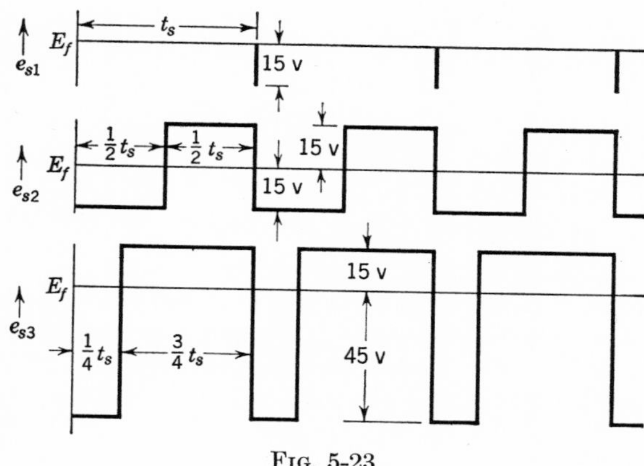

FIG. 5-23

5-17. (*a*) Verify Eq. (5-33) by direct solution from the conditions of triangular-wave synchronization.

(*b*) Calculate the slope of Eq. (5-33) at $x = 1$ as a function of n and compare it with the slope of the $t_{s,\min}/t_1$ line of the $n + 1$ region.

5-18. Consider that the signal available to synchronize a sweep at 10 kc must be derived from a 50-kc sinusoidal oscillator. It will be clipped to a symmetrical square wave and may also be differentiated. Calculate the optimum free-running sweep period and the optimum ratio of sweep to sync signal. Justify your answer. What is the maximum number of cycles over which the sweep can be synchronized if the free-running sweep has ± 3 per cent jitter?

BIBLIOGRAPHY

MacLean, W. R.: The Synchronization of Oscilloscope Sweep Circuits, *Communications*, March, 1943.

Millman, J., and H. Taub: "Pulse and Digital Circuits," McGraw-Hill Book Company, Inc., New York, 1956.

Puckle, O. S.: "Time Bases," 2d ed., John Wiley & Sons, Inc., New York, 1951.

CHAPTER 6

VACUUM-TUBE VOLTAGE SWEEPS

6-1. Introduction. Even a perfunctory reexamination of the simple gas-tube sweeps of Chap. 5 testifies to their inherent unsuitability for other than the most noncritical applications. Generation of very-short-duration sawtooths, smaller than about 20 μsec, was precluded by the circuit's excessively long recovery time. Instability, introduced by the dependence of the ionization potential on external factors, temperature, noise, etc., limited the longest sweep duration to approximately 0.1 sec. And only through severely restricting the amplitude could sweep linearity be maintained within acceptable tolerances. Consequently, when stringent specifications must be met, we are forced to look for other, better techniques of sweep generation.

In this chapter each of the three sweep essentials, rise, recovery, and switching, will be separately treated with a view toward optimizing the over-all performance. The first sections are concerned with the establishment of an almost ideal, linear charging path. For this purpose, it is necessary to employ active circuit elements, which we shall, in this chapter, limit to vacuum tubes. Three methods of linearization, all involving feedback, are in common use: current feedback for constant-current charging of the capacitor, positive-voltage feedback wherein the needed correction term is first developed and then applied, and finally the effective multiplication of the time constant and charging voltage, through the use of negative-voltage feedback. After examining each one of these methods of linearization, the improvement of the sweep recovery time and the nature of the switching process will be considered. Later sections will combine the individual circuits into two practical voltage sweeps, the Miller integrator and the phantastron.

6-2. Linearity Improvement through Current Feedback. If we were to examine the differential equation defining capacitor charging, we would conclude that its terminal voltage rises linearly with time only while being charged from a constant-current source. One method of approaching this ideal situation is through the application of current feedback, as illustrated in the sweep circuit of Fig. 6-1*a*. Here the complete capacitor current flows in R_K, producing a proportional voltage drop, which, together with E, determines the grid-to-cathode voltage ($e_{gk} = E - i_bR_K$). Any change in current automatically establishes the conditions which act to return the current flow to its original value. Quite possibly some factor may cause a momentary decrease in i_b, and the reduced current will, of course, reduce the voltage drop across R_K. But this increases e_{gk}, which, by inducing a resultant increase in tube current, effectively opposes the original change. An increase in load current produces just the opposite effect, again with the tube aiding in the effort to maintain the charging current constant.

This circuit, from grid to cathode, is simply a cathode follower. Therefore, provided that the plate voltage remains sufficiently high (maximum capacitor voltage limited), the grid will not draw current and we can assume unity gain as a reasonable first approximation. The drop across

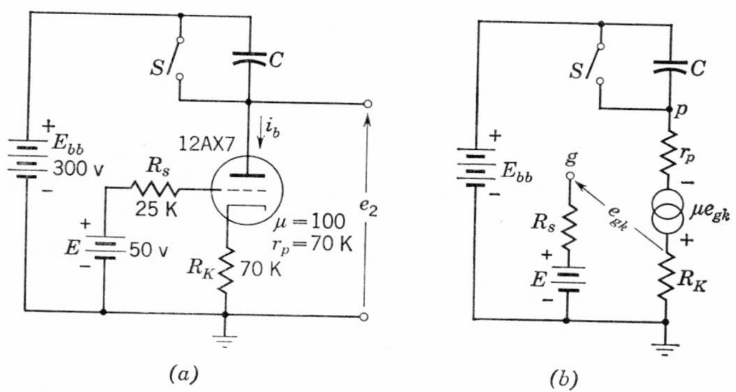

FIG. 6-1. (a) Sweep using current feedback for linearization; (b) equivalent circuit.

R_K is identically the grid-to-ground voltage E and it logically follows that the charging current must be

$$i_b \cong \frac{E}{R_K} = \frac{50}{70\text{ K}} = 714\ \mu\text{a} \tag{6-1}$$

In order to verify this rough approximation, we might calculate the Thévenin equivalent circuit across C. Referring to Fig. 6-1b,

$$R_{Th} = r_p + (\mu + 1)R_K = 70\text{ K} + 7{,}070\text{ K} \tag{6-2a}$$

$$E_{Th} = E_{bb} + \mu E = 300 + 5{,}000\text{ volts} \tag{6-2b}$$

With a high-μ tube, $\mu E \gg E_{bb}$, $(\mu + 1)R_K \gg r_p$, and Eq. (6-1) gives a reasonably correct answer. The actual short-circuit current E_{Th}/R_{Th} is only 4 per cent larger. Constraints, which are considered below, limit the maximum output sweep voltage to a very small percentage of the total Thévenin equivalent value given in Eq. (6-2). In spite of the actual exponential charging toward E_{Th} with the long time constant $(\mu + 1)R_KC$, the current varies but slightly over the restricted time range of interest.

The plate voltage falls from E_{bb} at a rate determined by the capacitor charging. Substitution of the approximately constant-current equation (6-1) into the charge equation yields

$$e_2 = E_{bb} - \frac{1}{C}\int i_b\,dt = E_{bb} - \frac{E}{R_KC}\,t \tag{6-3}$$

Equation (6-3) remains valid until the grid begins conducting. Its loading of the constant-voltage source will change the charging current and adversely affect the sweep linearity. The bottoming value of plate voltage is found from the circuit of Fig. 6-1*b* by setting $e_{gk} = 0$. At this point, the actual voltage drop across R_K is E, and since the current that flows through R_K also flows through r_p, the lower bounding value of the linear sweep output becomes

$$E_{2s} = \left(1 + \frac{r_p}{R_K}\right)E = 100 \text{ volts} \tag{6-4}$$

The capacitor discharge mechanism is usually triggered when the output falls to some preset voltage. In a fixed duration sweep, this might be the bottoming value found in Eq. (6-4). If, however, the charging current is adjusted by varying R_K, then the saturation voltage will also change. Decreasing R_K increases the current, thus decreasing the charging rate and lengthening the sweep. But any reduction in R_K also affects the possible sweep amplitude by raising the plate bottoming voltage. The discharge point must correspond to the worst condition, i.e., the solution of Eq. (6-4) for the smallest R_K. Hence, from Eq. (6-3), the sweep time becomes

$$t_1 = R_KC\,\frac{E_{bb} - E'_{2s}}{E} \tag{6-5}$$

where, for example, when $R_{K,\min} = 35$ K, $E'_{2s} = 150$ volts.

As the plate falls from 300 to its bottoming value of 150 volts, the capacitor charges by only 150 out of its equivalent steady-state value of 5,300 volts. Hence the sweep nonlinearity may be found from Eq. (5-22).

$$\text{NL} = \frac{150}{5{,}300}\,12.5\% = 0.36\%$$

In an equivalent *RC* sweep, where *C* charges by the same amount from a constant 300-volt source, the nonlinearity [Eq. (5-21)] is

$$\text{NL} = 12.5\% \ln\frac{300}{300 - 150} = 8.7\%$$

The improvement is quite impressive.

6-3. Bootstrap Sweep. Bootstrapping, a form of positive feedback, linearizes the sweep by first determining what voltage correction term is needed and then deriving it through acting on an already existing voltage. The necessary circuit modification usually follows directly from the analysis of the original problem posed. For example, the nonlinear charging in the RC circuit of Fig. 6-2 is a consequence of the dependency of the loop current upon the capacitor voltage.

$$i = \frac{E' - e_c}{R} \qquad (6\text{-}6)$$

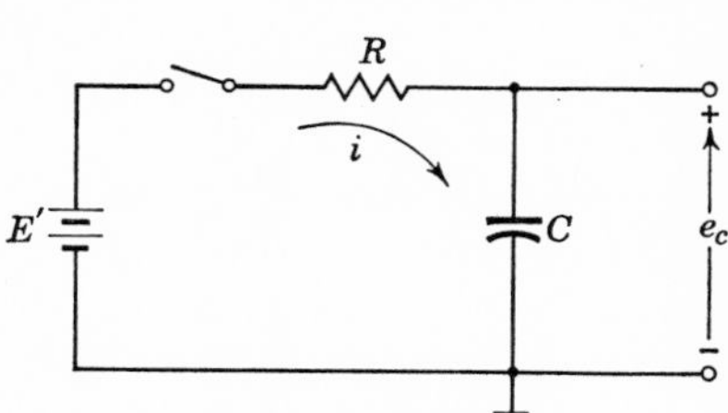

FIG. 6-2. Simple RC sweep.

If, somehow, we could cancel the effects of e_c, through the adjustment or replacement of one of the circuit components under our control, then the desired linear charging would be assured. One obvious course is to replace E' by $E + e_c$. This required drive can be developed quite easily by amplifying the capacitor voltage and connecting the charging resistor to the amplifier output instead of to the battery. Because of the special charging requirements, the output must have a d-c level of E. Thus it follows that Fig. 6-3 represents the general form of the bootstrap sweep. In this case positive-voltage feedback is employed to increase the effective charging source voltage at the same rate as the increase in the sweep voltage e_c.

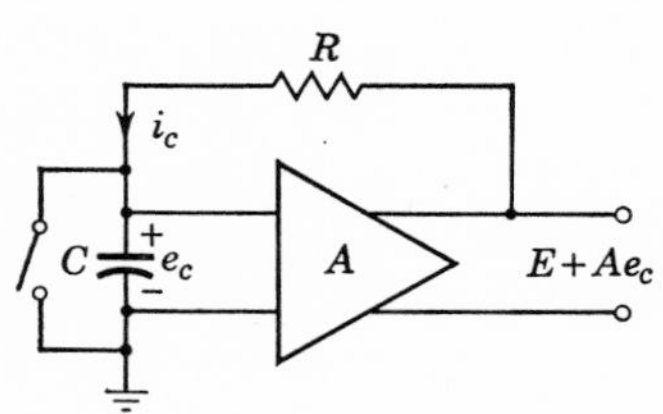

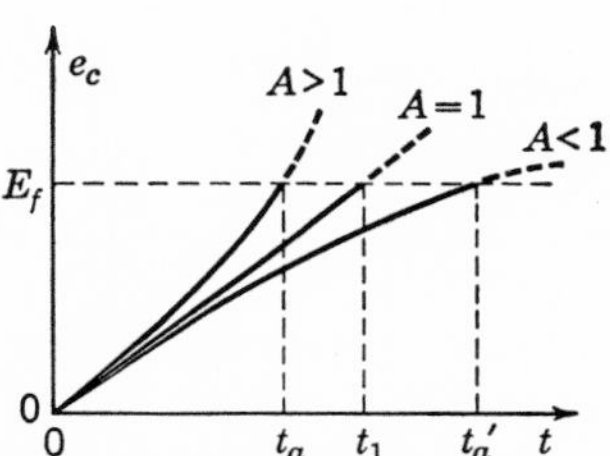

FIG. 6-3. General bootstrap sweep and output waveshapes.

Constant-current charging of C is contingent on the amplifier gain A remaining unity. Any variation is immediately reflected as a change in the output waveshape and sweep period (Fig. 6-3). This dependency on A may, if serious, prevent the use of the bootstrap circuit for all but noncritical applications.

The sensitivity of sweep duration with respect to the voltage amplification may be interpreted quantitatively by starting from the equivalent circuit controlling the charging current flow. Referring to Fig. 6-3 and writing the input node equation yields

$$i_c = \frac{E + Ae_c - e_c}{R} = \frac{E}{R} - \frac{(1 - A)e_c}{R} \tag{6-7}$$

The right-hand side of Eq. (6-7) represents the circuit as seen by the capacitor: it consists of a constant-current generator in parallel with its own internal admittance (Fig. 6-4).

We might observe, from Fig. 6-4, that when $A < 1$, the charging of C is exponential rather than linear. The final steady-state voltage, determined by setting $i_c = 0$, is $E/(1 - A)$, and by inspection of the circuit, we see that the charging time constant is $CR/(1 - A)$. Therefore the sweep voltage may be expressed as

$$e_c(t) = \frac{E}{1 - A}\left(1 - e^{-\frac{1-A}{RC}t}\right) \tag{6-8}$$

However, when $A = 1$, G_o becomes zero and C is charged directly from the ideal constant-current source.

$$A = 1 \qquad e_c = \frac{E}{RC}t \tag{6-9}$$

Suppose that a change in either tube or circuit parameters makes A slightly greater than unity. Under these circumstances G_o becomes negative and the terminal voltage increases exponentially toward infinity. The equation defining this region of operation is the same as Eq. (6-8). But $A > 1$ means that the time constant is now negative and that the system's single pole will move along the real axis into the right half plane. Since a physical device cannot handle infinite-amplitude signals, any slight disturbance immediately drives the amplifier toward saturation.

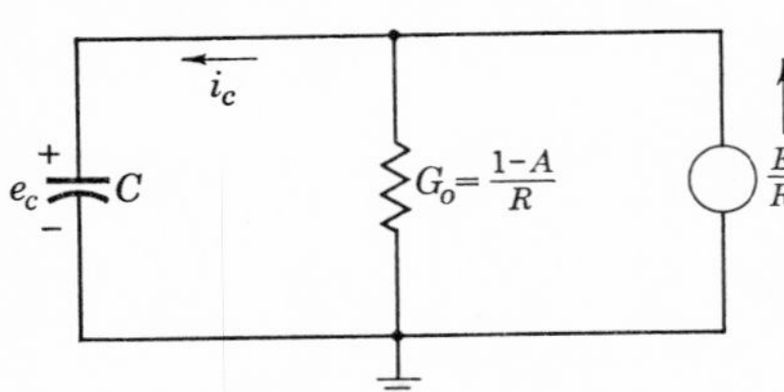

FIG. 6-4. Bootstrap equivalent circuit.

In order to see how the sweep time depends on A, we first calculate the sweep duration from Eq. (6-8).

$$t_a' = \frac{RC}{1 - A} \ln \frac{E}{E - (1 - A)E_f}$$

No generality is lost by choosing a convenient termination point, one which will keep A in the forefront and at the same time eliminate superfluous voltage terms. The greatest simplification occurs by setting

$E_f = E$:

$$t_a = \frac{RC}{1 - A} \ln \frac{1}{A} \tag{6-10}$$

As a basis for comparison, the duration of the linear sweep of the same amplitude is evaluated from Eq. (6-9).

$$t_1 = RC \tag{6-11}$$

And from Eqs. (6-10) and (6-11),

$$\frac{t_a}{t_1} = \frac{1}{1 - A} \ln \frac{1}{A} \tag{6-12}$$

For $A = 0.95$, 5 per cent below the optimum value of unity,

$$\frac{t_a}{t_1} = 1.082$$

or the sweep time is now 8 per cent longer than the perfectly linear sweep. When $A = 1.05$, the sweep duration is reduced to $0.976t_1$. The separation from the linear sweep with respect to changes in A becomes even

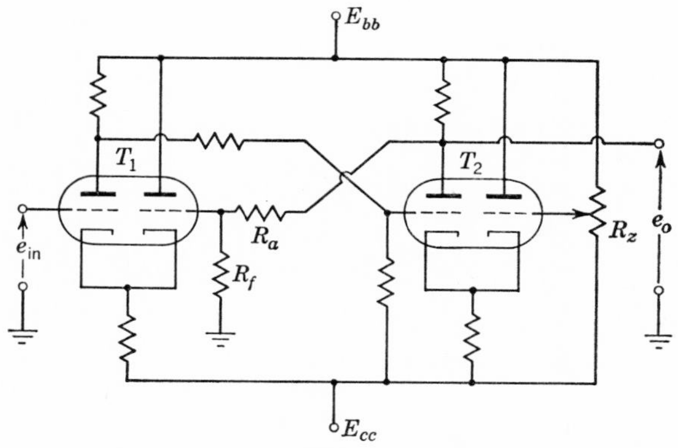

FIG. 6-5. Practical bootstrap amplifier.

more pronounced as the sweep amplitude increases. From the above discussion, the only possible conclusion drawn is that the gain of the bootstrap amplifier must be highly stabilized if we are to avoid sweep-duration instability. But even with the high degree of sensitivity of the sweep period to changes in A, the sweep linearity and maximum sweep amplitude are still superior to what it is possible to achieve with a simple RC network.

A practical, direct-coupled amplifier for bootstrapping applications appears in Fig. 6-5. Negative-voltage feedback, applied through the resistor network R_a and R_f, both sets and stabilizes the over-all positive gain. This amplifier's gain varies by less than 0.01 per cent, with regard to expected tube and parameter changes from its nominal unity gain value. R_z controls the output voltage level, and thus the charging current: it might also serve as the fine sweep control. An obvious circuit disadvantage is the need for two power supplies which, for optimum gain stability, must be highly regulated.

6-4. Miller Sweep. The Miller sweep, which utilizes negative-voltage feedback for sweep linearization, poses no problems as to poles in the right half plane. And, in addition, it generates a sweep virtually independent of the amplifier gain. Consider the basic circuit of Fig. 6-6*a*,

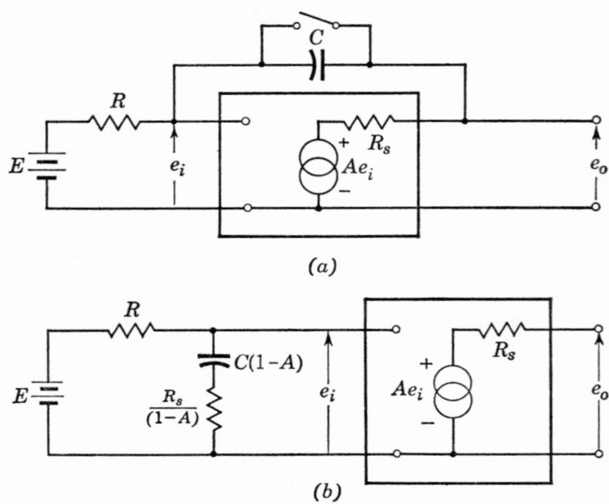

FIG. 6-6. (*a*) Basic Miller sweep; (*b*) Miller sweep—equivalent-circuit representation.

where the amplifier has a forward voltage gain A and an output impedance R_s. If, as was done for the bootstrap, we write the current equation at the input node,

$$i_i = \frac{e_i - Ae_i}{R_s + 1/pC}$$

We now, by solving this equation, find the input impedance,

$$Z_{\text{in}} = \frac{e_i}{i_i} = \frac{R_s}{1 - A} + \frac{1}{pC(1 - A)} \tag{6-13}$$

Equation (6-13), the Miller effect, expresses the effective multiplication of the feedback capacity and reduction of resistance due to the negative-voltage feedback. With current feedback (the circuit of Fig. 6-1), the opposite effect appeared. It follows, from Eq. (6-13), that the input circuit may be represented as shown in Fig. 6-6*b*. If the current flow from the output back to the input is kept small, then the drop across R_s

due to the feedback component may be neglected. R controls the charging rate as well as limiting the feedback-path current flow; it is usually very much larger than R_s. We have thus effectively isolated the input and output circuits, allowing an independent solution for the input voltage. It may then be reflected into the output by multiplying by the circuit gain $e_o = Ae_i$.

Since we are interested in generating a linear sweep, charging must be limited to a small portion of the total exponential. The input circuit will be treated as an integrator with the reflected resistance $R_s/(1 - A)$ contributing an additional small constant term.

$$e_i = \frac{R_s}{R_s + R(1 - A)} E + \frac{1}{\left(R + \frac{R_s}{1 - A}\right) C(1 - A)} \int_0^t E\, dt$$

And the amplified input voltage appears at the output:

$$e_o = Ae_i = \frac{AR_sE}{R_s + R(1 - A)} + \frac{AE}{\left(R + \frac{R_s}{1 - A}\right) C(1 - A)} t \qquad (6\text{-}14)$$

If the amplifier gain is a very large negative number, then $(1 - A) \cong |A|$ and A cancels out in the sweep term of Eq. (6-14). This necessary condition must be satisfied in order to make the sweep relatively independent of the amplifier parameters. As a further result of the large gain, $R \gg R_s/(1 - A)$ and

$$e_o = -\frac{R_s}{R} E - \frac{E}{RC} t$$

If the much more stringent requirement that $R \gg R_s$ is also satisfied, then this equation may be reduced even further:

$$e_o \cong -\frac{E}{RC} t \qquad (6\text{-}15)$$

Equation (6-15) has the same form as the charging equation derived for the bootstrap [Eq. (6-9)]. But while the linear charging in that circuit was critically dependent on the value of the amplifier gain, this is not true in the Miller sweep, where the only requirement is a large negative gain.

An amplifier with a gain of -100 and source voltage of 300 volts generates a sweep of 100 volts, while the input only changes by $1/A$ times as much, or by 1 volt. Since this is a very small portion of the possible 300-volt charging curve, the sweep will be extremely linear; nonlinearity of better than 0.1 per cent is easily achieved, and with a very-high-gain amplifier even 0.01 per cent nonlinearity becomes possible.

Triode Miller Sweep. The procedure used in calculating the circuit waveshapes and in subsequent verification of sweep linearity is outlined below for the triode Miller sweep of Fig. 6-7*a*. The solution follows in time sequence the behavior of the circuit. In each region we draw the model holding and use it to evaluate time constants and boundary conditions.

Along with the general solution outlined below, we shall consider the specific components of Fig. 6-7 to illustrate the order of magnitudes involved.

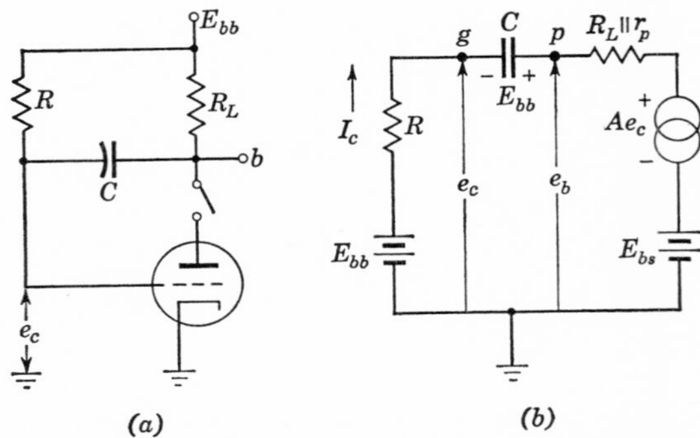

FIG. 6-7. (*a*) Triode Miller sweep; (*b*) model holding in the active region. For the purposes of illustration, the following typical values are assigned to this circuit: $\mu = 60$, $r_p = 10$ K, $r_c = 400$ ohms, $R_L = 50$ K, $R = 1$ megohm, $C = 0.001\ \mu$f, and $E_{bb} = 250$ volts.

Before closing the switch at $t = 0$, the grid, returned through R to E_{bb}, is conducting. Since the 400-ohm grid resistance is much less than R, the capacitor charges to E_{bb} with the polarity indicated. The grid is not actually at zero but at some small positive value, usually a fraction of a volt, as given by Eq. (6-16).

$$E_c(0^-) = \frac{r_c}{R} E_{bb} = \frac{400}{10^6} 250 = 0.1 \text{ volt} \tag{6-16}$$

Once the switch closes, the first question of interest is, What is the new value of grid and plate (point b) voltage? Our qualitative argument as to the circuit behavior follows. The voltage across the capacitor cannot change instantaneously; therefore any change at the plate must also appear as an equal change in grid voltage. When the switch closes, the grid either rises, falls, or remains constant at its slightly positive value. We shall first assume that it remains unchanged. The plate current corresponding to the positive grid voltage is very large, causing a large voltage drop at point b which, coupled by the capacitor, appears at the grid and cuts the tube off. Hence a contradiction arises, and the original assumption must have been incorrect.

This contradiction may be resolved by observing that only a small change of plate voltage may be tolerated without cutting off the tube. The plate current flow, after switching, must be small, and we conclude that the tube is driven almost to, but not quite into, cutoff.

The operation in the active region, including the initial drop at both the plate and grid, may be calculated from the model which holds immediately after switching. In Fig. 6-7*b*, the complete circuit, seen looking into the plate of the tube, was replaced by its Thévenin equivalent. E_{bs} is the saturation value of the plate voltage ($e_{gk} = 0$), and A

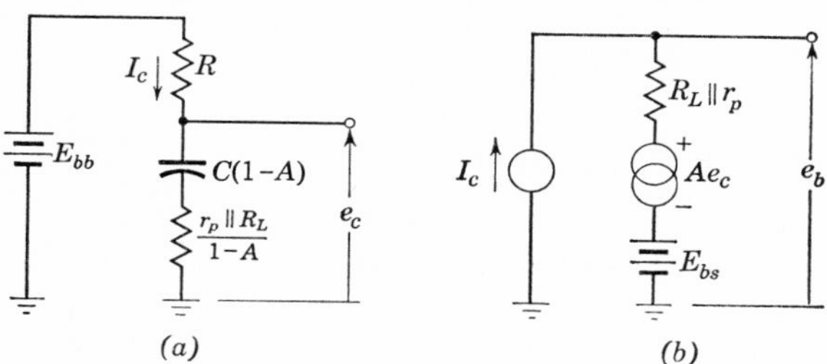

FIG. 6-8. Triode Miller-sweep models. (*a*) Grid circuit; (*b*) plate circuit.

is the voltage gain in the active region. From the unloaded plate-circuit model,

$$A = \frac{-\mu R_L}{r_p + R_L} \qquad E_{bs} = \frac{r_p}{r_p + R_L} E_{bb} \tag{6-17}$$

With the parameters given, the equivalent plate-circuit resistance ($R_s = r_p \| R_2$) is only 8.3 K, the gain is -50, and $E_{bs} = 41.7$ volts.

Following the argument presented with respect to the general Miller sweep, the complete timing can be reflected into the grid circuit (Fig. 6-8*a*). The only question remaining unanswered is, What is the initial voltage across the reflected capacity $C(1 - A)$? Just after switching, the loop voltage from grid to ground can be found from Fig. 6-7*b*.

$$E_c(0^+) = -E_{bb} + I_C(0^+)R_s + AE_c(0^+) + E_{bs}$$

Solving for the grid voltage yields

$$E_c(0^+) = \frac{-E_{bb} + E_{bs}}{1 - A} + \frac{R_s}{1 - A} I_C(0^+) \tag{6-18}$$

The first term in Eq. (6-18) is the voltage across $C(1 - A)$ immediately after the switch is closed.

Since the current through R remains invariant across the change in models from Fig. 6-7*b* to Fig. 6-8*a*, the second term of Eq. (6-18) can be identified as the drop across the reflected source resistance. The current which charges $C(1 - A)$ is

$$I_C(0^+) = \frac{E_{bb} - E_c(0^+)}{R}$$

but $E_c(0^+)$ must lie within the small grid base during the entire sweep. Hence $E_{bb} \gg E_c$ and

$$I_C \cong \frac{E_{bb}}{R} \tag{6-19}$$

The almost constant charging current indicated by Eq. (6-19) proves that the sweep produced will be highly linear.

By substituting the terms from Eqs. (6-17) and (6-19) into Eq. (6-18), we can also express the initial grid voltage as

$$E_c(0^+) = -\frac{R_L}{r_p + (\mu + 1)R_L} E_{bb} + \frac{R_s}{1 - A} \frac{E_{bb}}{R} \tag{6-20}$$

In this example, the reflected source resistance is only 160 ohms, which is very much less than the 1-megohm timing resistance. The second term of Eq. (6-20) is almost completely negligible; it is only 0.04 volt. With a high-μ tube the significant first term of Eq. (6-20) may be approximated as

$$E_c(0^+) = \frac{-E_{bb}}{\mu + 1} = -4.1 \text{ volts} \tag{6-21}$$

We might note that this is only slightly above the grid cutoff voltage of $-E_{bb}/\mu$ (−4.2 volts). This verifies our previous contention that the tube is driven to the verge of cutoff.

After the initial drop, the grid starts charging from $E_c(0^+)$ toward E_{bb}, with the long time constant

$$\tau_1 = C(1 - A)\left(R + \frac{R_s}{1 - A}\right) \cong RC(1 - A) \tag{6-22}$$

With the constant charging current assumed in Eq. (6-19), the small portion of the exponential rise used may be approximated by

$$e_c(t) = E_c(0^+) + \frac{E_{bb}}{RC(1 - A)} t \tag{6-23}$$

The grid rises at a rate of $E_{bb}/RC(1 - A)$ volts/sec from its initial value.

The abrupt change in voltage at the grid, as the tube turns on, is

$$\Delta E_{c1} = E_c(0^+) - E_c(0^-)$$

Since the plate and grid are coupled by C,

$$E_b(0^+) = E_{bb} - |\Delta E_{c1}| = 246 \text{ volts}$$

The plate waveshape will simply be an amplified version of the signal appearing at the grid. It follows that the plate will fall A times as fast as the grid rises.

$$e_b(t) = E_b(0^+) + \frac{E_{bb}A}{RC(1 - A)}t$$

and since A is a large negative number, the plate rundown is independent of the gain.

$$e_b(t) = E_b(0^+) - \frac{E_{bb}}{RC}t \tag{6-24}$$

The next change in the circuit state occurs when the grid reaches zero and starts conducting. From Eq. (6-23), the linear grid rise of $E_c(0^+)$ volts takes

$$t_1 = \frac{-E_c(0^+)}{E_{bb}}\tau_1 \qquad \text{sec} \tag{6-25}$$

With the values given in Fig. 6-7, the sweep lasts for approximately 800 μsec. Only a small fraction of the 50-msec grid time constant is used for the linear plate rundown, and over this interval the sweep nonlinearity is 0.16 per cent.

The plate voltage corresponding to zero grid voltage E_{b0} may be found in several ways. For example, the sweep time found from Eq. (6-25) can be substituted into the plate-voltage equation. A somewhat more accurate method is to solve the plate-circuit model of Fig. 6-8*b* with $e_c = 0$.

$$E_{b0} = I_C R_s + E_{bs} = \frac{R_s}{R}E_{bb} + E_{bs} \tag{6-26}$$

In the case where $R_s \ll R$, the bottoming voltage is almost exactly E_{bs}. In the example cited, $E_{b0} = 43.7$ volts, only 2 volts above E_{bs}.

The several answers for E_{b0} will not be in exact agreement because of the approximations made in the course of the analysis. The value found from the model is more nearly correct since it comes from the basic circuit instead of being the product of many intervening steps.

After the end of the linear rundown, the grid's conduction does not remove the tube from its active region; it only reintroduces r_c from grid to ground in Figs. 6-7*b* and 6-8*a*, changing the time constant and the steady-state voltage. From the Thévenin equivalent of the grid circuit, the new values are

$$\begin{aligned} E_{ss2} &= \frac{r_c}{R}E_{bb} = E_c(0^-) \\ \tau_2 &= C(1 - A)\left(r_c + \frac{r_p \parallel R_L}{1 - A}\right) \end{aligned} \tag{6-27}$$

In this region the 160-ohm contribution due to the reflected source impedance becomes significant compared with the 400-ohm grid resistance. The new time constant of 28 μsec is obviously much smaller than τ_1, and the rise rate is much faster. The positive grid resistance is introduced into the circuit at zero volts at a point where it cannot abruptly change the voltage anywhere within the timing capacitor loop. Consequently the sweep will enter the new region smoothly, without any jumps appearing in either the grid or plate waveshapes.

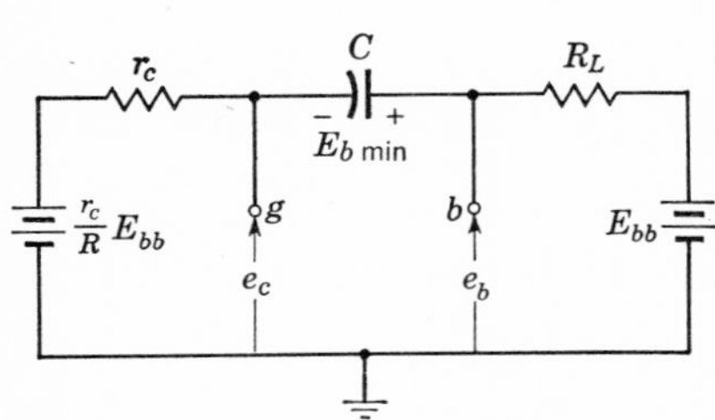

FIG. 6-9. Circuit model holding during recovery.

As the grid continues rising, the plate falls proportionately, finally bottoming at $E_{b,\min}$. We evaluate this voltage from the plate-circuit model (Fig. 6-8b) by setting $e_c = 0.1$ volt. Even in the positive grid region, the ratio of the change in plate voltage to the change in grid voltage is the circuit's amplification. Thus $E_{b,\min}$ might also be found by writing

$$E_{b,\min} = E_{b0} + AE_c(0^-) = 38.7 \text{ volts}$$

Once the tube bottoms, the sweep is absolutely stable and remains in this state until external conditions force a change. When we open the switch, we remove the active element and must again draw a new model, this time to define the behavior during recovery. Figure 6-9 illustrates the conditions prevailing.

Just before, and therefore just after, switching, the voltage across C is $E_{b,\min}$. The net change in the loop voltage will appear across the total series resistance. It will divide proportionately across R_L and r_c, but remember that the jump at both the grid and plate must be equal. The grid voltage jumps by $\Delta_2 E_c$, from $E_c(0^-)$ to a new value, $E_{c,\max}$.

$$E_{c,\max} = E_c(0^-) + \frac{r_c}{r_c + R_L}[E_{bb} - E_{b,\min} - E_c(0^-)]$$
$$\cong \frac{r_c}{R_L}(E_{bb} - E_{b,\min}) = 1.69 \text{ volts} \tag{6-28}$$

Point b rises by the same amount. Recovery now proceeds with the time constant

$$\tau_3 = (R_L + r_c)C \cong R_L C \tag{6-29}$$

toward the original steady-state voltages, E_{bb} and $E_c(0^-)$.

The complete waveshapes, with all voltages, times, and time constants indicated, are presented in Fig. 6-10.

Complete recovery requires $4\tau_3$ sec, or 200 μsec, which is on the same order of magnitude as the plate's linear rundown. Unless we do something to shorten this time (Sec. 6-5), an unreasonably long interval must elapse between sweeps.

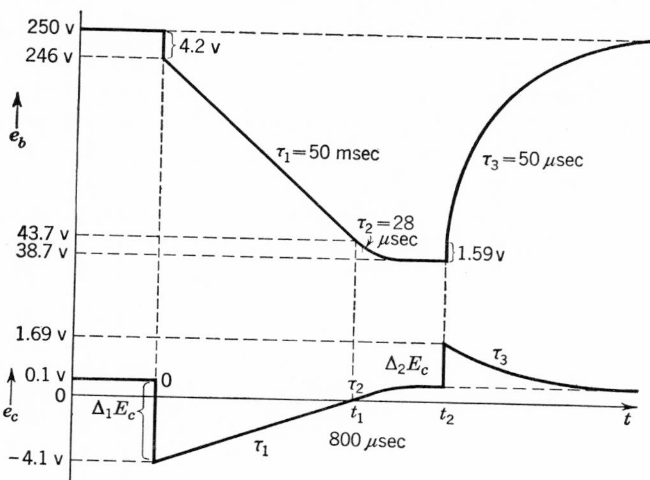

FIG. 6-10. Triode Miller-sweep plate and grid waveshapes (not to scale).

Voltage Control over Sweep Time. External voltage control of the sweep duration may be incorporated by coupling point b (the plate) of the Miller sweep through a plate catching diode to the control voltage E (Fig. 6-11). With the circuit in the normal, unexcited state, the switch is open and the diode conducts, maintaining point b at E volts.

The grid voltage just after switching can be found by following the procedure previously discussed, with, however, an initial voltage of E across C. If $R \gg R_L \parallel r_p$ and the contribution due the reflected resistance can be ignored, we obtain

$$E_c(0^+) = \frac{r_p E_{bb} - (r_p + R_L)E}{r_p + (\mu + 1)R_L} \qquad (6\text{-}30)$$

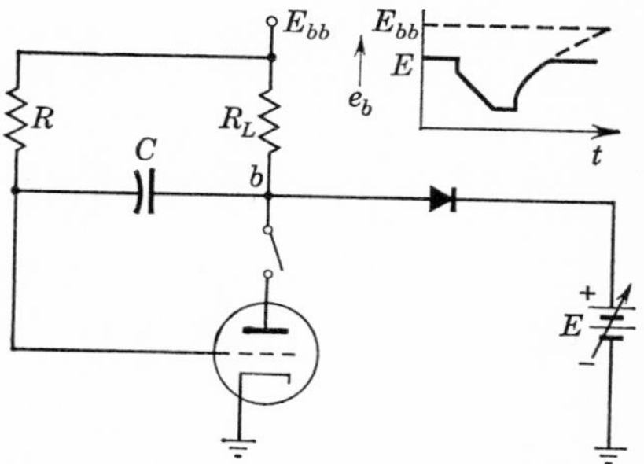

FIG. 6-11. Circuit for voltage control of sweep period—Miller sweep.

Equation (6-30) expresses the linear relationship existing between $E_c(0^+)$ and E. Since the sweep time is determined by the amount of the initial grid drop, it follows that the period is a linear function of E. However, E must be restricted to the range from E_{bb} to E_{bs}. When E reaches its maximum value E_{bb}, Eq. (6-30) reduces to Eq. (6-21), and when E is set equal to E_{bs}, $E_c(0^+)$ becomes, as expected, zero and the sweep time is also zero.

The initial drop in plate voltage, which brings it below E, back-biases the diode, effectively removing E from any further circuit control. Rundown and bottoming proceed as before, to the same final values, except that the starting point is from a lower initial voltage and the sweep ends sooner.

During the recovery of the plate toward E_{bb}, the diode conducts when E_b reaches E, stopping the recharging of C; the recovery time is reduced to some percentage of its previous value. And often, for just this important reason, a diode is connected between the plate and a voltage divider from E_{bb} to ground.

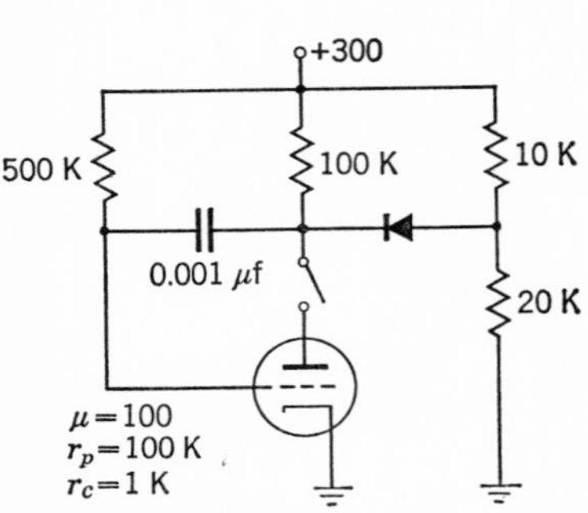

FIG. 6-12. Miller-sweep circuit for Example 6-1.

Example 6-1. Figure 6-12 shows a Miller sweep circuit which incorporates a plate bottoming diode, biased to conduct when the plate falls to 200 volts. Thus the duration of the linear sweep depends on the plate rundown rather than on the grid voltage rise. Furthermore, in this circuit the source impedance is relatively large and cannot be neglected.

The initial value of the grid voltage is

$$E_c(0^-) = \frac{1\text{ K}}{500\text{ K}}\,300 = 0.6\text{ volt}$$

After switching into the active region, $A = -50$, $r_p \parallel R_L = 50$ K, and the reflected source impedance is 1 K. From Eq. (6-20)

$$E_c(0^+) = -\frac{300}{102} + \frac{1\text{ K}}{500\text{ K}}\,300 = -2.34\text{ volts}$$

which is well above the cutoff value of -3 volts. The total grid change is -2.94 volts, and the plate drops by the same amount.

From Eq. (6-24),

$$e_b(t) = 297 - 0.6 \times 10^6 t$$

The plate runs down 97 volts to the 200 volts at which the diode conducts in

$$t_1 = \frac{97}{0.6} \times 10^{-6} = 162\ \mu\text{sec}$$

During this interval, the grid rises by

$$\Delta E_c = \frac{\Delta E_b}{A} = \frac{97}{50} = 1.94\text{ volts}$$

to

$$e_c(t_1) = -0.4\text{ volt}$$

6-5. Recovery-time Improvement. The long recovery time is primarily a function of the large plate load of the Miller-sweep tube. If in the capacitor charge and discharge paths we could somehow replace this large source impedance by a much smaller value without otherwise affecting the circuit, then the recovery time would be reduced proportionately. One convenient method is to isolate the capacitor from the plate circuit by means of an intervening cathode follower (Fig. 6-13*a*).

A cathode follower's gain, especially when using a high-μ tube and a large value of R_K, is almost unity. Since $A_{CF}E_b \cong E_b$, the cathode follower couples everything happening at the plate of T_1 to the capacitor through its very low output impedance (Fig. 6-13*b*). The over-all circuit is identical with those previously given in Figs. 6-7 to 6-9, except

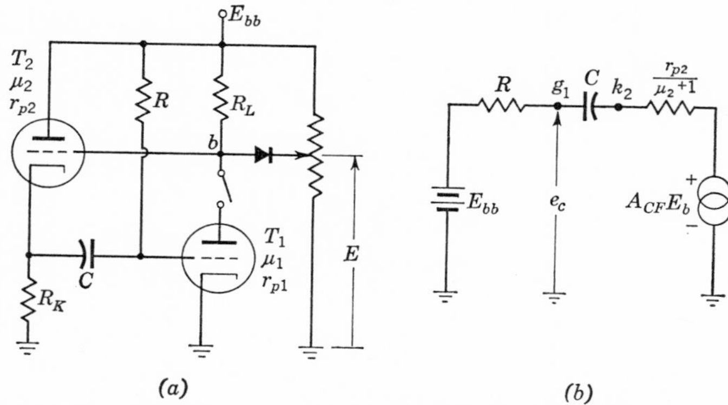

FIG. 6-13. (*a*) Miller sweep with a cathode follower included for fast recovery; (*b*) equivalent grid circuit of the sweep tube.

that the source impedance must be changed from R_L or $R_L \parallel r_p$, as the case may be, to

$$R_{s2} = \frac{r_{p2}}{\mu_2 + 1} \parallel R_K \cong \frac{r_{p2}}{\mu_2 + 1}$$

R_{s2} is quite small: in the normal triode it would lie between 200 and 500 ohms. If we compare this small resistance with the 10- to 100-K source impedance that was formerly present, we can see that the bottoming and recovery time constants (τ_1 and τ_2) will be greatly reduced. Conditions during the circuit-voltage jumps, rundown, and recovery remain as before, except for the introduction of R_{s2} in all pertinent equations.

The isolation of C from the plate of the Miller-sweep tube allows extremely rapid recovery of the plate, limited only by any stray circuit capacity from point b of the switch to ground. It is completely independent of the new Miller grid recovery time constant of [from Eq. (6-29)]

$$\tau_3' = \left(r_{c1} + \frac{r_{p2}}{\mu_2 + 1}\right) C \tag{6-31}$$

Assuming $R_{s2} = 500$ ohms in the circuit of Fig. 6-13, this time constant is reduced from 50 to 0.9 μsec. The new waveshapes are sketched in Fig. 6-14. Note that the rundown time constant [Eq. (6-21)] remains relatively unaffected by the circuit change. But bottoming occurs slightly faster, once the grid reaches zero, because of the reduction of τ_2, which was previously given by Eqs. (6-27). Just before opening the plate switch, the charge on C was approximately $E_{b,\min}$; just after the switch is opened the equivalent generator of the cathode follower jumps to E.

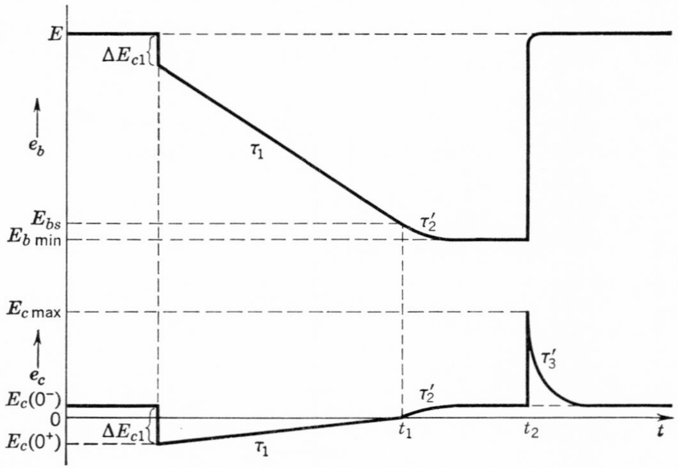

FIG. 6-14. Miller-sweep waveshapes when a cathode follower is used for fast recovery.

The change of circuit voltage divides proportionately across r_{c1} and $r_{p2}/(\mu_2 + 1)$, with the new grid voltage becoming

$$E_{c,\max} \cong \frac{r_{c1}}{r_{c1} + r_{p2}/(\mu_2 + 1)} (E - E_{b,\min}) \tag{6-32}$$

Equation (6-32) indicates that upon recovery a very large positive grid voltage pulse will appear. In an actual circuit, the peak will always be appreciably less than the value calculated above. Both the grid resistance, which decreases markedly at higher values of grid voltage, and any stray capacity present act to limit the maximum grid jump to 10 to 20 volts rather than the 50 or 100 volts calculated. This portion of the cycle appears after the region of major interest (the linear rundown), and therefore we can accept a very gross approximation for the solution. It still explains, as well as necessary, the waveshape that will be seen on an oscilloscope.

The cathode follower also performs an important secondary function by making the sweep voltage available at a low impedance level for coupling to other circuits. We can tolerate a much greater degree of external loading at the cathode, without affecting the sweep, than could possibly be applied at the plate of the sweep tube.

6-6. Sweep Switching Problems. The final sweep essential is the establishment of the capacitor discharge path which terminates each sweep cycle. Looking backward to Chap. 5, this function was served by the gas tube. However, any other bistate device, such as the controlled gates of Chaps. 3 and 4, might serve equally well. These circuits require an external control signal which opens or closes the gate at the proper point of the cycle and for a given time interval. But in reality the extra signal involves slight, if any, additional complexity. In order to stabilize the gas-tube sweep, we were also forced to inject an external voltage, the sync signal. Thus the gate control voltage might simultaneously perform two functions, switching and synchronization.

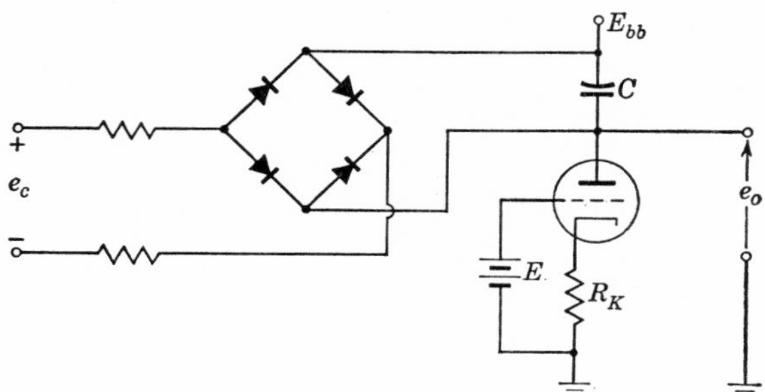

FIG. 6-15. Diode-bridge sweep discharge circuit.

Suppose we concentrate our attention on only one of the possible switches, the diode bridge of Sec. 3-6, and apply it to the three sweeps considered so far in this chapter. Each has its own special capacitor discharge or charge problems, and in the aggregate they adequately represent what might be expected in almost any switching situation.

First consider the current feedback sweep of Sec. 6-2 (Fig. 6-1). The diode bridge, applied across the capacity (Fig. 6-15), should normally be open: all diodes should be back-biased (e_c negative). Unless the diode's reverse resistance is very large, the shunting of C by r_r will adversely affect both sweep time and linearity. In addition, the diode capabilities limit the maximum sweep amplitude to somewhat less than twice the peak inverse voltage. The control pulse forces the bridge into conduction, shunting C with r_f and thus discharging C. For complete discharge the control-pulse duration must be at least $4r_fC$. Provided that the spacing between adjacent pulses is less than or equal to the maximum linear sweep time [Eq. (6-5)], the periodic discharge locks the sweep time to the control-pulse period.

The diode bridge may also be used in shunt with the capacitor of the bootstrap sweep of Sec. 6-3. Amplitude limitations, required control-pulse duration, and the mechanism of switching are identical with that of the current feedback sweep. However, in this sweep we can compensate for the shunting effect of r_r which had previously increased the sweep nonlinearity. The input impedance $R/(1 - A)$ is made negative and equal in value to r_r by making the base amplifier gain slightly greater than unity. The parallel-resistance combination becomes infinite, ensuring constant-current charging of C, even in the presence of the diode bridge.

In the triode Miller sweep (Sec. 6-4), the switching circuit and recovery path are completely independent. The bridge, inserted in series with the plate, simply replaces the switch of Fig. 6-7*a*. When it is pulsed to cutoff (diodes back-biased), the large reverse resistance r_r in series with the plate greatly reduces the loop gain and effectively opens the plate circuit, allowing recovery. When the bridge again conducts, the next sweep cycle starts. An alternative is to shunt R_L with a normally conducting bridge and by this means reduce the load resistance, and hence the gain, to zero. Once the pulse opens the gate, the change in resistance produces the initial grid drop, with the amplification, now permitted, starting the linear rundown.

The conclusion which can be drawn from the above arguments is that almost any means of discharging the energy-storage element, interrupting the feedback path, or reducing the loop amplification to zero will satisfactorily control the sweep operation. Of course, we must ensure that the circuit enters its active region upon switching; if it remains saturated or cut off, the sweep may be delayed or may never even get started.

6-7. Pentode Miller Sweep. Rather than separate the functions of gating and sweep into two independent circuits, they might well be incorporated in a single tube, a pentode. The suppressor is normally biased negatively enough to completely cut off the plate current. In order to turn the plate on and so complete the feedback loop, we must apply a positive control pulse at the suppressor. The subsequent circuit operation, the equal drop in plate and grid voltage, the linear charging and eventual bottoming, and finally the recovery are similar to those of the triode Miller sweep. Furthermore, with its greater amplification, the pentode improves the sweep linearity by a factor of 10 or more over that of the triode and also permits a greater sweep amplitude.

The basic differences between the pentode Miller sweep of Fig. 6-16 and the triode sweep appear in all boundary conditions dependent on the physical characteristics of the tube. Practically, this sweep would also include a cathode follower for fast recovery and a plate catching diode, but in the interests of circuit simplicity, these elements have been omitted from Fig. 6-16.

Under normal circuit operation, the initial conditions are the following. The control grid, returned through R to E_{bb}, conducts and therefore will be slightly positive, just as in the triode. Since the suppressor cuts off the plate, the cathode, control grid, and screen grid act as the three elements of a triode. As a direct consequence of the positive control grid, heavy screen current flows, with the resultant voltage drop in R_c lowering the screen voltage to 50 or 60 volts.

Once the positive gating pulse raises the suppressor voltage to, or more usually slightly above, zero, plate current will begin flowing. In order to maintain the gating voltage substantially constant over the sweep cycle, the control pulse must be applied either through the very long time constant C_sR_s or directly from a d-c source. An argument similar to the one employed with the triode sweep leads to the same conclusion; upon switching on, the plate and control grid both drop by an amount not quite sufficient to cut off the tube. Calculation of the exact initial drop (about 10 volts) is not as simple a process as previously described, because the screen characteristics now have the predominant control over the tube current (Sec. 6-9). The low grid voltage reduces the total pentode current almost to the vanishing point, and therefore the screen voltage simultaneously jumps to nearly E_{bb}.

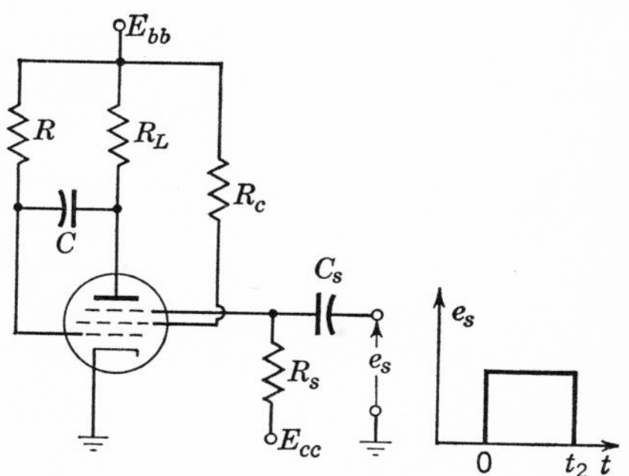

FIG. 6-16. Pentode Miller sweep.

After the initial jumps, the grid starts rising toward E_{bb} at a rate given by Eq. (6-23), beginning the corresponding plate rundown. The large time constant τ_1 is identical with that of the triode sweep [Eq. (6-22)]. The initial conditions, voltage jumps, linear rise, and recovery are illustrated in the sketch of the circuit waveshapes (Fig. 6-18), and for clarity we should periodically refer to them during the following discussion.

The next question facing us is, Where does the sweep end? The higher pentode gain ($A \cong 250$) permits the plate to fall to about zero while the grid rises by only 1 volt, or even less, from its approximate initial value of -10 volts. Consequently, the limits of sweep operation are no longer determined by the grid but depend instead on the plate's bottoming. Figure 6-17 shows a portion of pentode plate volt-ampere characteristics represented by a set of straight lines. The large value of load resistance

R_L was, of course, chosen for the highest possible amplification, and therefore the load line will be almost horizontal.

Note that no further voltage drop is possible after the plate falls to the point where the load line intersects the knee of the characteristics, $E_{b,\min}$. At this operating point the plate resistance changes to a very low value, about 10,000 ohms, and g_m is reduced to zero. Since the circuit amplification also becomes zero, the Miller effect ceases. Plate bottoming occurs at 2 to 10 volts, depending upon the characteristics of the particular tube and the load resistance chosen. This value is so very

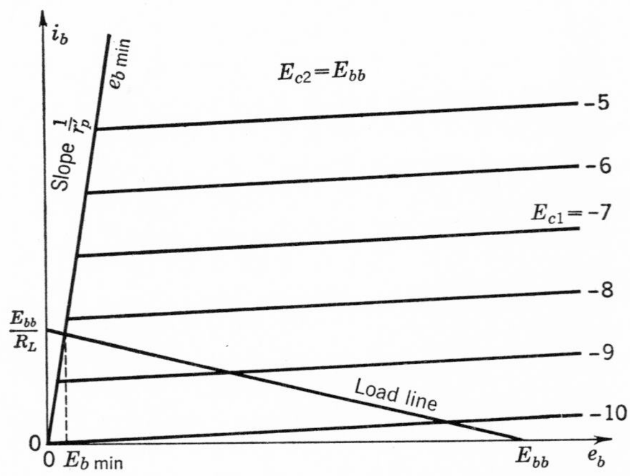

FIG. 6-17. Miller-sweep tube—plate characteristics and load line.

small in terms of the total sweep amplitude that it is often approximated as zero. A somewhat better approximation would be

$$E_{b,\min} \cong \frac{r'_p}{R_L} E_{bb}$$

where r'_p, the effective plate resistance, is the reciprocal of the slope of the $e_{b,\min}$ line.

Since the grid voltage of the pentode remains almost constant during the linear plate rundown, the capacitor charging current is best represented by $I_C(0^+)$. By substituting this current, instead of E_{bb}/R, the necessary time for the complete plate rundown, which starts at $E_{bb} + E_{c1}(0^+)$ and ends at $E_{b,\min}$, is

$$t_1 = RC \frac{E_{bb} + E_{c1}(0^+) - E_{b,\min}}{E_{bb} - E_{c1}(0^+)} = RC \frac{\Delta E_b}{E_{bb} - E_{c1}(0^+)} \qquad (6\text{-}33)$$

During this same interval, the grid rises by only $\Delta E_b/|A|$ volts, where ΔE_b is the total change in the plate voltage. If the maximum plate voltage is limited to an external control voltage E by a plate catching diode, the starting point of the rundown would be $E + E_{c1}(0^+)$ instead of $E_{bb} + E_{c1}(0^+)$. As in the triode circuit, the sweep duration is a linear function of this control signal.

In Eq. (6-33), the only terms dependent on the tube are $E_{c1}(0^+)$ and $E_{b,\min}$. These are directly proportional to E_{bb}, and therefore any small decrease or increase in the supply voltage would change both the numerator and denominator proportionately. Thus we conclude that both this sweep and the phantastron (Sec. 6-8) have excellent time stability with respect to power-supply variations.

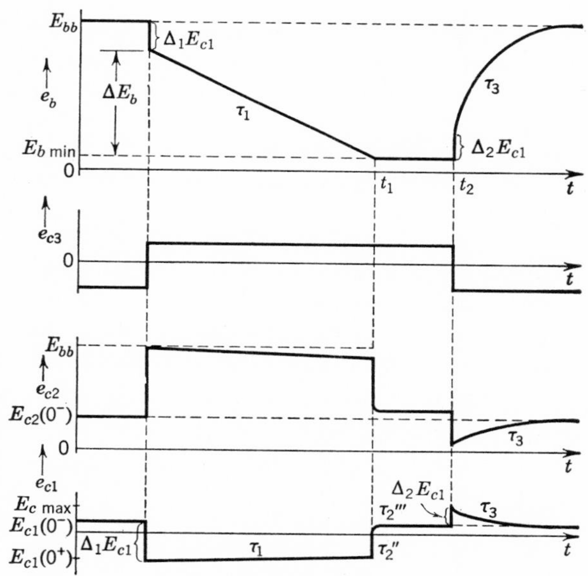

FIG. 6-18. Pentode Miller-sweep waveshapes.

Furthermore, the terms in Eq. (6-33) dependent on the tube, $E_{c1}(0^+)$ and $E_{b,\min}$, are both small compared with E_{bb}. By making R_L large, $E_{b,\min}$ is reduced almost to the vanishing point. The other term, $E_{c1}(0^+)$, remains relatively constant over the life of the tube and does not change much from tube to tube. To a very good approximation we can say that this sweep is virtually independent of the tube. This is one of the major advantages negative feedback offers over the positive feedback employed in the bootstrap sweep.

Even after the plate bottoms, the grid continues charging toward E_{bb}, but very much faster, with a time constant reduced from $\tau_1 = |A|RC$ to

$$\tau_2'' = C(R + r_p') \cong CR$$

The grid, charging from only a few volts negative, reaches zero in a comparatively short time and begins conducting. All circuit conditions again change; the time constant becomes

$$\tau_2''' = (r_{c1} + r_p')C$$

and the steady-state voltage changes back to its initial value $E_{c1}(0^-)$.

But the rapidly rising grid voltage increases the total cathode current, almost all of which now flows to the screen. Therefore the screen voltage will drop to slightly above its initial value, the small amount of current flowing to the plate accounting for the difference.

Immediately upon the removal of the suppressor gating pulse, the plate cuts off and recovery proceeds as in the triode sweep, with all the voltage jumps and time constants found in a similar manner. The only additional consideration is that the positive grid jump also appears as an amplified drop at the screen.

The pentode circuit, besides producing the linear plate rundown, simultaneously generates a large rectangular pulse of equal duration which has fast rise and fall times. This signal, which appears at the screen, is as important as the linear sweep. We might apply it to the normally cut-off grid of a cathode-ray tube, thus unblanking the oscilloscope only during the linear sweep (supplied by the plate rundown). Since its period is well defined, it can be used in conjunction with a gate for accurate time selection. If differentiated, the negative output trigger, which is delayed from the initial positive trigger by the sweep period, serves either for timing measurements or to start subsequent operations.

A few words are now in order concerning the special requirements we impose on the pentode used in this sweep. First, it should have sharp suppressor control over plate current flow to ensure definitive on-off circuit states. Secondly, since under plate-current cutoff conditions the total cathode current flows to the screen, the tube should have the capabilities necessary to dissipate the heat produced; its maximum screen dissipation must be large. Only slightly less important is a small control-grid–screen-grid transconductance to ensure that the screen voltage will remain reasonably constant during the linear grid rise. Otherwise the screen degeneration reduces the effective plate-circuit amplification and thus increases the sweep nonlinearity. Special tubes, such as the 6AS6 and the 6BH6, whose specifications satisfy the above requirements, have been developed primarily for Miller-sweep and phantastron applications.

6-8. The Phantastron. For optimum circuit response, the ideal Miller-sweep gating pulse would be one having exactly the same duration as the linear plate rundown. The circuit would recover immediately upon the plate's bottoming, becoming ready, in the shortest possible time interval, to react to the next input pulse. But the Miller sweep itself generates a pulse of just the proper duration, and therefore we might just as well let the circuit do its own gating. All that this requires is the coupling of the screen pulse directly into the suppressor. Since the two waveshapes, the sweep and gating pulse, are simultaneously produced, we are not forced to cope with the problems of synchronization and phasing that we would be sure to meet in attempting to generate an independent control signal.

Figure 6-19*a* shows the complete phantastron circuit including a cathode follower for fast recovery and a plate catching diode D_1 for voltage control of sweep duration. We normally adjust the coupling network R_c, R_a, and R_s to keep the suppressor at about -20 volts, i.e., sufficiently negative to ensure plate cutoff. And as in the Miller sweep, the screen conducts heavily, setting the quiescent voltage level at 50 or 60 volts.

Application of a narrow positive trigger at either the suppressor or the screen starts the sweep by raising the suppressor voltage to zero or even slightly higher, thus bringing the plate out of cutoff. The resultant drop in control-grid voltage almost cuts off the entire tube, and consequently the screen will jump toward E_{bb}. This jump, coupled through C_c and the resistor network, keeps the suppressor turned on, even after the starting trigger disappears. C_c serves to speed up the switching action by immediately coupling the sharp rise and fall of the screen voltage into the suppressor, thus counteracting the retarding effects of the stray circuit capacity. It functions in a manner similar to the capacitor in a compensated attenuator which is adjusted somewhat overcompensated; usually C_c is very small, only 25 to 100 $\mu\mu$f.

Diode D_2 limits the maximum positive suppressor voltage to about 5 volts, set by the voltage divider R_1 and R_2. We pick this voltage to give the largest possible gain, since g_m reaches its maximum value at a slightly positive suppressor voltage. In addition, the suppressor current increases with increasing voltage, and unless limited to a very low value, the power dissipation may exceed the tube's ratings.

Until the plate bottoms, the sweep operation is identical with that of the Miller sweep of Sec. 6-7, taking the same time to generate the same waveshapes (Fig. 6-19). However, after the plate bottoms, the drop in screen voltage is directly coupled to the suppressor and turns the plate off. The cathode follower allows fast plate recovery to its initial value E and also contributes a large positive grid jump, which, as we expect, appears amplified at the screen. But this additional drop can only help to turn the suppressor off even faster.

The grid-circuit recovery is extremely rapid, because of the cathode follower and the control-grid conduction path. And the system is now ready for the next input trigger.

We may inject the positive trigger pulse at either the screen or suppressor, the speed-up capacitor effectively applying it at both elements simultaneously. The trigger not only starts the suppressor into the plate conduction region, but also aids the initial screen rise. Its amplitude and duration are not critical, provided, however, that it at least exceeds the threshold necessary for guaranteed switching.

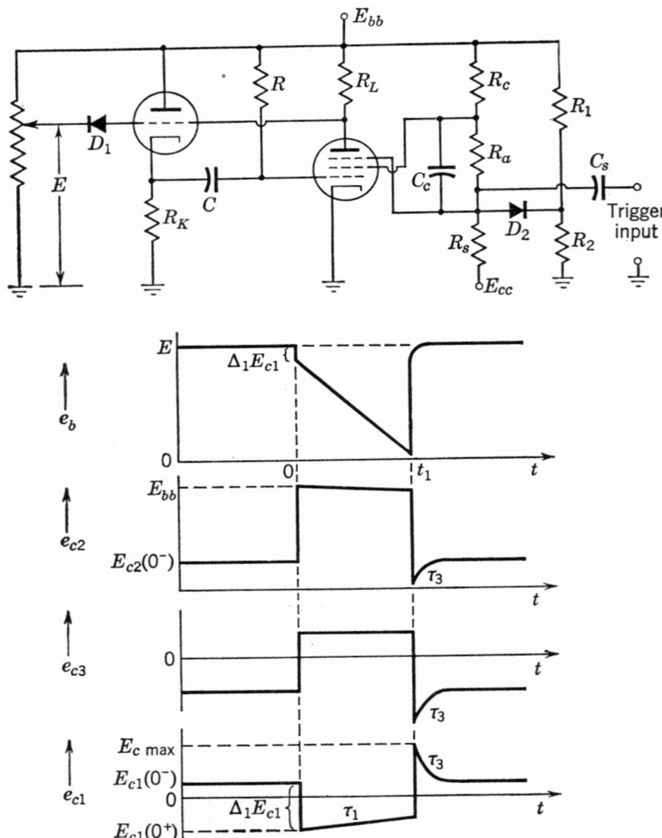

FIG. 6-19. Phantastron circuit and waveshapes.

Example 6-2. The phantastron of Fig. 6-19 employs a 6AS6 with the plate load adjusted to give a gain of 250. We can assume that initially the grid drops to -10 volts and that the plate finally bottoms at 5 volts. Furthermore, in this circuit, $E_{bb} = 300$ volts and $E = 200$ volts.

(*a*) What RC product is required to give a sweep time of 500 μsec?

(*b*) Under these circumstances, what is the sweep nonlinearity?

(*c*) Assuming that $E_{c1}(0^+)$ changes by 10 per cent, by what percentage would the sweep duration change?

Solution. (*a*) The total plate rundown is

$$\Delta E_b = 200 - 10 - 5 = 185 \text{ volts}$$

From Eq. (6-33),

$$RC = t_1 \frac{E_{bb} + 10}{185} = 500 \times 10^{-6} \times \frac{310}{185} = 825 \times 10^{-6} \text{ sec}$$

Let $R = 1.65$ megohms and $C = 500$ $\mu\mu$f.

(*b*) The change in the grid voltage over the complete linear rundown is only

$$\Delta E_c = \frac{\Delta E_b}{A} = \frac{185}{250} = 0.74 \text{ volt}$$

Thus the grid rises from -10 to -9.26 volts out of a charging curve having a 300-volt maximum value. Substituting these limits into the linearity equation (5-22) yields

$$\text{NL} = 12.5\% \times \frac{0.74}{300} \cong 0.03\%$$

Actually, this value may be too small to have any significance. The nonlinearity of C over this voltage range and the various second-order effects would, at the very least, double the calculated value.

(*c*) From Eq. (6-33), with $E_{c1}(0^+) = -9$ volts,

$$t_1' = RC \times {}^{186}\!/_{309}$$

The normal sweep is

$$t_1 = RC \times {}^{185}\!/_{310}$$

Thus, by dividing and expanding,

$$\frac{t_1'}{t_1} = \left(\frac{186}{185}\right)\left(\frac{310}{309}\right) = \frac{(185 + 1)(309 + 1)}{(185)(309)} \cong 1 + \frac{496}{(185)(309)} = 1.0087$$

The sweep time is increased by only 0.87 per cent when the initial grid drop is reduced by 10 per cent.

Free-running Phantastron. The phantastron lends itself to self-triggering or free-running operation. By simply setting the quiescent suppressor bias within its base, the plate is normally conducting. Consider the circuit behavior immediately following plate bottoming. The screen voltage drop, together with the large sharp spike (contributed by the control grid's positive jump), momentarily drives the suppressor below plate cutoff. As the control grid recovers, both the screen and suppressor voltage follow it toward their quiescent values. But the suppressor eventually reaches a point where the plate can turn back on, and as a consequence, the switching cycle repeats. The screen, driven back toward E_{bb}, pulls the suppressor up along with it. Rundown begins again, and the cycle keeps repeating.

Synchronization of the phantastron is usually effected by converting the input signal to pulses, which are then used to turn the sweep on or maybe to turn it off. These control either the start or the sweep bottoming point, and the resultant regions of synchronization may be defined in exactly the manner of Sec. 5-6.

6-9. Miller Sweep and Phantastron—Screen and Control-grid Voltage Calculations. To attempt an exact solution for the pentode screen and control-grid voltages is to attempt an extremely difficult task. We would need a complete set of both plate and screen volt-ampere characteristics, and even then probably the best approach would be one of successive approximations, i.e., making a guess, checking it, and then making a more educated guess, until finally some guess agrees with the checked answer.

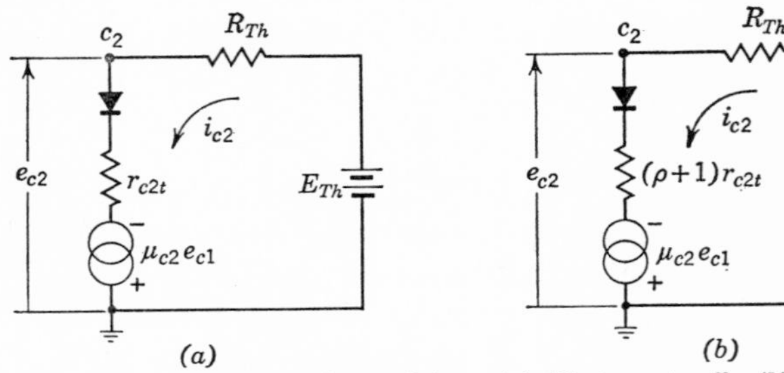

FIG. 6-20. Pentode screen circuit models. (a) Plate cut off; (b) plate conducting.

However, we can quite simply find an approximate solution, by a method which still keeps the essential circuit behavior in the forefront. This is through treating the cathode, control grid, and screen as a triode. It follows that the screen model of Fig. 6-20a represents the circuit when the suppressor cuts off the plate and the total current flows to the screen. R_{Th} and E_{Th} are actually the Thévenin equivalents of the screen network. The screen parameters r_{c2t} and μ_{c2} are determined from the tube under triode operating conditions, plate and screen connected together so that $i_{c2} = i_k$.

$$\mu_{c2} = \left.\frac{\partial e_{c2}}{\partial e_{c1}}\right|_{\Delta i_{c2}=0} \qquad r_{c2t} = \frac{\partial e_{c2}}{\partial i_{c2t}} = \left.\frac{\partial e_{c2}}{\partial i_k}\right|_{\Delta e_1=0} \tag{6-34}$$

The parameters of Eqs. (6-34) may be found directly from the manufacturer's curves by adding the screen and plate current characteristics. For the two widely used sweep tubes, reasonable values are:

Sweep tube	μ_{c2}	r_{c2t}, kilohms	ρ
6AS6..........	25	5	3
6BH6.........	20	4.5	2

Using these values, and with $e_{c1} = 0$, the quiescent value of e_{c2} may readily be calculated from Fig. 6-20*a*.

$$E_{c2}(0^-) = \frac{r_{c2t}}{R_{Th} + r_{c2t}} E_{Th} \tag{6-35}$$

Once the suppressor pulse allows plate current flow, then its sole role is to regulate the percentage of the total cathode current that flows in the plate circuit. But the total current remains predominantly a function of the screen and control-grid voltages, and therefore the form of the screen model is still consistent with the tube's physical behavior. In the positive suppressor region, the division of current between the plate and screen is almost constant and is independent of the suppressor voltage. This ratio may be expressed as

$$\rho = \frac{I_b}{I_{c2}} \tag{6-36}$$

The constant ρ depends on tube geometry and is also found from the manufacturer's curves; it may be taken as 3 for the 6AS6 and 2 for the 6BH6. When ρ is 3, only one-quarter of the total cathode current flows to the screen. With the tube now operating as a pentode,

$$i_k = i_b + i_{c2} = (1 + \rho)i_{c2}$$

and

$$i_{c2p} = \frac{i_k}{\rho + 1}$$

Substituting into Eqs. (6-34) yields

$$r_{c2p} = \frac{\partial e_{c2}}{\partial i_{c2p}} = (\rho + 1)\frac{\partial e_{c2}}{\partial i_k} = (\rho + 1)r_{c2t}$$

Thus r_{c2t} must be multiplied by $(\rho + 1)$ in order to account for the effects of plate current flow and the screen model will be changed to the one shown in Fig. 6-20*b*.

The equal drop in plate and control-grid voltage, upon switching, may be expressed solely in terms of the screen current by noting that

$$E_{c1}(0^+) \cong -i_b R_L = -\rho i_{c2} R_L \tag{6-37}$$

where R_L is the effective plate load resistance. Substitution of Eq. (6-37) into the model of Fig. 6-20*b* establishes all the conditions necessary to solve for $E_{c1}(0^+)$. And it follows directly that

$$E_{c1}(0^+) = -\frac{\rho E_{Th} R_L}{\mu_{c2}\rho R_L + (\rho + 1)r_{c2t} + R_{Th}}$$

But since $r_{c2t}(\rho + 1) + R_{Th} \ll \mu_{c2}\rho R_L$,

$$E_{c1}(0^+) \cong -\frac{E_{Th}}{\mu_{c2}} \tag{6-38}$$

Equation (6-38) is just the cutoff voltage of the screen circuit, treated as a triode, which verifies our assumption that the tube is driven almost to cutoff. At the same time the screen rises to nearly E_{Th}, as might be found from Fig. 6-20*b*.

During the control-grid rise, the screen voltage droops slightly because of the amplification from control grid to screen,

$$A_{c1c2} = -\frac{\mu_{c2}R_{Th}}{(\rho + 1)r_{c2t} + R_{Th}} \tag{6-39}$$

In order to prevent excessive changes in the screen voltage, the amplification must be kept small. To this end we usually choose R_{Th} to be of the same order of magnitude as $r_{c2t}(\rho + 1)$. Therefore the gain is only 10 or 12. Since the control-grid voltage changes by a fraction of a volt over the whole sweep cycle, the screen voltage will remain substantially constant.

Example 6-3. We shall now consider the design of the screen-suppressor coupling circuit for the phantastron of Example 6-2 (Fig. 6-19). The desired quiescent conditions are $E_{c2} = 50$ volts and $E_{c2} = -20$ volts. The two supplies at our disposal are +300 and −200 volts.

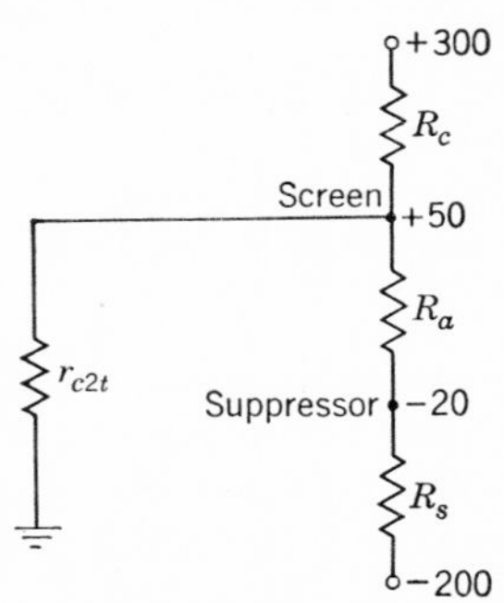

FIG. 6-21. Model for Example 6-3.

Solution. The model holding under plate cutoff conditions is shown in Fig. 6-21. We arbitrarily choose a 1-ma bleeder current through R_a and R_s. If this current is too large, appreciable power would be wasted; if too small, the resistors would become excessively large. Therefore

$$R_a = \frac{70 \text{ volts}}{1 \text{ ma}} = 70 \text{ K}$$

$$R_s = \frac{180 \text{ volts}}{1 \text{ ma}} = 180 \text{ K}$$

Since $r_{c2t} = 5$ K, the screen current at 50 volts is 10 ma. Thus 11 ma must flow through R_L and

$$R_c = \frac{250}{11 \text{ ma}} = 23 \text{ K}$$

From these values, we can find the Thévenin equivalent of the screen circuit. It is a 278-volt source having an internal impedance of 22 K and 250 K in parallel, or, to a good approximation, 20 K. The grid voltage after switching becomes, from Eq. (6-38),

$$E_{c1}(0^+) = -{}^{278}\!/_{25} \cong -11 \text{ volts}$$

The grid-to-screen amplification is [Eq. (6-39)]

$$A_{c1c2} = -\frac{25 \times 20 \text{ K}}{(3+1)5 \text{ K} + 20 \text{ K}} = -12.5$$

In the previous example the control-grid voltage only changed by 0.74 volt. Consequently the screen voltage will run down by only 9 volts from its starting point of approximately 278 volts. These values check quite closely with laboratory measurements.

PROBLEMS

6-1. (*a*) Prove that varying E in the circuit of Fig. 6-1 is a very unsatisfactory method of adjusting the sweep time. Consider the sweep linearity as E charges from 10 to 100 volts. The final voltage remains constant at $E_{2s,\max}$.

(*b*) Under the conditions of part *a*, how will the sweep duration change if the plate is always allowed to bottom before the capacitor is discharged?

6-2. The sweep of Fig. 6-1 uses a 0.05-μf capacitor for timing. Once the switch is opened, it remains open. Sketch the plate waveshape if the grid resistance in the positive grid region is 1 K. The model which should be used for the plate bottoming region is a resistor of $r_p = 700$ ohms (no controlled source) from the plate to the cathode. This model holds for $e_c \geq e_b$ (Prob. 4-4).

6-3. Assume that we desire to construct a bootstrap sweep but that we are unable to obtain an amplifier with a sufficiently stable gain A. Instead, we can make R a function of A, so that, within rather narrow limits, the change in R will compensate for the change in A and thus maintain the sweep time invariant. Find the required functional relationship, that is, $R = f(A)$. Find the approximate relationship when A is close to unity. Repeat if $R = f(E_R)$.

6-4. The only tube available for the sweep of Fig. 6-1 has $\mu = 5$ and $r_p = 5$ K. The other circuit values are $E_{bb} = 300$ volts, $E = 100$ volts, $R_k = 50$ K, and $C = 0.002$ μf.

(*a*) Sketch the plate waveshape, giving all values if the switch is opened at $t = 0$ and closed when e_{gk} reaches zero.

(*b*) Calculate the NL of this sweep.

(HINT: All the equations in Sec. 6-2 may not hold with a low-μ tube.)

6-5. (*a*) Draw the capacitor and output waveshape on the same axis if $A = 0.95$, $E = 100$ volts, $R = 1$ megohm, and $C = 100$ $\mu\mu$f in the circuit of Fig. 6-3. The capacitor is discharged when its terminal voltage reaches 100 volts.

(*b*) Calculate the sweep NL.

(*c*) Compare the results of part *a* with the results obtained when $A = 1$. For this comparison the capacitor is adjusted to maintain the same sweep period.

(*d*) This sweep is adjusted by varying E. Plot the time duration versus K if $E = 1/KE_f$ $(A = 1)$.

6-6. The bootstrap of Fig. 6-22 employs a cathode follower as its base amplifier.

(*a*) Sketch the voltage waveshape appearing at the cathode if the switch is opened at $t = 0$ and closed once the grid-to-cathode voltage reaches zero. Label all voltage values, time constants, and times. (HINT: Replace the tube by the equivalent circuit seen when looking into the cathode.)

(*b*) Show that within its active region this circuit may be represented by the model of Fig. 6-4. Specify the parameters.

(*c*) Calculate and compare the sweep amplitude and linearity when the battery in series with the charging resistor is present and when it is absent.

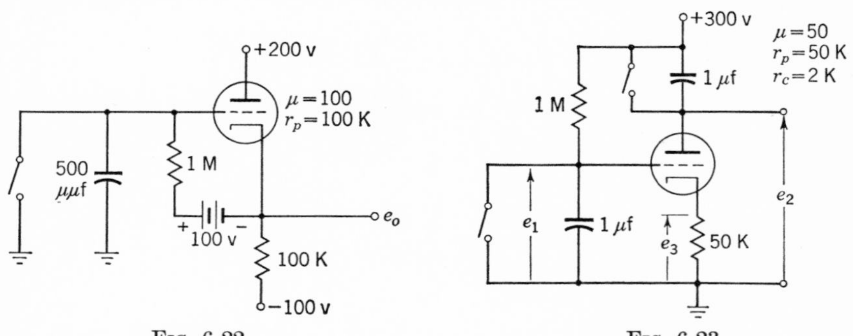

FIG. 6-22 FIG. 6-23

6-7. The circuit of Fig. 6-23 makes use of the techniques discussed in Sec. 6-2 to generate a specific nonlinear sweep. Sketch e_1, e_2, and e_3 to scale if both switches are opened at $t = 0$ and closed when the voltage across the tube, e_{bk}, drops to 200 volts. What function does this circuit generate? Make all reasonable approximations in your solution. Justify any assumptions made.

6-8. In the Miller sweep of Fig. 6-7, the switch is closed at $t = 0$ and opened a short time after the plate falls to its lowest value. Sketch the plate and grid waveshapes, giving the values of all voltages, times, and time constants. Compute the sweep nonlinearity of the linear plate rundown. The tube and circuit parameters are

$$R_L = 240 \text{ K} \qquad r_p = 50 \text{ K}$$
$$R = 1 \text{ megohm} \qquad r_c = 2 \text{ K}$$
$$C = 1{,}000\ \mu\mu\text{f} \qquad E_{bb} = 300 \text{ volts}$$
$$\mu = 100$$

6-9. Repeat Prob. 6-8 if the plate is returned through a plate catching diode to +200 volts. Pay particular attention to the time required for the linear plate rundown and for the time required for the complete plate recovery.

6-10. (*a*) Compare the sweep linearity of the triode Miller sweep under the following conditions:

1. The charging resistor is returned to E_{bb}.

2. The charging resistor is returned to a voltage equal to $0.1E_{bb}$. Express the answer as a ratio (assume $|A| \gg 1$).

(*b*) Prove that the sweep period is a linear function of the control voltage E.

(*c*) Prove that the sweep period varies inversely with the voltage to which the grid resistor is returned.

6-11. Figure 6-24 represents a variation in switching the Miller sweep on and off. Sketch the grid and plate waveshapes, labeling all times and break voltages. (HINT: Be careful in evaluating the initial conditions of each region.) The switch is opened at $t = 0$ and closed soon after D_2 conducts. What is the largest voltage which can be used to back-bias the tube and still allow the sweep to start as soon as the switch is opened?

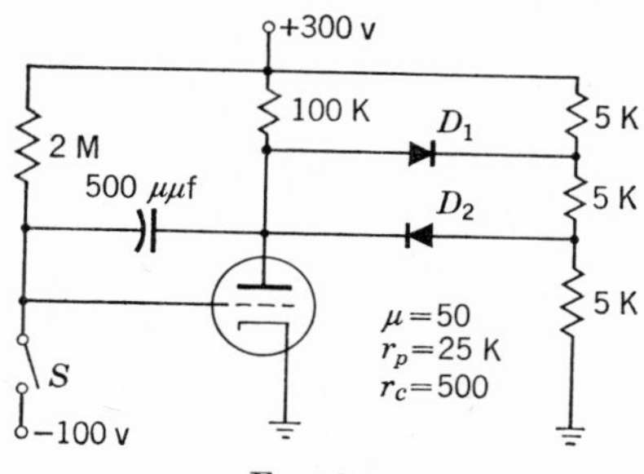

FIG. 6-24

6-12. (*a*) Compute the initial grid drop, the time required for the linear plate rundown, and the recovery time in the improved sweep of Fig. 6-13*a*. The circuit components are

$$\begin{aligned} E_{bb} &= 300 \text{ volts} & R &= 1 \text{ megohm} & \mu_2 &= 20 \\ E &= 0.75E_{bb} & R_k &= 40 \text{ K} & r_{p2} &= 10 \text{ K} \\ R_L &= 200 \text{ K} & \mu_1 &= 100 \\ C &= 1\ \mu\text{f} & r_{p1} &= 100 \text{ K} \end{aligned}$$

Assume that the total stray capacity from the plate of T_1 to ground is 50 $\mu\mu$f.

(*b*) Sketch the waveshape at the cathode of the cathode follower and calculate the internal impedance at this point.

(*c*) What is the maximum possible value of E before the grid of the cathode follower is forced into conduction? If E exceeds this voltage, what happens to the circuit response?

6-13. The sweep of Fig. 6-25 is placed in operation by opening the switch S at $t = 0$. It is closed again at $t = 200$ μsec. Plot the grid and plate voltage to scale from before $t = 0$ until the circuit completely recovers.

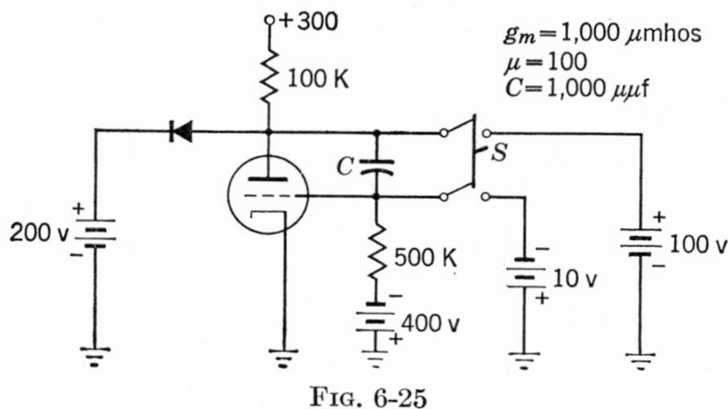

FIG. 6-25

6-14. Show three methods of switching the triode Miller sweep which are adaptable to diode or triode gating circuits. Discuss any limitations on or modifications in the basic sweep behavior when each gate is inserted. Give the circuit of these gates together with their points of insertion and the gating signal requirements.

6-15. In the phantastron circuit of Fig. 6-26, assume that the plate falls by 10 volts when the pulse is injected. The plate rundown ends when D_2 conducts. If the loop gain is assumed to be −200, sketch the plate and grid waveshapes. Label these plots with all voltage and time values. Calculate the sweep nonlinearity.

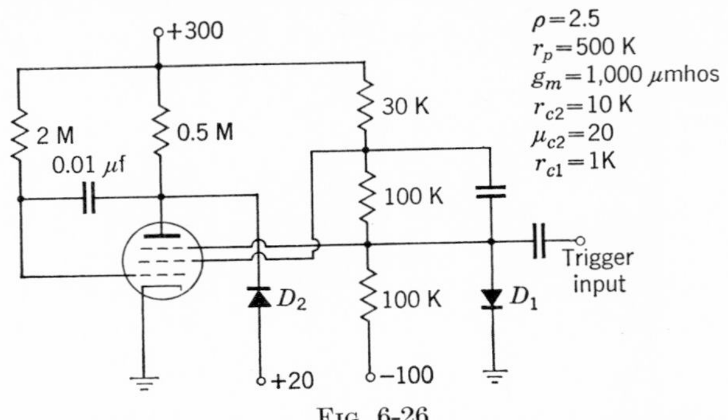

FIG. 6-26

6-16. Plot the correct suppressor, screen, plate, and control-grid waveshapes for the circuit given in Fig. 6-26. Assume that screen degeneration results in a 40 per cent decrease in the control-grid to plate-circuit gain. Give all voltage values, times, and time constants.

6-17. The circuit of Fig. 6-26 has been modified to the circuit of Fig. 6-19. Repeat the calculations of Prob. 6-15 if the additional circuit parameters are

Triode $\mu = 100$	$E = 200$ volts
$r_p = 100$ K	$R_1 = 100$ K
$R_k = 200$ K	$R_2 = 5$ K

Make all reasonable approximations in your calculations and assume that the stray capacity loading the pentode elements is completely negligible.

6-18. A phantastron used as a linear sweep is shown in Fig. 6-27. As a first approximation assume:

1. Cathode-follower gain ≅ 1
2. An initial drop of 10 volts at the plate
3. r_p = 525 K and g_m = 2,000 μmhos during rundown

Given the cathode voltage waveform as shown in Fig. 6-27, calculate the approximate plate waveform for the first 300 μsec after a trigger is applied. At the end of this interval the tube is turned off. If the total capacitance from the phantastron plate to ground is 100 μμf, calculate the flyback time.

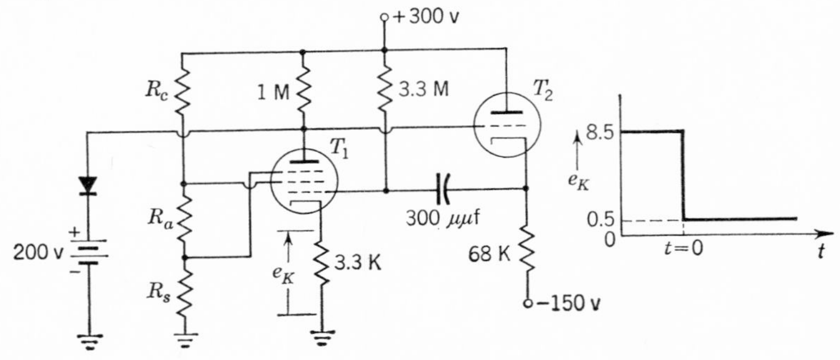

FIG. 6-27

6-19. The phantastron circuit of Fig. 6-19 is adjusted so that the normal suppressor voltage is zero (free-running sweep).

(*a*) Discuss the effects on the sweep waveshape of injecting a synchronizing signal into the grid, screen grid, suppressor, and plate. This signal consists of a pulse train of equally spaced positive and negative pulses with a spacing between adjacent pulses of 75 μsec. The phantastron free-running sweep period is 1,000 μsec. Which point would be the best place to synchronize the sweep?

(*b*) Plot the regions of pulse synchronization if the sync signal is applied as shown in Fig. 6-28.

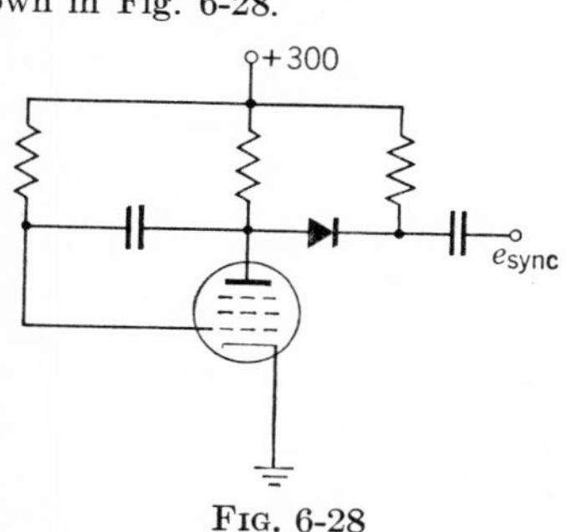

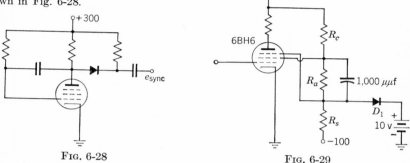

FIG. 6-28

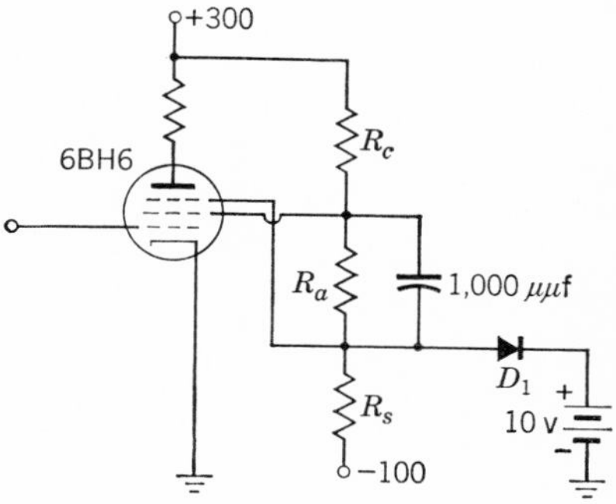

FIG. 6-29

6-20. This problem is designed to investigate the region of free-running phantastron operation between the time that the plate bottoms and the time that the next sweep starts. We do not have to consider the sweep rundown, but can concentrate attention on the screen and suppressor coupling. Suppose that a 6BH6 is used in this circuit, biased at E_{c2} = 100 volts and E_{c3} = 40 volts when the plate circuit is opened and when D_1 is removed. With the plate supply used, the suppressor cutoff may be taken as −15 volts. Assume that the positive grid jump drives the screen down to 10 volts, from where it recovers with the grid time constant of 2 μsec. The plate and grid are decoupled by a cathode follower.

(*a*) Calculate the value of resistors in the bleeder network of Fig. 6-29 needed for proper biasing.

(*b*) Sketch the screen and suppressor waveshapes, giving all voltage values and times. Assume that the plate starts at 300 volts and runs down (after the initial drop) to zero in 50 μsec.

BIBLIOGRAPHY

Briggs, B. H.: The Miller Integrator, *Electronic Eng.*, vol. 20, pp. 243–247, August, 1948; pp. 279–284, September, 1948; pp. 325–330, October, 1948.

Chance, B.: Some Precision Circuit Techniques Used in Wave-form Generation and Measurement, *Rev. Sci. Instr.*, vol. 17, p. 396, October, 1946.

——— et al.: "Waveforms," Massachusetts Institute of Technology Radiation Laboratory Series, vol. 19, McGraw-Hill Book Company, Inc., New York, 1949.

Close, R. N., and M. T. Kibenbaum: Design of Phantastron Time Delay Circuits, *Electronics*, vol. 21, no. 4, pp. 100–107, 1948.

Puckle, O. S.: "Time Bases," 2d ed., John Wiley & Sons, Inc., New York, 1951.

Williams, F. C., and N. F. Moody: Ranging Circuits, Linear Time Base Generators and Associated Circuits, *J. IEE (London)*, pt. IIIA, vol. 93, no. 7, pp. 1188–1198, 1946.

CHAPTER 7

LINEAR TRANSISTOR VOLTAGE SWEEPS

We rightly expect that almost all the basic sweeps of Chap. 6 may be adapted for transistor operation. Of course, the reverse transmission path present within the transistor and the vast difference in impedance levels do not permit its automatic substitution for the vacuum tube. But if the required minor circuit modifications are made, a transistor will perform at least as well as a triode in many of the voltage sweeps, and even somewhat better in some of them.

Throughout the following discussion the reader should refer back to the appropriate sections of Chap. 6, both to review the basic concepts of the active-element sweeps and as a means of recognizing the differences between the transistor and vacuum-tube circuits. Even though the fundamental defining equations may be the same, it is these very differences which account for the proper operation of each sweep. However, the basic similarity that does in fact exist broadens our outlook by enabling us to separate the system's behavior from the individually chosen components. If the same circuit operates with either a triode or a transistor, what is to prevent it from also working when some other active element is substituted?

7-1. Constant-charging-current Voltage Sweep. One of the simplest possible voltage sweeps makes use of the current source of the transistor for the linear charging of the sweep capacitor (Fig. 7-1). This circuit's operation is analogous to that discussed in Sec. 6-2, but as we note, the almost constant current output makes the introduction of additional current feedback unnecessary for many applications. Furthermore, since the collector current is controlled by the emitter input, a means of adjusting the charging rate is afforded at a terminal well removed from the sweep output.

The approximate model given in Fig. 7-1*b* adequately represents the circuit behavior because the emitter and base resistances are so very small compared with the external controlling resistance R that their neglect will have no appreciable effect on the operation. From this model we see that the essentially constant emitter current is given by

$$I_e = \frac{E_{cc}}{R} \tag{7-1}$$

where E_{cc} is the emitter bias source. After the switch is opened, the collector charges from its initial value of E_{bb} toward the Thévenin steady-state voltage of

$$E_{2ss} = -\alpha I_e r_c = -\frac{\alpha E_{cc}}{R} r_c$$

with the long time constant $\tau_1 = r_c C$.

But in order to have a reasonably large value of current flow, R will have to be relatively small, i.e., no greater than several thousand ohms. Since r_c is normally greater than 1.0 megohm, the output apparently charges toward a very large negative voltage. Once the collector drops to zero, the transistor saturates with the now conducting collector diode,

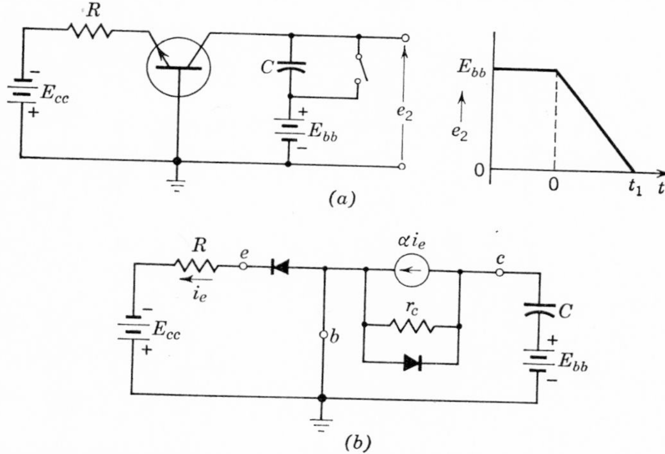

FIG. 7-1. (a) Constant-current sweep and output waveshape; (b) active-region model.

shorting the capacitor to ground. Only a very small percentage of the total exponential appears at the output, and therefore it seems reasonable to approximate this voltage by an absolutely linear rundown.

$$e_2(t) = E_{bb} - \frac{1}{C}\int_0^t i\,dt = E_{bb} - \alpha\frac{E_{cc}}{RC}t \tag{7-2}$$

Substitution of the bottoming value of zero into Eq. (7-2) yields a maximum sweep duration of

$$t_1 = RC\frac{E_{bb}}{\alpha E_{cc}} \tag{7-3}$$

Equation (7-3) points up the dependency of this sweep on the value of α and hence the necessity of recalibration upon the replacement of the individual transistor.

Referring to Eq. (7-3), we see that since a low value of resistance was used in the emitter circuit in an effort to maintain linearity, we are forced to turn to relatively large capacity for any given sweep duration. The use of high capacitor values is one of the characteristics of transistor sweep circuits that differentiates them from their vacuum-tube equivalents.

If this sawtooth is intended to drive a following transistor stage, the relatively low input impedance to be expected may load the capacitor excessively, with a corresponding deterioration in sweep quality.

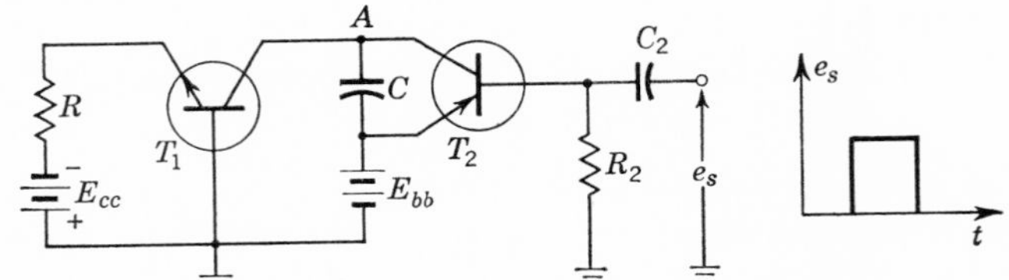

FIG. 7-2. Transistor switching of the sweep circuit.

Switching in the circuit of Fig. 7-1 may be accomplished by shunting the sweep capacitor by the complementary *p-n-p* transistor shown in Fig. 7-2. Under normal conditions the additional transistor T_2 conducts heavily and shunts C with its low saturation resistance. Injection of a positive pulse through the input coupling capacitor C_2 raises the base voltage of T_2 above E_{bb} and rapidly cuts off the switching transistor. During the presence of the pulse, the very high back impedance of T_2 will not prevent the expected linear rundown. Of course, this switching pulse should be long enough to allow bottoming of the sweep.

Example 7-1. The recovery of the sweep of Fig. 7-2 is effected by recharging C from an almost constant current source. This current must be of the opposite polarity to that used for the original linear charging, and it is supplied from the complementary *p-n-p* transistor. The amplitude of the recharge current, and hence the time required for recovery, depends directly on the size of R_2. Consider a circuit where $E_{bb} = |E_{cc}| = 10$ volts, $R = 1$ K, and $\alpha_1 = \alpha_2 = 0.98$ and where the recovery

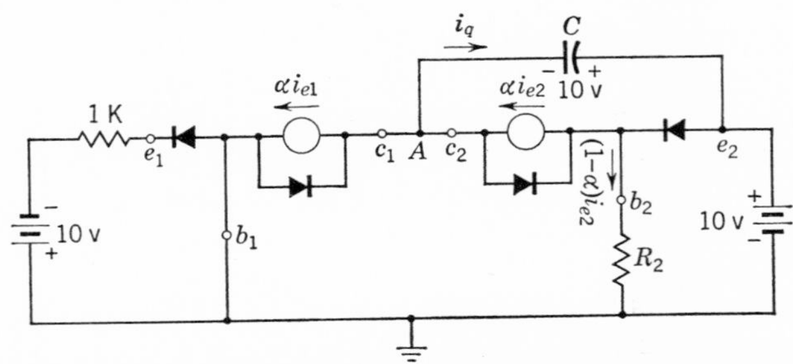

FIG. 7-3. Model of the circuit of Fig. 7-2 holding in the recovery region.

time must not exceed 5 per cent of the linear rundown. Under these conditions, what is the limiting size of R_2?

Solution. To a good approximation, the circuit of Fig. 7-3 represents the behavior of the sweep immediately after T_2 is switched back on. Both transistors are in their active regions, and C is fully charged. Moreover, in approximating this circuit's response, the small emitter input resistance is assumed to be zero and the shunting collector resistance is assumed to be too large to influence either the sweep or recovery times. During the linear sweep, T_2 is off and the total current flowing into C is

$$i_{q1} = -\alpha i_{e1} = -\alpha \frac{E_{cc}}{1\text{ K}} = -9.8\text{ ma}$$

During the discharge interval, the capacitor current can be found by writing the node equation at point A:

$$i_{q2} = \alpha i_{e2} - \alpha i_{e1} = \alpha i_{e2} - 9.8\text{ ma}$$

where

$$i_{e2} = \frac{E_{bb}}{(1-\alpha)R_2} = \frac{10}{0.02R_2}$$

Since the charge and discharge of C are always from constant-current sources, the ratio of times is inversely proportional to the current flow. Therefore, under the conditions of the problem, for the recovery time to be 5 per cent of the sweep time,

$$i_{q2} = 20i_{q1}$$

Or to satisfy this condition,

$$i_{e2} = 21i_{e1} = 210\text{ ma}$$

Substituting and solving for R_2 yields

$$R_2 = \frac{1}{21} R \frac{E_{bb}}{(1-\alpha)E_{cc}} = 2{,}375\text{ ohms}$$

Once C is completely discharged, current can no longer flow into it. To do so would forward-bias the collector of T_2, and this would shunt C with the two conducting diodes of the transistor.

7-2. Bootstrap Voltage Sweep. Bootstrapping entails positive feedback of the sweep voltage around an amplifier having essentially unity voltage gain. By this method we endeavor to maintain a constant voltage drop across, and consequently a constant current flow through, the charging resistor. One transistor bootstrap, illustrated in Fig. 7-4, employs an emitter follower as its base amplifier. Over its complete active region, the output is almost exactly equal to the applied base voltage (the drop from the base to emitter is quite small). However, the small voltage difference that does exist is inadequate to ensure sufficient charging current flow, and therefore an additional battery must be inserted in series with the feedback resistor.

Our starting point in the analysis of this emitter follower is the selection of the proper model for the transistor. By choosing one based on Fig. 4-23, rather than a T model, the circuit is reduced to the two-node network of Fig. 7-4*b*, where, in addition, the feedback network (R and E) was replaced by its Norton equivalent. Furthermore, the large collector resistance r_d is essentially in parallel with the much smaller R_e, and therefore it may be neglected.

Since the transistor is a current-controlled device, it is more informative to consider any variation in the circuit current instead of the resultant change in voltage. The input controlling current i_1 divides between the external base-emitter resistance R and the transistor internal input impedance r'_{11}. The actual base input is

$$i_b = \frac{R}{r'_{11} + R} i_1 \tag{7-4}$$

where r'_{11} may also be expressed in terms of the T parameters as

$$r'_{11} = r_b + r_e(1 + \beta)$$

By substituting Eq. (7-4) into the model, the controlled source may be written as $\beta' i_1$ instead of as βi_b. Here

$$\beta' = \frac{R}{r'_{11} + R} \beta \tag{7-5}$$

As a result, the circuit of Fig. 7-4*b* may be replaced by the simplified model shown in Fig. 7-5.

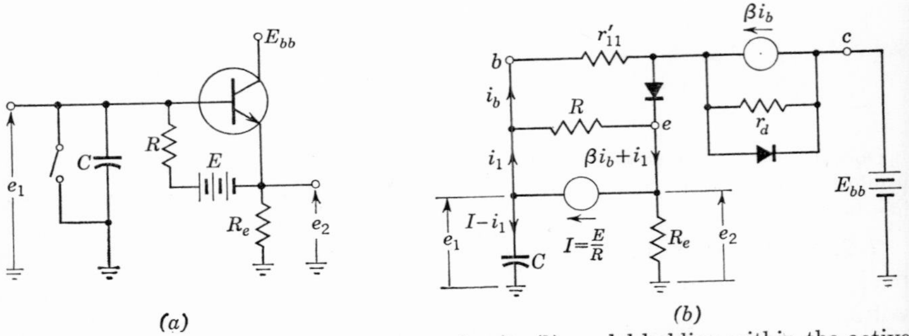

FIG. 7-4. (*a*) Transistor bootstrap sweep circuit; (*b*) model holding within the active region.

With the switch closed, the transistor must be in its active region. It cannot be cut off because the supply current I flowing through R and R_e produces a voltage drop which forward-biases the emitter base diode. The current through R_e in the active region is found from the model of Fig. 7-5:

$$i_a = (1 + \beta')i_1 - I$$

But the drop across $R \parallel r'_{11}$ must also equal the drop across R_e. Hence

$$E_2(0^-) = [(1 + \beta')i_1(0^-) - I]R_e = -i_1(0^-)R \parallel r'_{11}$$

Solving this equation yields

$$i_1(0^-) = \frac{IR_e}{R \parallel r'_{11} + (1 + \beta')R_e} \tag{7-6}$$

Once the switch is opened, the current that formerly bypassed C begins charging it. The circuit is not disturbed when the sweep starts, and no voltage jumps appear. Thus the initial value of the charging current is

$$i_q(0^+) = I - i_1(0^-) = \frac{R \parallel r'_{11} + \beta' R_e}{R \parallel r'_{11} + (1 + \beta')R_e} I$$

In general, $\beta' R_e \gg R \parallel r'_{11}$ and

$$i_q(0^+) \cong \frac{\beta'}{1 + \beta'} I \qquad (7\text{-}7)$$

We might now note that almost the complete bias current goes to charge the capacitor. The remaining small amount sustains the proper operating point of the transistor.

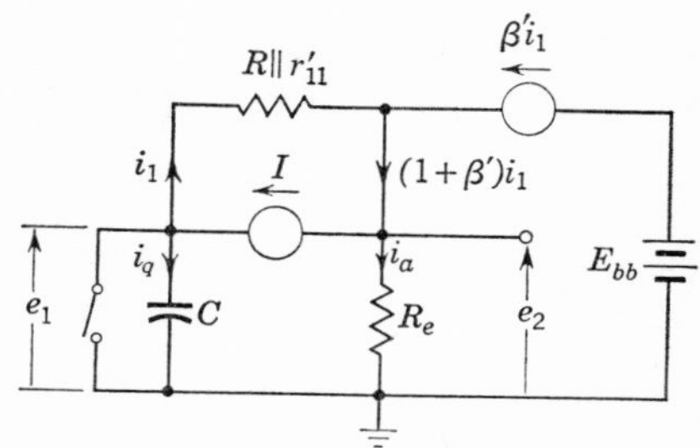

FIG. 7-5. Simplified model of the transistor bootstrap of Fig. 7-4.

Charging continues until the transistor saturates. But the point at which this occurs is known; it is when the drop across R_e rises to E_{bb}. The corresponding limit of i_1 is found from

$$E_{2s} = E_{bb} = [i_{1s}(1 + \beta') - I]R_e$$

or

$$i_{1s} = \frac{IR_e + E_{bb}}{(1 + \beta')R_e}$$

Referring back to the input node, the final value of charging current in the linear portion of the sweep becomes

$$i_q(t_1) = I - i_{1s} = \frac{\beta'}{1 + \beta'} I - \frac{E_{bb}}{(1 + \beta')R_e} \qquad (7\text{-}8)$$

The second term in Eq. (7-8) is the change in current over the sweep interval, and for maximum linearity it must be small compared with the initial value. From Eqs. (7-7) and (7-8),

$$\beta' I = \beta' \frac{E}{R} \gg \frac{E_{bb}}{R_e}$$

For the purposes of comparison, we shall set $E = E_{bb}$. By also substituting the value of β' given in Eq. (7-5), the necessary inequality reduces to

$$\beta R_e \gg r'_{11} + R \qquad (7\text{-}9)$$

We conclude that R should be small and that a transistor with a large β should be used if acceptable linearity is to be achieved. Usually R, limited solely by the current capabilities of the bias source, would be on the same order of magnitude as r'_{11}, i.e., about 200 to 1,000 ohms. With the β's available of 60 to 100 or higher, the inequality of Eq. (7-9) is not difficult to satisfy with reasonable values of R_e.

Example 7-2. Suppose that $\beta = 50$, $R = r'_{11} = 1{,}000$ ohms, $R_e = 2{,}000$ ohms, and $E_{bb} = E = 10$ volts. Under these circumstances $\beta' = \beta/2 = 25$ (from Eq. 7-5). The initial charging current, given by Eq. (7-7), is

$$i_q(0^+) = \frac{25}{25+1} \times \frac{10}{1{,}000} = 9.62 \text{ ma}$$

This is only 4 per cent less than I. At saturation the charging current is reduced to

$$i_q(t_1) = 9.62 - \frac{10}{26(2{,}000)} = 9.43 \text{ ma}$$

The total change of current is only 2 per cent, and linear charging of C appears to be an acceptable approximation. Actually, the sweep is exponential, with the current decreasing toward zero.

From Eq. (5-22), the sweep nonlinearity may be expressed as

$$\text{NL} = 12.5\% \frac{9.62 - 9.43}{9.62} = 0.26\%$$

Various second-order effects which have been neglected in this discussion, such as the decrease in β as the transistor enters the saturation region, may even increase the NL by a factor of 2.

Since the preceding argument proves that sweep nonlinearity is small, the input voltage may be approximated by the linear rise due to constant current charging of C.

$$e_1(t) = \frac{It}{C} = \frac{E}{RC}\,t \tag{7-10}$$

and the time required to saturate the transistor is

$$t_1 = RC\,\frac{E_{bb}}{E} \tag{7-11}$$

R must be small for good linearity, and consequently we are again forced to turn to large values of C to establish the required RC product. To generate a 1.0-msec sweep with the circuit of Example 7-2, C would have to be slightly larger than 1 μf. It must be emphasized that the RC term in Eq. (7-11) is not the sweep time constant but only a product resulting from the analysis.

The approximate waveshape produced at the emitter is sketched in Fig. 7-6. This point is isolated from the timing circuit and serves as a convenient low-impedance point from which to take the output.

Any circuit, such as the one of Fig. 7-4, requiring an expensive, isolated power supply is quite unsatisfactory for general use. However, in this particular sweep it is possible to replace the battery by a charged capacitor (C_1 of Fig. 7-7), and provided that we allow only a slight discharge of this energy source over any cycle, the basic mode of operation will be quite unaffected. Of course, some provision must be incorporated for automatic recharging. Examination of Fig. 7-7 will show how this is accomplished.

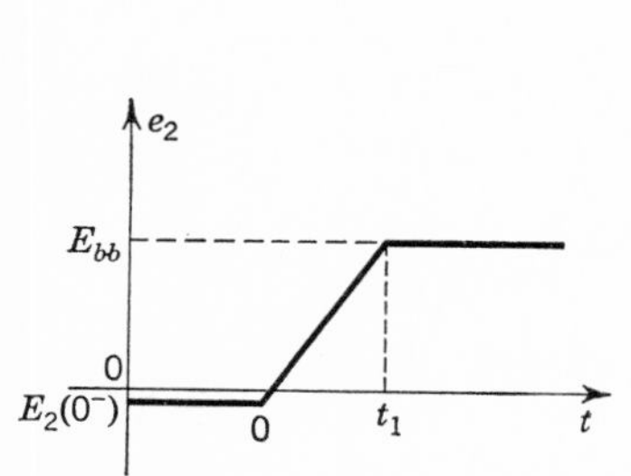

FIG. 7-6. Output voltage of the bootstrap sweep of Fig. 7-4.

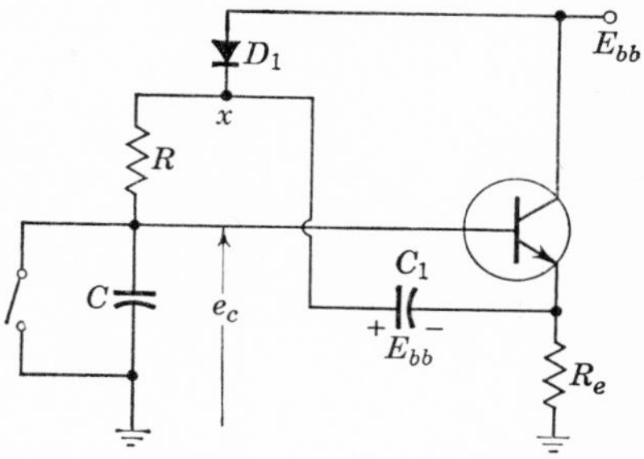

FIG. 7-7. Bootstrap sweep containing a self-charging current source.

Under the normal operating condition of this circuit, the switch across C is closed. This permits the energy-storage capacitor to charge through R_e and the conducting diode to E_{bb}. Upon opening the switch, the sweep begins. As the base starts rising, the emitter voltage follows it. Since C_1 remains almost fully charged over the complete sweep cycle, the voltage at the bottom of the diode, point x, becomes

$$e_x = E_{bb} + Ae_c$$

where the gain A is very close to unity.

Hence the very slightest increase of the sweep voltage automatically back-biases the charging diode D_1, and it may be removed from our consideration during the linear sweep interval. At the end of the sweep, the switch is closed, C discharges, and the diode again conducts, finally allowing C_1 to recover toward E_{bb}.

If we neglect the small base current which is also supplied from the charge stored in C_1, then during the sweep, charge is simply transferred from C_1 to C. Since the total charge in the circuit must remain constant, it follows that

$$\Delta Q = CE_{bb} = C_1\,\Delta E \tag{7-12}$$

where ΔE is the drop in voltage across C_1 over the complete sweep interval. For best linearity ΔE should be as small as possible, leading us to conclude that C_1 must be very large compared with C. An adverse effect introduced by the large storage capacity is the long time required for circuit recovery, a time primarily determined by the time constant R_eC_1.

In this sweep the mechanism employed for switching might be identical with that discussed in Sec. 7-1. Alternatively, any of the controlled gates would function equally well. The time constant and switching time of the discharge path established would have to be included in any calculation of the total recovery time of the circuit.

7-3. Miller Sweep. The voltage Miller sweep (Fig. 7-8) depends for its proper functioning, as did the bootstrap, upon the conversion of the current response of the transistor into proportional voltage amplification, which is now used to multiply the feedback capacity. Before we can

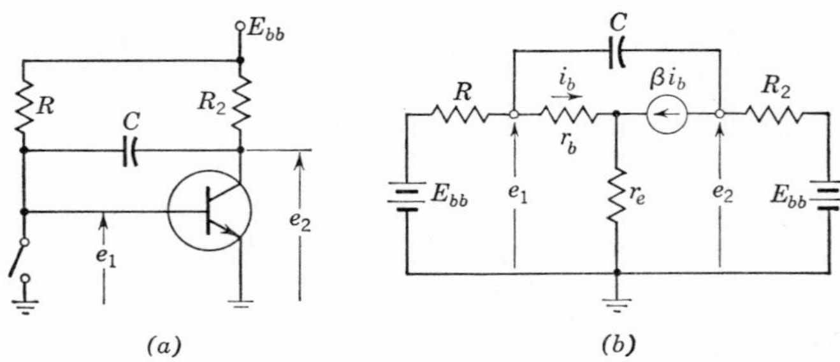

FIG. 7-8. (a) Transistor Miller sweep; (b) model holding within the active region.

discuss the over-all sweep-circuit response we must evaluate the voltage gain. The input voltage may be expressed as

$$e_1 = r'_{11} i_b \tag{7-13}$$

where $r'_{11} = r_b + (1 + \beta)r_e$. The change in collector voltage corresponding to this driving signal is simply

$$e_2 = -\beta i_b R_2 \tag{7-14}$$

Any loading of the output by the feedback capacity has been neglected. Solving Eqs. (7-13) and (7-14) simultaneously yields the voltage gain

$$A = -\frac{\beta R_2}{r'_{11}} = -g_m R_2 \tag{7-15}$$

Equation (7-15) might be interpreted as saying that the transistor has an effective g_m of β/r'_{11}. With $\beta = 100$, $r_e = 10$, and $r_b = 200$, the g_m is 82.6 millimhos, which is so very much larger than can possibly be obtained from any triode that a reasonable gain is ensured, even when using very small load resistors.

After the switch is opened and the circuit becomes active, Fig. 7-8*b* represents the complete equivalent model. In calculating the initial base voltage by the method developed with respect to the grid voltage of the triode sweep of Sec. 6-4, we obtain

$$E_1(0^+) = \frac{R_2}{1 - A} I \cong \frac{r'_{11}}{\beta} I \qquad (7\text{-}16)$$

where I is the capacitor charging current and where the approximation is the result of substituting the high gain given by Eq. (7-15). The equation indicates that there is a small positive jump due solely to the current flow through the reflected resistance (Fig. 7-9*a*). It follows that the reflected capacity $C(1 - A)$ will be initially uncharged.

The charging current at $t = 0^+$ is

$$I(0^+) = \frac{E_{Th} - E_1(0^+)}{R_{Th}} \cong \frac{E_{bb}}{R} \qquad (7\text{-}17)$$

where $E_1(0^+) \ll E_{Th}$, $R_{Th} = R \parallel r'_{11}$, and $E_{Th} = r'_{11}E_{bb}/(R + r'_{11})$. The change in base voltage over the complete charging interval must be small

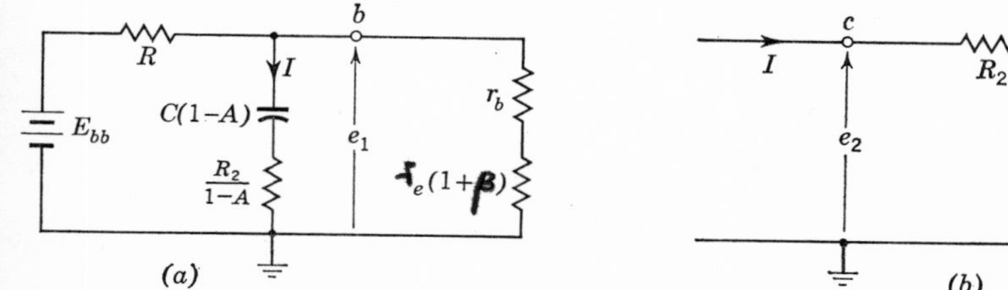

FIG. 7-9. (*a*) Equivalent base input circuit—Miller sweep; (*b*) collector equivalent circuit.

compared with E_{Th} for maximum sweep linearity. Consequently, constant current charging may be assumed and

$$e_1(t) = \frac{r'_{11}}{\beta}\frac{E_{bb}}{R} + \frac{E_{bb}}{RC(1 - A)} t \qquad (7\text{-}18)$$

Since $\beta R \gg r'_{11}$, the initial jump is quite insignificant.

From the collector model of Fig. 7-9*b*, the output voltage may be expressed as

$$e_2(t) = E_{bb} + IR_2 + \frac{AE_{bb}}{RC(1 - A)} t$$
$$\cong E_{bb}\left(1 + \frac{R_2}{R} - \frac{1}{RC} t\right)$$

The time required for the collector to bottom at zero is

$$t_1 = (R + R_2)C \qquad (7\text{-}19)$$

After bottoming, the base voltage continues rising toward a new steady-state voltage with a much faster time constant. We find these from the model of Fig. 7-8*b* by shunting the current source βi_b with a conducting diode. This also reduces the input resistance.

When the switch is finally closed, the base immediately drops back to zero. This same change in voltage must be coupled by C to the collector and will drive it even further into saturation. Recovery of the collector toward zero is quite rapid, with the time constant primarily depending on the resistance of the now conducting collector-base diode. Above zero, the capacitor recharges toward E_{bb} with the time constant $\tau_4 = CR_2$. The complete base and collector waveshapes are sketched in Fig. 7-10.

7-4. Compound Transistors. Both voltage sweeps depended for their linearity improvement on the gain of the feedback amplifier: the bootstrap on maintaining a gain close to unity, and the Miller sweep on developing the largest possible negative gain. If the two appropriate equations are examined, we conclude that for optimum operation the

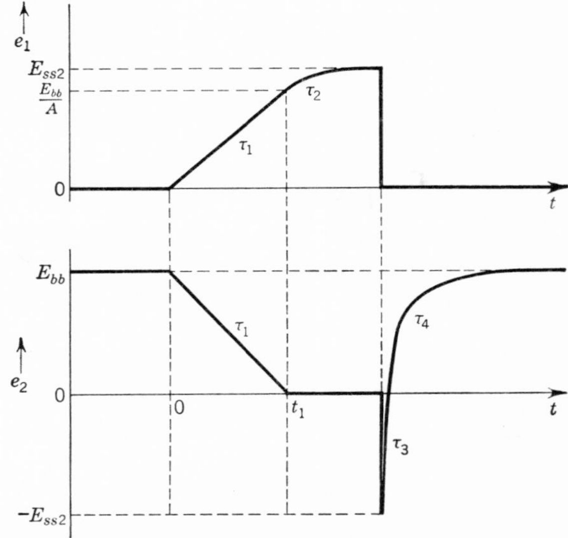

FIG. 7-10. Transistor Miller-sweep waveshapes (e_1 and e_2 are not drawn to the same scale).

transistor having an α closest to unity should be chosen (β very large).

In an effort to approach unity α, and at the same time to reduce the dependency of the circuit behavior on the individual transistor, Darlington proposed using a compound arrangement in place of a single transistor. Figure 7-11 illustrates the suggested configuration: for our convenience in the later discussion the approximate current flow into and out of each transistor element is indicated. The arrows mark the actual direction of the current in the *p-n-p* transistors shown.

The small base current of the primary transistor (T_1), $i_{e1}(1 - \alpha_1)$, is amplified by the correction transistor (T_2) and added to the output of

T_1. Thus the composite collector current is composed of two terms:

$$i_c = i_{c1} + i_{c2} = \alpha_1 i_{e1} + (1 - \alpha_1)\alpha_2 i_{e1}$$

The first term is the normal current transmission through any transistor, and the second term represents a small additional correction current flow from T_2 that raises the over-all output to a value much closer to the input driving current. We should note that as long as the individual transistor α's are less than 1, the total output current will always be less than i_{e1}. The two transistors, taken together, can be said to act as a single compound transistor, one having

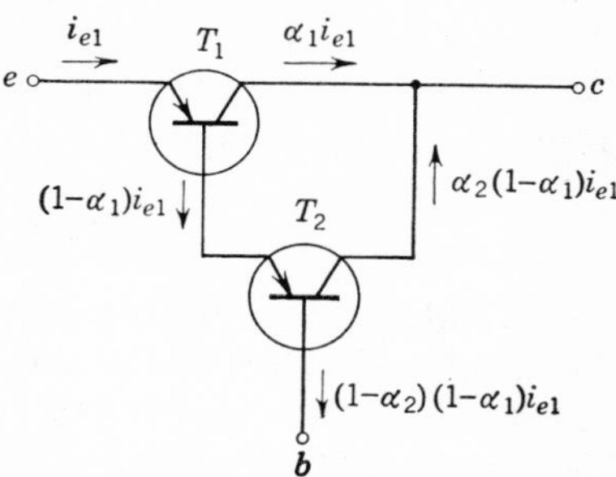

FIG. 7-11. Compound transistor circuit.

$$\begin{aligned}\alpha_c &= \alpha_1 + (1 - \alpha_1)\alpha_2 \\ &= 1 - (1 - \alpha_1)(1 - \alpha_2)\end{aligned} \qquad (7\text{-}20)$$

For example, when $\alpha_1 = 0.98$ and $\alpha_2 = 0.97$, the composite current gain is 0.9994.

Additional transistors may also be incorporated for further correction, each amplifying the base current of the previous transistor and adding it to the over-all output. They raise α_c by multiplying the second term of Eq. (7-20) by additional factors of the form $(1 - \alpha_i)$. But regardless of the number used, α_c will never quite reach unity. These additional transistors have a progressively decreasing effect on α_c, and therefore the composite unit is usually composed of no more than two or three junction transistors.

Stability of the composite element with respect to the individual α's is also much better than that of a single transistor. If only small variations are considered, then

$$\frac{d\alpha_c}{d\alpha_1} = 1 - \alpha_2 \qquad \frac{d\alpha_c}{d\alpha_2} = 1 - \alpha_1 \qquad (7\text{-}21)$$

Using the figures given above, a 1.0 per cent change in α_1 would cause only a 0.03 per cent change in the over-all current gain α_c. Equation (7-21) is not valid with respect to large variations of α_1 or α_2, and in this case the effect on α_c would have to be found by evaluating Eq. (7-20) over the expected range of α_1 and/or α_2.

The composite transistor is not an unmixed blessing; further examination of the circuit of Fig. 7-1 exposes serious drawbacks which severely limit the possible applications. For example, the temperature-dependent reverse collector current I_{c0} of T_2 still flows unchanged at the base of the composite unit. Since the value of β_c is very large, only a very small base current is needed to control the complete collector current flow. But I_{c0} may well be of the same order of magnitude, making the problem of temperature stabilization extremely difficult.

Furthermore, it can be shown that the input impedance at the composite base may be approximated by

$$r_{in,b} \cong [r_{e1}(1 + \beta_1) + r_{b1}](1 + \beta_2) \tag{7-22}$$

As β_1 and β_2 are very large, the base input will no longer approximate the ideal short circuit which is desirable in a current-controlled device. But for just this reason, this circuit configuration is more convenient for use as a voltage amplifier; the loading of the external source decreases with the increase in β_c (refer to the requirements given in Secs. 7-2 and 7-3). If ever a higher impedance were needed, additional padding resistance would be inserted in series with the emitter. It would be multiplied by the product $(1 + \beta_1)(1 + \beta_2)$ as it is reflected into the base circuit.

PROBLEMS

7-1. Compare the sweep linearity if the transistor sweep of Fig. 7-1 is first used in a grounded base connection and then as a grounded emitter circuit. In both cases R_2 is adjusted to make the sweep period 1.0 msec. The other circuit parameters are $\alpha = 0.98$, $r_c = 0.5$ megohm, $C = 0.1\ \mu$f, $E_{bb} = 10$ volts, and $E_{cc} = -10$ volts. Specify the required values for R_2.

7-2. (*a*) Plot the locus of operation (i_c versus e_c) of the sweep of Fig. 7-2 on the collector characteristics and evaluate the sweep and recovery times. The component values are $\alpha_1 = \alpha_2 = 0.99$, $r_c = 1$ megohm, $C = 1\ \mu$f, $R = 2$ K, $R_2 = 5$ K, $E_{bb} = 10$ volts, and $E_{cc} = -10$ volts.

(*b*) Modify this circuit so that a very short input pulse will periodically discharge the capacitor, with the sweep starting immediately upon the termination of the pulse. Sketch the new circuit. Specify the necessary value of R_2 if the discharge must be complete within 10 μsec.

(*c*) Compare the necessary power requirements for the circuits in parts *a* and *b*. Which one offers the most efficient operation if the spacing between sweeps is $0.1t_1$, t_1, $5t_1$? (t_1 is the sweep period.)

7-3. The switching transistor in Prob. 7-2*a* presents a resistance of 25 ohms from the collector to the emitter when saturated.

(*a*) How will this term affect the output waveshape and period? Write an expression for the sweep interval in general terms, calling the conduction resistance r_s, and then evaluate this equation.

(*b*) Plot both the output waveshape and the locus of operation for the above circuit.

7-4. We wish to evaluate the performance of the sweep of Fig. 7-12 to see whether it yields the same response as the circuit of Fig. 7-1 without having recourse to two power supplies. We have at our disposal a transistor having $\beta = 50$ and $r_c = 1$ megohm, a 20-volt power supply, and a capacitor of 1,000 $\mu\mu$f.

(*a*) What values of R_e and R_B are needed to give a sweep amplitude of 15 volts and a sweep duration of 15 μsec?

(*b*) What value of L is required so that the change in emitter current over the complete sweep period will be less than 0.1 per cent?

(*c*) Sketch e_2, specifying all values.

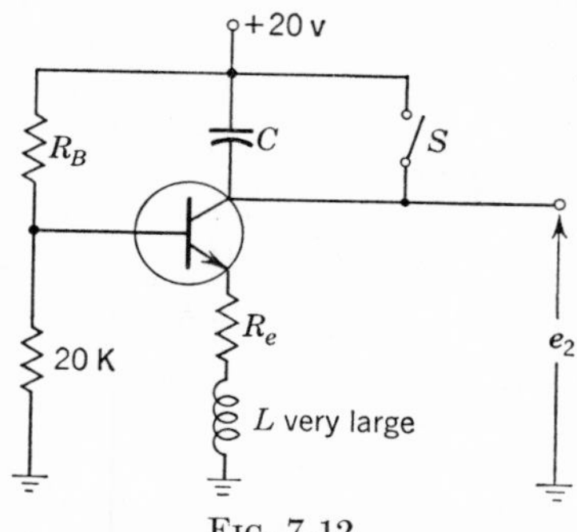

FIG. 7-12

7-5. The bootstrap sweep of Fig. 7-4 has the following component values:

$$r_b = 200 \qquad E = 6 \text{ volts}$$
$$r_c = 1 \text{ megohm} \qquad E_{bb} = 12 \text{ volts}$$
$$r_e = 20 \qquad R_e = 1{,}000$$
$$\beta = 50 \qquad C = 0.04\ \mu\text{f}$$
$$R = 800$$

(*a*) Sketch the sweep output, labeling all voltages and times.

(*b*) Evaluate the sweep nonlinearity.

7-6. (*a*) Express the sweep nonlinearity of the circuit of Fig. 7-4*a* as a function of β.

(*b*) The circuit and parameters are $E_{bb} = E = 10$ volts, $r'_{11} = 1{,}000$, $R_e = 1{,}000$, and $R = 500$ ohms. For what range of β will the NL fall between 0.5 and 1.0 per cent?

7-7. Prove that the bootstrap sweep of Fig. 7-4 may be represented by the model of Fig. 7-13. Find the values of R_n, A, and I for the circuit of Example 7-2. Compare the sweep duration and nonlinearity with that given in the text.

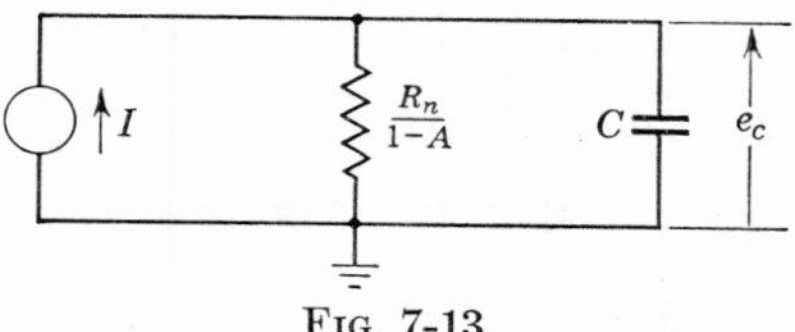

FIG. 7-13

7-8. (*a*) In the bootstrap sweep of Fig. 7-4, the bias source E is equal in value to E_{bb}, but it remains constant, whereas E_{bb} varies by ± 20 per cent from its nominal value of 10 volts. Calculate the change in sweep duration when $r'_{11} = 1{,}200$, $\beta = 50$, $R = 1$ K, $R_e = 1$ K, and $C = 0.05$ μf.

(*b*) The sweep of part *a* is connected in the configuration of Fig. 7-7 with $C_1 = 10$ μf. Compare the sweep duration at the limits of E_{bb} with the answers found in part *a*.

7-9. Figure 7-14 represents an alternative mode of switching the bootstrap sweep of Sec. 7-2. However, once the collector is opened, the conducting base-emitter diode presents a resistance of only 20 ohms, instead of the 1,000 ohms (r'_{11}) seen with the switch closed. Plot the emitter voltage and the controlling current i_1 to scale, after the switch is closed at $t = 0$. Pay particular attention to the circuit behavior as the switch closes. The other components are $R = 500$, $R_e = 2$ K, $\beta = 100$, $C = 2\ \mu$f, and $E = E_{bb} = 20$ volts.

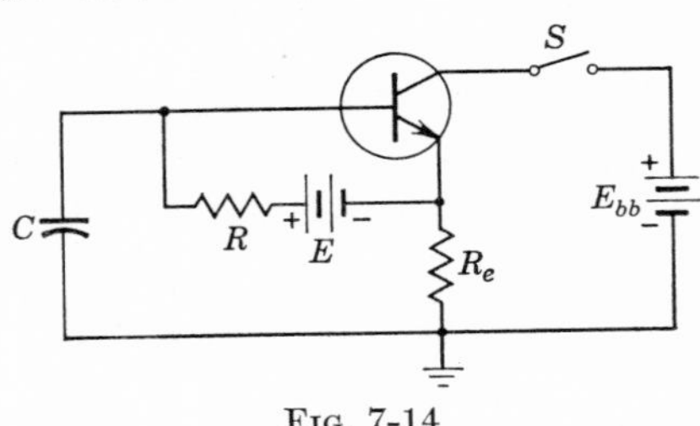

FIG. 7-14

7-10. The bootstrap circuit of Fig. 7-7 uses a transistor with the following parameters: $r'_{11} = 900$, $\beta = 10$. With this transistor and with $R_e = 5$ K, $R = 1.5$ K, $C = 1\ \mu$f, and $E_{bb} = 20$ volts, find

(*a*) The waveform at the emitter when the switch S is opened at $t = 0$ and closed when the voltage is equal to E_{bb}. (Note that β is relatively small, which invalidates some of the approximations made in Sec. 7-2.) Label all time constants and find the time when S is closed.

(*b*) The sweep nonlinearity.

7-11. In the Miller sweep of Fig. 7-8 the switch is opened at $t = 0$ and closed once the collector falls to 1 volt. The transistor employed has the identical characteristics of the one used in Prob. 7-5, and the other circuit values are $R_2 = 10$ K, $R = 5$ K, $C = 0.01\ \mu$f, and $E_{bb} = 15$ volts.

(*a*) Sketch the collector waveshape, making all approximations given in Sec. 7-3. Calculate the sweep nonlinearity.

(*b*) Repeat part *a* if R is reduced to 1,000 ohms and C increased so that the period remains the same as in part *a*.

(*c*) If r_e varies by a factor of 2 over the dynamic range of the transistor, how will this affect the sweep period? Give a qualitative answer.

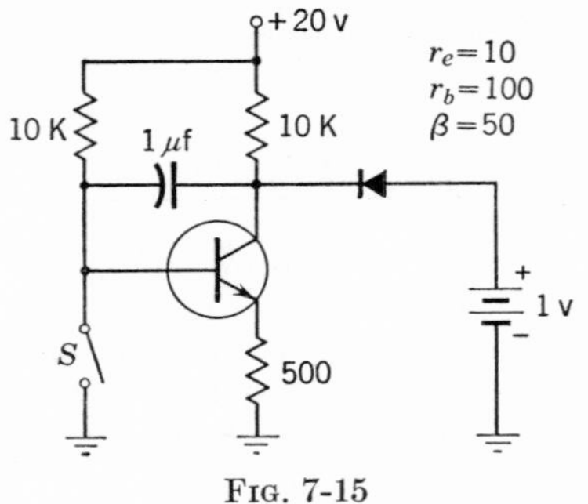

FIG. 7-15

7-12. We shall use the circuit of Fig. 7-15 as an alternative to the Miller sweep of Fig. 7-8. The external emitter padding resistance minimizes the effects of the changing r_b and r_e during the collector rundown. Furthermore, to prevent the transistor from being driven completely into saturation, a bottoming diode is connected to the collector. For the circuit values given below, calculate the complete collector and base waveshapes, from $t = 0$ until steady state is reached.

7-13. Repeat Prob. 7-10 when the single transistor is replaced by the compound circuit of Fig. 7-11. Each transistor has the identical parameters given in Prob. 7-10. Do the approximations of Sec. 7-2 now hold? How would a third transistor affect the sweep period? Discuss the effects of the increasing input impedance on the sweep waveshape.

7-14. Prove that the maximum base input resistance of a composite transistor, composed of two identical units, must be less than the collector resistance r_c of one. Show that this holds regardless of the size of the padding resistance inserted in series with the composite emitter.

7-15. The composite transistor of Fig. 7-11 is composed of a high-power transistor T_1 with its characteristics improved through the addition of T_2. If these two transistors have the parameters listed below, what is the equivalent base input impedance, emitter input impedance, base-to-collector current gain, and maximum power dissipation of the composite unit?

T_1	T_2
$\alpha_1 = 0.95$	$\alpha_2 = 0.99$
$r_b = 100$	$r_b = 400$
$r_e = 20$	$r_e = 15$
$P_m = 5$ watts	$P_m = 200$ mw

7-16. Calculate the composite characteristics of the *n-p-n* and *p-n-p* transistor shown in Fig. 7-16 ($r_{in,e}$, $r_{in,b}$, α_c, and β_c). Assume that the two units are identical

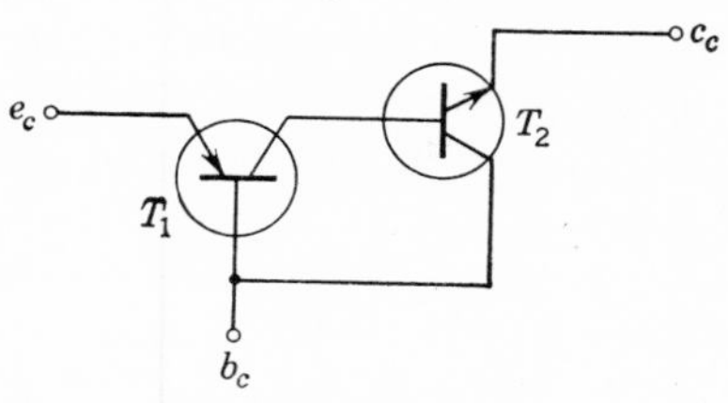

FIG. 7-16

in all respects except the direction of current flow. Would this configuration be helpful in linearizing any of the voltage or current sweeps discussed in this chapter? Explain how.

BIBLIOGRAPHY

Clarke, K. K., and M. V. Joyce: "Transistor Circuit Analysis," Addison-Wesley Publishing Company, Reading, Mass., in press.

Darlington, S.: Patent No. 2,663,806 (assigned to Bell Telephone Laboratories).

Nambiar, K. P. P., and A. R. Boothroyd: Junction Transistor Bootstrap Linear Sweep Circuits, *Proc. IEE (London)*, pt. B, vol. 104, pp. 293–306, 1957.

CHAPTER 8

LINEAR CURRENT SWEEPS

The electric deflection of a high-energy electron beam imposes a severe strain on the circuit designer in that it requires an excessively large sweep amplitude. For this reason magnetic deflection, which is produced by a linearly increasing current in the deflection coil, is used instead. The most common example is a television receiver where the raster is generated by the magnetic deflection of the beam: a single horizontal scan taking about 53 μsec and a vertical scan about 16 msec. Radar display scopes and some electromechanical systems employ similar deflection circuits. Furthermore, a coil excited with a linear current may be mechanically rotated, thus generating a spiral sweep.

Our treatment of current sweeps in this chapter will closely parallel the development of the various voltage sweeps, with, however, an inductance replacing the capacitor as the basic timing element. We should expect our thinking to be influenced by the previous discussion and should feel free to adapt any existing circuit to our current need. For purposes of comparison and in order to gain perspective, the reader might occasionally refer back to the appropriate sections of Chaps. 6 and 7.

8-1. Basic Current Sweeps. If the ideal inductance did exist, as does the almost ideal capacitor, then the problem of producing a linearly increasing current would become trivial; simply switching a constant voltage across the coil would suffice. Because $E = L\,di/dt$, the current would immediately become

$$i = \frac{E}{L} t \tag{8-1}$$

Unfortunately all coils have distributed winding resistance and interwinding and stray capacity; a typical iron-core deflection coil of 50 mh may have a resistance of 70 ohms and an effective capacity of 200 μμf. These parasitic elements are generally represented by the lumped parameters (R_L, C) shown in the basic sweep circuit of Fig. 8-1a, and their effects on the sweep waveshape must be accounted for in any analysis.

Since we are interested in a linear sweep, the portion of the cycle devoted to the initial charging of C must be much smaller than the time required for the coil current to build up to its final value. Immediately upon closing the switch in Fig. 8-1a, the complete circuit current flows into C. Thus the beginning of the sweep may be represented by the model of Fig. 8-1b, which implicitly assumes that the start of the

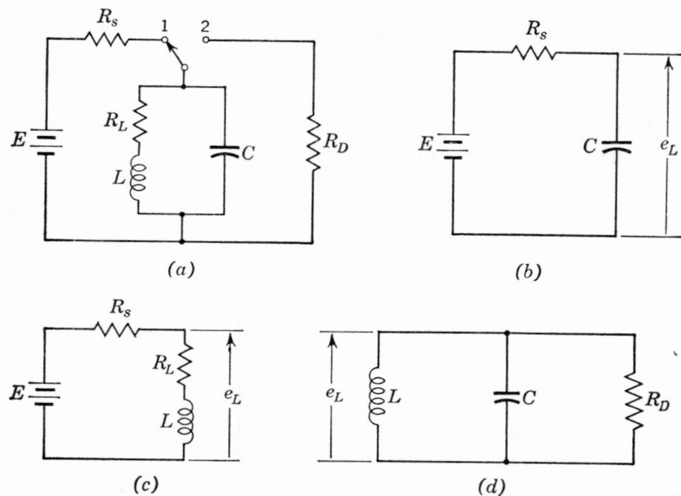

FIG. 8-1. (a) Basic current sweep; (b) approximate model holding during initial charging; (c) model representing the current-sweep region; (d) recovery-region model.

inductive-current build-up will be delayed until the terminal voltage reaches E. The time constant of this circuit,

$$\tau_1 = R_s C \tag{8-2}$$

is quite small, and the delay is proportional ($t_1 = 4\tau_1$); even when charging through 500 ohms, the 200-$\mu\mu$f capacity introduces a delay of less than 0.5 μsec (Fig. 8-2).

Sweep Region. We can now assume that the circuit enters into its sweep region, which is defined by the model given in Fig. 8-1c. Neglecting the small current change occurring during the charging of C, the time response becomes

$$i_L = \frac{E}{R_s + R_L}(1 - e^{-t/\tau_2}) \qquad \tau_2 = \frac{L}{R_2 + R_s} \tag{8-3}$$

To justify our separating the response into these two segments, the sweep time constant τ_2 must be much longer than τ_1. In the case considered above (L = 50 mh, R_L = 70 ohms, and R_s = 500 ohms), τ_2 = 88 μsec. If R_s is further reduced, the separation between τ_1 and τ_2 increases and the assumption made above becomes even more valid.

Moreover, in order to ensure good sweep linearity, the charging interval t_2 must be limited to some small fraction of τ_2.

Suppose that we employ this coil in a deflection circuit where the current must reach a peak of 200 ma in 53 μsec. From Eqs. (8-3), the necessary supply voltage is found to be

$$E = \frac{570 I_m}{1 - e^{-0.602}} = 252 \text{ volts}$$

The inductive component of the voltage decays to 138 volts over the sweep interval. An additional 14 volts (200 ma through 70 ohms) appears across the resistive component, raising the final coil voltage to 152 volts.

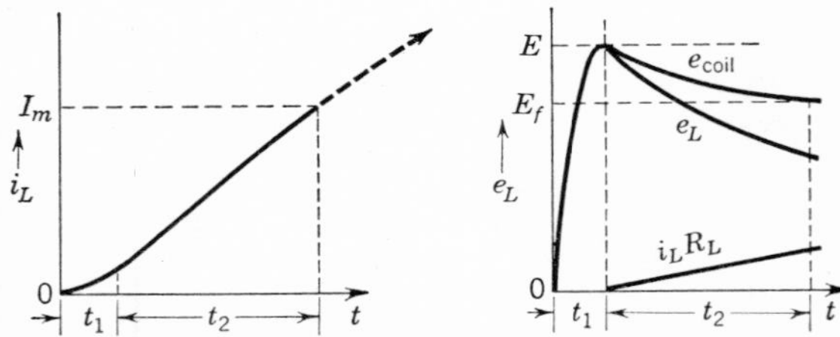

FIG. 8-2. Sweep current and voltage waveshapes for the basic sweep of Fig. 8-1 (switch in position 1).

The waveshapes produced during this portion of the cycle are sketched in Fig. 8-2. Note the delay in starting the sweep and the comparatively small voltage change across the complete coil and the large voltage change across the inductive component.

Sweep Recovery. At the end of the required sweep interval, the switch is thrown to position 2. The response of the coil with its parasitic capacity and external damping, R_D, is found from the single node equation of the circuit in Fig. 8-1*d*. We assume, in writing Eq. (8-4), that the series coil resistance will have but little influence during the portion of the recovery time with which we shall be concerned.

$$i_c + i_L + i_R = C\frac{de}{dt} + \frac{1}{L}\int e\,dt + \frac{e}{R_D} = 0 \tag{8-4}$$

The roots of Eq. (8-4) are

$$p_{1,2} = -\frac{1}{2R_DC} \pm \sqrt{\left(\frac{1}{2R_DC}\right)^2 - \frac{1}{LC}} \tag{8-5}$$

Two bounding possibilities serve to delineate the response characteristics of the network. In one case, $(1/2R_DC)^2 < 1/LC$ and the circuit exhibits a damped sinusoidal response. Here the poles are located at

$$p_{1,2} = -\alpha \pm j\beta$$

where $\alpha = \dfrac{1}{2R_DC} \qquad \beta = \sqrt{\omega_0^2 - \alpha^2} \qquad \omega_0^2 = \dfrac{1}{LC}$

The complete solution of Eq. (8-4) may be expressed as

$$i_L = Ae^{-\alpha t} \cos(\beta t + \phi)$$

If the system is but slightly damped, $\alpha \ll \beta$. By including the initial conditions, which are the final voltage and current reached during the linear sweep (E_f and I_m of Fig. 8-2),

$$i_L = I_m e^{-\alpha t} \cos \omega_0 t \tag{8-6}$$

$$e_L \cong -\sqrt{\frac{L}{C}}\, I_m e^{-\alpha t} \sin \omega_0 t \tag{8-7}$$

Since the damping factor α is so very small, the maximum coil voltage occurs when $\sin \omega_0 t = 1$ (in ¼ cycle of f_0 or at $t = \pi\sqrt{LC}/2$):

$$e_{L,\max} \cong -\sqrt{\frac{L}{C}}\, I_m \tag{8-8}$$

For the coil considered above, this peak reaches almost $-3{,}200$ volts only 4.98 μsec after recovery begins. Figure 8-3*a* illustrates the rapid oscillation and slow decay of the recovery portion of the sweep waveshape.

A second bounding location of the roots of Eq. (8-4) occurs when R_D is adjusted to critically damp the response ($R_D = \sqrt{L/4C}$). The two roots are now identical, both lying on the real axis at

$$p_{1,2} = -\frac{1}{\sqrt{LC}}$$

When the initial conditions are included, the solutions for the critically damped case become

$$i_L = \left[I_m + \left(\frac{E_f}{L} + \frac{I_m}{\sqrt{LC}}\right)t\right] \exp \frac{-t}{\sqrt{LC}} \tag{8-9a}$$

$$e_L = \left[E_f - \left(\frac{E_f}{\sqrt{LC}} + \frac{I_m}{C}\right)t\right] \exp \frac{-t}{\sqrt{LC}} \tag{8-9b}$$

The peak voltage is much smaller, and it occurs sooner; for the same coil considered above, it reaches $-2{,}380$ volts at $t = 3.16$ μsec. Figure 8-3*b* shows this portion of the complete waveshape. As R_D is further reduced, the poles separate along the real axis. Even though the peak voltage is reduced below the value shown in Fig. 8-3*b*, the increase in the time required for final recovery generally prevents the use of a very small damping resistance.

In comparing Fig. 8-3*a* and *b*, we conclude that the fastest possible recovery corresponds to a single half cycle in the completely undamped case. For periodic sweeps the "switch" is returned to position 1 at the time that the coil current reaches its minimum point and the capacitor voltage returns to zero. The current will build up from approximately $-I_m$ instead of from zero, and the sweep amplitudes and time will increase accordingly.

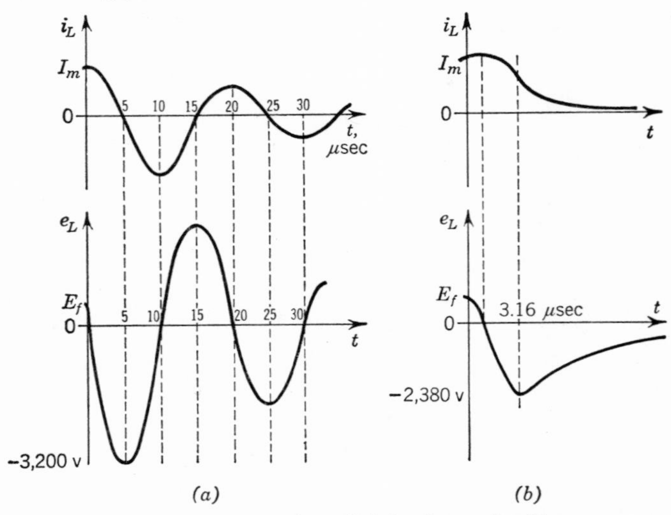

FIG. 8-3. (*a*) Recovery waveshape when lightly damped; (*b*) recovery waveshape when critically damped.

8-2. Switched Current Sweeps. Figure 8-4 illustrates the application of a transistor to the basic sweep of Fig. 8-1. We shall first assume that the circuit is initially inert; i.e., it contains no stored energy. When a pulse is injected, the transistor switches from cutoff to saturation, connecting the full supply voltage across the inductive component of the circuit. (See the model of Fig. 8-5*a*.) Because the saturation resistance of the transistor r_s is quite small, the delay in starting the sweep, due to the stray coil capacity, will be insignificant. Therefore, except during the oscillatory recovery interval, our discussion of this circuit will completely neglect C.

Immediately after switching, the operating point moves to the origin of the collector volt-ampere characteristics and the current starts increasing toward the intersection of the steady-state load line, $-1/R_L$, with the saturation resistance line of the transistor characteristics (Fig. 8-6).

This steady-state current and the charging time constant may be found directly from the model of Fig. 8-5*a*.

$$I_{ss1} = \frac{E_{bb}}{R_L + r_s} \qquad \tau_1 = \frac{L}{R_L + r_s} \tag{8-10}$$

In general, $R_L \gg r_s$ and both terms of Eqs. (8-10) are primarily determined by the coil and battery; they are almost completely independent of the transistor.

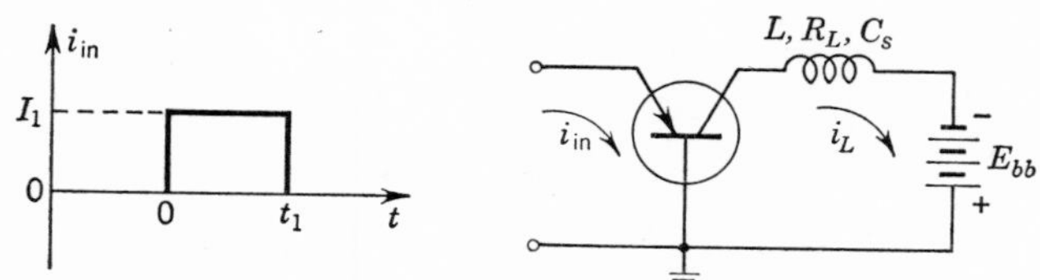

FIG. 8-4. A switched current sweep—the transistor is driven from cutoff to saturation.

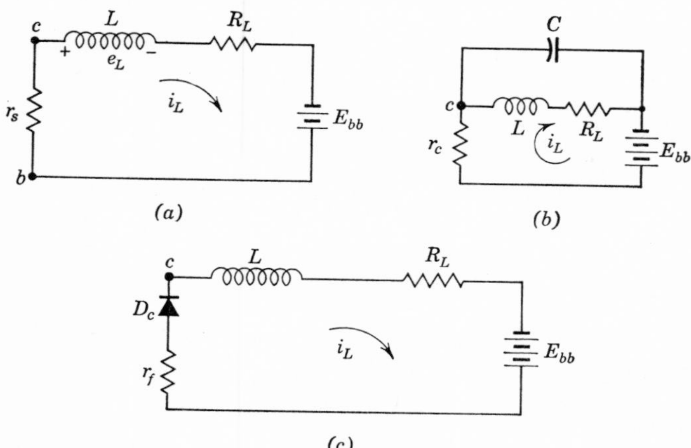

FIG. 8-5. Models for the sweep of Fig. 8-4. (*a*) Charging region—transistor saturated; (*b*) recovery region—transistor cut off; (*c*) recovery region—collector-base diode conducting.

The collector current build-up is permitted to continue until it reaches I_m, a value somewhat less than αI_1, where I_1 is the peak injected emitter current. If the current build-up continues past this point, the transistor will enter its active region and the increase of the collector resistance (from r_s to r_c) will radically distort the sweep waveshape.

After the input pulse is removed, the transistor becomes back-biased. Since the only damping present is the very large reverse resistance of the transistor and the small coil resistance (Fig. 8-5*b*), the output waveshape is a damped oscillation similar to that shown in Fig. 8-3*a*.

In this region the coil current and collector voltage follow the elliptical trajectory drawn on the collector characteristics of Fig. 8-6. At point A, the energy of the complete system,

$$W_L = \tfrac{1}{2} L I_m^2 \tag{8-11}$$

is stored in the magnetic field of the coil. Along the path AB the stored energy is transferred to the electric field of the capacitor. As the coil

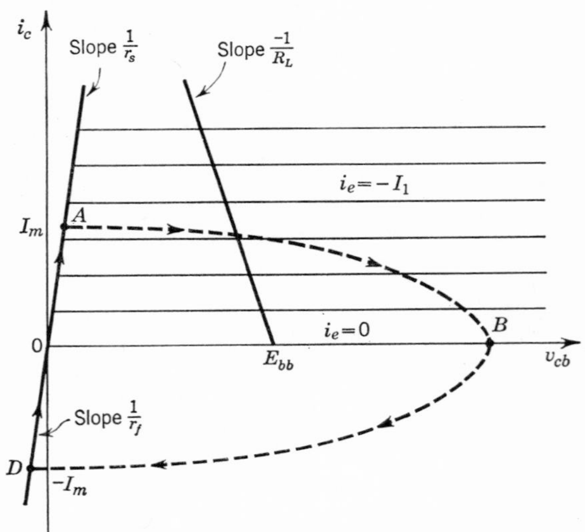

FIG. 8-6. Trajectory of the collector voltage and coil current for the switched sweep of Fig. 8-4. The dashed portion is the path taken in the oscillatory recovery region; the solid-line segments, the path followed in the linear-sweep region.

voltage reverses and builds up to the negative peak of E_p, the coil current decreases to zero. At point B,

$$W_C = \tfrac{1}{2} C E_p^2 \tag{8-12}$$

From Eqs. (8-11) and (8-12),

$$E_p = \sqrt{\frac{L}{C}}\, I_m$$

which is identical with the result given in Eq. (8-8).

Because of the transistor's limitations, only a small voltage can be tolerated during retrace. By shunting the coil with additional resistance and capacity the peak can be reduced to an acceptable value, but this also reduces the frequency of oscillation and increases the portion of the sweep which must be allocated to recovery. If this time must be minimized, while still limiting the peak voltage, either smaller inductance deflection coils can be used or two transistors may be placed in series, reducing the drop across each to one-half the total voltage present.

Along the second portion of the elliptic trajectory BD, the energy is retransferred from C to the magnetic field of the deflection coil. The voltage now decreases, and the current builds up to $-I_m$. The dashed portion is the path taken in the oscillatory recovery region and the solid-line segments, the path in the linear-sweep region.

Slightly after one-half cycle of the oscillation (Figs. 8-6 and 8-7), the positive voltage developed across the coil exceeds the negative supply and the collector becomes forward-biased with respect to the base. A conduction path through this diode now exists irrespective of the emitter condition. The model holding changes from that of Fig. 8-5*b* to the one of Fig. 8-5*c*. Current now builds up from the negative peak of $-I_m$ toward a new steady-state value

$$I_{ss2} = \frac{E_{bb}}{R_L + r_f}$$

with a new time constant

$$\tau_2 = \frac{L}{R_L + r_f}$$

The charging path is now along the straight-line segment DO in Fig. 8-6. In order for the two portions of the sweep to have an equal slope and the same steady-state current, a transistor with $r_f = r_s$ must be selected. When R_L is large, it will predominate and a much greater degree of unbalance in r_f and r_s can be tolerated.

To generate a periodic sweep, the emitter must be periodically switched from off to on. The time of the application of the input gating pulse is not extremely critical provided that it occurs before the coil current rises to zero. Under these conditions the transistor changes state smoothly, from its operation as a forward-conducting collector-base diode to its saturation region. Build-up continues along the path DOA to I_m. Along this line segment the charging equation is

$$i_L(t) = I_{ss} - (I_{ss} + I_m)e^{-t/\tau} \tag{8-13}$$

And from Eq. (8-13), the time required for the current sweep to build up from $-I_m$ to I_m is

$$t_1 = \tau \ln \frac{I_{ss} + I_m}{I_{ss} - I_m} \tag{8-14}$$

At the end of the linear-sweep interval the excitation is removed and the circuit recovers as discussed above. The portion of the period devoted to the flyback constitutes only one half cycle of the oscillatory wave, or

$$t_r = \frac{1}{2f_0} = \frac{\pi}{\omega_0} = \pi\sqrt{LC} \tag{8-15}$$

We have seen how a periodic excitation leads directly to a periodic sweep with half of the linear-sweep interval depending on the saturated transistor (external excitation) and the other half upon the self-excitation (stored energy) of the diode characteristics.

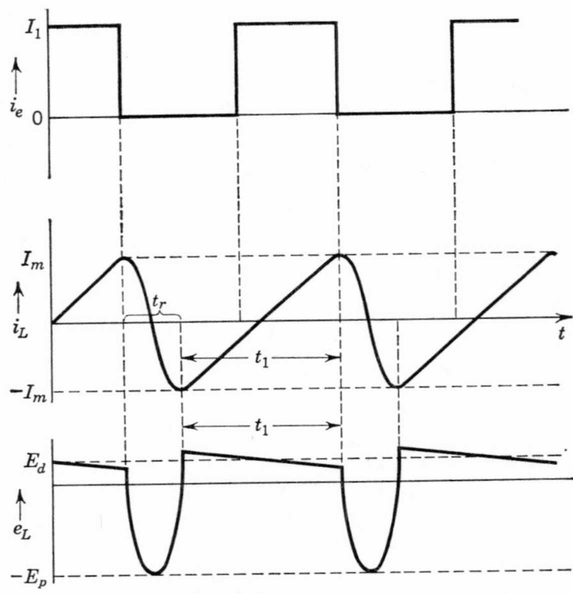

FIG. 8-7. Periodic sweep produced by the circuit of Fig. 8-4 upon square-wave excitation.

We should note that this sweep circuit is extremely efficient. During the half cycle that the transistor is saturated, energy is transferred from E_{bb} to the coil. During the half cycle when the reverse current flows through the conducting collector-base diode, the stored energy is returned to the power supply. Of course, some power is dissipated over each half cycle in the circuit resistance.

Satisfactory switching may be obtained from a square wave of current coupled into the emitter through an emitter follower. The sweep produced is shown in Fig. 8-7.

Example 8-1. We wish to see whether the sweep of Fig. 8-4 can be used in the horizontal-deflection circuit in a portable television receiver. Of the 63-μsec total period, the linear sweep requires 55 μsec, with 8 μsec allowed for the sweep recovery.

The deflection yoke, which must be excited by a peak-to-peak current of 1.0 amp, has the following parameters: $L = 0.5$ mh, $R = 4.5$ ohms, and $C_s = 50\ \mu\mu$f.

(a) With this coil, what supply voltage must be used?

(b) How can the peak reverse voltage be minimized?

(c) What is the sweep nonlinearity?

Solution. Assume that both the saturation and the forward resistance of the transistor employed are 1 ohm. The time constant of the sweep interval is $\tau_1 = 91\ \mu$sec. Solving Eq. (8-14) with $I_m = 0.5$ amp yields

$$I_{ss} = 1.7 \text{ amp}$$

Hence $E_{bb} = 1.7(r_p + R_L) = 7.65$ volts.

As C is increased, the peak reverse voltage decreases. The upper limit of C is that value that increases the half period of the recovery sinusoid to 8 μsec. From Eq. (8-15),

$$C_m = \frac{1}{L}\left(\frac{t_r}{\pi}\right)^2 = 0.013\ \mu\text{f}$$

Thus the peak voltage becomes

$$E_p = 0.5\sqrt{\frac{0.5 \times 10^{-3}}{1.3 \times 10^{-8}}} = 106 \text{ volts}$$

Sweep nonlinearity is given by Eq. (5-20):

$$\text{NL} = 12.5\% \times 55/91 = 7.5\%$$

For acceptable linearity the coil inductance must be increased or the total resistance decreased.

Pentode Switched Sweeps. If a pentode is used as the switching element (Fig. 8-8) because of the higher saturation resistance, the start of the sweep will be slightly delayed. As the stray capacity charges, the operating point moves to the origin of the volt-ampere characteristic and the full supply voltage appears across the coil. This effectively places the tube in the region where it has a small value of r_p, i.e., along the $E_{b,\min}$ line, where r_p drops to r_p'. When a power pentode is used as the switching tube, r_p' may be as low as 100 or 200 ohms. (The process described is similar to the bottoming of the pentode Miller sweep of Sec. 6-7.)

The coil current increases exponentially from zero, with the time constant $\tau = L/(r_p' + R_L)$, and as it does so, the operating point travels up the $E_{b,\min}$ line of the pentode characteristics toward the intersection with the load line. In order to maintain an almost linear build-up, the sweep will be terminated long before it reaches this steady-state current and before the tube becomes active.

The removal of the control-grid signal turns the tube off. The large pulse now developed at the plate-coil current can be limited to a safe value by the addition of a suitable damping resistance. In the circuit of Fig. 8-8a, it is included in series with a diode, which is connected so that it will conduct only when the coil voltage reverses.

Since the tube cannot tolerate any reverse current flow, if we wish to adapt the pentode circuit for the most efficient recurrent operation, the coil must be shunted by a path which will support the sweep when $i_L < 0$. In the transistor circuit of Fig. 8-4 this path was established

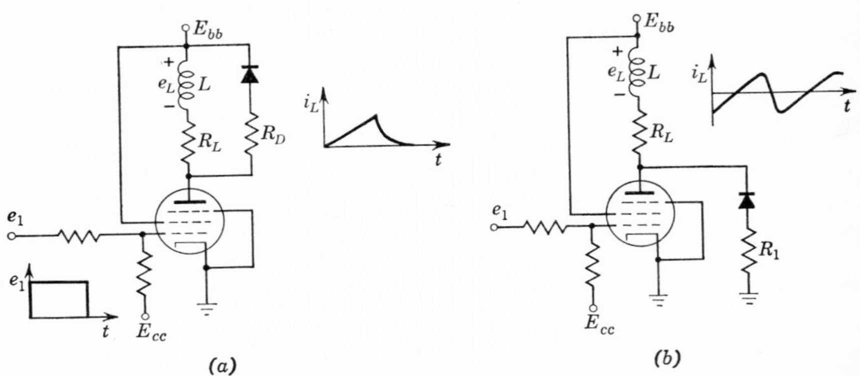

FIG. 8-8. Pentode switched sweeps. (a) Single-shot sweep circuit showing the connection of the damping diode; (b) periodic sweep showing the connection of the energy-recovery diode.

through the collector-base diode; by analogy, an energy-recovery diode can be connected across the tube (Fig. 8-8b). Just as in the transistor sweep, the diode will start to conduct slightly after the first half cycle of the damped sinusoid. At this time the coil voltage exceeds E_{bb}, making the plate of the pentode negative with respect to ground. A comparison of the vacuum-tube circuit of Fig. 8-8 with the transistor sweep of Fig. 8-4 convinces us that the transistor is much more suitable for periodic current sweeps than the vacuum tube. The only advantage offered by the tube is that it can tolerate large reverse voltages during recovery.

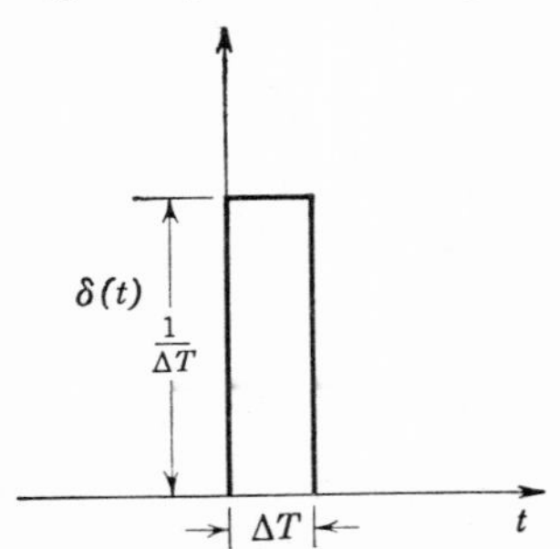

FIG. 8-9. Defining the unit impulse.

8-3. Current Sweep Linearization. The constant voltage charging of Sec. 8-1 is not a very satisfactory sweep for critical applications because of its delay in starting and its inherent nonlinearity. We now propose to reexamine the basic sweep of Fig. 8-10b and ask, What applied wave shape will ensure a linearly increasing current flow?

In order to minimize the sweep delay, the initial portion of the excitation waveshape should be a voltage impulse. The impulse, shown in Fig. 8-9, is a pulse whose amplitude increases toward infinity as its duration decreases toward zero. Its area remains constant during the limiting process. It follows that the unit impulse $\delta(t)$ may be defined by the area integral

$$\int_0^{0^+} \delta(t)\, dt = \int_0^{\Delta T} \frac{1}{\Delta T}\, dt = 1 \tag{8-16}$$

where, in the limit, $\Delta T = 0^+ - 0$.

If we excite the coil through the source impedance R_s with a voltage impulse of area K, then the stray capacity would be charged by the current

$$i = \frac{K\delta(t)}{R_s}$$

From Eq. (8-16), the voltage across C is given by

$$E_C(0^+) = \frac{1}{C}\int_L^t dt = \frac{K}{CR_s}\int_0^{0^+} \delta(t)\, dt = \frac{K}{CR_s}$$

In order for this voltage to equal E at $t = 0^+$, the weight of the impulse must be

$$K = CR_sE$$

It is impossible to generate the ideal impulse, but it is possible to inject a finite-amplitude pulse at the institution of the sweep to speed the charging of C. Any large-amplitude pulse will reduce the sweep starting time by an appreciable factor.

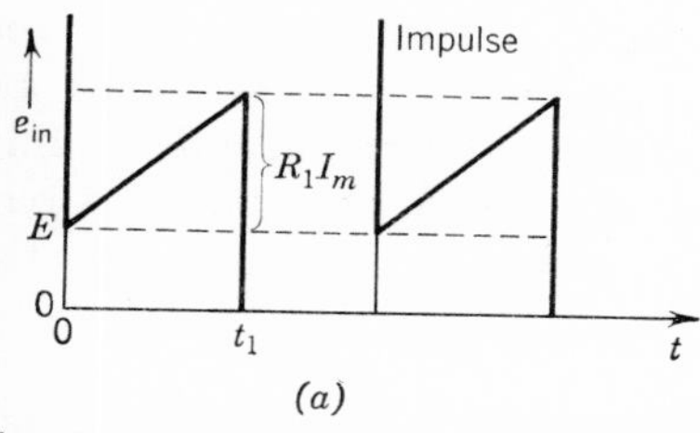

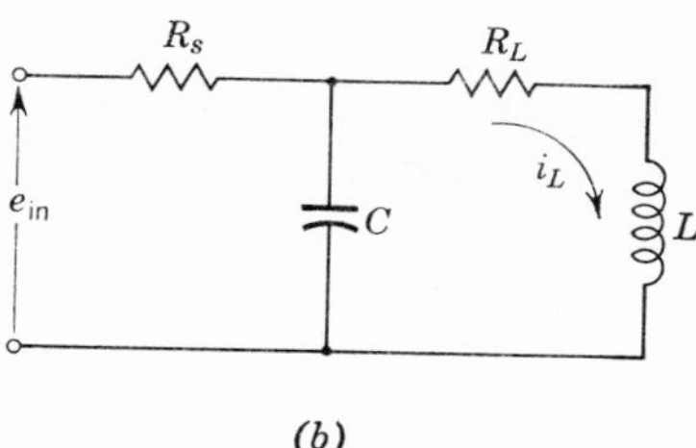

FIG. 8-10. (a) Required drive for the ideal current sweep; (b) equivalent circuit of the sweep.

To find the required drive voltage over the sweep region, we assume that the desired linearly increasing current is already flowing.

$$i = kt = \frac{I_m}{t_1}t \tag{8-17}$$

Substitution of this linear term into the circuit loop equation results in

$$e_{in} = L\frac{di}{dt} + R_1 i = Lk + R_1kt \tag{8-18}$$

where $R_1 = R_L + R_s$. Equation (8-18) defines the trapezoidal driving voltage shown in Fig. 8-10*a*. The first term in the above equation ($Lk = E$) is the magnitude of the pedestal; i.e., it is the constant voltage which must be developed across an ideal inductance if the current is to increase linearly with time. The second term represents the linearly increasing voltage drop appearing across the resistive components of the circuit due to the current sweep produced in the coil.

The individual components of the trapezoidal drive voltage necessary for a linear sweep may be generated separately, added together, and used to excite the coil. For example, by integrating a rectangular voltage wave in the input circuit of the emitter follower of Fig. 8-11, or alternatively in the grid circuit of a cathode follower, the voltage impressed across the coil would be of the proper trapezoidal form. The

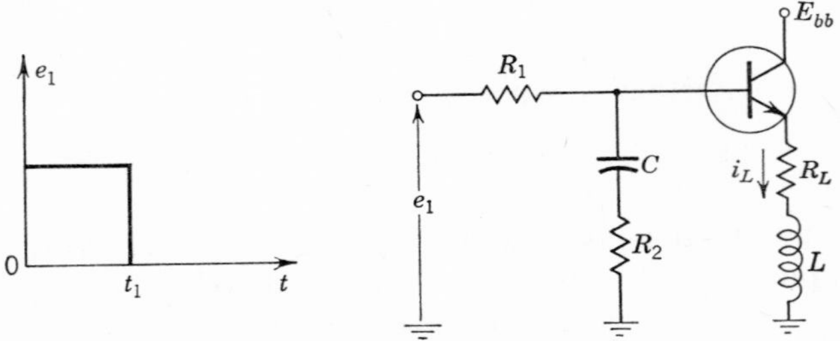

FIG. 8-11. Emitter-follower drive circuit for a current sweep.

low source impedance of the driver stage limits the peak excursion of the output voltage to a reasonable value. A starting impulse must be separately injected. Many other modes of signal generation and coupling are also possible—through a transformer from a high-impedance source, capacitive coupling to eliminate the d-c component in the coil, or directly from a push-pull circuit.

Example 8-2. The emitter follower used in the sweep of Fig. 8-11 employs as its active element the composite transistor of Sec. 7-4. Each unit has an $\alpha = 0.98$. The 200-mh 30-ohm deflection coil must be excited by a linear-sweep current which reaches a maximum of 0.5 amp in 20 msec. In generating the input signal, the end of R_1 is connected directly to the 50-volt supply. What must R_1, R_2, and C be to satisfy the necessary sweep conditions?

Solution. With the composite transistor, the large value of α_c (0.9996) given by Eq. (7-20) means that the over-all gain is extremely close to unity. Consequently, the reflected input impedance of the emitter load (R_L and L) back into the base will be large enough so that its loading of the input RC network will be negligible. From Eq. (8-18), the height of the pedestal must be

$$E = Lk = 200 \times 10^{-3} \times \frac{0.5}{20 \times 10^{-3}} = 5 \text{ volts}$$

The maximum height of the triangle, neglecting the small emitter resistance, is

$$E_{tm} = R_L I_m = 30 \times 0.5 = 15 \text{ volts}$$

Assume that the initial current through the RC network is 1.0 ma. To obtain a 5-volt jump at the base input upon excitation,

$$R_2 = \frac{5 \text{ volts}}{1 \text{ ma}} = 5 \text{ K}$$

The remaining 45 volts must be developed across the other input resistor:

$$R_1 = \frac{45 \text{ volts}}{1 \text{ ma}} = 45 \text{ K}$$

The base must charge from 5 to 20 volts in the 20-msec sweep duration. From the exponential charging equation,

$$t_1 = \tau \ln \frac{50 - 20}{50 - 5} = 49.5 \text{ msec}$$

Since $R_1 + R_2 = 50$ K, $C = 0.99\ \mu$f. We should note that the sweep duration is independent of the 6.7-msec coil time constant; in fact, the approximately linear sweep is now three times as long.

8-4. A Transistor Bootstrap Sweep. For a second method of linearizing the current sweep we might consider a circuit which is the dual of the RC voltage sweep of Fig. 6-2, i.e., the parallel combination of a coil and a conductance charged from a constant current source (Fig. 8-12). This circuit's node equation may be written as

$$e_L = \frac{I' - i_L}{G} \qquad (8\text{-}19)$$

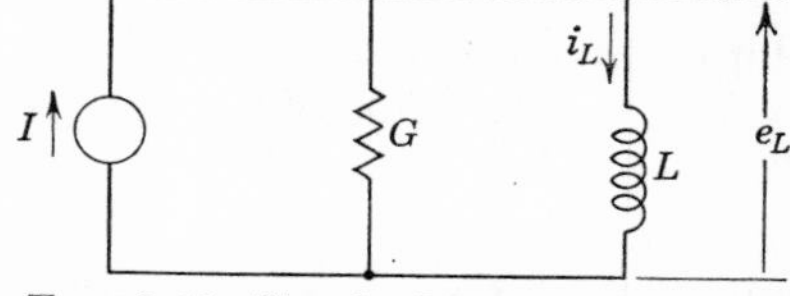

FIG. 8-12. Simple LG current sweep.

At this point Eq. (8-19) should be compared with the equation written for the voltage sweep [Eq. (6-6)] and the argument employed with respect to that circuit reread.

We know that bootstrapping generates an extremely linear voltage sweep. Since we now have at our disposal a current-controlled active circuit element, the transistor, we should consider the possibility of developing the dual circuit, a current bootstrap, as our current sweep. Choosing Eq. (8-19) for the starting point, we see that the replacement of I' by $I + A_c i_L$ provides the correction term which is so essential. When this is done,

$$e_L = \frac{I + A_c i_L - i_L}{G} \qquad (8\text{-}20)$$

where A_c is the current gain of the feedback amplifier. Figure 8-13a and b illustrate the current bootstrapping process defined in Eq. (8-20). It should be noted that the role of the current amplifier is analogous to that performed by the voltage amplifier in the voltage bootstrap. Both supply the additional energy made necessary by the dissipative elements of the external circuit. By this means the system maintains either constant current or constant voltage charging of the energy-storage element. Since under these circumstances the dissipative energy remains constant (I^2R or E^2G), the system must supply an ever-increasing amount of energy for storage in the capacitor or inductance. Unless an active circuit element is present to cancel the effects of the circuit resistance (which limits the available storage energy), it is impossible to achieve an absolutely linear sweep.

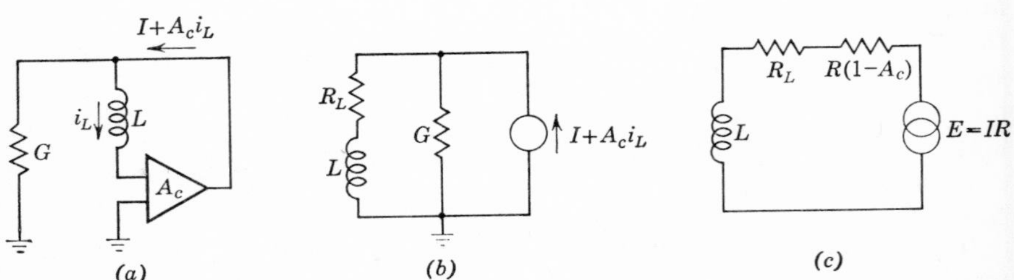

FIG. 8-13. Basic current bootstrap circuit. (*a*) Circuit connection; (*b*) schematic representation; (*c*) Thévenin equivalent circuit.

The role of the amplifier becomes somewhat clearer if we solve for the Thévenin equivalent of the current generator and its internal conductance in Fig. 8-13*b*. One of the two voltage generators resulting is of the form

$$e_a = RA_c i_L$$

where $R = 1/G$. But since this voltage rise is proportional to the series current flow, it may be replaced by a negative resistance $-RA_c$, as shown in Fig. 8-13*c*. The amplifier's action serves to reduce the over-all series resistance and to increase the circuit time constant. The current sweep is now defined by

$$i_L = \frac{E}{R_L + R(1 - A_c)} (1 - e^{-t/\tau}) \qquad \tau = \frac{L}{R_L + R(1 - A_c)}$$

It is immediately apparent that there will be no improvement over the first circuit discussed unless A_c is positive and greater than unity. When $A_c < 1$ there will actually be deterioration of the sweep quality as a result of the decrease in the steady-state current and the time constant. Since both terms change in the same direction, the slope at the origin remains invariant with respect to any instability of A_c. Any improvement in the sweep permits a larger amplitude output before the nonlinearity becomes excessive.

Ideal constant voltage charging occurs when there is complete cancellation of the resistance. From Fig. 8-13c we see that the necessary amplifier gain is

$$A_c = 1 + \frac{R_L}{R} \tag{8-21}$$

Usually $R \gg R_L$, and consequently the current gain required for linear charging will be but slightly greater than unity. Since we are dependent on the cancellation of two terms of equal magnitude for sweep linearization, any instability in A_c will have pronounced repercussions on the current waveshape, particularly on the time required to reach a predetermined final value [Eq. (6-10)]. Generally, the amplifier is adjusted so that the net resistance will be small but positive and so that any expected gain instability will never result in a net negative circuit resistance. The high degree of stabilization necessary, if the sweep time is to be very long, sets extremely stringent requirements on the base current amplifier.

Previously, we proved that a trapezoidal voltage drive must appear across the physical inductance when a linear-sweep current flows through it [Eq. (8-18)]. Substituting the assumed ideal current $i_L = kt$ into the bootstrap equation (8-20) and equating the result to the known drive signal affords another method of determining the essential system conditions:

$$e_L = R_L kt + Lk = \frac{I + (A_c - 1)kt}{G}$$

Comparing similar terms on both sides of the above equation yields two relationships:

$$A_c - 1 = R_L G = \frac{R_L}{R} \tag{8-22}$$

$$I = LkG \tag{8-23}$$

The first of the above equations establishes the necessary system gain, and, as expected, it is identical with Eq. (8-21). The second condition [Eq. (8-23)] expresses the constant voltage charging of the inductive component of the external circuit. By rewriting this in the form

$$E = IR = L\frac{di}{dt} = Lk$$

it also offers a convenient design criterion for the choice of the parallel resistance.

The positive current gain of a single transistor is necessarily limited to somewhat less than α, and consequently a multiple-stage amplifier must be used in this bootstrap sweep. Figure 8-14 illustrates an appropriate circuit, which employs current feedback both to increase the gain stability and as a means of adjusting the gain to the optimum value. This will generally be somewhat less than that given by Eq. (8-21), thus allowing a margin for any remaining amplifier instability. Since the coil resistance will not be completely canceled, if originally R_L was small, little or nothing will be gained by bootstrapping and the switched sweep of Fig. 8-4 might prove to be just as satisfactory.

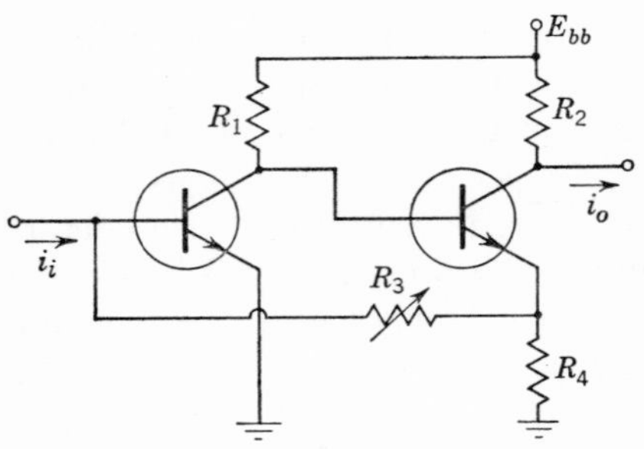

FIG. 8-14. Base amplifier for a current bootstrap circuit.

The current sweep discussed above is the dual of the bootstrap voltage sweep treated in Chaps. 6 and 7. By analogy it would seem likely that a current-controlled Miller sweep, depending for its timing on the inductance, might also be practical. However, the impossibility of isolating the coil resistance causes any operation on the inductance to be accompanied by an equal effect on the associated coil resistance. Multiplying or dividing both L and R_L by the same factor leaves the time constant unchanged. Because there is no improvement, this method of linearization is never used. It is worth noting that not all forms of voltage-operated systems can, in fact, be converted to their duals. Often, as in this case, the unavailability of the needed ideal circuit element (pure inductance) will be the decisive factor.

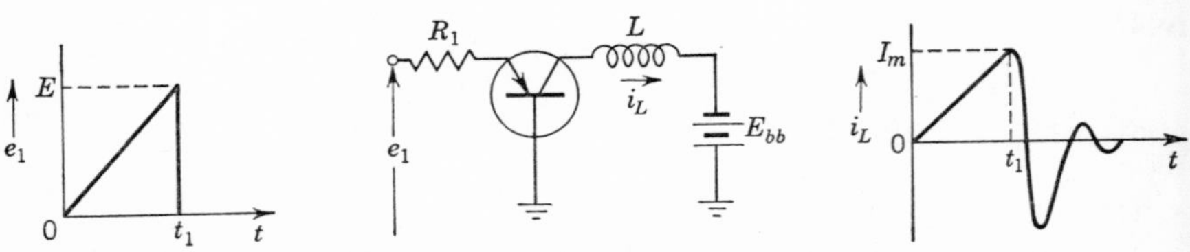

FIG. 8-15. Current sweep generated from a constant-current source.

8-5. Constant-current-source Current Sweep. A contrasting line of thought actually obviates the generation of a current sweep. The tube or transistor is utilized solely as a voltage-to-current converter. A highly accurate voltage sweep is generated elsewhere and applied as a drive: in Fig. 8-15 the constant-current output of the transistor furnishes a driving current proportional to this voltage. We thus bypass the need to develop separately the trapezoidal voltage across the coil, the negative resistance in series with the coil, or any other correction term necessitated by the nonideal inductance. Moreover, by restricting the sweep generation to voltage waveshapes, we are able to employ an almost ideal energy-storage element (i.e., a capacitor), with consequent ease of linearization.

The current flow through L, found from the model holding for the active region, is

$$i_L = \alpha \frac{e_1}{R_1} + \frac{E_{bb} - E_d}{r_c} \tag{8-24}$$

where E_d is the drop across the inductance. In general, $R_1 \ll r_c$ and the small current component due to E_{bb} will be negligible; the coil current becomes a linear function of the driving voltage.

At the end of the sweep cycle the input voltage drops to zero. The turnoff process is identical with the removal of the excitation in the switched sweeps of Sec. 8-2. Here also the recovery would be controlled either by an external damping diode and resistance or by a recovery diode for recurrent sweeps.

PROBLEMS

8-1. A coil having an inductance of 100 mh, a resistance of 20 ohms, and stray capacity of 200 $\mu\mu$f is charged through a source impedance of 1,000 ohms (Fig. 8-1). The sweep current must reach 150 ma in 50 μsec.

(*a*) Specify the necessary charging voltage and calculate the sweep linearity.

(*b*) Sketch the current and voltage waveshapes when the circuit is critically damped.

(*c*) Repeat part *b* when the damping resistance is reduced to 1,000 ohms. Specify the peak voltage and the time at which it occurs. Make all reasonable approximations. (HINT: Treat in the same way as the double-energy circuit of Chap. 1.)

8-2. The coil of Prob. 8-1 is shunted with additional capacity so that one half cycle of the oscillatory recovery lasts for 60 μsec ($R_d = \infty$). Calculate the peak voltage and compare with the value found for the coil without additional shunting capacity. What does the additional capacity do to the initial sweep delay?

8-3. The transistor used in the sweep of Fig. 8-4 is excited by a 1.0-msec-period current square wave. Both r_s and r_f at the collector are 5 ohms, r_c = 100 K, $\alpha = 0.97$, E_{bb} = 20 volts, and the coil parameters are L = 0.05 henry, R = 10 ohms, and C = 500 $\mu\mu$f.

(*a*) What is the minimum amplitude input that will ensure the transistor's remaining saturated over the full half of the sweep cycle?

(*b*) Sketch the current and voltage waveshapes.

(*c*) Calculate the sweep nonlinearity.

8-4. As an alternative to the sweep of Fig. 8-4, the square-wave excitation is applied to the base as shown in Fig. 8-16. For the purposes of analysis assume that each equivalent diode in the transistor has a forward resistance of 5 ohms and a reverse resistance of 100 K. In addition, the collector-to-emitter saturation resistance is 10 ohms. The coil parameters are L = 100 mh, R = 20 ohms, and C = 100 $\mu\mu$f. (For this problem, remove the diode shunting the coil.)

(*a*) Sketch the current if the 100-μsec square wave drives the transistor into saturation.

(*b*) How might this circuit be modified to linearize the sweep? Explain your answer.

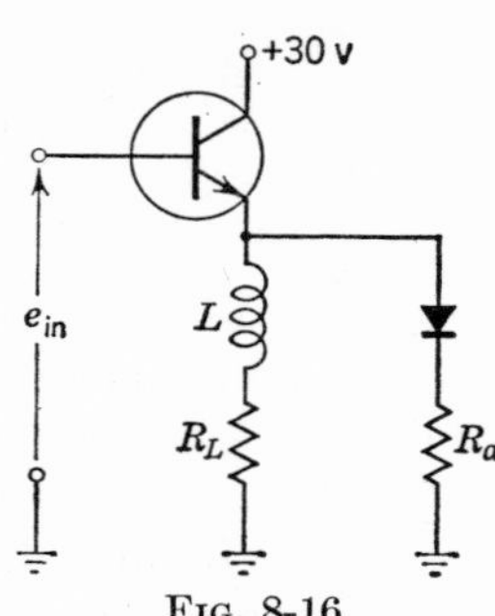

FIG. 8-16

8-5. In the switched sweep of Fig. 8-8*a* the plate resistance of the pentode, when operating along the $e_{b,\min}$ line, is 400 ohms. The coil used has an additional resistance of 100 ohms and an inductance of 500 mh. Once the current builds up to 100 ma, the tube is switched off (the plate voltage will not leave the $e_{b,\min}$ line until this point). $E_{bb} = 300$ volts.

(*a*) Sketch the sweep current waveshape, specifying all times and time constants.

(*b*) Evaluate the sweep linearity.

(*c*) Repeat part *a* when the tube is not switched off until the current builds up to its maximum value. Assume that the plate resistance in the active region is 100 K. Calculate the peak plate voltage and give the time at which it occurs. Plot the operating locus on the plate volt-ampere characteristics.

8-6. (*a*) If the coil of Prob. 8-5 has associated shunt capacity of 500 $\mu\mu$f, calculate the value of R_D necessary for critical damping.

(*b*) Calculate the R_D that will result in a damping equation of the form

$$i \cong ke^{-\alpha t} \cos \beta t$$

where $\alpha = \beta$.

(*c*) Plot the voltage and current recovery waveshapes for parts *a* and *b* on the same graph. Which condition gives the best recovery response?

8-7. Assume, for this problem, that the coil capacity in the switched sweep of Fig. 8-17 is zero. The plate resistance in the saturation region is $r_p' = r_p/(\mu + 1)$, and this region corresponds to $E_{b,\min} \leq E_{c,\max}$.

(*a*) Sketch the voltage and current waveshapes to scale.

(*b*) Plot the locus of operation on the piecewise-linear tube characteristics.

(*c*) Prove that the tube remains conducting when the pulse first disappears.

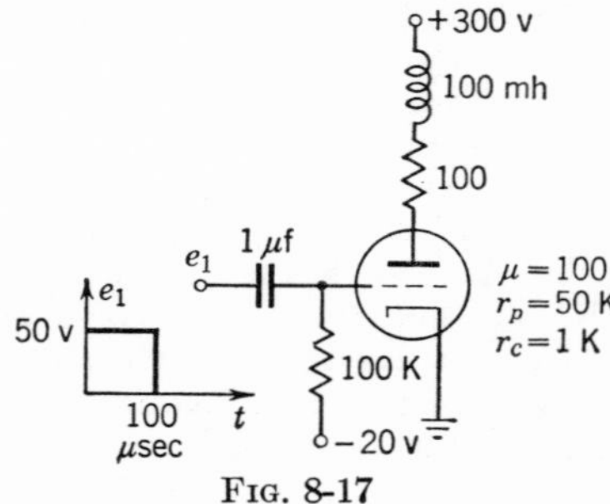

FIG. 8-17

8-8. A power-amplifier pentode having a saturation resistance of 200 ohms is used to excite a 50-mh 50-ohm coil in the periodic sweep of Fig. 8-8*b*. The maximum saturation current of this tube, with zero control-grid voltage, is 250 ma. $E_{bb} =$ 400 volts.

(*a*) Calculate the optimum value of R_1 if the coil current must vary from -100 ma to $+100$ ma over the sweep interval.

(*b*) Sketch the plate current, diode current, and coil current to scale. The oscillatory recovery time is limited by external capacity to 10 per cent of the linear-sweep interval.

(*c*) Sketch the plate voltage waveshape.

(*d*) Plot the plate characteristic trajectory of this sweep.

(*e*) Calculate the sweep nonlinearity.

8-9. The coil of Prob. 8-1 is driven by the output of an emitter follower as shown in Fig. 8-11. Assume that the output impedance of the approximately unity gain stage is only 10 ohms. The peak current of the single sweep cycle is 200 ma, and this circuit has a recovery diode and resistance critically damping the response. In addition, shunting capacity is added to reduce the peak voltage across the coil to 100 volts.

(*a*) If a 25-volt supply is used, what is the fastest possible sweep?

(*b*) Calculate the necessary drive for a single sweep of 5 msec duration.

(*c*) Sketch the voltage and current waveshapes to scale, paying particular attention to the recovery portion of the cycle.

(*d*) Repeat part *c* when the diode is removed.

8-10. The circuit of Fig. 8-16 is used as a periodic sweep. The transistor has $\alpha = 0.98$, $r_e = 10$ ohms, $r_b = 100$ ohms, $r_d = 100$ K, and the 10-mh coil being driven has a resistance of 10 ohms and 100 $\mu\mu$f stray capacity.

(*a*) What is the highest frequency sweep possible if the recovery is limited to 10 per cent of the sweep period? The peak-to-peak sweep current must be 0.5 amp, and $E_{bb} = 30$ volts.

(*b*) Calculate the drive waveshape, at the base of the transistor, required to produce a periodic sweep of one-half the frequency determined in part *a*. Ensure that the transistor will be back-biased during the recovery interval. Calculate the optimum value of R_a. What function does this resistor perform?

8-11. A power-amplifier triode is used as a cathode-follower driver with the deflection coil inserted in the cathode circuit. For this tube $\mu = 10$, $r_p = 1.5$ K, and the plate supply is 400 volts. The same basic circuit is used for both horizontal and vertical deflection in a television receiver. Both deflection coils have $L = 50$ mh, $R = 150$ ohms, and $C = 250$ $\mu\mu$f. For a single horizontal scan the current must increase to 200 ma in 55 μsec with 8 μsec allowed for recovery. The vertical scan requires a peak of 150 ma in 16 msec with 700 μsec left for the recovery.

(*a*) Specify the necessary trapezoidal drive signal for the horizontal sweep.

(*b*) Complete the design by calculating the diode resistance and recovery capacity.

(*c*) Sketch the circuit waveshapes.

(*d*) Repeat parts *a*, *b*, and *c* for the vertical sweep.

8-12. The coil of Prob. 8-11 is excited from a generator having 200 ohms source impedance.

(*a*) Specify the drives necessary to produce a 200-ma peak 10-msec-duration periodic sweep of the following geometry: a parabola, $i = Kt^2$; an isosceles triangle; a truncated isosceles triangle where the flat top is 3.3 msec long.

(*b*) Sketch the waveshapes produced on the oscilloscope screen if the coil is rotated at 300 revolutions/sec and the sweeps are those given in part *a*.

8-13. Prove that the current bootstrap circuit employing only a single transistor, such as the one shown in Fig. 8-18, produces a sweep of poorer quality than the simple switched coil of Fig. 8-4. ($\alpha = 0.98$, $r_e = 10$ ohms, $r_b = 100$ ohms, and $r_c = 1$ megohm.)

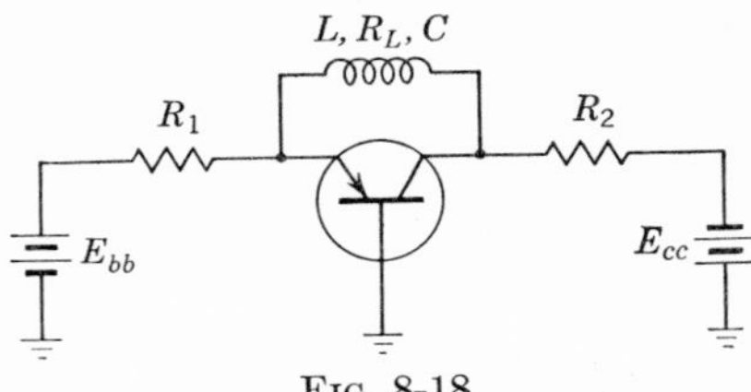

FIG. 8-18

8-14. In the base amplifier of Fig. 8-14 the two transistors are identical, each having $\beta = 50$, $r_e = 10$, $r_b = 200$, and $r_d = 100$ K. The power supply $E_{bb} = 30$ volts, and $R_1 = R_2 = R_4 = 1$ K. Plot the current gain as a function of R_3.

8-15. We wish to use the circuit of Fig. 8-19*a* to produce a perfectly linear current sweep $i = kt$ after the switch is closed at $t = 0$.

(*a*) For this condition, sketch the volt-ampere characteristic of N, labeling all slopes.

(*b*) If $i = kt$ with N properly adjusted, what is the value of k?

(*c*) When N is represented by a two-stage current amplifier with feedback (Fig. 8-19*b*), specify the necessary current gain β in terms of R_1, r_s, and r_L.

(*d*) How does the time constant of the circuit vary as a function of β, for small variations in β, in the vicinity of the optimum value?

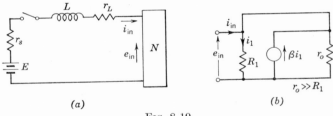

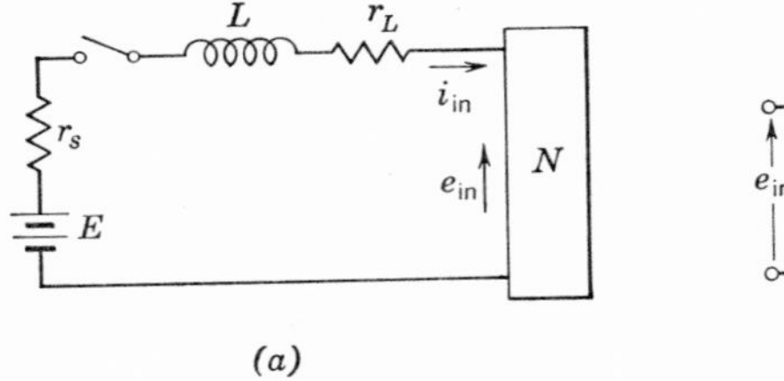

FIG. 8-19

8-16. In the current sweep of Fig. 8-15 the driving voltage increases linearly from 0 to 10 volts in 100 μsec. The circuit components are $R_1 = 100$ ohms, $L = 500$ mh, $R_L = 50$ ohms, $C = 0.01$ μf, $E_{bb} = 20$ volts, $\alpha = 0.98$, $r_e = 20$ ohms, and $r_c = 500$ K.

(*a*) Sketch the coil current and voltage to scale, specifying all values. Make all reasonable approximations.

(*b*) Calculate the value of the damping resistance which should be included across the coil if the maximum collector voltage must be limited to 40 volts. Repeat part *a*, first when this resistor is directly across the coil, and then when it is in series with a damping diode.

8-17. A series *RL* circuit is excited by a linear-sweep voltage from a low-impedance source such as a cathode follower. The total series resistance is 500 ohms, and the coil inductance is 1 henry. Evaluate and sketch the current and voltage waveshapes appearing across L

(*a*) When τ is long compared with the time duration of a single applied drive signal.

(*b*) When τ is short compared with the time duration of the drive signal.

(c) When the applied voltage has a peak amplitude of 100 volts and a duration of 100 μsec.

8-18. The triode current sweep of Fig. 8-20 is driven by a perfectly linear sweep voltage of 100 volts peak amplitude and 50 μsec duration. The tube used is a 12AU7.

(a) Sketch both the plate voltage and plate current waveshapes when the damping diode is omitted. (Make all reasonable approximations.)

(b) Calculate the value of R_D necessary to limit the maximum plate-to-cathode voltage to 600 volts.

(c) Repeat part *a* when the diode is included and when R_D is given by the answer of part *b*.

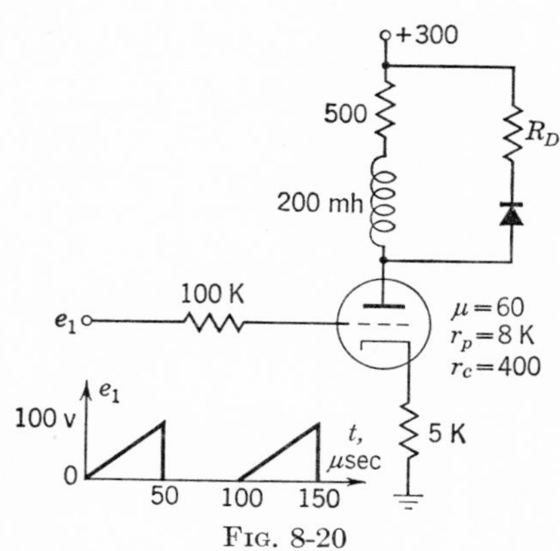

FIG. 8-20

8-19. (a) Prove that the coil current in the sweep of Fig. 8-15 may be expressed as

$$i = Ae^{-t/\tau} + Bt + C$$

where A, B, C, and τ are constants of the circuit.

(b) Evaluate the above constants in terms of the circuit and transistor parameters.

(c) Is it possible to generate a perfectly linear sweep? What conditions must be satisfied if the sweep nonlinearity is to be minimized?

BIBLIOGRAPHY

Chance, B., et al.: "Waveforms," Massachusetts Institute of Technology Radiation Laboratory Series, vol. 19, McGraw-Hill Book Company, Inc., New York, 1949.

Goodrich, H. C.: A Transistorized Horizontal Deflection System, *RCA Rev.*, vol. 18, pp. 293–321, September, 1957.

Millman, J., and H. Taub: "Pulse and Digital Circuits," McGraw-Hill Book Company, Inc., New York, 1956.

Soller, T., et al.: "Cathode-ray Tube Displays," Massachusetts Institute of Technology Radiation Laboratory Series, vol. 22, McGraw-Hill Book Company, Inc., New York, 1948.

Sziklai, G. C., R. D. Lohman, and G. B. Herzog: A Study of Transistor Circuits for Television, *Proc. IRE*, vol. 41, no. 6, pp. 708–717, 1953.

PART 3

SWITCHING

CHAPTER 9

PLATE-GRID- AND COLLECTOR-BASE-COUPLED MULTIVIBRATORS

9-1. Basic Multivibrator Considerations. Any closed-loop regenerative system having two or more clearly defined stable or quasi-stable states, each of which is maintained without recourse to external forcing, might well be categorized as a multivibrator. The application of a low-energy-content stimulus, a trigger, starts the switching action which drives the operating point away from one stable state and toward the next. But the important attribute of the multivibrator which differentiates it from other multistate systems, such as a switch or relay, is that once the trigger brings the circuit into its regenerative region, the additional energy necessary to complete the transition is supplied by the system itself.

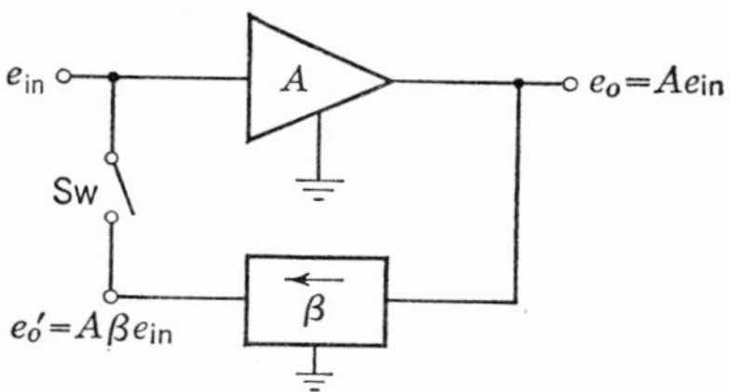

FIG. 9-1. Basic regenerative system.

The necessary and sufficient conditions for any system to operate as a multivibrator may best be established by considering the functional form of the multivibrator, shown in the block diagram of Fig. 9-1. At least two active elements are assumed included in A, contributing the necessary positive gain.

Upon the application of an input stimulus, e_{in}, the signal returned through the amplifier and feedback network β is

$$e_o' = \beta A e_{in} \tag{9-1}$$

When $\beta A > 1$, the returned signal is larger than the applied stimulus, and once the switch is closed, it will reinforce the original signal. The closed-loop system is unstable, with build-up continuing until the balance of returned signal and input is achieved, either through a decrease in the amplifier gain (limiting) or by the destruction of the transmission path (active element cut off).

Balance conditions require that when the switch is closed

$$e_o' = e_{in} \tag{9-2}$$

For possible switching, the system must have more than one stable point satisfying Eq. (9-2).

Figure 9-2, where we have superimposed the unity gain locus ($e_o' = e_{in}$) on the loop transfer characteristic of a typical amplifier, i.e., $\beta A e_{in}$ versus e_{in}, serves to illustrate the switching action. If the particular point selected to break the system's loop, for the evaluation of this curve, is normally restricted to positive or negative voltages (e.g., at the plate of a tube), then the whole curve will be shifted along the balance line into either the first or third quadrant. Inherent circuit limitations will always account for the two horizontal regions.

Satisfaction of the unity-loop-gain criterion is a necessary but insufficient condition for stable operation. Consider point Y (where $e_o' = e_{in}$

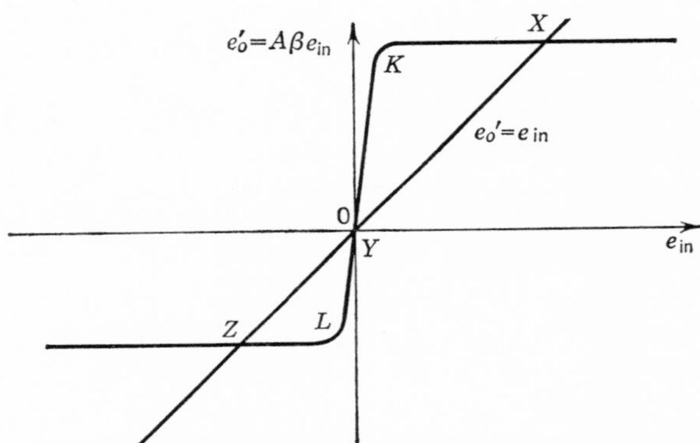

FIG. 9-2. Loop transfer characteristics for circuit of Fig. 9-1.

$= 0$), which, at first glance, appears stable. The slope of the transfer characteristic, evaluated at a particular point, is simply the value of the corresponding loop gain βA. At the origin, $\beta A > 1$, and thus any slight perturbation which might momentarily shift the operating point into the first quadrant will be amplified and returned as a much larger disturbance. The operating point travels up the transfer characteristic from Y to point X, where the balance condition is again satisfied. Here the incremental gain βA is less than 1; it is in fact zero. Any small disturbance away from X rapidly damps out, and the operating point returns to X, one of the two stable points. Similar reasoning shows that the other one is point Z.

We conclude, from the previous discussion, that the second necessary condition for stable switching is that $\beta A > 1$ in the active region and that $\beta A < 1$ at the stable point. It also follows that there always must be a point of unstable equilibrium between each set of stable points. As an exercise, the reader may furnish the proof of this statement.

If the active elements were transistors instead of vacuum tubes, we would modify the previous discussion and define the regenerative action in terms of the essential loop current gain.

The initial start from any unstable point, such as Y, would be caused by circuit noise or some other small perturbation. However, in order to switch from one absolutely stable point to the other, we must disturb the system at least enough to shift the operating point into the regenerative region where $\beta A > 1$. This region is easily delineated by marking its boundary points ($\beta A = 1$). We simply find the two points on the characteristic with unity slope (K, L). Thus the trigger size required for switching from X to Z becomes

$$e_T > e_K - e_X$$

To shift back from Z, we must introduce a positive disturbance greater than ZL.

When energy-storage elements are included in the internal transmission path, the exponential decay will eventually bring the circuit from the limiting to the regenerative region. As a consequence, the multivibrator switches between the points satisfying the balance conditions without resorting to external triggers. But since the system remains at each particular state for a well-defined interval, this only changes the stable to a quasi-stable point.

The flat portions of the transfer characteristic arise as a direct result of driving one of the active elements into saturation or cutoff. It follows that if we modify the load of the active element by the addition of diode wave-shaping circuits (Chap. 2), multiple limiting regions become feasible. Each diode introduces an additional break into the transfer characteristics and may thus create a new stable, or if energy-storage elements are also included, a new quasi-stable, point.

Transition from state to state takes some small finite time interval, primarily the time required to store or dissipate energy in the parasitic elements. In addition, when the base amplifier contains transistors, their on-off and carrier storage times will further affect the switching speed. These delays are not germane to the system's basic behavior, and we shall therefore ignore them in the following discussion.

9-2. Vacuum-tube Bistable Multivibrator. The circuit of a vacuum-tube bistable multivibrator (bistable indicating two absolutely stable states) appears in Fig. 9-3. Sometimes this circuit is also referred to as an Eccles-Jordan circuit, a flip-flop, or a binary. On being triggered, each tube switches between two of its three possible states, full on, active, or cut off; the particular two depend upon the adjustment of the circuit parameters.

It is easy to show that both tubes are normally in different states except during the transition interval when they simultaneously become active. Assume that both tubes are on, with E_{cc}, a negative voltage, chosen to place them in their active regions. Any slight disturbance, such as noise, may momentarily raise the plate current of T_1. The resultant drop in plate voltage is coupled by R_1, R_2, and the speed-up capacitor C_1 to the grid of T_2. The cross-coupling reapplies the amplified signal (now a voltage rise) back to the grid of T_1, where it reinforces the original perturbation. Thus the regenerative action drives T_1 toward saturation and T_2 toward cutoff. Switching ceases when one or both tubes reach their limit.

Three possible models exist for each tube, one when the tube is cut off (Fig. 9-4*a*), the second when it is in its active region (Fig. 9-4*b*), and the

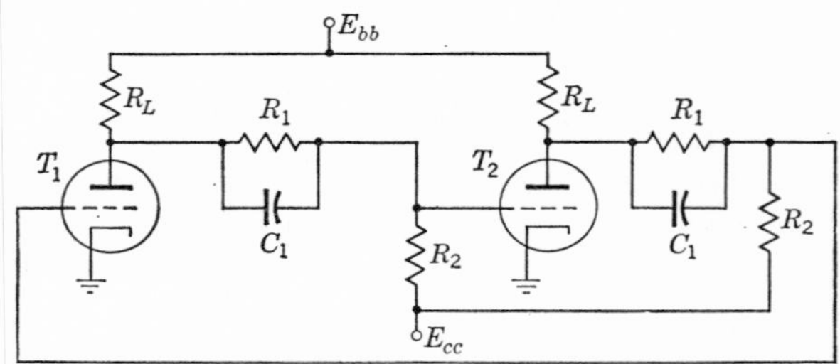

FIG. 9-3. Vacuum-tube bistable multivibrator.

third when it is saturated (Fig. 9-4*c*). (Figure 9-4*a* and *c* are degenerate forms of the general plate-circuit model shown in Fig. 9-4*b*.) In drawing the model holding during saturation, we neglected the effect of the slight positive grid excursion. When this term becomes significant, the model of Fig. 9-4*b*, with the appropriate positive value of e_c, will be used instead.

In attempting to analyze a multivibrator, a circuit where many combinations of tube states are possible, where and how do we begin? The answer is "anywhere"; any logical initial assumption serves as a convenient starting point and, if incorrect, will eventually lead to a contradiction. One of the limited number of other choices will then be the correct tube state. Since both tubes cannot remain in the same condition, the only permissible combinations of tube states are those tabulated below. We assume that the circuit has been triggered so that T_1 is the on (active) tube and T_2 is the off tube.

PERMISSIBLE STATES OF TUBES

T_1	T_2
Full on.........	Active
Full on.........	Cut off
Active..........	Cut off

Our object thus is to start, say, by assuming T_1 fully on, and then to carry the steady-state-circuit analysis through to its logical conclusion. Usually $(R_1 + R_2) \gg R_L$ and the loading of the plate by the coupling network may be ignored. From Fig. 9-4c,

$$E_{bs1} = \frac{r_p}{R_L + r_p} E_{bb} \tag{9-3}$$

And by superposition

$$E_{c2} = \frac{R_1}{R_1 + R_2} E_{cc} + \frac{R_2}{R_1 + R_2} E_{bs1} \tag{9-4}$$

where E_{bs1} is given by Eq. (9-3). Cutoff for this circuit is

$$E_{co} = -\frac{E_{bb}}{\mu} \tag{9-5}$$

Now if the actual grid voltage E_{c2} is more negative than E_{co}, then T_2 is cut off and Fig. 9-4a is the applicable model for calculation of

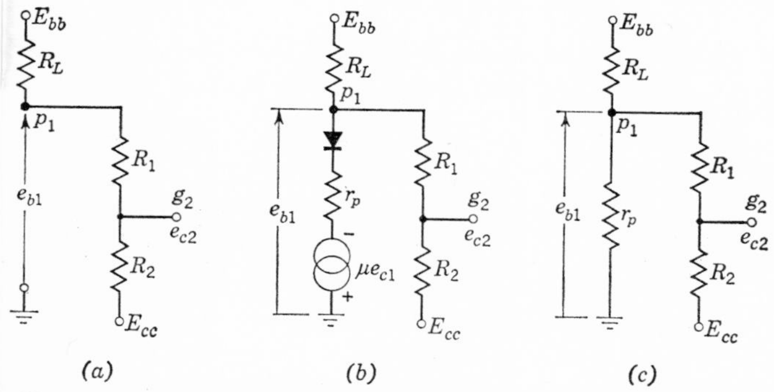

FIG. 9-4. Vacuum-tube circuit models. (a) Cutoff region; (b) active region; (c) saturation.

E_{b2} and E_{c1}. But if $0 > E_{c2} > E_{co}$, T_2 is in its active region and we must use the model of Fig. 9-4b. At the stable point both tubes cannot be active; if T_2 is part on, then T_1 must be full on, and our original assumption as to the circuit state was correct.

To continue, suppose that in this circuit $E_{c2} < E_{co}$ (T_2 cut off); then it follows from Fig. 9-4a that

$$E_{c1} = \frac{R_2}{R_1 + R_2} E_{bb} + \frac{R_1}{R_1 + R_2} E_{cc} \tag{9-6}$$

But to verify the initial assumption, namely, T_1 full on, the solution of Eq. (9-6) must be $E_{c1} > 0$.

Grid-circuit limiting prevents the grid from becoming more than slightly positive regardless of the solution of Eq. (9-6). In the model used, the grid loading was omitted in order to simplify the calculations.

The alternative solution of Eq. (9-6), $E_{co} < E_{c1} < 0$, contradicts our original assumption, and therefore the problem must be repeated from the now known tube states, T_1 part on and T_2 cut off. Because Eq. (9-6) was written for T_2 off, the substitution of the value of E_{c1} given by it into the model of Fig. 9-4*b* enables us to resolve the contradiction and find the correct values of e_{b1} and e_{c2}.

The switching process, the injection of a trigger turning the off tube on or the on tube off, will just interchange the states of the two tubes of the symmetrical circuit of Fig. 9-3. In an asymmetrical multivibrator, all voltages must be recalculated as a completely independent problem. The widest separation between the two stable states, and consequently the easiest to distinguish, occurs when each tube switches between full on and cut off. Under these circumstances the total plate voltage swing becomes

$$\Delta e_{b\,\max} = S_{\max} = E_{bb} - E_{bs1} = \frac{R_L E_{bb}}{R_L + r_p} \tag{9-7}$$

Proper multivibrator operation is predicated on our establishing the correct grid voltages in each of the two circuit states. Since this depends

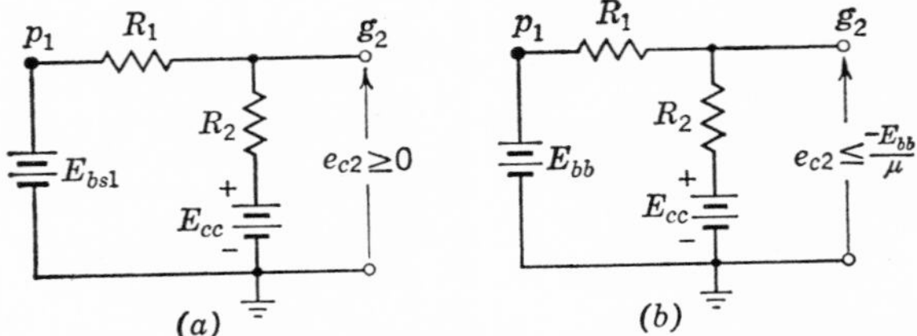

FIG. 9-5. Circuit models under limiting conditions. (*a*) Both tubes saturated; (*b*) both tubes cut off.

on E_{cc}, R_1, and R_2, we should determine their interrelationships, at least at the limits, as a guide in circuit design. One limit occurs when both tubes are always saturated, the other when both are cut off. The circuit models holding under the limiting conditions, and where $(R_1 + R_2) > R_L$, are sketched in Fig. 9-5.

In order to prevent complete circuit saturation, from Fig. 9-5*a* we see that

$$E_{cc} < -\frac{R_2}{R_1} E_{bs1} \tag{9-8}$$

where E_{bs1} is given by Eq. (9-3). The other circuit limit, found from Fig. 9-5*b*, is expressed in Eq. (9-9).

$$E_{cc} > -\frac{R_2}{R_1} E_{bb} \left(\frac{\mu + 1}{\mu} + \frac{R_1}{\mu R_2} \right) \cong -\frac{R_2}{R_1} E_{bb} \tag{9-9}$$

The above approximation holds only for high-μ tubes. Generally, the center value of Eqs. (9-8) and (9-9) represents a good choice in that it allows for the greatest possible variation in the tube and circuit parameters before the multivibrator will cease functioning.

Rather than switch the multivibrator from one state to the other by first injecting a positive trigger to turn the tube on and then a negative one to turn it off, we might much more conveniently apply a train of

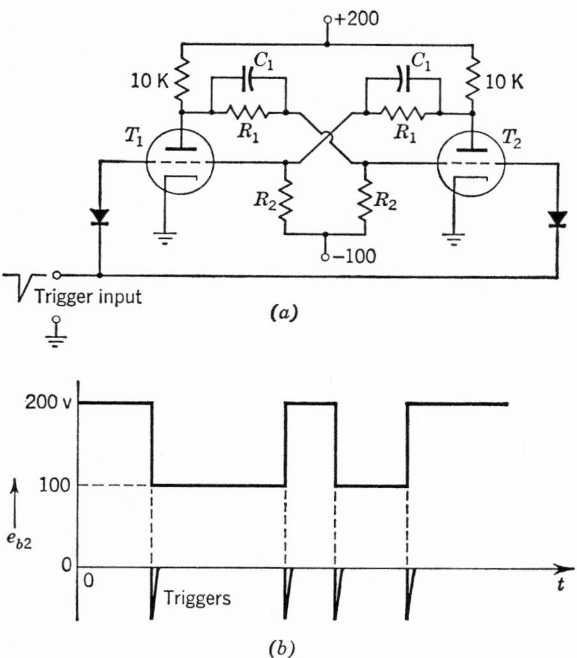

FIG. 9-6. (a) Bistable multivibrator triggered by a negative pulse train; (b) resultant plate waveshapes.

only positive or negative pulses. In order to maintain grid-to-grid isolation, the pulses are coupled into the tubes through diodes (Fig. 9-6a), producing the change in state at the plate of T_2 shown in Fig. 9-6b. The negative pulse drives the on tube into its active region. The positive amplified pulse appearing at the plate is coupled into the off tube and pulls it into conduction. For positive trigger inputs, the diodes are reversed.

Example 9-1. In this problem we shall investigate the role performed by the speed-up capacitor C_1 in the bistable multivibrator of Fig. 9-6. The circuit is excited by negative triggers injected into both grids through diodes. The tube used has $\mu = 20$, $r_p = 10$ K, $r_c = 200$ ohms, $C_{gk} = 10\ \mu\mu$f, and $C_{gp} = 10\ \mu\mu$f.

From Eqs. (9-3) and (9-7) we see that the plate voltage will swing from 200 volts, when the tube is cut off, to 100 volts, when the grid is driven slightly positive. To prevent false triggering, the grid of the off tube should be maintained somewhat below cutoff, say 10 volts below the cutoff value of -10 volts. Assuming that $R_1 + R_2 \gg R_L$, then with the grid of the off tube at -20 volts, the drop across R_2 must be 80 volts (Fig. 9-4c). Since the plate of the on tube is at 100 volts, the drop across R_1 will be 120 volts. Hence

$$\frac{R_1}{R_2} = \frac{120}{80}$$

and we can, quite arbitrarily, choose $R_2 = 0.5$ megohm and $R_1 = 0.75$ megohm.

We must now check that the on tube is saturated when these coupling resistors are used. Substituting the circuit values into the model of Fig. 9-4a, the grid voltage of T_1 becomes

$$e_{c1} = 20 \text{ volts}$$

Of course, this calculation neglected the positive-grid limiting and e_{c1} would actually be only a fraction of a volt.

When the external pulse is injected, the cutoff grid of T_2 will charge from -20 volts toward the new value established by the input trigger, with the time constant

$$\tau_a = R_1 \parallel R_2 C_{gk} = 2.85 \ \mu\text{sec}$$

Once the tube becomes active, the input capacity seen looking into the grid becomes

$$C_{\text{in}} = C_{gk} + C_{gp}(1 - A) = 10 + 10[1 - (-10)] = 120 \ \mu\mu\text{f}$$

Thereafter the charging continues with the much longer time constant of

$$\tau_b = R_1 \parallel R_2 C_{\text{in}} = 34 \ \mu\text{sec}$$

If the input pulse is extremely narrow, the net change in the grid voltage may be insufficient to maintain the switched tube states after the trigger is removed; the multivibrator will subsequently return to its original condition.

By shunting R_1 with C_1, the coupling network is changed into the compensated attenuator discussed in Sec. 1-9. Usually, for the fastest possible switching, it is adjusted slightly overcompensated. However, for the purpose of this discussion, assume that $C_1R_1 = R_2C_{\text{in}}$ or that

$$C_1 = 80 \ \mu\mu\text{f}$$

This capacity is far from critical, and in an actual circuit it may vary from 25 to 200 $\mu\mu$f. The switching time constants now become, from Eq. (1-34),

$$\tau_a' = \frac{C_1 C_{gk}}{C_1 + C_{gk}} R_s = 0.045 \ \mu\text{sec}$$

$$\tau_b' = \frac{C_1 C_{\text{in}}}{C_1 + C_{\text{in}}} R_s = 0.245 \ \mu\text{sec}$$

where R_s is the 5-K source impedance seen looking into the plate of the active tube. We see that the presence of C_1 reduces the critical time constant by a factor of more than 100.

The above argument attempted to show, in a relatively qualitative manner, that C_1 speeds up the switching process and permits operation with quite narrow trigger pulses. Many factors are changing during the interval considered: one tube is turning off; the other tube first becomes active and then its grid rapidly saturates. Therefore no attempt will be made to define the required pulse width. We can, however, say that it should be somewhat wider than the calculated time constant τ_b' but very much narrower than the pulse needed in the uncompensated circuit.

The bistable multivibrator is a device widely used in digital computers and in control equipment for counting. Each unit registers two counts: the first input trigger turns off the tube, and the second one turns it back on. Thus, if we differentiate the plate waveshape (Fig. 9-6*b*), we shall derive only one negative trigger for every two applied. By coupling the output pulse to another bistable we count down by four, and finally the cascading of n circuits allows counting by 2^n, yielding one output pulse per 2^n inputs. Various feedback arrangements, which preset the cascaded binary chain, will present a single output pulse for any desired count.

9-3. Transistor Bistable Multivibrator. A collector-base-coupled multivibrator is the transistor equivalent of the plate-grid-coupled multivibrator previously discussed. The mode of operation is now determined

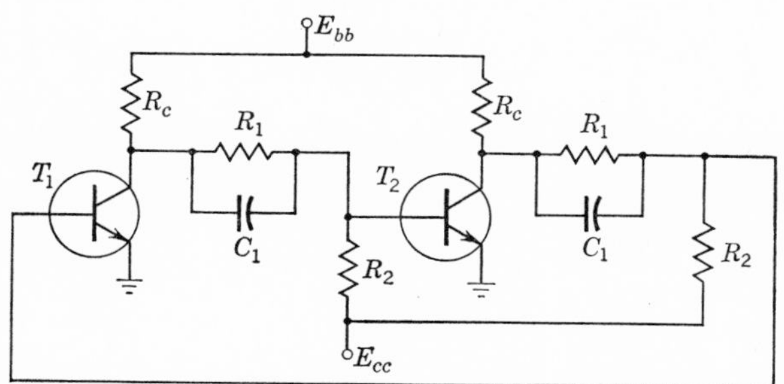

FIG. 9-7. Transistor bistable multivibrator.

by the base current flow, and therefore, for ensured regenerative switching, the loop current gain must be greater than unity. If we keep these specific features in mind, then this circuit is also amenable to the arguments employed in Sec. 9-2.

Assume that T_1, of the transistor bistable of Fig. 9-7, is in its active region. (The circuit shown uses *n-p-n* transistors; for *p-n-p* transistors all polarities are reversed.) Any increase in its base current causes a proportional increase in collector current. But this is reflected as a decrease in the base current of T_2, where it is amplified and finally reapplied as an increase in the base current of T_1. The original current change has thus been multiplied by the total loop current gain. Eventually the circuit limits with either T_1 full on or T_2 cut off. Since the speed-up capacitor couples the full change of collector current into the other transistor's base, the build-up process is extremely rapid. And as in our analysis of the vacuum-tube circuit, transition time will be ignored.

A separate model might be drawn for each of the three regions of transistor operation. If, as is normally the case, R_c is very much smaller than the transistor output impedance and if $R_1 \parallel R_2$ is very much larger than the small input impedance, then the models become extremely simple. Figure 9-8*a* shows the model holding for cutoff, 9-8*b* the one defining the active region, and 9-8*c* that holding under saturation conditions.

For the solution of this circuit, we shall start by assuming T_1 cut off. The model of Fig. 9-8*a* gives the base current of T_2 as

$$i_{b2} = \frac{E_{bb}}{R_1 + R_c} + \frac{E_{cc}}{R_2} \tag{9-10}$$

Models for the active and saturation region must agree at the boundary. From Fig. 9-8*c*, we see that the collector-emitter voltage of a saturated transistor is zero. Substitution of this limit into the model of the active region (Fig. 9-8*b*) results in

$$e_{ce} = 0 = E_{bb} - \beta i_b R_c$$

or

$$i_b \geq \frac{E_{bb}}{\beta R_c} \tag{9-11}$$

Equation (9-11) expresses the bounding condition for maintaining a transistor in saturation.

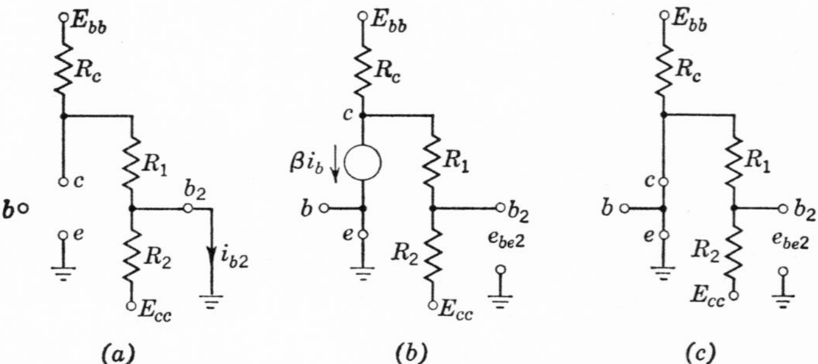

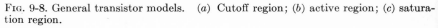

FIG. 9-8. General transistor models. (*a*) Cutoff region; (*b*) active region; (*c*) saturation region.

A comparison of Eqs. (9-10) and (9-11) determines the actual state of T_2 and enables us to choose the appropriate model. E_{c2} and I_{b1} or E_{be1} are now calculated, and the initial assumption checked.

If T_1 is not cut off, the contradiction must be resolved by a new solution from the other possible starting point, T_1 active and T_2 full on. It is, of course, necessary to modify the general models of Fig. 9-8 so that they satisfy the now known transistor states. In particular, we must connect the base junction of the coupling network in Fig. 9-8*b* to ground when solving for E_{c1} and I_{b2}.

The limits of E_{cc} or the coupling resistors are found at the two boundaries, complete saturation and complete cutoff. From Eq. (9-10), the minimum value of E_{cc} for $i_{b2} > 0$ is

$$E_{cc} > -\frac{R_2}{R_1 + R_c} E_{bb} \tag{9-12}$$

The maximum value of E_{cc}, above which both transistors are always saturated, will be found directly from Eq. (9-11) through recognizing that, under this condition, the total base current must be supplied by E_{cc}. Therefore

$$E_{cc} < \frac{R_2}{\beta R_c} E_{bb} \tag{9-13}$$

To ensure that one transistor is driven into cutoff while the other remains in the active region, much more stringent limitations must be placed on E_{cc} [Eq. (9-14)]. If we assume that T_2 is on and solve for the condition that the voltage at the base of T_1 must be less than zero, we obtain

$$E_{cc} < -\frac{R_2}{R_1} E_{c2} \tag{9-14}$$

where E_{c2} is the collector voltage of the conducting transistor.

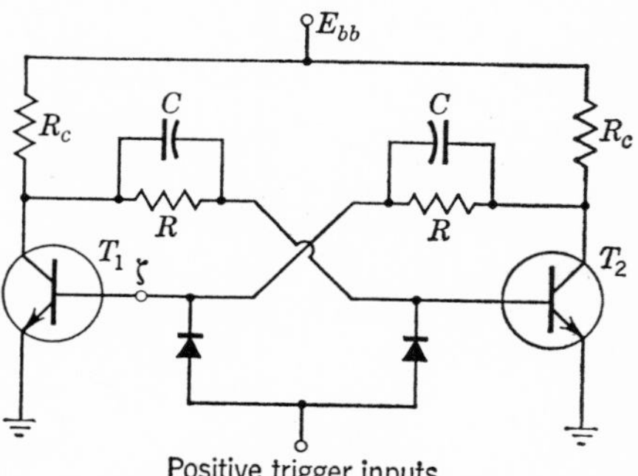

FIG. 9-9. Simple transistor multivibrator using one power supply and switching between full on and cutoff.

It should be noted that with T_2 full on ($E_{c2} = 0$), T_1 is cut off for all $E_{cc} \leq 0$ [Eq. (9-14)]. By setting $E_{cc} = 0$, only one power supply is required instead of two. Furthermore, since the multivibrator switches between full on and full off, current never flows in R_2 and it also may be omitted. The very simple multivibrator of Fig. 9-9 results.

The stable-state current and voltage values for this circuit, with T_1 cut off and T_2 full on, are

$$i_{b1} = 0 \qquad i_{b2} = \frac{E_{bb}}{R_c + R}$$

$$e_{c2} = 0 \qquad e_{c1} = \frac{RE_{bb}}{R_c + R}$$

But in order to ensure the saturation of T_2, i_{b2} must satisfy the condition given in Eq. (9-11):

$$i_{b2} = \frac{E_{bb}}{R_c + R} \geq \frac{E_{bb}}{\beta R_c} \tag{9-15}$$

The solution of Eq. (9-15) establishes the maximum value of R as

$$R \leq (\beta - 1)R_c \tag{9-16}$$

By treating this circuit as a current amplifier, we shall now demonstrate that the condition described above is the very one necessary for guaranteed regenerative switching. Suppose that the loop is broken at the base of T_1 and that point ζ is shorted to ground. Then the loop current gain, from an input of T_1 to point ζ, is

$$\frac{i_\zeta}{i_{b1}} = A_c = \left(\frac{R_c}{R_c + R}\right)^2 \beta^2 \tag{9-17}$$

For regenerative operation $A_c > 1$, and thus

$$R < (\beta - 1)R_c$$

which is identically the condition previously given by Eq. (9-16). A similar inequality must also be satisfied in the first multivibrator discussed in this section.

The change of circuit state, on to off and back on again, is effected by positive triggers injected into both bases through diodes. They drive the off transistor into the conduction region, and the resultant of the amplified pulse and the original triggers turn the on transistor off. Negative triggers will also work, but the diodes would have to be reversed.

Collector waveshapes, except for voltage values, are of identical form with those of the vacuum-tube multivibrator of Fig. 9-6. The maximum swing will, of course, be much smaller, and the minimum voltage value can now go to zero, but the two circuit states are still clearly delineated, one at zero and the other close to E_{bb}.

9-4. A Monostable Transistor Multivibrator. The introduction of a single energy-storage element in the regenerative transmission path creates a circuit having one stable and one quasi-stable state. If we examine the resultant monostable circuit of Fig. 9-10, we note that since the base of T_2 is returned to E_{bb}, this transistor must be on, either in its active region or saturated. The polarity of E_{cc} is always opposite to that of E_{bb}, and it is relatively easy to ensure that T_1 will be cut off.

In the particular multivibrator shown, *p-n-p* transistors are used as the active elements. E_{bb} will therefore be negative, and E_{cc} positive. If

n-p-n transistors were used instead, all voltages and currents would be reversed.

The quasi-stable circuit state, T_2 cut off, is contingent on the charge in the coupling capacitor maintaining $e_{be2} > 0$. However, a discharge path exists and, regardless of the initial condition, C must decay with e_{be2} subsequently reaching zero. At this point T_2 turns back on. Regeneration turns T_1 off, and the multivibrator is back in its one "mono" stable state.

Analysis of this circuit will proceed on the assumption that it is designed for the maximum possible collector voltage variation, i.e., both transistors driven between saturation and cutoff. If any particular answer does not support this contention, then the problem must be re-solved by drawing new models that will yield consistent results.

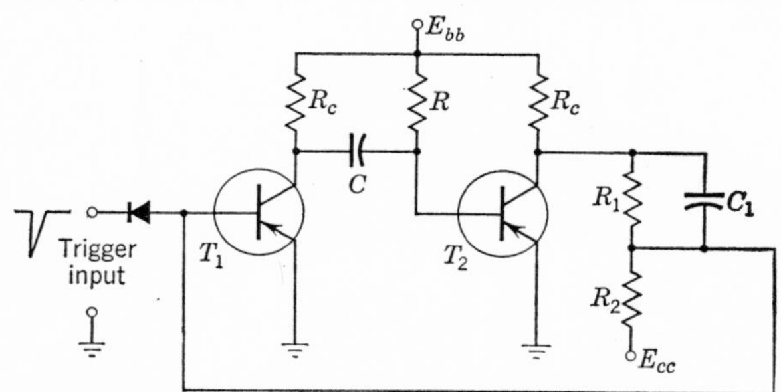

FIG. 9-10. Collector-base-coupled monostable multivibrator using p-n-p transistors. E_{bb} is negative and E_{cc} positive for proper biasing.

The stable circuit conditions are (from the models of Fig. 9-8)

$$T_1 \text{ off:} \qquad e_{c1} = E_{bb} \qquad e_{be1}(0^-) = \frac{R_1}{R_1 + R_2} E_{cc}$$

$$T_2 \text{ on:} \qquad e_{c2} = 0 \qquad i_{b2}(0^-) = \frac{E_{bb}}{R}$$

If T_2 is to be saturated, i_{b2} must also satisfy Eq. (9-11), leading to the following restriction on R:

$$R \leq \beta R_c \tag{9-18}$$

If this inequality is not satisfied, then, in its normal state, T_2 will be active instead of being saturated.

A negative trigger injected at the base of T_1 turns this transistor on, and the change in its collector voltage is immediately coupled through C to the base of T_2, turning it off. The circuit has now entered its quasi-stable region, and the new models needed to define operation are those given in Fig. 9-11.

We determine the time elapsed before the circuit can return to its stable state from Fig. 9-11*a*. As the right-hand side of C charges from

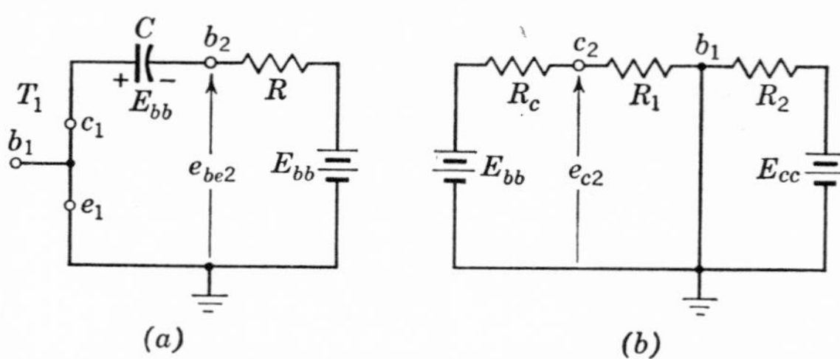

FIG. 9-11. Circuit models holding under quasi-stable conditions. (*a*) Collector of T_1 to the base of T_2; (*b*) collector of T_2 to the base of T_1.

its original value of $-E_{bb}$ toward E_{bb}, the equation of the base voltage of T_2 becomes

$$e_{b2}(t) = E_{bb} - 2E_{bb}e^{-t/\tau_1} \qquad \tau_1 = RC$$

At $t = t_1$, $e_{b2} = 0$, and T_2 again conducts. Substitution of the boundary value into the equation defining $e_{b2}(t)$ results in

$$t_1 = \tau_1 \ln 2 \tag{9-19}$$

To guarantee the saturation of T_1 during the unstable period, the following relationship must be satisfied [from Fig. 9-11*b* and Eq. (9-11)]:

$$i_{b1} = \frac{E_{bb}}{R_c + R_1} + \frac{E_{cc}}{R_2} \geq \frac{E_{bb}}{\beta R_c} \tag{9-20}$$

After the circuit reswitches and recovery begins, the models of Fig. 9-11 are no longer valid. We must consider the new problem posed in Fig. 9-12, where C recharges toward E_{bb} from its initial value of zero. The collector of T_1 recovers toward its stable state, also E_{bb}, with the recovery time constant $\tau_2 = R_cC$.

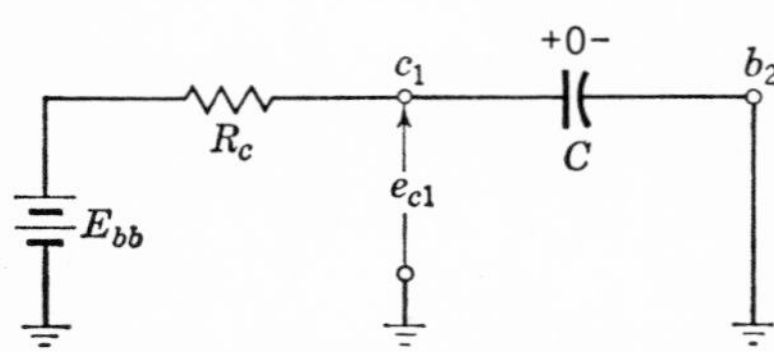

FIG. 9-12. Recovery circuit.

Within four time constants, recovery is virtually complete. Since we wish the recovery time to be small compared with the output pulse width, $R_c \ll R$. This multivibrator is also open to simplification by omitting R_2 and E_{cc} just as discussed in Sec. 9-3. Their presence aids in maintaining T_2 well below cutoff while the circuit is in its normal state and consequently prevents false triggering by small noise pulses.

Circuit waveshapes are shown in Fig. 9-13, and we might note that the output pulse having the best shape appears at the collector of T_2.

Since this point is isolated from the single RC timing circuit, external loading, introduced by the coupling to the next stage, will not affect the pulse duration. If we differentiate the output pulse, the resultant

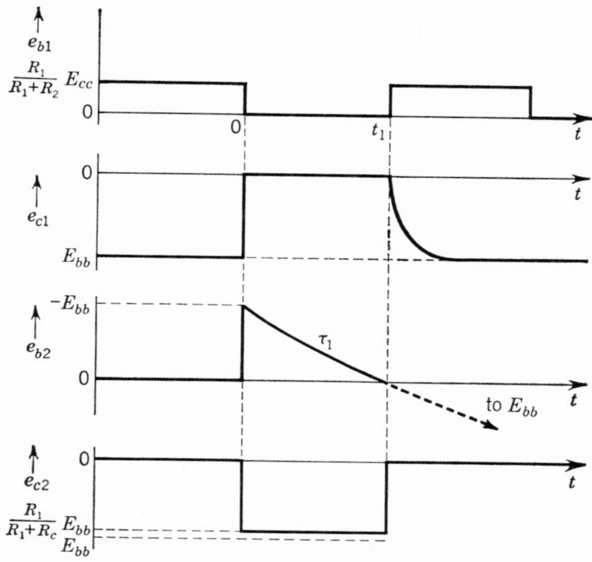

FIG. 9-13. Monostable multivibrator waveshapes for the p-n-p circuit of Fig. 9-10.

positive trigger is delayed from the applied input by the pulse duration t_1. Therefore the monostable multivibrator may be used as either a pulse or a delay trigger generator.

9-5. A Vacuum-tube Monostable Multivibrator. Even a perfunctory inspection of the monostable of Fig. 9-14 indicates that in its normal state

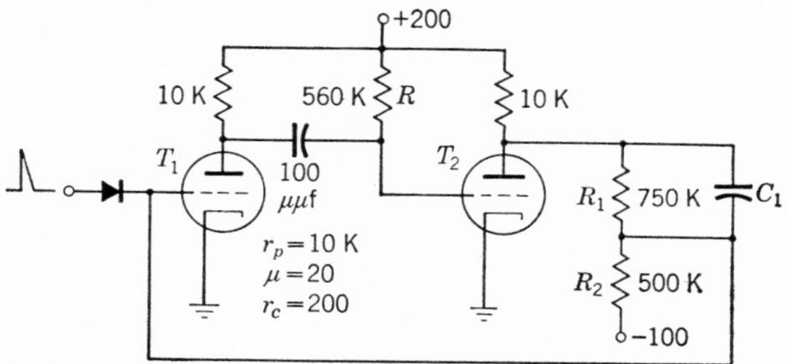

FIG. 9-14. Vacuum-tube monostable multivibrator.

T_2 is fully on (the grid returned through R to E_{bb} will be slightly above zero, and the plate will be slightly below its saturation value of 100 volts). Proper choice of E_{cc} will bias T_1 well below cutoff and yet allow it to switch fully on when the circuit is triggered into the unstable state.

If we neglect both the small positive grid voltage and the loading of R_L by the resistive-coupling network, the grid of the off tube will be at

$$e_{c1}(0^-) \cong \frac{R_2}{R_1 + R_2} E_{bs} + \frac{R_1}{R_1 + R_2} E_{cc} = -20 \text{ volts} \qquad (9\text{-}21)$$

which is below the cutoff value of -10 volts. This tube's plate is, of course, at E_{bb}. The only other unknown initial condition is the voltage across C, which remains invariant across the transition from the stable to the unstable state. Since one end of C is returned to ground through

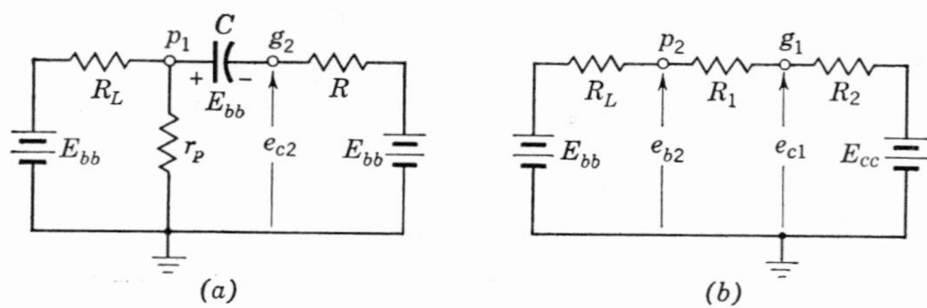

FIG. 9-15. Quasi-stable state circuit models. (a) Plate of T_1 to the grid of T_2; (b) plate of T_2 to the grid of T_1.

the conducting grid of T_2 and the other end is connected to the plate of the off tube,

$$e_q(0^-) = e_{b1}(0^-) - e_{c2}(0^-) \cong E_{bb}$$

After a positive trigger at the grid of T_1 switches the circuit into its quasi-stable state, the models defining the behavior become those shown in Fig. 9-15. Figure 9-15a is the more important of the two because it contains the circuit's single energy-storage element. The model can be further simplified by replacing the tube with its Thévenin equivalent—a 100-volt source (E_{bs}) together with a 5,000-ohm resistance ($R_L \parallel r_p$). This approximation neglects the slight positive grid excursion that will lower the plate to somewhat below E_{bs}. By using the reduced circuit we can now solve for the grid voltage of T_2.

$$e_{c2}(0^+) = E_{bb} - \frac{2E_{bb} - E_{bs}}{R + R_L \parallel r_p} R \qquad (9\text{-}22)$$

But since $R \gg R_L \parallel r_p$

$$e_{c2}(0^+) \cong -(E_{bb} - E_{bs}) = -S_1 = -100 \qquad (9\text{-}23)$$

where S_1, the total plate voltage swing of T_1 as it switches from cutoff to saturation, is also given by

$$S_1 = \frac{R_L}{r_p + R_L} E_{bb} \qquad (9\text{-}24)$$

The grid starts recovering from -100 toward 200 volts with the time constant

$$\tau_1 = (R + R_L \parallel r_p)C \cong RC = 56 \ \mu\text{sec}$$

Once it reaches the cutoff value of -10 volts, T_2 becomes active and the circuit regeneration will rapidly turn T_1 off and T_2 fully on. Consequently, the duration of the quasi-stable state, as evaluated from the exponential-response equation, is

$$t_1 = \tau_1 \ln \frac{E_{bb} + S_1}{E_{bb} + \dfrac{E_{bb}}{\mu}} = 20 \ \mu\text{sec} \tag{9-25}$$

Since, at least to a first approximation, all the voltage terms of Eq. (9-25) are linear functions of E_{bb}, we expect that the pulse duration will be relatively independent of any variations in the plate supply voltage. Both μ and r_p will vary with the current flow, μ only slightly but r_p drastically. As a consequence S_1 will vary somewhat with E_{bb}, and so will the pulse duration.

The final charge on C at the instant before switching back to the stable state is

$$e_q(t_1) = E_{bs} + \frac{E_{bb}}{\mu} = 110 \text{ volts}$$

This value must be used to calculate the initial value of the recovery waveshape from the model of Fig. 9-16. Since the transition occurs at

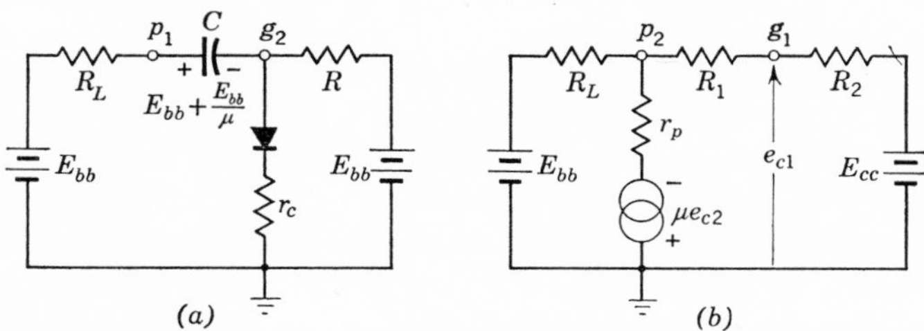

FIG. 9-16. Recovery models for plate-grid-coupled monostable multivibrator. (a) p_1 to g_2; (b) p_2 to g_1.

$-E_{bb}/\mu$ instead of at zero, during the switching process the tube goes directly from cutoff to saturation. As a result, jumps appear at both the grid of T_2 and the plate of T_1. From Fig. 9-16a,

$$E_{c2,\max} = \frac{E_{bb} - (E_{bs} + E_{bb}/\mu)}{R_L + r_c} r_c$$

but since $r_c \ll R_L$,

$$E_{c2,\max} \cong \frac{r_c}{R_L}\left(S_1 - \frac{E_{bb}}{\mu}\right) = 2.2 \text{ volts} \tag{9-26}$$

We might note that the voltage term in Eq. (9-26) is simply the total change of loop voltage due to the change of the circuit state and that it divides proportionately across r_c and R_L. The total jump at the grid of 12.2 volts (from -10 to $+2.2$ volts) will also appear at the plate of T_1, raising its voltage from 100 to 112.2 volts. After the jump, recovery is rapid—back to the initial steady-state value with the fast time constant of

$$\tau_2 = (R_L + r_c)C \cong R_L C = 1\ \mu\text{sec}$$

To obtain the recovery waveshapes at the plate of T_2 and the grid of T_1 we must treat the model of Fig. 9-16*b*. These are most easily

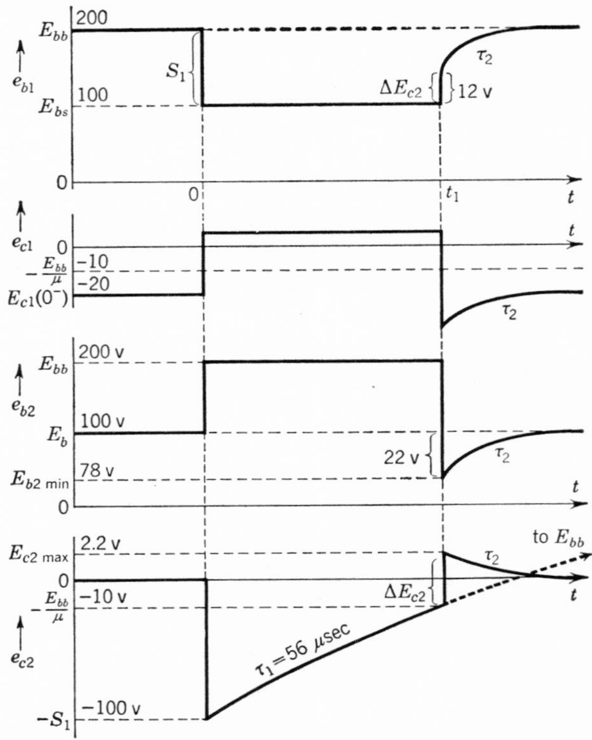

FIG. 9-17. Waveshapes of plate-grid-coupled monostable multivibrator of Fig. 9-14.

found by imposing the effect of the positive grid voltage on the quiescent values. The 2.2-volt grid excursion is amplified ($A = -10$) and reflected into the plate of T_2, causing the voltage to drop 22 volts below the nominal value of 100 volts:

$$E_{b2,\min} = E_{bs} - \frac{\mu R_L}{r_p + R_L} E_{c2,\max} = 78 \text{ volts} \tag{9-27}$$

The plate now recovers toward E_{bs} at a rate controlled by the grid circuit charging. In addition, this large drop is coupled through the speed-up capacitor to the grid of T_1 and can only aid in driving it to well below cutoff.

Equation (9-27) may yield a negative answer for $E_{b,\min}$. Obviously, this must be rejected since the model representation has led us to an impossible solution. Once the tube is driven into the high-grid-current region, both r_p and r_c change markedly from the constant values assumed in drawing the piecewise-linear models, and these variations, if taken into account, would resolve the contradiction.

The waveshapes shown in Fig. 9-17 are of the same general form as those found for the transistor monostable, and if we had accounted for the small base region (about 200 mv), the transistor circuit also would have exhibited some very small overshoots. The excursion below E_{bs}, appearing at the plate of T_2, can be easily eliminated by incorporating a plate bottoming diode which will conduct and limit the plate voltage to some value slightly above E_{bs}.

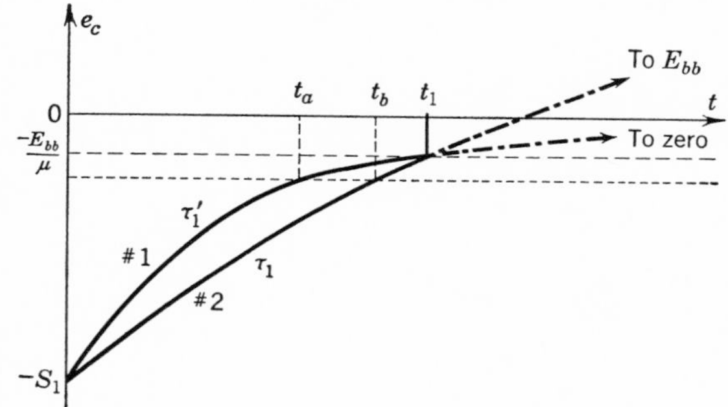

FIG. 9-18. Firing-line intersection by charging exponentials.

As an alternative to the circuit of Fig. 9-14, we might return R to ground instead of to E_{bb}. The switching sequence still remains the same, with the same size plate swing and time constant; the grid, however, now charges toward zero. The conduction point $-E_{bb}/\mu$ is not affected by this circuit change, but since the multivibrator switches state closer to the final value, the pulse duration will be much longer than that given by Eq. (9-25):

$$t_1' = \tau_1 \ln \frac{\mu S_1}{E_{bb}} \tag{9-28}$$

and for a high-μ tube, which fires almost at zero, this sweep takes approximately four time constants.

Suppose that we adjust the RC time constant of the particular multivibrator having its grid returned to zero so that its period is identical with that of the original circuit (Fig. 9-18). The curve charging toward zero (1) crosses the $-E_{bb}/\mu$ line at an extremely shallow angle, in fact almost horizontally. This is in sharp contrast to curve 2, which exponentially charges toward E_{bb} and which intersects the firing line closer to the perpendicular. Any noise introduced into the system effectively lowers the cutoff line to the dotted line of Fig. 9-18. Curve 1 fires quite a bit prematurely (at t_a), while curve 2 is only slightly affected (fires at t_b). Thus we conclude that by returning the grid to the highest possible voltage, the pulse duration is made much less susceptible to random disturbances.

9-6. Vacuum-tube Astable Multivibrator. The insertion of a second capacitor in the transmission loop, i.e., capacitive coupling from each plate to the other tube's grid, makes both circuit states quasi-stable. Figure 9-19 shows the circuit of the resultant astable multivibrator. If both tubes are assumed to be in their active regions, regeneration will rapidly drive one into cutoff and the other to saturation. This state is unstable, lasting only until the particular capacitor that is keeping the tube cut off discharges, at which point the switching action reverses

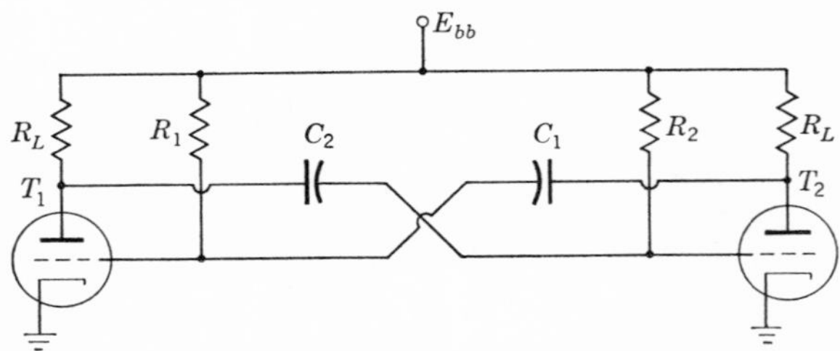

FIG. 9-19. Plate-grid-coupled astable multivibrator.

the tube states: the off tube goes on and the on tube goes off. The astable multivibrator is self-starting and free-running.

We might note that the timing network coupling each plate to the next grid is exactly the same as the single timing circuit of the monostable multivibrator (Fig. 9-14). The astable multivibrator may well be considered as two monostable circuits operating sequentially, one triggered off whenever the other one turns on. The previous techniques are readily applicable, and by starting anywhere we shall, within no more than 2 cycles, reach the final periodic solution.

Since the exponential timing after the change of circuit state depends upon the conditions existing immediately before switching, probably the best starting point is where T_2 is full on, just going off, and T_1 is full off, just going on. At this instant the model holding (Fig. 9-20a) is identical with the one defining the stable state of the monostable multivibrator (Fig. 9-15a). In our initial analysis, so as not to confuse or conceal the basic simplicity of the behavior of this circuit beneath the mathematical manipulations, we shall ignore the effects of any positive grid voltage. In fact, we may even limit $e_c \leq 0$ by simply setting $r_c = 0$. The initial circuit voltages, from Eqs. (9-21), (9-22), and the assumed starting point, are

$$e_{c1} = \frac{-E_{bb}}{\mu} \qquad e_{b1} = E_{bb}$$

$$e_{c2} = \frac{r_c}{R_2} E_{bb} \cong 0 \qquad e_{b2} = E_{bs2} = \frac{r_{p2}}{r_{p2} + R_L} E_{bb}$$

These values determine the initial charge across each coupling capacitor and therefore enable us to calculate the voltages at each tube element just after switching. The models holding appear in Fig. 9-20 with the charge indicated.

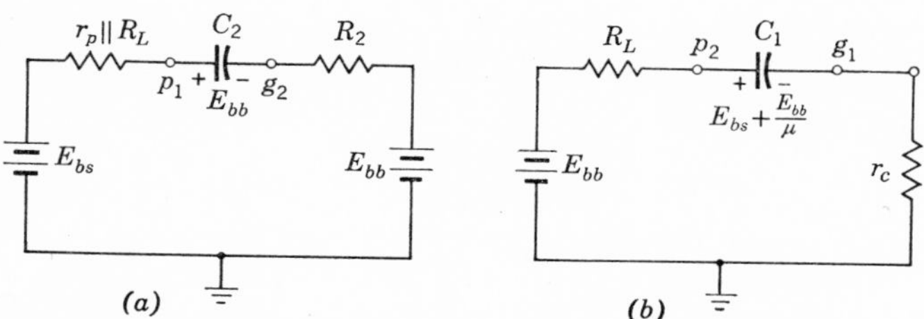

FIG. 9-20. Astable circuit models (T_1 on, T_2 off). (a) Sweep model p_1 to g_2; (b) positive grid recovery model p_2 to g_1.

As the circuit changes state, the plate voltage of the formerly off tube T_1 drops from E_{bb} to E_{bs1}. This swing S_1 is coupled by C_2 to the grid of T_2 and will cut off that tube. Since $R_2 \gg R_L$, the effect of the capacitor charging current in determining the plate swing is insignificant. Figure 9-20*a* shows the timing circuit holding during the unstable interval. The grid of T_2 recovers from $-S_1$ toward E_{bb}, with the tube turning back on when it reaches $-E_{bb}/\mu$. The time required is

$$t_2 = \tau_2 \ln \frac{E_{bb} + S_1}{E_{bb} + E_{bb}/\mu} \qquad \tau_2 \cong R_2C_2 \tag{9-29}$$

When the multivibrator reswitches, the sequence of events repeats in the network coupling the plate of T_2 to the grid of T_1.

$$t_1 = \tau_1 \ln \frac{E_{bb} + S_2}{E_{bb} + E_{bb}/\mu} \qquad \tau_1 \cong R_1C_1 \tag{9-30}$$

The two waveshapes generated are displaced in time from one another, one starting when the other ends (Fig. 9-21). Thus the total period is the sum of the times given in Eqs. (9-29) and (9-30). If a square-wave output is desired, the circuit is made completely symmetrical and $t_1 = t_2$.

Up to this point we have concerned ourselves only with the circuit behavior during the off period and we have ignored anything that happened at the grid of the on tube. When T_1 switches on (Fig. 9-20*b*), the change in the grid circuit and the introduction of a finite value of r_c produce a positive grid jump [Eq. (9-26)], with a subsequent recovery back to zero.

$$e_{c1}(t) \cong E_{c1,\max}e^{-t/\tau_3} \qquad \tau_3 = R_L C_1 \tag{9-31}$$

Normally, $\tau_3 \ll \tau_2$ and the recovery of T_1 is completed within a very short period compared with the off time of T_2. The grid jump also

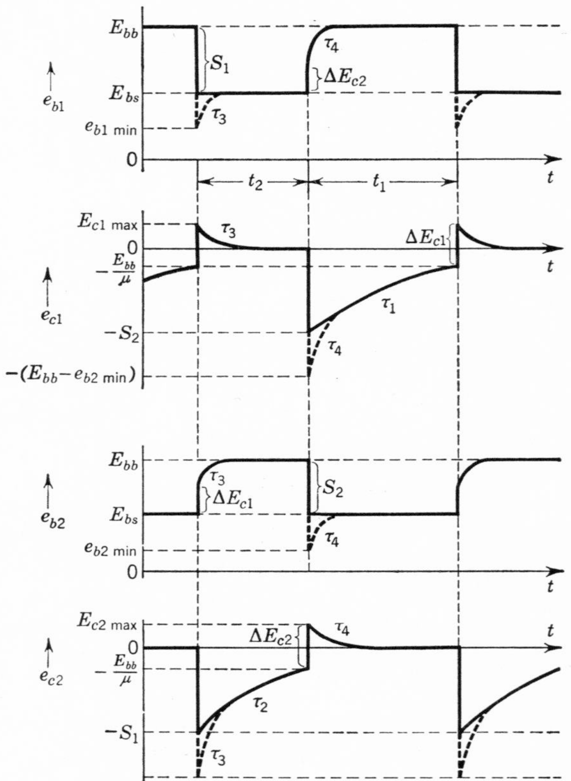

FIG. 9-21. Waveshapes appearing in the plate-grid-coupled astable multivibrator.

appears amplified at the plate of T_1 and helps drive the other tube off. Thus two driving source components must be considered in calculating the exact response of the grid circuit of T_2, the simple plate drop from E_{bb} to E_{bs1} (previously considered), and the amplified exponential grid decay of Eq. (9-31).

Since the positive grid recovery of T_1 is assumed complete while the grid of the off tube is still well below the cutoff value, there will be but slight modification needed as to the actual duration of the off period.

It seems that a reasonable approach is to simply amplify the grid recovery waveshape [Eq. (9-31)] and superimpose it on the sweep waveshapes which were found by ignoring the positive grid jump. This is indicated by the broken lines of Fig. 9-21. If we should require a more exact answer as to the sweep duration, we would have to solve for the response of the appropriate plate-to-grid RC circuit to the applied driving function, $-S_1 + Ae_{c1}(t)$, where $e_{c1}(t)$ was defined in Eq. (9-31).

9-7. Transistor Astable Multivibrator. The circuit of a symmetrical astable multivibrator using *n-p-n* transistors appears in Fig. 9-22. Each transistor sequentially switches between full on and full off and behaves in a manner similar to the single unstable state of the monostable multivibrator. The circuit waveshapes are also basically those of the monostable (Fig. 9-13), with the alternate transistor states displaced by half of the total period (Fig. 9-23).

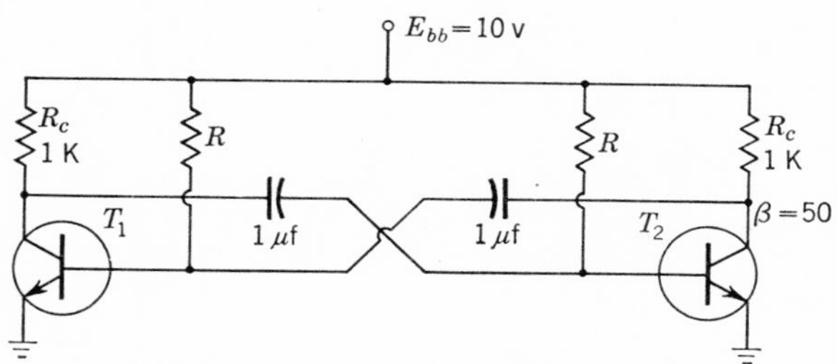

FIG. 9-22. Transistor astable multivibrator.

Once T_2 goes full on, the base of T_1 is driven to -10 volts and the collector of T_1 recovers to E_{bb} with the time constant R_cC. To ensure complete recovery before the circuit reswitches, the half period, identically that given in Eq. (9-19), must be longer than the recovery time.

$$RC \ln 2 \geq 4R_cC \tag{9-32}$$

If, in addition, we should want to ensure that the on transistor remains saturated over the complete half cycle, then a further limitation, defined by Eq. (9-18), must also be imposed on R. Combining Eqs. (9-18) and (9-32), we see that R should be restricted to the range

$$\beta R_c \geq R \geq 5.8R_c \tag{9-33}$$

In the circuit of Fig. 9-22, R must lie between 5.8 and 50 K. Currently available transistors have β values of 50 or more; hence the limitation on R is not particularly severe. Since C is the same in both charging paths, the larger the size of R, consistent with Eq. (9-33), the smaller the percentage of the half period devoted to the collector recovery exponential. The waveshapes of one transistor are shown in

Fig. 9-23; those at the other transistor are identical but displaced by a half period.

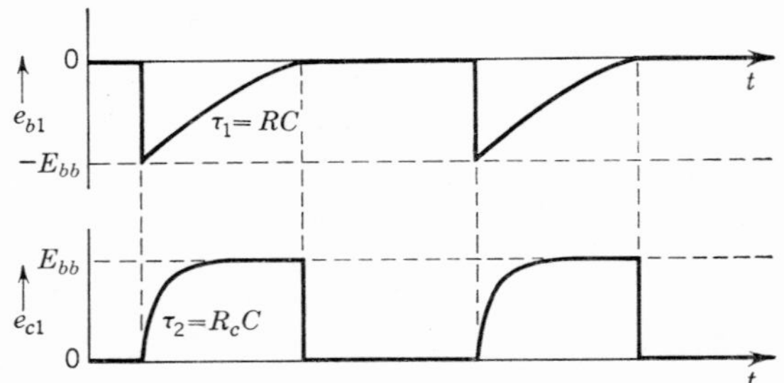

FIG. 9-23. Waveshapes of transistor astable multivibrator (taken at transistor T_1).

Example 9-2. By setting $R = 75$ K in the circuit of Fig. 9-22, Eq. (9-33) is not satisfied and the transistors switch between their cutoff and active regions. This mode of operation is somewhat different from that previously considered for the transistor, but since the basic behavior remains the same, we may use the standard method of analysis.

As our arbitrary starting point, we shall assume that T_1 is off, on the verge of switching on, and that T_2 is in the opposite state. In the initial discussion the contribution of the charging current through C_2 and the base of T_1 will be neglected, and we shall further assume that the total bias current is E_{bb}/R. When T_1 turns on, its collector falls from 10 volts to

$$E_{c1}(0^+) = E_{bb} - \beta i_b R_c = 10 - \beta \frac{10}{75 \text{ K}} 1 \text{ K} = 2.5 \text{ volts}$$

The base of T_2 falls by the same amount and immediately starts charging from -7.5 volts toward 10 volts with the time constant

$$\tau_1 \cong RC = 75 \text{ msec}$$

Since the turn-on point is zero volts, all the information necessary to calculate the switching time is now known. The half period is

$$t_1 = 75 \ln \frac{10 + 7.5}{10} \cong 42 \text{ msec}$$

In the previous calculations we neglected the component of the base current of T_1 contributed by the recharge of C_2. This current flows through the 1-K collector load resistor, starting from a peak of

$$I_m = \frac{7.5 \text{ volts}}{R_c} = 7.5 \text{ ma}$$

and decays toward zero with the fast time constant

$$\tau_2 = R_cC = 1 \text{ msec}$$

The extra current flow drives the transistor into saturation for a portion of the cycle. This phenomenon is almost identical with the positive grid jump in the vacuum-tube circuit where the fast overshoot brought the plate voltage below E_{bs}. Just as in that case, $\tau_2 \ll \tau_1$ and the extra recovery exponential will not influence the sweep timing. It may simply be superimposed on the normal sweep as shown by the heavy broken lines in Fig. 9-24.

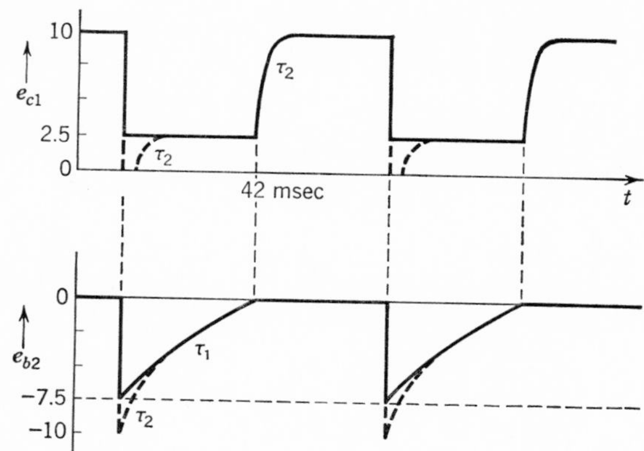

FIG. 9-24. Waveshapes for the multivibrator of Example 9-2.

Under the conditions of this problem, the initial drop, and hence the half period, are dependent on the value of β. A 10 per cent reduction, from 50 to 45, reduces the size of the voltage drop to 6.75 volts and the sweep time to 39 msec. If the transistor switched between cutoff and saturation, as it does when generating the waveshapes of Fig. 9-23, then the period is determined solely by the RC network and not by the parameters of the active circuit element.

Incomplete Circuit Recovery. We now propose to consider the additional complexity introduced in calculating the duration of the half period, if the collector recovery is not complete when the multivibrator switches states. The symmetrical astable is relatively easy to treat, once it builds up to periodicity, since the waveshapes of both transistors are identical. The base of one transistor is driven off by the drop in the collector voltage of the other transistor as it switches full on. At the end of the unknown half period t_1, the collector voltage has risen only from zero to the value found from the recovery exponential [Eq. (9-34)]. (Also see the waveshape in Fig. 9-25.)

$$e_c(t_1) = E_{bb}(1 - e^{-t_1/\tau_2}) \qquad \tau_2 = R_cC \tag{9-34}$$

Therefore the off transistor is driven only to $-e_c(t_1)$ instead of to $-E_{bb}$. The equation defining the rise of base voltage becomes

$$e_b(t) = E_{bb} - [E_{bb} + e_c(t_1)]e^{-t/\tau_1} \qquad \tau_1 = RC \tag{9-35}$$

A change of state again occurs when $e_b(t_1) = 0$. But the elapsed time depends on the initial drop [Eq. (9-34)], which itself is determined by the unknown half period. The interrelationships of the two equations are illustrated in Fig. 9-25, especially by comparing it with Figs. 9-23 and 9-24.

The above argument has furnished us with two transcendental equations [(9-34) and (9-35)] which must be simultaneously solved for the unknown half period t_1. One standard method of solution is to graph e_{c1} as a function of various values of t_1, as individually found from each equation. The intersection represents the unique solution for both e_{c1} and t_1.

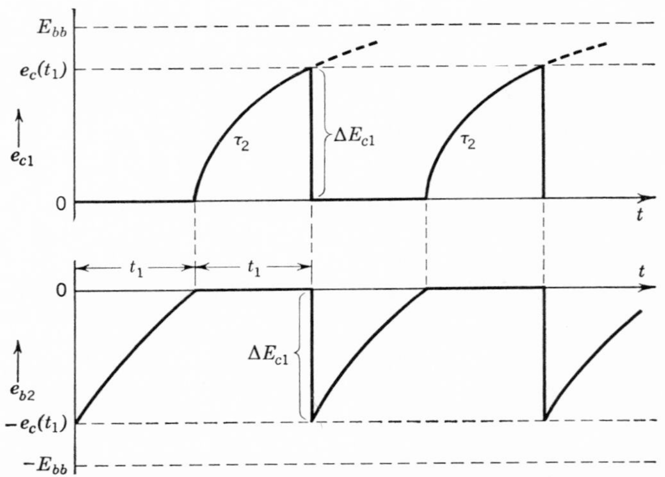

FIG. 9-25. Collector and base waveshapes due to incomplete recovery.

In the special case of a symmetrical transistor multivibrator, by substituting Eq. (9-34) into (9-35), we find that the half period t_1 corresponds to the solution of

$$1 - 2e^{-t_1/\tau_1} + e^{-t_1/\tau_1}e^{-t_1/\tau_2} = 0 \tag{9-36}$$

By making the following additional substitutions,

$$\tau_1 = \lambda\tau_2 \qquad x = e^{-t_1/\tau_1}$$

Eq. (9-36) reduces to

$$x^{\lambda+1} - 2x + 1 = 0 \qquad x \leq 1 \tag{9-37}$$

The restriction on x must be imposed so that the solution of Eq. (9-37) for the half period will correspond to real values of time.

In general, λ is not an integer and Eq. (9-37) would have to be solved by numerical or graphical methods for the single root lying within

$$0 < x_1 < 1$$

Finally, since $x_1 = \exp[-(t_1/\tau_1)]$, the half period is

$$t_1 = \tau_1 \ln \frac{1}{x_1}$$

For λ large, the recovery time constant τ_2 is very much smaller than that of the rise and the root of Eq. (9-37) is located at

$$x_{1,\min} = \tfrac{1}{2}$$

This simply yields the half period for the complete recovery waveshape, i.e., the maximum possible sweep duration of

$$t_1 = \tau_1 \ln 2$$

which was given in Eq. (9-19). The second limiting location of the timing root appears where $\tau_1 = \tau_2$ (i.e., when $\lambda = 1$). Under this condition, Eq. (9-37) may be expressed as

$$(x - 1)^2 = 0$$

and the half period is reduced to zero.

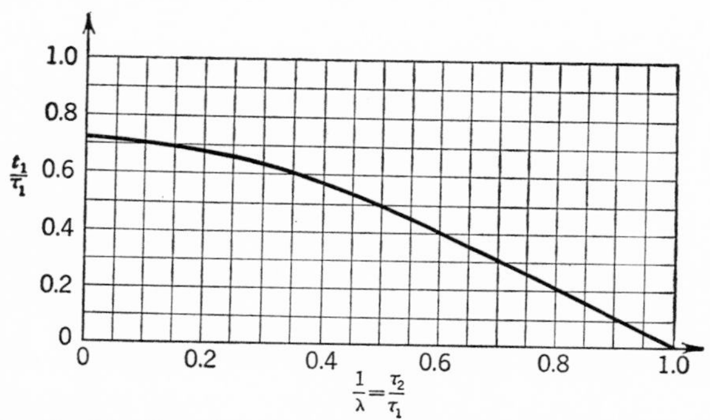

FIG. 9-26. Normalized half period as a function of the ratio of time constants [Eq. (9-37)].

A plot of the solution of Eq. (9-37) appears in Fig. 9-26. We can see that the recovery exponential has almost no effect on the sweep period when $\tau_2 < 0.2\tau_1$, but as τ_2 approaches the sweep time constant τ_1, the sweep time rapidly decreases toward zero. Operation in this mode is usually avoided since the slightest variation in circuit parameters has pronounced repercussions on the waveshape produced. There are multivibrators, however, which depend on the incomplete recovery behavior to generate extremely fast pulses. In this case, the transistor would never be allowed to saturate (Sec. 9-9) and the analysis would be slightly more complicated than that given above.

If the multivibrator is asymmetrical, we shall be faced with four transcendental equations, two for each half cycle. The evaluation of the two unknown time intervals and the two starting voltages would clearly be most tedious.

Returning briefly to the vacuum-tube astable, incomplete recovery also means that the double exponential grid waveshape, shown by the broken lines of Fig. 9-21, persists until the off tube turns on. The plate voltage of the on tube reflects the positive grid-recovery exponential into the circuit which maintains the next grid cut off. Even in a symmetrical circuit, each of the two equations would involve double-energy-storage conditions and would be extremely difficult to solve.

9-8. Inductively Timed Multivibrators. In the capacitively timed circuits discussed above, the regenerative loop was interrupted and the quasi-stable state established by cutting off the tube (transistor). This

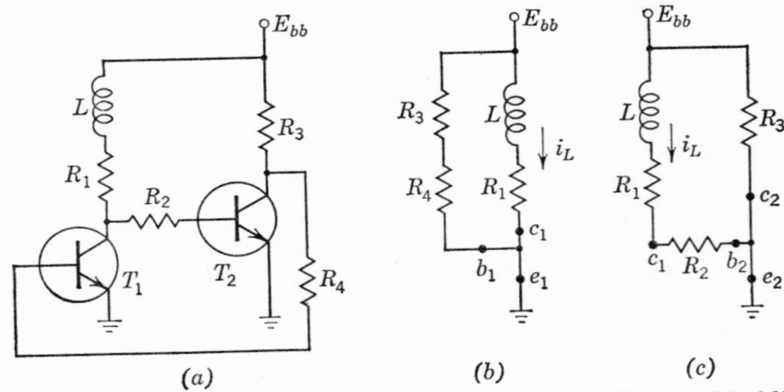

FIG. 9-27. (a) Inductively timed monostable multivibrator; (b) model holding during the stable state; (c) model defining the timing interval.

action was voltage-controlled, with the amount of stored energy and the discharge path determining the duration of the pulse generated. As an alternative, the loop gain can be reduced to below unity by keeping the transistor saturated for a controlled time interval. Because this is a current-dependent action, we shall use an inductance as the timing element.

Let us consider the monostable multivibrator of Fig. 9-27a, where, in the normal state, T_1 is saturated. Since its collector voltage is zero, T_2 must be cut off. The initial circuit conditions, from the model of Fig. 9-27b, are

$$I_{b1}(0^-) = \frac{E_{bb}}{R_3 + R_4} \tag{9-38a}$$

$$I_L(0^-) = I_{c1}(0^-) = \frac{E_{bb}}{R_1} \tag{9-38b}$$

$$E_{c1}(0^-) = E_{b1}(0^-) = E_{b2}(0^-) = 0 \tag{9-38c}$$

$$E_{c2}(0^-) = \frac{R_4}{R_3 + R_4} E_{bb} \tag{9-38d}$$

and to ensure the saturation of T_1, $\beta R_1 > (R_3 + R_4)$. Because $R_4 \gg R_3$, the drop across R_3 may be neglected in any computations.

The injection of a negative pulse at the base of T_1 turns off this transistor. The current previously flowing through L must remain constant across the switching interval. $I_L(0^-)$ will now flow into the base of T_2, driving it far into saturation. The current in L immediately starts flowing through the path shown in Fig. 9-27c, decaying toward

$$I_{ss} = \frac{E_{bb}}{R_1 + R_2} \tag{9-39}$$

with the time constant $\tau_1 = L/(R_1 + R_2)$. For regenerative switching, the circuit must enter the active region by itself. This requires that I_{ss}, given in Eq. (9-39), must be less than the saturation value of the base current of T_2; i.e., it must be below

$$I_{s2} = \frac{E_{bb}}{\beta R_3} \tag{9-40}$$

By writing the required inequality, the condition which must be satisfied may be expressed as $\beta R_3 < R_1 + R_2$.

Once T_2 enters the active region, the increase in its collector voltage forward-biases T_1, bringing it from cutoff into conduction. Regeneration completes the switching, carrying T_1 into saturation and turning T_2 back off.

The duration of the pulse generated may be found from the exponential charging equation. Substituting the initial current [Eq. (9-38b)], the final current [Eq. (9-40)], and the steady-state current [Eq. (9-39)], this time becomes

$$t_1 = \tau_1 \ln \frac{I_{ss} - I_{c1}(0^-)}{I_{ss} - I_{s2}} \tag{9-41}$$

The various current limits are indicated in the waveshapes of Fig. 9-28.

Care must be taken to limit the maximum voltage appearing at the collector of T_1. On starting, when the coil current switches from the collector of T_1 to the base of T_2, this voltage jumps from zero [Eq. (9-38c)] to

$$e_{c1}(0^+) = I_{c1}(0^-)R_2 = \frac{R_2}{R_1} E_{bb}$$

In general, $R_2 > R_1$ and the peak collector voltage will be several times as large as E_{bb}.

At the end of the pulse, the inductance must recharge to its initial state (the saturation current of T_1). Since T_1 is again saturated (Fig. 9-27b), it does so with the relatively long time constant $\tau_2 = L/R_1$, and because the recovery time is much longer than the pulse width, this circuit is only applicable where the wide pulse spacing can be tolerated.

Thermal instability in a transistor multivibrator is due to the temperature-dependent I_{c0}, which also flows into C, increasing the total charging current. This reduces the sweep duration, and when attempting to generate long-duration pulses, the large resistance used in the capacitive timed circuit compounds this instability. On the other hand, if an inductance is used as the timing element, the series resistance must be

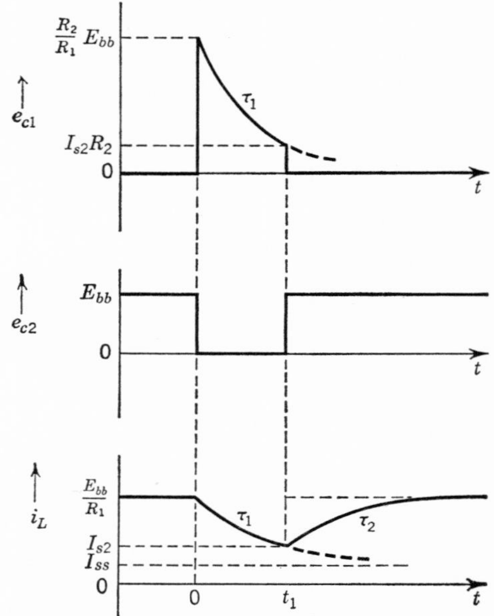

FIG. 9-28. Inductively timed monostable multivibrator waveshapes.

minimized if we wish to have a long time constant. The effects of I_{c0} become almost negligible and pulse time stability is ensured.

Inductive Astable Operation (?). It is quite difficult to design a simple, easily controlled, astable version of the inductively timed multivibrator. In the symmetrical circuit of Fig. 9-29, depending solely on the LR charging (the coil capacity assumed completely negligible), the time constant which maintains the saturation of one transistor is

$$\tau_1 = \frac{L}{R_1 + R_2}$$

But the coil recovers with the much longer time constant

$$\tau_2 = \frac{L}{R_1}$$

The argument employed with respect to the incomplete recovery in the capacitively timed circuit, which led to Eq. (9-37), also holds for this circuit. We draw the conclusion that no root corresponding to real time can be found for the condition of $\tau_1 \leq \tau_2$, and consequently the period of this multivibrator must be zero.

In the special case where the coupling resistor R_2 is set equal to zero and where R_1 is very small, the transistor parameters may play a major role in determining the two time constants of the circuit. During the saturation interval, the conduction path is through the base-to-emitter resistance of the transistor. Recovery is through the much larger saturation resistance of the collector emitter path, and therefore with a faster time constant. Thus $\tau_2 < \tau_1$, and the period may be found by solving an equation similar to Eq. (9-37). It should again be noted that this multivibrator depends for its timing on the second-order effects of the circuit and its operation may not be very dependable.

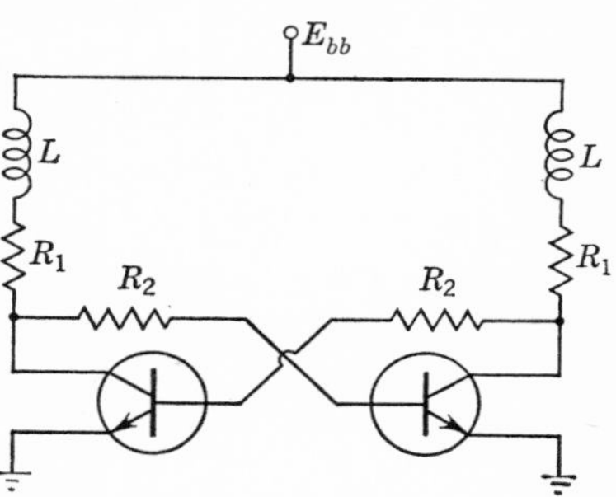

FIG. 9-29. Symmetrical circuit with inductive energy-storage elements (not an astable circuit).

Several free-running circuits exist that apparently use inductive timing for their operation. In all cases, either a second energy-storage element is present, making the coil a resonant circuit, or the two coils are coupled and the core driven into saturation on alternative half cycles. These circuits depend for their timing on other than a single mode of energy storage. Their solution is somewhat more complicated than the simple multivibrators discussed and is therefore beyond the scope of this section of the text.

9-9. Multivibrator Transition Time. A number of approximations were made in the course of our analysis of the multivibrator in the interest of keeping the important characteristics of the circuit in the forefront. The major assumption was that the multivibrator switched states in zero time, which allowed us to treat only the circuit behavior on both sides of the boundary. Calculation of the exact switching interval is much too complex for a simple piecewise-linear approach, especially since many of the significant terms were thrown out in linearizing the circuit. A qualitative discussion will still point out the problems involved in the switching process and will lead to the necessary conditions for optimization.

The transition time of a vacuum-tube multivibrator is primarily limited by the parasitic capacity and inductance present in the circuit. For ideal operation, the change of tube state, i.e., from on to off, should be accompanied by large instantaneous changes in both tube current and voltage, but lead inductance limits the time rate of change of current and stray capacity will prevent any instantaneous change of circuit voltage. The response to a change of state is quite similar to the transient response of the tubes and coupling networks to an applied unit step of grid voltage. For switching rates up to about 100 kc this is not very important; but if we try to design multivibrators to operate at several megacycles, the transition time is often the limiting factor.

The conclusions to be drawn from the above discussion are that the switching time may be improved by using small plate load resistors, by keeping the stray capacity low, and, if necessary, by high-frequency compensation. Pentodes, with their improved high-frequency response, are also occasionally used in high-speed multivibrators.

Transistor multivibrators normally operate with very small values of collector resistance, which makes the effects of the parasitic elements relatively unimportant. The basic limitations on switching time are due to the properties of the transistor itself. Three factors must be considered:

1. The transit time in the transistor
2. The cutoff frequency of the transistor
3. The storage time of the minority carriers

Current carrier velocity in a transistor, or any other semiconductor, is quite slow compared with the speed of electron travel in the high-vacuum interelectrode space of a tube. Any abrupt change of the external forcing function requires some finite time before it makes itself felt as the collector. First carriers must be injected, and then they have to travel across the junction. In turning off the transistors, current will continue flowing until the carriers, previously injected, are swept out. The transistor on and off times are proportional to the spacing of the base-collector, base-emitter junctions. With the new diffusion techniques of producing thin base films and extremely small junctions, the transit time can be made quite short. Special switching transistors having on-off times of less than 25 mμsec are currently available, and improved manufacturing techniques give promise of even further reduction.

The transistor current-amplification factor falls off with increasing frequency as

$$\alpha(f) = \frac{\alpha}{1 + j(f/f_\alpha)}$$

where f_α is the α cutoff frequency. When we use the transistor in a grounded-emitter circuit, the transformation $\beta = \alpha/(1 - \alpha)$ yields the expression for the β variation with frequency

$$\beta(f) = \frac{\beta}{1 + j[f/f_\alpha(1 - \alpha)]}$$

Thus the β cutoff frequency is $f_\alpha(1 - \alpha)$, and since α is only slightly less than 1, f_β is a very small percentage of f_α. In poor transistors, the β frequency may even be as low as 5 kc, but in the better ones it rises to 100 or 200 kc. At some sufficiently high frequency the reduction in β will cause the loop gain to drop below unity. There can no longer be any regenerative action above this point. If excessively narrow pulses are used for switching, the loop amplification of their high-frequency components may be insufficient to ensure a change of circuit state. For high-speed switching, we must always look for transistors having a high α cutoff frequency.

Operation in the transistor saturation region is accompanied by the injection of minority carriers into the base region from both the collector and the emitter. When we try to turn off the transistor, forward current continues flowing until these carriers are swept or diffused out. But this takes an appreciable time, usually about ten times as long as the on-off time of the transistor in its active region. Therefore the transistor must never be allowed to saturate in high-speed switching circuits.

If we attempt to prevent transistor saturation by increasing the size of the bias resistor, so that $R > \beta R_c$ [Eq. (9-18)], then both the collector drop and the unstable period become dependent on β. In addition, during the collector recovery, the charging current also flows through the base emitter circuit of the on transistor. Unless the collector voltage change is severely restricted to allow for the additional base current flow, the transistor may be driven into saturation for a portion of the cycle.

Our object, then, is to prevent the transistor from bottoming. One method which might be used is to connect a diode from the collector to a small external bias voltage. Once the collector falls to this voltage, the diode conducts and maintains the transistor in its active region. Only diodes which have fast recovery time may be used; otherwise the storage problem will simply be transferred from the transistor to the diode.

A second possible circuit configuration involves shunting the collector load by a Zener diode (Fig. 9-30*a*). This diode fires when the drop across R_c equals E_z and subsequently operates in a region where there are no carrier storage delays. The load resistance is now shunted by r_z, reducing the loop gain well below the value needed to sustain regeneration. Figure 9-30*b* illustrates the abrupt change in the path of operation once the diode fires. In addition, if the circuit is designed to saturate in the absence of the Zener diode, then the change in the collector voltage is always E_z and the sweep period is again independent of the transistor parameters.

Many alternative methods of preventing transistor saturation are in common use. They differ only in the circuit location of the diodes and in their particular firing points.

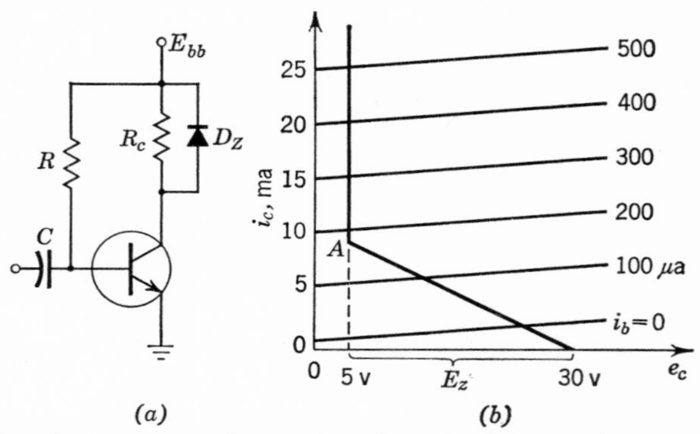

FIG. 9-30. Circuit to prevent bottoming through the use of a Zener diode. (a) Transistor collector circuit; (b) transistor characteristic and path of operation.

9-10. Multivibrator Triggering and Synchronization. The minimum trigger amplitude depends on its point of insertion. Once this has been decided, we can draw a model of the multivibrator and include the pulse generator along with its source impedance. Since we know the loading introduced and the change-over point of the circuit, the required pulse amplitude is easily calculated.

As an example, consider the problem involved when we apply a negative pulse to the grid of the on tube. It must be large enough so that the amplified plate pulse, which is coupled to the grid of the off tube, can turn the second tube on. We gain one stage of amplification, but the trigger source is loaded by the low impedance of a conducting grid. On the other hand, a positive pulse applied to the off grid will have absolutely no effect until it is large enough to bring the tube into the active region. It will always see a very high impedance, that of a nonconducting grid.

Exactly the same problems must be faced in triggering the transistor multivibrator except that now the trigger source should be able to supply the base current requirements when turning it on or off, as the case may be.

Diodes are almost always used in injecting the trigger pulses, for two reasons: first, to decouple the two bases or grids until the application of a trigger and, second, to prevent a pulse of the wrong polarity from falsely triggering the multivibrator. This might happen if a rectangular pulse were coupled to both grids through a small capacitor. It would be differentiated, and the positive input trigger, produced from the leading edge, would turn the off tube on. The trailing edge of the applied input also supplies a trigger, a negative pulse which may now turn the on tube off and thus return the circuit to its original state. Decoupling through diodes would prevent the second pulse from ever appearing at a grid and falsely retriggering the tube.

We may also inject a synchronizing signal into one or both bases (grids) of the astable multivibrator and lock its free-running period to some submultiple of the sync frequency. The charging curve would no longer be a simple exponential but would have the external signal superimposed. The tube conducts when the total grid voltage reaches cutoff (Fig. 9-31*a*). And as was done in Chap. 5, the sync signal might be considered as

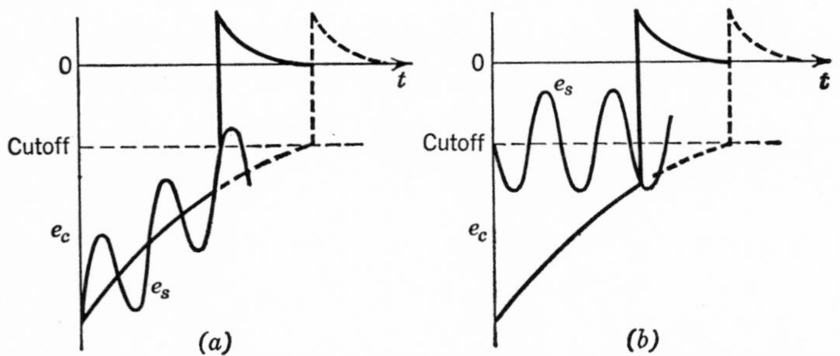

FIG. 9-31. Sine-wave synchronization of a vacuum-tube multivibrator.

effectively changing the tube cutoff voltage (Fig. 9-31*b*). If we approximate the exponential sweep by a straight line, then all the results of Chap. 5 dealing with synchronization may be applied to the astable multivibrator. In Fig. 9-31, the broken lines indicate the normal free-running waveshapes, while the solid curves are the ones due to synchronization by the sinusoidal signal e_s.

PROBLEMS

9-1. Assuming that the amplifier of Fig. 9-1 is a perfect amplifier having a constant gain $A = 10$, design a two-diode feedback network β, such that the system's stable points are at $e_{in} = \pm 10$ volts and the switching points are at $e_{in} = \pm 5$ volts. You may use any required resistances and voltage sources in addition to two diodes in designing the passive network. Let the smallest resistor equal 10 K. Sketch the transfer characteristics and the operating line.

9-2. (*a*) Draw the loop transfer characteristics for the active network of Fig. 9-32. Assume that all amplifiers and feedback networks are ideal over the complete range. What are the coordinates of the stable points, and how large must the input pulses be for triggering?

(*b*) Repeat part *a* when β_1 is changed from 0.1 to 0.01.

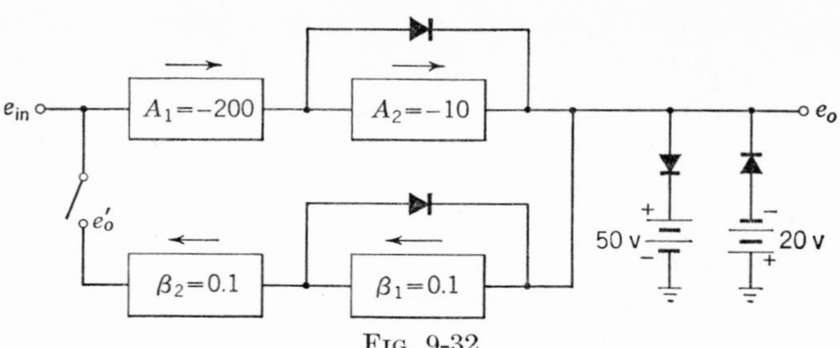

FIG. 9-32

9-3. The bistable multivibrator of Fig. 9-3 employs a 12AU7 with equal plate resistors of 20 K. The plate supply is 200 volts, and the coupling network consists of $R_1 = 0.5$ megohm and $R_2 = 1$ megohm. Evaluate the states of the two tubes as a function of E_{cc}. Tabulate the results and state which conditions will give the greatest output swing.

9-4. An asymmetrical bistable multivibrator uses tubes having $\mu = 25$, $r_p = 10$ K, and $r_c = 1$ K. One plate resistor is 40 K, and the other is 10 K. The coupling networks are identical with $R_1 = R_2 = 200$ K. $E_{bb} = 250$ volts, and $E_{cc} = -200$ volts.

(*a*) Sketch and label the waveshape at each plate when alternate positive and negative pulses are injected into the grid of T_1.

(*b*) What are the minimum amplitude pulses required to cause switching? To which grid must they be applied?

9-5. Design a bistable multivibrator using a 12AX7 and two 200-volt power supplies. The plate swing must be 125 volts as the tube switches from cutoff to full on. Specify all resistors and show how this circuit would be triggered by a chain of negative pulses.

9-6. By coupling the cathodes of the two tubes of a bistable multivibrator together, as shown in Fig. 9-33, the need for a second power supply is eliminated. For this circuit calculate the values of R_K and R_L that are required to keep one tube just cut off when the other tube just reaches saturation. What is the function of C_K, and must it be very large or can it be relatively small?

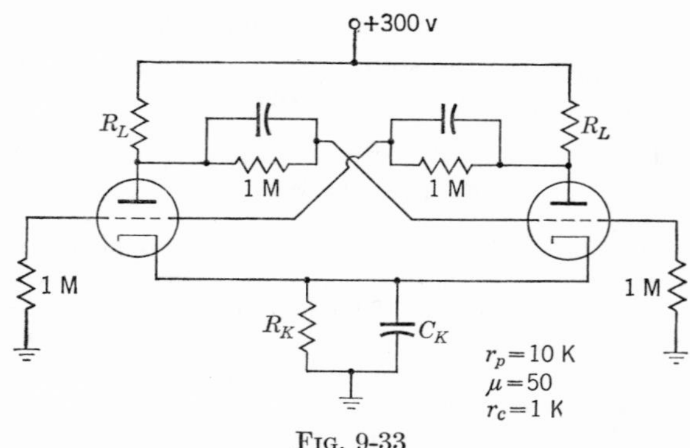

FIG. 9-33

9-7. During the transition from on to off, the behavior of the bistable multivibrator may be approximately represented by the model of Fig. 9-34*a*. In this model C includes the stray, interelectrode, and speed-up capacity. By taking the Thévenin equivalent across each capacitor, the model may be simplified to the two-loop network shown in Fig. 9-34*b*, where e_n is the equivalent pulse source inserted for triggering.

(*a*) Find the poles of the equivalent network by writing the mesh equations as a function of p, setting the network determinant equal to zero, and solving for p_1 and p_2.

(*b*) Show that the form of the transient response of the networks is

$$e_o = Ae^{p_1 t} + Be^{p_2 t}$$

(*c*) If $\mu = 100$, $C = 50\ \mu\mu\text{f}$, $R_2 = 10$ K, $R_1 = 500$ K, and the impulse of voltage applied is infinitesimally narrow but with an area of 10^{-7} volt-sec, find the time required for e_o to increase by 100 volts.

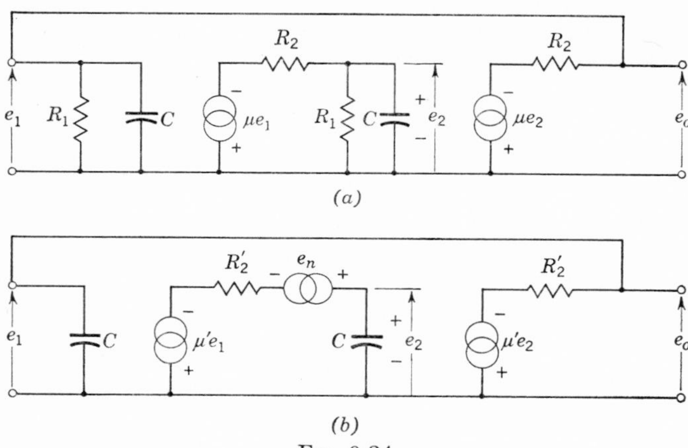

FIG. 9-34

9-8. Sketch the waveshapes at the base of T_1 and the collector of T_2 from $t = 0$ for the circuit of Fig. 9-35. Initially, T_1 is cut off.

9-9. (*a*) Draw the transfer characteristics and the unity gain line for the multivibrator of Fig. 9-35. Evaluate the minimum-size trigger (current) necessary for proper switching.

(*b*) Calculate the maximum-size resistive-coupling network necessary to ensure reliable operation. Repeat part *a* for this condition.

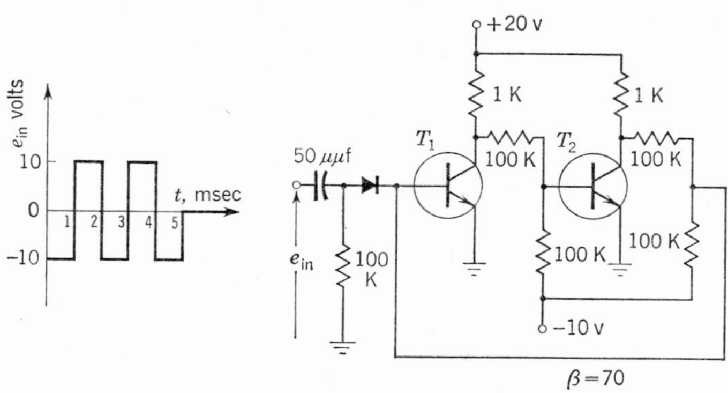

FIG. 9-35

9-10. A transistor having $\beta = 25$ is to be used in the circuit of Fig. 9-9. If $R_c = 1$ K and $E_{bb} = 2$ volts, specify a value for R that will allow for a ± 50 per cent variation in β between transistors and will still permit reliable operation. Calculate the change in collector voltage from state to state.

9-11. A simple direct-coupled bistable multivibrator makes use of the small back voltage which must be overcome before the transistor turns on. In addition to the characteristic shown in Fig. 9-36, the collector-to-emitter saturation resistance of the transistor is 50 ohms and in the active region $\beta = 40$.

(*a*) Show that the circuit of Fig. 9-36 is a perfectly stable circuit having two distinct states.

(*b*) Derive the magnitude of the minimum switching pulse.

(*c*) Calculate the voltage change at the collector.

(*d*) To what value must the collector resistor be changed if we want to ensure that the transistor is never driven into saturation? Would the circuit function properly under this condition?

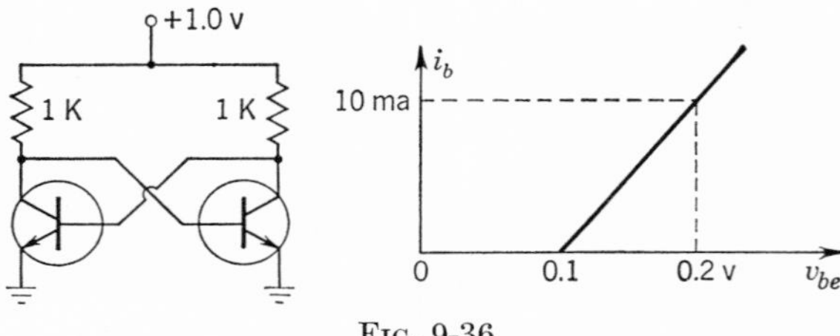

FIG. 9-36

9-12. (*a*) Show at least three ways of ensuring the triggering of a bistable vacuum-tube multivibrator on each pulse. A train of positive pulses or a train of negative pulses is all that is available.

(*b*) Repeat part *a* for the transistor multivibrators of Sec. 9-3.

(*c*) Discuss the behavior of a bistable if a narrow pulse is coupled into both active elements simultaneously through a small capacitor. Consider both polarity pulses injected into the control terminals (i.e., the base or the grid).

9-13. We wish to complete the design of the monostable circuit shown in Fig. 9-37.

(*a*) Calculate the value of R_c needed to drive T_2 just to saturation in the stable state.

(*b*) What value of C is required to keep the circuit in its quasi-stable state for 1 msec?

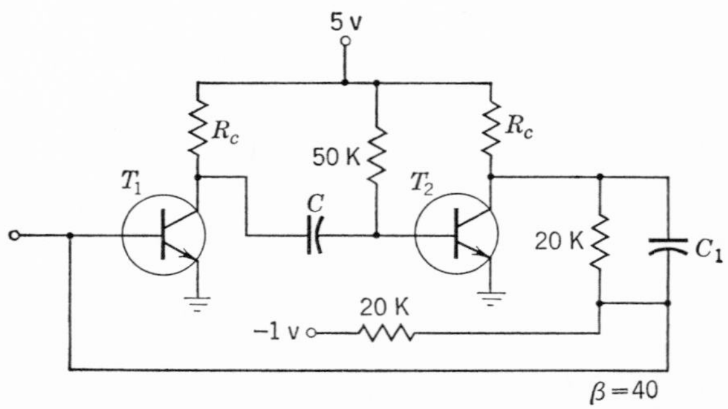

FIG. 9-37

(*c*) Sketch the waveforms of the base and collector voltages of both transistors when a pulse is applied to the base of T_1 at $t = 0$. Label all break points and time constants numerically.

9-14. The transistor monostable of Fig. 9-38 is triggered at $t = 0$. Calculate the waveshapes at the base and at the collector of T_2, giving all times and time constants.

9-15. In Fig. 9-38, the timing resistor R is returned to a variable supply rather than to 10 volts. Plot the pulse duration as a function of this control voltage E for the range of 1 to 25 volts.

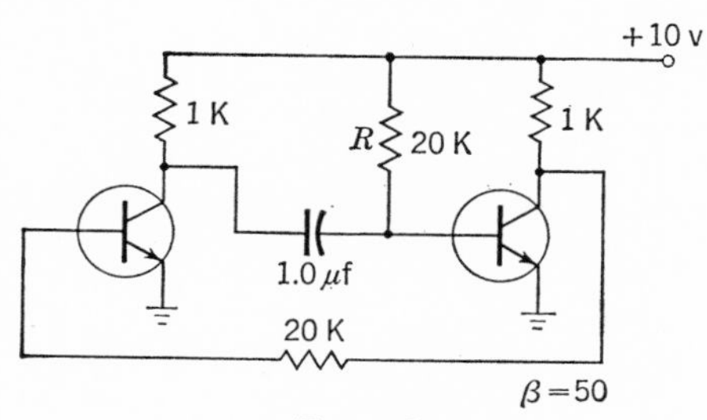

FIG. 9-38

9-16. The monostable multivibrator of Fig. 9-38 is modified by connecting a Zener diode which will fire at 6 volts from each collector to E_{bb}. This prevents the transistors from being driven into saturation and improves the recovery time (Sec. 9-9).

(*a*) Draw the resultant circuit.

(*b*) Repeat Prob. 9-14 for this new circuit.

(*c*) Plot the operating locus of the transistor on the collector characteristics.

9-17. The monostable multivibrator of Fig. 9-14 employs a 12AX7 adjusted so that the grid of the off tube is normally at -30 volts. Calculate the required value of E_{cc} if the other components are $R_L = 100$ K, $R = 1$ megohm, $R_1 = 1$ megohm, $R_2 = 2$ megohms, and $E_{bb} = 250$ volts. Find the required value of C to make the output pulse duration 100 μsec. Sketch and label the waveshapes appearing at the grid and plate of the normally off tube after a trigger is injected.

9-18. Design a monostable multivibrator that will generate a 150-volt 2-msec pulse at the plate of the normally on tube. Use a 12AU7 returned to 250 volts, $E_{cc} = -150$ volts, and a +20-volt trigger pulse. Specify all component values and show where and how the trigger is applied.

9-19. Consider the monostable circuit of Fig. 9-39, where the voltage at both plates is limited by bottoming diodes.

(*a*) Sketch to scale the waveshapes appearing at the plate and grid of T_2 after a large positive trigger is momentarily applied to the grid of T_1.

(*b*) Repeat part *a* when the timing resistor R_1 is returned to ground and adjusted to produce the same duration pulse as found in part *a*. Specify the new value of R_1.

(*c*) The tube parameters may be expected to vary by ±30 per cent from the nominal values. In light of these expected variations from tube to tube, what function do the diodes perform?

9-20. The monostable circuit of Fig. 9-39 is triggered by a pulse applied through a diode to one grid. If the internal impedance of the trigger generator is 500 ohms, calculate the minimum-amplitude trigger (open-circuit) under the following conditions:

(a) A positive trigger is injected at the grid of T_1.

(*b*) A negative pulse is applied to the grid of T_2.

Be careful to check the state of each tube immediately after switching.

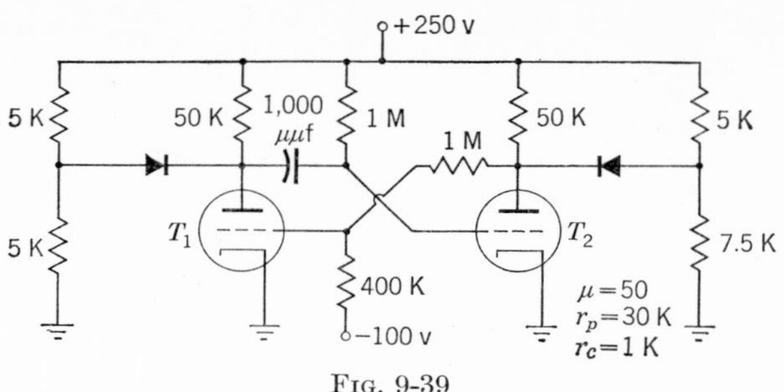

FIG. 9-39

9-21. When the astable multivibrator of Fig. 9-19 is made symmetrical, it will generate a square wave. Calculate and sketch the waveshapes at one tube if E_{bb} = 300 volts, R_L = 50 K, μ = 70, r_p = 20 K, r_c = 500, R = 500 K, and C = 0.001 μf.

9-22. Design an astable multivibrator using a 12AU7 and having a plate swing of 150 volts. T_1 should be on for 100 μsec, and T_2 for 900 μsec. Use a plate supply of 250 volts. Sketch the plate and grid waveshapes, checking that each tube recovers completely before reswitching.

9-23. We desire to build an astable multivibrator for use as a square-wave generator. The output at the plates should be 200 volts peak to peak and should have a d-c level of 200 volts and a period of 10 msec. At each plate we insert a limiting diode to remove any overshoot which would otherwise appear. If the tube available has μ = 70 and r_p = 50 K, specify all other circuit components.

9-24. Consider the application of the complete plate waveshape of Fig. 9-21 (broken line) to the grid-circuit timing network of the astable multivibrator. This may be represented as shown in Fig. 9-40. Assume that the capacitor is initially uncharged and that the output voltage e_c is zero at $t = 0$. The excitation e_1 is

$$e_1 = -150 - 50e^{-t/\tau_4} \qquad \tau_4 = 50 \ \mu\text{sec}$$

The interval of interest to us is where $e_c \leq -10$ volts.

(*a*) Calculate the exact output waveshape during the interval that the second tube is maintained off. What is the length of this interval? Compare this result with the approximate solution.

(*b*) The recovery time constant τ_4 is increased until the time at which the next tube turns on is changed by 5 per cent. What is the ratio of the excitation time constant τ_4 to the circuit time constant under this condition? Is the approximation made in the text valid?

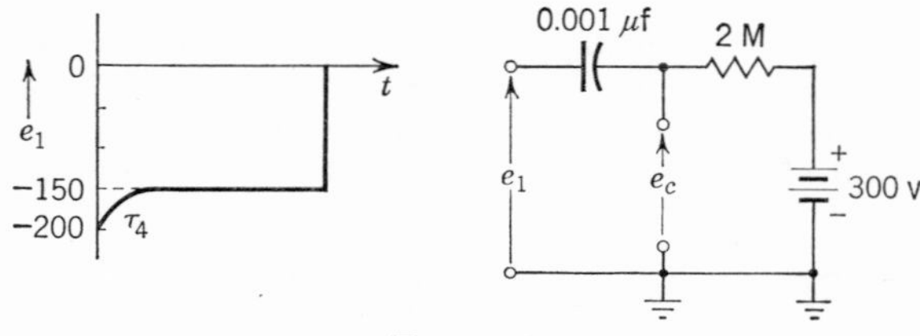

FIG. 9-40

9-25. Design an astable multivibrator that will generate a pulse whose duration is one-tenth that of the total period of 2 msec. Use transistors having β = 30, a power supply of 10 volts, and two collector resistors of 500 ohms. Make allowance in your design for a 20 per cent variation in β; check to see if recovery is complete before the circuit reswitches.

9-26. In a symmetrical transistor astable multivibrator (Fig. 9-22), the supply voltage varies from 10 to 30 volts. $R < \beta R_c$, where R is the base bias resistor and R_c is the collector load resistor. Calculate the variation in the period of the multivibrator due to the power-supply variation. Explain your answer.

9-27. The symmetrical astable of Fig. 9-22 employs the following components: $E_{bb} = 10$ volts, $R_c = 1$ K, $R = 50$ K, $C = 1$ μf, and $\beta = 25$. Sketch the base and collector waveshapes of one transistor for a complete cycle, labeling them with all voltage values, times, and time constants.

9-28. In the multivibrator of Prob. 9-27, R is reduced to 20 K, a value that ensures transistor saturation. Moreover, to guarantee fast recovery, the collector resistance is shunted by a Zener diode which will fire at 8 volts (Fig. 9-30).

(*a*) Plot the collector and base waveshapes, giving all times and time constants.

(*b*) Plot the volt-ampere characteristics of the collector load.

(*c*) How will the Zener diode influence the sweep time stability of this circuit?

9-29. The inductively timed monostable of Fig. 9-27 uses a coil having $L = 2$ henrys and $R_1 = 10$ ohms as its basic timing element. As the collector load of the second transistor we use a 2-ohm resistor, with $R_2 = 90$ ohms and $R_4 = 200$ ohms. The power supply is 5 volts, and the switching transistor has $\beta = 25$ in its active region.

(*a*) Calculate the current and voltage waveshapes at the collector of T_1 after the injection of a trigger.

(*b*) Repeat part *a* when β is reduced to 20.

(*c*) If the base-to-emitter resistance of the saturated transistor is 2 ohms and the collector-to-emitter resistance is 5 ohms, how would the waveshapes of part *a* be modified?

9-30. Figure 9-41 illustrates an alternative configuration for an inductively timed multivibrator. Show that the normal state is with T_1 on and T_2 cut off. Sketch the collector and base waveshapes of T_2 and the current in the coil after a trigger is applied. Give all times and time constants and the voltage and current coordinates at the break points. What are the advantages or disadvantages of this multivibrator compared with the circuit of Fig. 9-27?

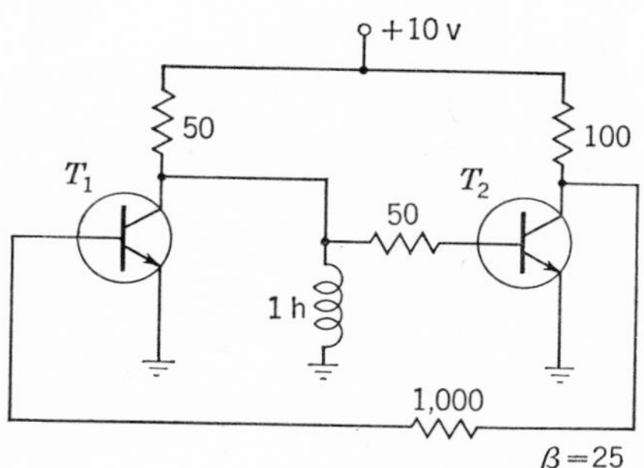

FIG. 9-41

9-31. (*a*) Derive Eq. (9-37).

(*b*) Show that the complete restriction on x must be

$$0.5 \leq x \leq 1.0$$

(*c*) For the case of $\tau_1 = \tau_2$, what are the stable states of the two transistors?

(*d*) Under the conditions of part *c*, calculate the loop current gain of the circuit. Explain the significance of your answer.

9-32. The symmetrical multivibrator of Fig. 9-22 is synchronized by injecting positive pulses into both bases through diodes. Because of the loading by the on transistor, we can assume that these pulses will affect only the off transistor and that they will act to shorten the off time. For simplicity, we shall further assume that the base charging curve is absolutely linear, taking t_1 sec to rise from $-E_{bb}$ to zero.

(*a*) Calculate and plot the regions of synchronization for $n = 1$ and $n = 2$.

(*b*) Repeat part *a* if the pulses are injected into only one base.

BIBLIOGRAPHY

Abraham, H., and E. Bloch: Le Multivibrateur, *Ann. phys.*, vol. 12, p. 237, 1919.

Chance, B., et al.: "Waveforms," Massachusetts Institute of Technology Radiation Laboratory Series, vol. 19, McGraw-Hill Book Company, Inc., New York, 1949.

Clarke, K. K., and M. V. Joyce: "Transistor Circuit Analysis," Addison-Wesley Publishing Company, Reading, Mass., in press.

Eccles, W. H., and F. W. Jordan: A Trigger Relay Utilizing Three Electrode Thermionic Vacuum Tubes, *Radio Rev.*, vol. 1, no. 3, pp. 143–146, 1919.

Feinberg, R.: Symmetrical and Asymmetrical Multivibrators, *Wireless Eng.*, vol. 26, pp. 153–158, 326–330, 1949.

Linvill, J. G.: Non-saturating Pulse Circuits Using Two Junction Transistors, *Proc. IRE*, vol. 43, no. 12, pp. 1826–1834, 1954.

Millman, J., and H. Taub: "Pulse and Digital Circuits," McGraw-Hill Book Company, Inc., New York, 1956.

Puckle, O. S.: "Time Bases," 2d ed., John Wiley & Sons, Inc., New York, 1951.

Reintjes, J. F., and G. T. Coate: "Principles of Radar," 3d ed., McGraw-Hill Book Company, Inc., New York, 1952.

Toomin, H.: Switching Action of the Eccles-Jordan Trigger Circuit, *Rev. Sci. Instr.*, vol. 10, pp. 191–192, June, 1939.

CHAPTER 10

EMITTER-COUPLED AND CATHODE-COUPLED MULTIVIBRATORS

10-1. Transistor Emitter-coupled Multivibrator—Monostable Operation. The emitter-coupled multivibrator and the equivalent vacuum-tube circuit, the cathode-coupled multivibrator, are circuits worthy of more than a cursory glance, illustrating as they do the possibility of one circuit operating in any one of several modes. Selection of the particular mode and a measure of control over the performance within this mode are a function of the control voltage E_1, which is labeled in the emitter-coupled circuit of Fig. 10-1.

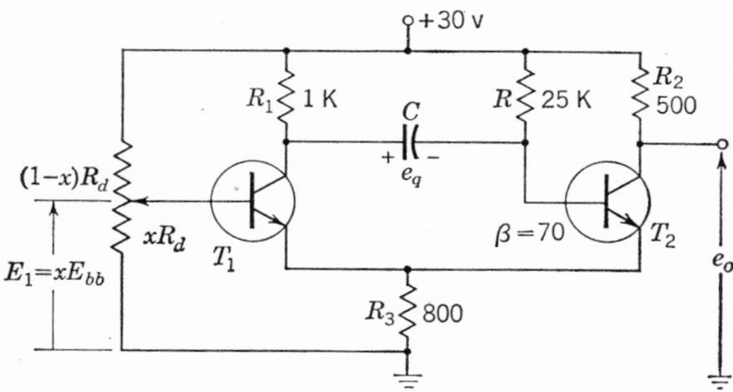

FIG. 10-1. Emitter-coupled multivibrator—component values shown for Examples 10-1 and 10-2.

Because a general treatment often obscures the detailed functioning of the switching circuit, as an introduction, one operating point will be explicitly stated and the resultant circuit analyzed. By doing this, a straightforward study may be made of the time response without, at the same time, being forced to account for the effects of a varying control voltage. In Sec. 10-2 the possible modes will be defined and any required modification of our original treatment may then be considered.

We shall assume that the circuit of Fig. 10-1 is adjusted so that, in its normal state, T_2 is full on and T_1 is cut off. The application of a positive trigger at the base of T_1 switches the multivibrator into the single quasi-stable state: T_1 is driven into its active region, and its collector voltage drop, coupled through C, turns T_2 off. Transistor T_1, now operating as an emitter follower, stabilizes with an emitter-to-ground voltage of approximately E_1. As C begins charging, the base-to-ground voltage of T_2 rises toward E_{bb}. Once it reaches the new emitter voltage and e_{be2} equals zero, T_2 will turn back on. The increased current in R_3 raises the common-emitter voltage above E_1, and it follows that T_1 must be cut off. E_{c1} jumps to a higher value, driving T_2 back into saturation.

Note that the coupling from T_1 to T_2 is through both the common-emitter resistance R_3 and the collector base network of C and R. But coupling from T_2 back to T_1 is only through the emitter resistor, which leaves R_2 relatively isolated from the transmission path. It therefore serves as a convenient place from which to take the output. At this point a small amount of capacitive loading may be tolerated without seriously affecting the pulse duration.

In order to simplify the quantitative analysis of the multivibrator of Fig. 10-1, we shall make the following further assumptions:

1. β is very large, allowing $R \gg R_1$ and $R \gg R_2$.
2. The Thévenin equivalent impedance looking from the base of T_1 into the control voltage potentiometer is so very small that it also will be neglected.

Preceding switching, the values of all voltages, measured with respect to ground, are

$$e_{c1}(0^-) = E_{bb} \tag{10-1a}$$

$$e_{b1}(0^-) = xE_{bb} = E_1 \tag{10-1b}$$

$$e_{b2}(0^-) = e_{c2}(0^-) = e_e(0^-) = \frac{R_3}{R_2 + R_3} E_{bb} \tag{10-1c}$$

$$e_q(0^-) = E_{bb} - \frac{R_3}{R_2 + R_3} E_{bb} = \frac{R_2}{R_2 + R_3} E_{bb} \tag{10-1d}$$

where $e_q(0^-)$ is the initial charge on the capacitor.

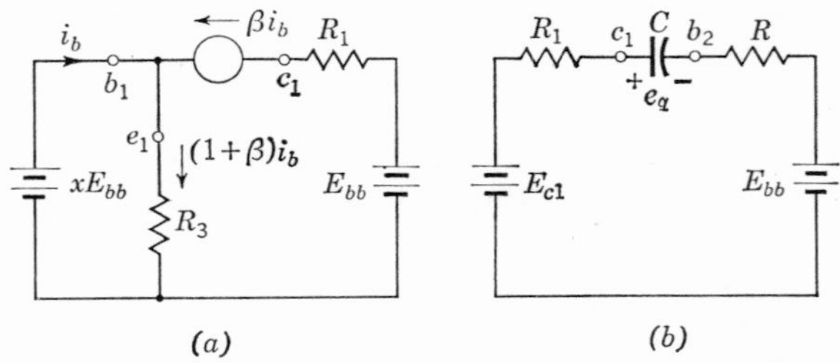

FIG. 10-2. Emitter-coupled multivibrator—models holding for the quasi-stable state. (a) Circuit of T_1; (b) Thévenin equivalent circuit coupling the collector of T_1 to the base of T_2.

Immediately after switching, the models of Fig. 10-2 represent the multivibrator's state and must be used for the calculation of the system's time response. From Fig. 10-2a, we can see that the conditions at the base and emitter of T_1, subsequent to its transition into the unstable region, are

$$e_{b1}(0^+) = e_e(0^+) = xE_{bb} \tag{10-2a}$$

$$i_{b1}(0^+) = \frac{xE_{bb}}{(\beta + 1)R_3} \tag{10-2b}$$

Therefore its collector voltage becomes

$$\begin{aligned} e_{c1}(0^+) &= E_{bb} - \beta i_{b1} R_1 \\ &\cong E_{bb}\left(1 - \frac{xR_1}{R_3}\right) \end{aligned} \tag{10-3}$$

where the second term of Eq. (10-3) is simply the drop in collector voltage upon switching. Because our original assumption ($R \gg R_1$) allows us to ignore the loading of R_1 by R, the voltage fall at the base of T_2 will be identically the drop of Eq. (10-3). We may immediately write

$$e_{b2}(0^+) = \frac{R_3}{R_2 + R_3} E_{bb} - \frac{xR_1}{R_3} E_{bb} \tag{10-4}$$

Recovery from this sharp change of voltage is toward E_{bb}, with the time constant

$$\tau_1 = (R_1 + R)C \cong RC$$

Once $e_{be2} = 0$, or from Eq. (10-2a), once the base-to-ground voltage of T_2 reaches

$$e_{b2}(t_1) = e_e = xE_{bb}$$

T_2 turns back on. We now know the initial, the final, and the steady-state voltage at the base of T_2; their substitution into, and the solution of, the exponential response equation yields

$$t_1 = \tau_1 \ln \frac{E_{bb}\left(1 - \dfrac{R_3}{R_2 + R_3} + \dfrac{xR_1}{R_3}\right)}{E_{bb}(1 - x)} \tag{10-5}$$

for the pulse duration.

The multivibrator reenters the regenerative transition region with the base of T_2 at a level lower than its steady-state voltage [Eq. (10-1c)]. We suspect that there will be a voltage jump, with the probability that this jump will be larger than necessary to return the base to its original point. The new base, emitter, and collector voltages can easily be calculated by drawing the model holding after the jump, i.e., during recovery (Fig. 10-3).

Just before the multivibrator switches, the final voltage across C is

$$e_q(t_1) = E_{c1} - xE_{bb} = E_{bb}\left[1 - x\left(1 + \frac{R_1}{R_3}\right)\right] \tag{10-6}$$

By substituting this value into Fig. 10-3, we arrive at the new operating point of the transistor. The algebra is much simpler when we can use numbers, and the solution will therefore be left to the reader as a part

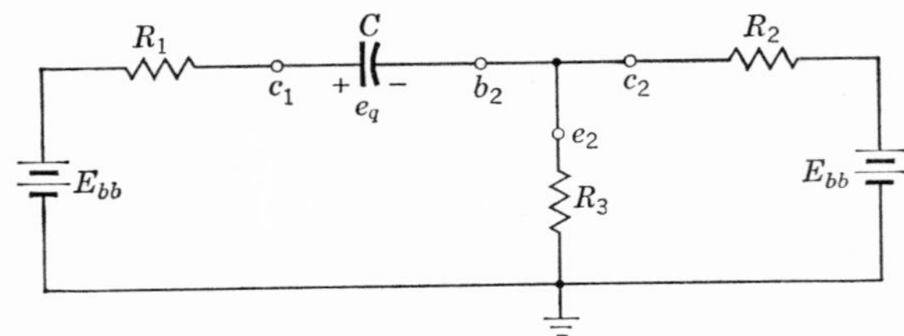

FIG. 10-3. Recovery model of the emitter-coupled multivibrator.

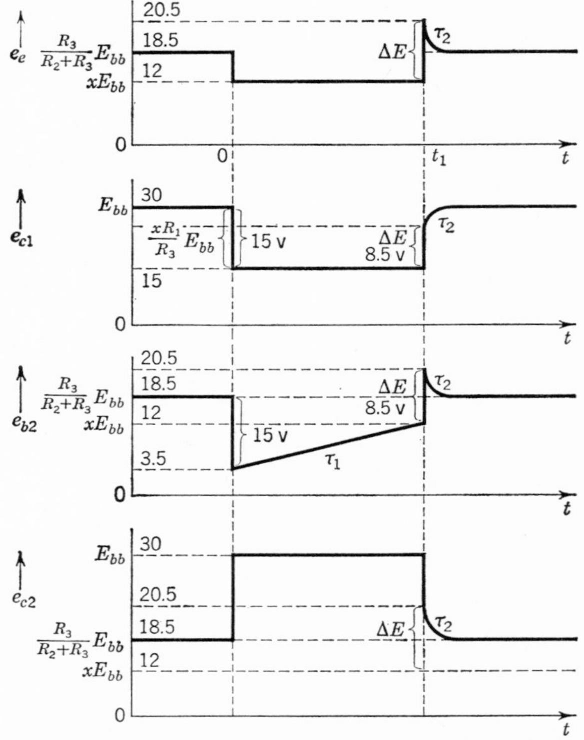

FIG. 10-4. Emitter-coupled multivibrator waveshapes—monostable operation—mode 12. Values given are for the solution of Example 10-1.

of his analysis of specific problems and to the calculations performed in Example 10-1.

After the final jump, the complete circuit recovers toward the original steady-state conditions, with the time constant

$$\tau_2 = C(R_1 + R_2 \parallel R_3)$$

Waveshapes appear in Fig. 10-4 with all jumps and time constants indicated. Observe that the base, emitter, and collector of T_2 all have identical recovery waveshapes (the saturated transistor is a short circuit).

Example 10-1. By setting $x = 0.4$, the monostable multivibrator of Fig. 10-1 is adjusted to operate in the mode described above, where T_1 switches between its cutoff and active regions. All circuit components are as given in Fig. 10-1. We do not need to specify C for the following analysis, since it would be selected on the basis of the required pulse width.

The duration of the unstable state, which is of primary interest, is controlled by the charge in C, maintaining T_2 cut off. Only two unknown voltages must be found in order to evaluate this interval, the initial value at the base of T_2 as the circuit enters its unstable region and the voltage at which T_2 again turns on.

From Eq. (10-1c) the stable base voltage of T_2 is

$$e_{b2}(0^-) = \frac{800}{1{,}300} 30 \text{ volts} = 18.5 \text{ volts}$$

With $x = 0.4$, the voltage at the base of T_1 remains fixed at

$$e_{b1} = E_{bb} = 12 \text{ volts}$$

When the trigger is injected, T_1 turns on and the common-emitter voltage drops from 18.5 to 12 volts (xE_{bb}).

If the small base current flow is neglected, the voltage drop across R_1 will be proportional to the 12-volt drop across R_3:

$$\frac{R_1}{R_3} = \frac{\Delta E_{c1}}{xE_{bb}}$$

or $\Delta E_{c1} = 15$ volts. C couples this change to base of T_2, driving it from its original value of 18.5 down to 3.5 volts. It immediately starts charging, as shown in Fig. 10-2b, toward 30 volts, with the time constant τ_1. When $e_{be2} = 0$ or when $e_{b2} = 12$ volts, T_2 turns back on. Consequently

$$t_1 = \tau_1 \ln \frac{30 - 3.5}{30 - 12} = 0.388\tau_1$$

At the end of the sweep interval the voltage across C is only 3 volts. Substituting this value into the model of Fig. 10-3, we find that the base of T_2 jumps from 12 to 20.5 volts. With the time constant

$$\tau_2 = 1{,}310C$$

the circuit returns to the original conditions. These voltages are used to label the typical circuit waveshapes of Fig. 10-4.

10-2. Modes of Operation of the Emitter-coupled Multivibrator.

The common-element (emitter) coupling permits this multivibrator to operate in a possible multiplicity of modes in each of its two classes. Since T_2 is always conducting in the normal state, these classes might well be defined in terms of the quiescent condition of this transistor: class 1 existing when the bias current is adjusted so that T_2 is placed in its active region, and class 2 when it is saturated. The particular class depends solely on the relationship of R to R_2; for T_2 saturated (class 2)

$$R < \beta R_2$$

We can prove the sufficiency of this condition by considering the transistor model holding under saturation [also see the derivation of Eq. (9-18)].

Class 2 operation is to be preferred over class 1; here both the initial conditions and sweep duration are relatively independent of the transistor parameters. However, the saturated transistor has a long recovery time and we would be forced to incorporate antibottoming diodes. We thus transfer the minority-carrier-storage problem from the transistor to the diodes, where it is more readily handled.

The various possible modes, within each class, are determined by the switching conditions of T_1, i.e., its starting and ending states. Modes will be classified by two numbers, the first describing the state of T_1, as listed below, and the second the class (state of T_2).

STATES OF T_1

	Before switching	After switching
0	Cut off	Cut off
1	Cut off	Part on
2	Cut off	Full on
3	Part on	Full on
4	Full on	Full on

Since the state of T_1 is a direct function of E_1, investigation of the multivibrator's performance will proceed, following the potentiometer setting, from $x = 0$ to $x = 1$. Each mode will be delineated by establishing the boundary values (of x) in terms of the circuit parameters. At any particular setting of x, detailed time-response calculations would simply follow the analysis outlined in Sec. 10-1.

We shall mainly concern ourselves with modes $n2$, representing as they do the more stable operation of the emitter-coupled multivibrator. In order to complete the discussion one astable mode of group $n1$ is briefly treated in Sec. 10-4. All approximations and assumptions made in Sec. 10-1 are also applicable in the following arguments.

Mode 02. In this mode T_1 is normally off. Application of a trigger turns T_1 part on, but not far enough on so that its collector voltage change can drive T_2 into cutoff. Upon removal of the trigger, T_2 is still in the active region, and it immediately switches back to its normal state, full on. The output pulse generated is of small amplitude and of exactly the same duration as the input trigger.

By assuming that T_2 has turned full off and that T_1 is still part on, the model drawn is much simpler than the one required if both transistors are taken in their active regions (the model for T_1 is given in Fig. 10-2a). The region's boundary remains the same regardless of the direction from which we approach it. If T_2 is cut off, the initial value of its base voltage is given by Eq. (10-4). Whenever T_1 is on, the drop across the emitter resistor is always the control voltage xE_{bb}. In order for T_2 to be part on,

$$e_{be2} = \left(\frac{R_3}{R_2 + R_3} - \frac{xR_1}{R_3}\right) E_{bb} - xE_{bb} > 0 \tag{10-7}$$

Solving Eq. (10-7) for the limit of x, which satisfies the inequality stated, we find that the limits of mode 02 are

$$0 < x < \frac{R_3}{R_1 + R_3} \frac{R_3}{R_2 + R_3} \tag{10-8}$$

This calculation serves mainly to define the lower limit of mode 12, the first useful range.

Mode 12. An input trigger will again switch T_1 part on, but now the drop in its collector voltage is sufficient to drive T_2 into cutoff. The upper limit of x is at that particular potentiometer setting that would allow T_1 to switch from cutoff to saturation upon being triggered. To find this setting, we should draw the model holding for T_1 full on (Fig. 10-5) and solve for the corresponding emitter-to-ground voltage.

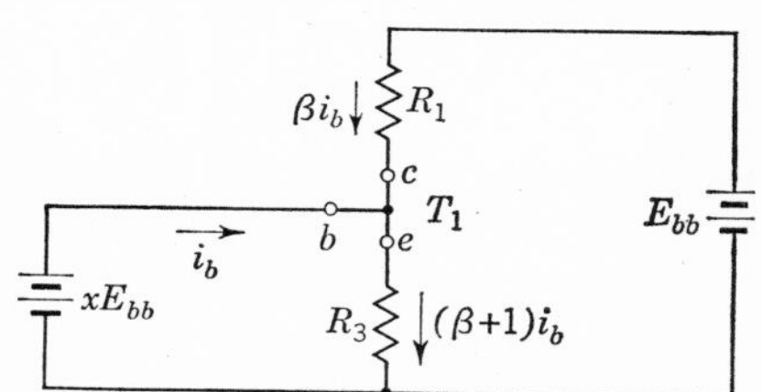

FIG. 10-5. Model for the upper limit of mode 12.

But for $\beta \gg 1$, $\beta + 1 \cong \beta$, and therefore

$$e_e = xE_{bb} \cong \frac{R_3}{R_1 + R_3} E_{bb} \tag{10-9}$$

The limits of x for operation in mode 12 are from the upper limit of mode 02 to the value found from Eq. (10-9):

$$\frac{R_3}{R_1 + R_3} \frac{R_3}{R_2 + R_3} < x < \frac{R_3}{R_1 + R_3} \tag{10-10}$$

For the multivibrator of Example 10-1 the limits are $0.273 < x < 0.445$.

Mode 12 was the one treated in detail in Sec. 10-1. Its pulse width, defined by Eq. (10-5), is a function of the potentiometer setting x. Increasing the setting increases both the drop in the base voltage of T_2

and the value of the emitter voltage after switching into the unstable state. As a consequence of the greater separation between the initial and final values of the base voltage, the pulse duration increases with potentiometer rotation. Substituting the limits of x into Eq. (10-5) gives the permissible range of output pulse width as

$$0 < t_1 < \tau_1 \ln \left[1 + \frac{R_2(R_1 + R_3)}{R_1(R_2 + R_3)} \right] \tag{10-11}$$

When the circuit is symmetrical ($R_1 = R_2$), the maximum pulse width generated is $t_{1,\max} = \tau_1 \ln 2$.

Mode 22. In this mode T_1 switches from cutoff to full on. The next possible circuit change occurs when the normal state of T_1 changes from cutoff to part on. But with T_1 cut off, Eqs. (10-1*b*) and (10-1*c*) hold: by solving for $e_{be1} = 0$, we find the upper limit of mode 22.

$$e_{be1} = xE_{bb} - \frac{R_3}{R_2 + R_3} E_{bb} \leq 0 \tag{10-12}$$

The limits of x for this mode become

$$\frac{R_3}{R_1 + R_3} < x < \frac{R_3}{R_2 + R_3} \tag{10-13}$$

and in Example 10-1, the upper limit is located at 0.615.

Note that unless $R_1 > R_2$, mode 22 will not exist and the transition will be directly from mode 12 to 32. Furthermore, if $R_1 = R_2$, the range of voltage settings for mode 22 operation degenerates into a single point.

When T_1 goes full on, the drop across R_3 is xE_{bb}. The remaining voltage must appear across R_1; therefore the drop in the collector voltage of T_1 will now be

$$\Delta e_{c1} = (1 - x)E_{bb} \tag{10-14}$$

This same drop appears at the base of T_2, turning it off. The base charges from its initial voltage, found from Eqs. (10-1*c*) and (10-14),

$$e_{b2}(0^+) = \frac{R_3}{R_2 + R_3} E_{bb} - (1 - x)E_{bb} \tag{10-15}$$

toward E_{bb}, with the time constant τ_1. It finally conducts when

$$e_{b2}(t_2) = xE_{bb}$$

Consequently, in mode 22, the pulse width becomes

$$t_2 = \tau_1 \ln \frac{2 - R_3/(R_2 + R_3) - x}{1 - x} \tag{10-16}$$

Mode 32. Under the circuit conditions existing within this mode of operation, T_1 always conducts, maintaining the emitter voltage fixed at xE_{bb} across the complete transition region. Limits, on x, are from the upper limit of mode 22 to that value which puts both transistors into permanent saturation (Fig. 10-6).

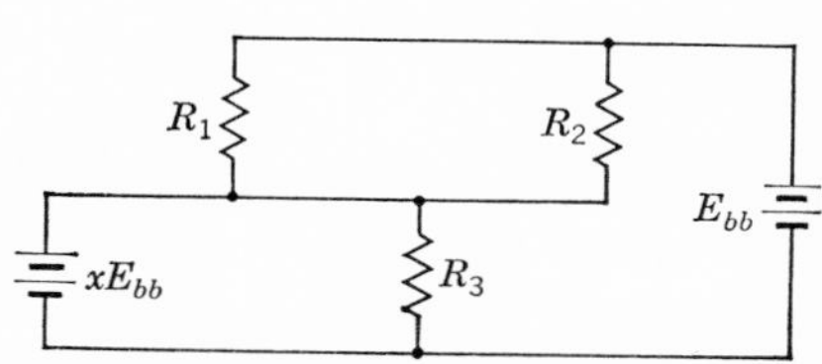

FIG. 10-6. Both transistors in saturation.

The upper limit, found from the model of Fig. 10-6, is

$$xE_{bb} < \frac{R_3}{R_1 \parallel R_2 + R_3}$$

Thus, in mode 32, the range of x becomes

$$\frac{R_3}{R_2 + R_3} < x < \frac{R_3}{R_1 \parallel R_2 + R_3} \qquad (10\text{-}17)$$

When R_3 is very large compared with R_1 and R_2, the limits of x for which this mode holds shrink almost to the vanishing point. The circuit conditions before switching are determined from the appropriate model (T_1 part on and T_2 saturated):

$$e_{b1}(0^-) = e_{b2}(0^-) = e_e(0^-) = xE_{bb} \qquad (10\text{-}18a)$$

$$e_{c1}(0^-) = E_{bb} - E_{bb}\left[\frac{xR_1}{R_3} - \frac{(1-x)R_1}{R_2}\right] \qquad (10\text{-}18b)$$

But after switching,

$$e_{c1}(0^+) = xE_{bb} \qquad (10\text{-}19)$$

The net change in the collector voltage of T_1 [Eqs. (10-18*b*) and (10-19)] is coupled to the base of T_2, and as the multivibrator enters the quasi-stable region, Δe_{c1} determines the initial value of e_{b2}:

$$e_{b2}(0^+) = (2x - 1)E_{bb} + \left[\frac{xR_1}{R_3} - \frac{(1-x)R_1}{R_2}\right]E_{bb} \qquad (10\text{-}20)$$

As in all the other modes, the base charges toward E_{bb}, switching at xE_{bb}. The pulse duration, still a function of x, turns out to be

$$t_3 = \tau_1 \ln \frac{2 + \dfrac{R_1}{R_2} - \left(2 + \dfrac{R_1}{R_3} + \dfrac{R_1}{R_2}\right)x}{1 - x} \qquad (10\text{-}21)$$

In the three modes of operation that generate a usable pulse, its duration, at least to the first approximation, is independent of E_{bb}, resulting in extremely good pulse stability.

Mode 42. This mode exists when both transistors are always saturated. Thus an input trigger will have absolutely no effect. The limits are

$$\frac{R_3}{R_1 \parallel R_2 + R_3} < x < 1 \tag{10-22}$$

It is included only to complete the range of setting of the potentiometer and, as mode 02, is of no practical use.

A summary of the results is presented in Tables 10-1 and 10-2. Table 10-1 shows the operating regions. Within each mode the normalized pulse duration is given by

$$\frac{t_n}{\tau} = \ln \frac{b + ax}{1 - x} \tag{10-23}$$

The constants a and b are listed in Table 10-2.

TABLE 10-1. TRANSISTOR STATES, EMITTER-COUPLED MULTIVIBRATOR

Mode	Upper limit of x	T_1	T_2
02	$\frac{R_3}{R_1 + R_3} \frac{R_3}{R_2 + R_3}$	Off	Full on
12	$\frac{R_3}{R_1 + R_3}$	Off ↓ part on	Full on ↓ cut off
22	$\frac{R_3}{R_2 + R_3}$	Off ↓ full on	Full on ↓ cut off
32	$\frac{R_3}{R_1 \parallel R_2 + R_3}$	Part on ↓ full on	Full on ↓ cut off
42	1	Full on	Full on

To summarize further the behavior of the multivibrator in terms of the particular modes, the complete normalized period is plotted as a function of x for the circuit of Example 10-1. The solid curve 1 of Fig. 10-7 illustrates the varying pulse duration as a function of x when the impedance of the control potentiometer is negligible. This corresponds to the mode boundaries discussed above. Both the demarcation between the individual modes and the different rates of pulse-width variation with x within each mode are quite clear. It might be noted that, in this special case, the pulse duration appears to vary almost linearly with x within mode 12.

TABLE 10-2. PULSE DURATION OF EMITTER-COUPLED MULTIVIBRATOR—MODES $n2$

Mode	b*	a*
12	$1 - \dfrac{R_3}{R_2 + R_3}$	$\dfrac{R_1}{R_3}$
22	$2 - \dfrac{R_3}{R_2 + R_3}$	-1
32	$2 + \dfrac{R_1}{R_2}$	$-\left(2 + \dfrac{R_1}{R_3} + \dfrac{R_1}{R_2}\right)$

* Constants for Eq. (10-23).

Effects of Finite Potentiometer Impedance. When the control potentiometer is of appreciable size, we must include its equivalent source impedance in all calculations involving the actual base and emitter voltage of T_1. The dashed curve 2 of Fig. 10-7 shows the effect of a 10-K potentiometer

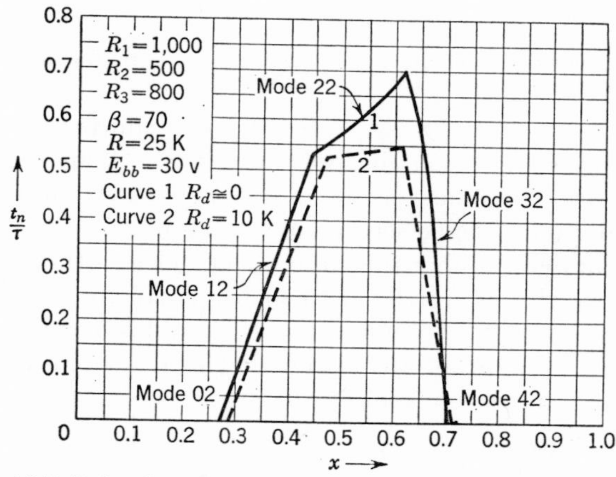

FIG. 10-7. Pulse duration as a function of potentiometer setting.

on the pulse duration in the various modes of operation. This plot is the result of inserting the Thévenin equivalent impedance of

$$R_s = x(1 - x)R_d \tag{10-24}$$

in series with xE_{bb}.

For mode 12, the input model is shown in Fig. 10-8a. Here, for any setting of x, the source impedance is much less than the active-region input impedance $(\beta + 1)R_3$ of the transistor. With the specific circuit values of Example 10-1, the input impedance is 56 K compared with the maximum R_s value of 2.5 K. The loading of the potentiometer is negligible, and the base voltage is but slightly less than the open-circuit voltage xE_{bb}. To generate a given-duration pulse, the value of x must be set slightly higher than previously found, in order to compensate for the voltage drop across R_s.

Once the multivibrator begins operating in mode 22, the input model must be changed to the one shown in Fig. 10-8b, which is obtained by replacing the transistor by the Thévenin equivalent circuit seen looking into the saturated base. The input impedance is reduced from 56 K to the parallel combination of R_1 and R_3 (445 ohms). Furthermore, the potentiometer is varying about the mid-point of its setting, and its impedance remains close to the maximum possible value (R_s = 2,500 ohms). Because most of the voltage will be developed across R_s, any change in the control-voltage setting will have but small

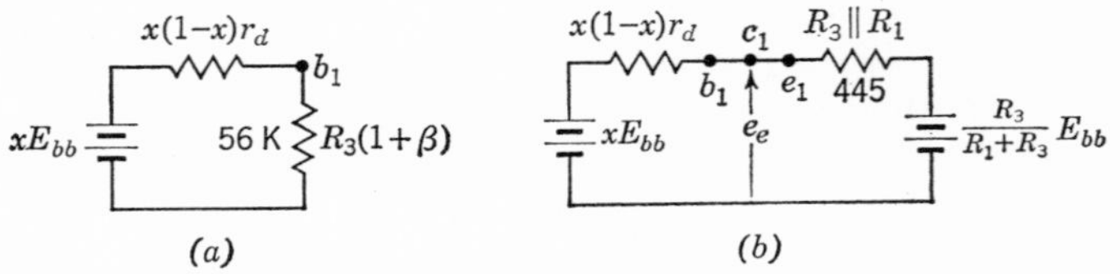

FIG. 10-8. Equivalent input circuit of T_1, including the potentiometer source impedance. (a) Mode 12 operation; (b) T_1 saturated (mode 22).

effect on the base voltage of T_1. The common-emitter voltage will not vary much, and neither will the pulse duration. This segment of the curve in Fig. 10-7 becomes much more horizontal. In Example 10-2 we shall consider one specific setting of x, lying in this mode, to illustrate the role of R_s in determining the circuit voltages and timing.

Mode 32 operation is restricted to such a small fraction of the range that, in general, it is of little interest. R_s would be treated as above, by including it in the appropriate models. The reader may perform this substitution and calculation himself.

Example 10-2. The multivibrator of Fig. 10-1 uses a 10-K potentiometer for its timing control. When it is set at $x = 0.55$ the circuit is operating near the center of mode 22. All other circuit components are the same as in Example 10-1, and the results of that problem may be used in this solution.

The initial voltage at the base of T_2, before triggering, is 18.5 volts (from Example 10-1). After the trigger turns T_1 on, the saturated transistor voltage may be found from the model of Fig. 10-8b. Here xE_{bb} = 16.5 volts, and R_s = 2,475 ohms. From Fig. 10-8b,

$$\begin{aligned} e_{c1} = e_{b1} = e_e &= 13.33 + \frac{445}{2{,}920} \times (16.5 - 13.33) \\ &= 13.81 \text{ volts} \end{aligned}$$

If R_s were 0, this voltage would be xE_{bb} = 16.5 volts. The loading of the potentiometer reduces the transistor voltage to slightly above its saturation value. Thus, as T_1

turns on, the drop at its collector is only

$$\Delta e_{c1} = 30 - 13.81 = 16.2 \text{ volts}$$

This drop is coupled by C, driving the base of T_2 down to

$$e_{b2}(0^+) = 18.5 - 16.2 = 2.3 \text{ volts}$$

Recovery is toward 30 volts, with the circuit reswitching at the common-emitter voltage of 13.8 volts:

$$t_1' = \tau_1 \ln \frac{30 - 2.3}{30 - 13.8} = 0.542\tau_1$$

When the source impedance is small enough to be neglected, the voltage at the terminals of T_1 will be xE_{bb} (16.5 volts). In this case, the change in collector voltage is only 13.5 volts and the base of T_2 is driven to 5 volts. The reswitching value is also higher, 16.5 volts, and since a greater percentage of the total exponential is used, the sweep period becomes somewhat longer:

$$t_1 = \tau_1 \ln \frac{30 - 5}{30 - 16.5} = 0.615\tau_1$$

10-3. Monostable Pulse Variation. The question confronting us in this section is, What circuit relationships must be satisfied to achieve some physically permissible variation of the pulse duration with respect to x? In modes 12 and 32, the function might well be a linear one, and in mode 22 it might be either constant or linear. One commonly used method of attacking this problem is first to expand the general time equation (10-23) into some series and then, by examining the individual terms, attempt to eliminate those that contribute the nonlinearity. But since x takes on a relatively large range of values, there is no possible series that will converge fast enough so that all the higher-order terms in x can be eliminated. A solution of this type is quite tedious, and in addition, the design requirements are often obscured beneath the algebra needed in handling the existent higher-order terms.

A second, more fruitful approach is through an investigation of the properties of the slope of the curve rather than of the curve itself. When we differentiate Eq. (10-23) with respect to x, the resultant expression for the slope is no longer an exponential function of x, and consequently it is of simpler form than the original equation:

$$S = \frac{d(t_1/\tau_1)}{dx} = \frac{-(b + a)}{ax^2 - (a - b)x - b} \tag{10-25}$$

In order for the pulse-width variation with respect to changes in x to be linear, the slope must be independent of x; it should be a constant. But this requires that the denominator of Eq. (10-25),

$$y = ax^2 - (a - b)x - b \tag{10-26}$$

must also be a constant for all values of x within any one mode. Equation (10-26) is the equation of a parabola, and therefore it is impossible to satisfy the required condition; we can never expect a completely linear relationship. A good compromise will keep the change in y small for the range of x within the mode under investigation.

We would conclude, from scrutinizing the properties of a parabola, that it is most nearly constant with respect to small variations of x in the vicinity of its vertex. The best design would adjust the circuit parameters so that the point of inflection of Eq. (10-26) lies in the middle of the mode in which the linear function is desired. Differentiating Eq. (10-26) and equating to zero locates the vertex at

$$x_m = \frac{a - b}{2a} \tag{10-27}$$

For mode 12 of the multivibrator that was treated in making the plot of Fig. 10-7 (zero control-source impedance), x_{m1} is at 0.345 compared with the lower and higher limits of $x_{l1} = 0.272$ and $x_{h1} = 0.444$. It is quite close to the optimum placement of the vertex at $x = 0.358$. But in mode 22 of the same circuit x_{m2} is at 1.19, well outside the mode limits of $x_{l2} = 0.444$ and $x_{h2} = 0.614$. The difference in linearity is quite apparent.

The second condition for good linearity also comes from the examination of the properties of the parabola. If the focus is close to the vertex, then the parabola is wide open and will be more nearly constant in the vicinity of the vertex, further improving the linearity. This distance, for the parabola of Eq. (10-26), is

$$D = \frac{1}{4a}$$

Generally it is not possible to make D small and still satisfy Eq. (10-27). Setting $D = 0$ in mode 12 is a trivial case, requiring a zero value for R_3, which would make the multivibrator inoperative. But even in this case, setting R_3 as small as possible compared with R_1 minimizes D within the other design constraints that now determine the lower limit of R_3. The more important condition is the one given by Eq. (10-27), and this is the one which must be satisfied for best linearity.

Under some other circumstances it may be desirable to make the pulse width relatively independent of x. From Eq. (10-25) it can be seen that this requires $a = -b$. All modes give ridiculous answers in satisfying this condition, either a pulse duration of zero or negative values of circuit resistors.

By including the source impedance of the control path in the derivation of the timing waveshape, we would find it possible to maintain the pulse width almost constant with respect to small changes in x in mode 22.

The equation resulting would be in the same form as Eq. (10-23), with, of course, different constants. Either from this equation or by considering the effect on the base voltage of T_1 (as in Example 10-2), the slope of the time-versus-x curve can be minimized by maximizing R_s. Any changes in the transistor parameters would now have but little influence on the timing, and the sweep stability would be greatly improved.

10-4. Emitter-coupled Astable Multivibrator. Astable operation, at least according to Sec. 9-7, apparently is dependent upon two independent energy-storage elements maintaining first one and then the other transistor cut off. But in the circuit configuration of Fig. 10-1 or 10-9, a single capacitor controls the duration of both unstable states. To see how, suppose that, with the feedback loop broken and by satisfying the following conditions, we bias both transistors in their active region.

For T_2 active:

$$R > \beta R_2$$

For T_1 active:

$$\frac{(1+\beta)R_3}{R+(1+\beta)R_3} < x < \frac{R_3R+(1+\beta)R_3R_1}{R(R_1+R_3)+(1+\beta)R_3R_1} \tag{10-28}$$

The complete limits of astable operation expressed by Eq. (10-28) are readily derived from the appropriate models, one with T_1 cut off and T_2 active, and the other for T_1 saturated while T_2 remains active.

Once the feedback loop is again closed, the regenerative action of the multivibrator rapidly drives T_2 into cutoff. As C recovers toward E_{bb}, the base of T_2 eventually reaches the emitter voltage xE_{bb}, at which point T_2 reenters its active region. The increased current through R_3 now raises e_e above xE_{bb} and thus drives T_1 off. The resultant jump in the collector voltage of T_1 forces T_2 toward, or even into, full conduction, capacitor charging current contributing the necessary additional base current flow. However, C will again recover. In the process, the total emitter current drops; the base voltage of T_2 and the common-emitter voltage exponentially decay, finally recrossing the xE_{bb} line. At this instant T_1 turns back on, and the cycle repeats. We see that the single capacitor performs both timing functions; first it maintains T_2 cut off, and next it supplies the additional current that keeps T_2 turned on and/or T_1 cut off.

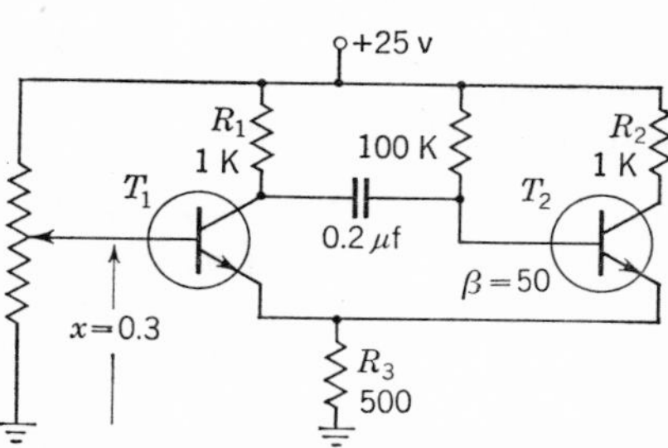

FIG. 10-9. An astable emitter-coupled multivibrator.

As a convenient starting point for the purpose of computation, we might well look at the conditions of Fig. 10-9 while T_2 is on, just going off, and T_1 is off, on the verge of turning on. The initial voltages at $t = 0^-$, neglecting any charging current which might be flowing, are

$$e_{c1} = E_{bb} = 25 \text{ volts}$$
$$e_{b1} = e_{b2} = e_e = xE_{bb} = 7.5 \text{ volts}$$
$$e_q = e_{c1} - e_{b2} = 17.5 \text{ volts}$$

Immediately after the circuit changes state, at $t = 0^+$, T_2 becomes cut off and T_1 active. Therefore the model with which we must be concerned is the one shown in Fig. 10-10*a*. Since the 100-K base bias resistor of T_2 is so very much larger than the 1-K collector resistor of T_1, we may

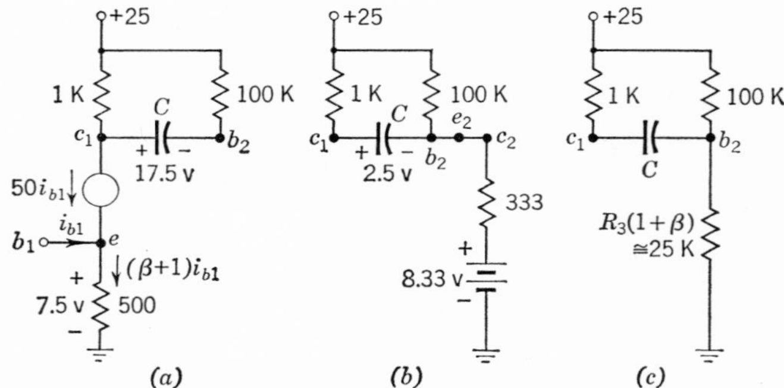

FIG. 10-10. Transistor models used for the calculation of astable operation. (*a*) T_1 on, T_2 off; (*b*) T_1 off, T_2 saturated; (*c*) T_1 off, T_2 active.

ignore the additional loading introduced by R. From Fig. 10-10*a*, the conditions at $t = 0^+$ are

$$e_{b1} = e_e = 7.5 \text{ volts}$$
$$i_{b1} = \frac{7.5 \text{ volts}}{(50 + 1)500} = 0.3 \text{ ma}$$
$$e_{c1} = E_{bb} - 50i_{b1} \text{ (1 K)} = 25 - 15 = 10 \text{ volts}$$

The collector voltage falls 15 volts, and the base of T_2 drops by the same amount, from 7.5 to -7.5 volts. It immediately starts charging toward E_{bb} with the time constant

$$\tau_1 = RC = 20 \text{ msec}$$

But T_2 turns back on once $e_{b2} = e_e = 7.5$ volts, and thus the first portion of the cycle lasts for

$$t_1 = \tau_1 \ln \frac{E_{bb} - E_i}{E_{bb} - E_f} = 20 \ln \frac{25 - (-7.5)}{25 - 7.5} = 12.36 \text{ msec}$$

The final charge in C, which we shall need as a boundary condition in the next operating region, is

$$e_q(t_1) = e_{c1}(t_1) - e_{b2}(t_1) = 2.5 \text{ volts}$$

After T_2 turns back on, the jump in the collector voltage of T_1 as it turns off, coupled through C, forces T_2 into saturation (Fig. 10-10*b*). Before we can calculate the time response, we must verify the correctness of this assumption. From the model drawn for the saturated transistor, we see that the equivalent-emitter voltage is

$$\frac{E_{bb}R_3}{R_1 + R_3} = 8.33 \text{ volts}$$

The additional capacitor charging current flowing through the 333-ohm source impedance ($R_3 \parallel R_1$) raises the voltage of all the elements of T_2 to 11.87 volts, a value well above the saturation-threshold voltage. The initial current flow through C and the base of T_2 becomes

$$i_{b2}(0) = \frac{25 - 2.5 - 8.33}{1{,}333} = 10.6 \text{ ma}$$

However, the base current necessary to sustain saturation is merely

$$i_{b2} = \frac{e_{es}}{(\beta + 1)R_3} = \frac{8.33}{25 \text{ K}} = 0.333 \text{ ma}$$

and of this, the amount contributed by the normal bias current flow through R is

$$i_{b2R} = \frac{E_{bb} - e_{es}}{R} = \frac{25 - 8.33}{100 \text{ K}} = 0.167 \text{ ma}$$

Thus the equation of the base current component due to the capacitor charging current becomes

$$i_{b2C}(t) = 10.6e^{-t/\tau_2}$$

where $$\tau_2 = (R_1 + R_2 \parallel R_3)C = 0.266 \text{ msec}$$

T_2 finally enters its active region (from saturation) when

$$i_{b2C}(t_2) = 0.167 \text{ ma}$$

As a consequence of the large initial and small final value of current flow, the duration of the first portion of the recovery period takes virtually the complete exponential:

$$t_2 = \tau_2 \ln \frac{10.6}{0.167} \cong 4\tau_2 = 1.06 \text{ msec}$$

At the end of this interval, a new model is needed for T_2, one representing the active region (Fig. 10-10*c*). The transistor input resistance, measured from base of T_2 to ground, is $(\beta + 1)R_3 = 25$ K, and the equivalent input open-circuit voltage is

$$E_{Th} = \frac{(\beta + 1)R_3}{R + (\beta + 1)R_3} E_{bb} = \frac{25 \text{ K}}{100 \text{ K} + 25 \text{ K}} 25 \text{ volts} = 5 \text{ volts}$$

Moreover, since the transition from the saturation to the active region will be smooth (without any voltage jump), there is no need to calculate the initial charge on C. Charging continues, but now toward 5 volts, with a new time constant $\tau_3 = [(\beta + 1)R_3 \parallel R]C = 6.7$ msec. Once the common-emitter voltage falls to 7.5 volts, T_1 again conducts, the circuit reswitches, and the cycle repeats:

$$t_3 = \tau_3 \ln \frac{5 - 8.33}{5 - 7.5} = 1.94 \text{ msec}$$

During this final interval T_2 is in its active rather than its saturated state. As its base current continues to decrease, the collector voltage now starts rising. The generated waveshapes at the base of T_2 and at the common-emitter junction appear in Fig. 10-11.

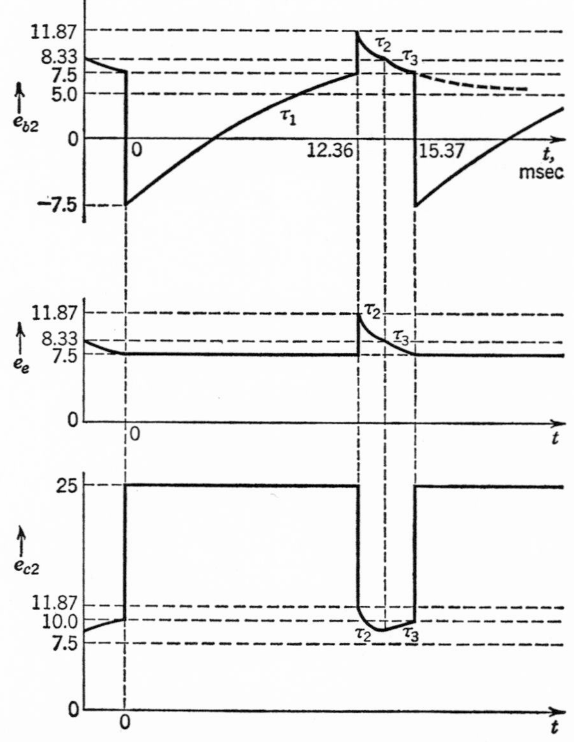

FIG. 10-11. Controlling waveshapes of emitter-coupled astable multivibrator.

10-5. Cathode-coupled Monostable Multivibrator. A vacuum-tube cathode-coupled circuit (Fig. 10-12) functions in a manner quite similar to that of the common-emitter transistor multivibrator; the principal differences involve the circumstances that surround the change of circuit state. These naturally arise from the physical properties of the vacuum tube and will be represented in the circuit models. The various operating modes would be defined for the same switching conditions as in the transistor circuit.

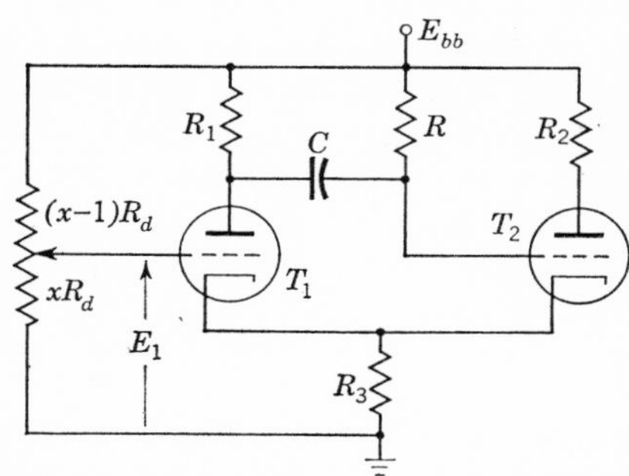

FIG. 10-12. Cathode-coupled monostable multivibrator.

All aspects of this multivibrator's operation in mode 12, the only one with which we shall be concerned, are presented in the two models drawn below. The first represents the circuit conditions both during recovery and while the multivibrator is in its normal state (Fig. 10-13*a*), and the second, when it is in its quasi-stable state (Fig. 10-13*b*).

In an effort to simplify computations, we shall make the following assumptions:

1. The equivalent grid resistance in the positive grid region, r_c, is small compared with R.
2. R is sufficiently large so that its loading of R_1 may be neglected.
3. The contribution of grid current in developing the voltage across R_3 is insignificant.

From Fig. 10-13*a* (T_1 off, T_2 saturated), the quiescent circuit voltages are

$$e_{gk2}(0^-) \cong 0 \tag{10-29a}$$

$$e_{c2}(0^-) \cong e_k(0^-) = \frac{R_3}{R_2 + R_3 + r_p} E_{bb} \tag{10-29b}$$

$$e_{b2}(0^-) = \frac{r_p + R_3}{R_2 + R_3 + r_p} E_{bb} \tag{10-29c}$$

$$e_q(0^-) = E_{bb} - e_{c2}(0^-) = \frac{r_p + R_2}{R_2 + R_3 + r_p} E_{bb} \tag{10-29d}$$

For proper operation in this mode, T_1 must be cut off. The required minimum bias voltage (grid to cathode) is determined by the plate-to-cathode drop.

$$E_{co1} = -\frac{E_{b1}}{\mu} = -\frac{E_{bb} - e_k}{\mu} \tag{10-30}$$

and to ensure that T_1 remains off in its normal state,

$$e_{gk1} = xE_{bb} - e_k < -\frac{E_{bb} - e_k}{\mu} \tag{10-31}$$

where $e_k = R_3E_{bb}/(r_p + R_2 + R_3)$.

As the multivibrator enters upon its quasi-stable state, after the application of an external trigger, T_1 switches from cutoff to its active region. The plate and cathode voltages become (Fig. 10-13*b*)

$$e_k(0^+) = \frac{R_3(E_{bb} + \mu xE_{bb})}{r_p + R_1 + (\mu + 1)R_3} \tag{10-32}$$

$$e_{b1}(0^+) = E_{bb} - \frac{R_1(E_{bb} + \mu xE_{bb})}{r_p + R_1 + (\mu + 1)R_3} \tag{10-33}$$

We must check that $e_k(0^+) > xE_{bb}$, because if this inequality is not satisfied, the model of Fig. 10-13*b* is no longer valid. It must then be

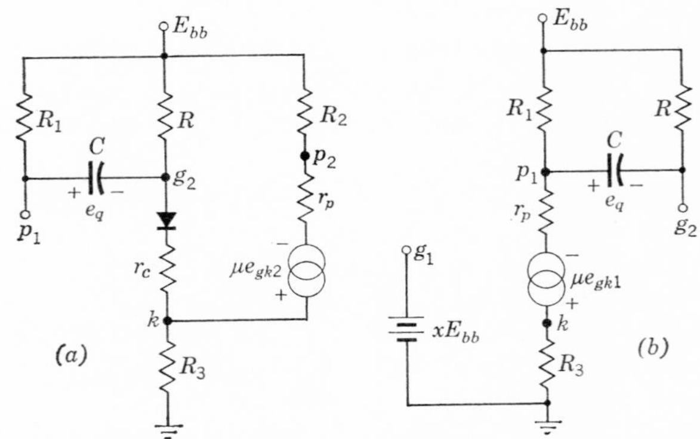

FIG. 10-13. Cathode-coupled multivibrator circuit models. (*a*) Normal state; (*b*) quasi-stable state.

replaced by the model representing positive grid operation. The second term of Eq. (10-33), the drop in plate voltage upon switching (Δe_{b1}), is coupled to the grid of T_2, driving it well below cutoff:

$$\begin{aligned} e_{c2}(0^+) &= e_{c2}(0^-) - \Delta e_{b1} \\ &= \frac{R_3E_{bb}}{R_2 + R_3 + r_p} - \frac{R_1(1 + \mu x)E_{bb}}{r_p + R_1 + (\mu + 1)R_3} \end{aligned} \tag{10-34}$$

The grid of T_2 charges from its initial value [Eq. (10-34)] toward E_{bb}, finally switching at $t = t_1$ as it reaches its particular cutoff voltage:

$$e_{c2}(t_1) = e_k(0^+) - \frac{E_{bb} - e_k(0^+)}{\mu} \tag{10-35}$$

where $e_k(0^+)$ was given in Eq. (10-32). And for high-μ tubes, where $(\mu + 1)R_3 \gg r_p + R_1$,

$$e_{c2}(t_1) \cong E_{bb}\frac{1 + \mu x}{\mu} - \frac{E_{bb}}{\mu} \cong xE_{bb}$$

The charge time constant, again found from Fig. 10-13*b*, is

$$\tau_1 = C\{R + R_1 \parallel [r_p + R_3(\mu + 1)]\} \cong RC$$

and thus the pulse duration becomes

$$t_1 = \tau_1 \ln \frac{E_{bb} - e_{c2}(0^+)}{E_{bb} - e_{c2}(t_1)} \tag{10-36}$$

If we substitute the two values of e_{c2} found above into Eq. (10-36), we shall see that the pulse width is independent of E_{bb} and, in addition, that the resultant equation is of the same form as the general timing equation (10-23). For the particular case of a high-μ tube, we obtain the equation

$$t_1 = \tau_1 \ln \frac{1 - \dfrac{R_3}{R_2 + R_3 + r_p} + \dfrac{1 + \mu x}{\mu}\dfrac{R_1}{R_3}}{1 - x} \tag{10-37}$$

At the end of the unstable state, the voltage across C is

$$e_g(t_1) = e_{b1}(0^+) - e_{c2}(t_1)$$

and by substituting this value into the circuit of Fig. 10-13*a*, we can compute the initial value of the positive grid excursion as the multivibrator starts recovering toward its normal state. Recovery at the plate of T_1 and the grid of T_2 is with the time constant

$$\tau_2 = C[R_1 + r_c(1 - A_k)]$$

where the positive gain from grid to cathode effectively multiplies the grid resistance ($A_k < 1$). We see, at both the plate and cathode of T_2, the reflected grid recovery waveshape (Fig. 10-14), amplified by the appropriate factor. Waveshapes of all tube elements, further illustrating the performance of this circuit, appear in Fig. 10-14.

Limits of the various operating modes of the vacuum-tube multivibrator are computed from the appropriate models by simply solving for their boundary values. Since, in its active region, the vacuum tube operates within a grid base, dependent not only upon the voltage across the tube but also on the tube parameters, the factors defining the limits become quite unwieldy. In the special case of the high-μ tube, there will be considerable simplification. However, for any specific multivibrator, where subcalculations using the circuit resistance and the tube parameters are usually performed, the problem is straightforward and not at all difficult.

10-6. Limitation of Analysis. Physical multivibrators differ in several important aspects from the idealized circuits treated in this chapter. Experimentally measured results cannot be expected to agree exactly with those calculated on the basis of our previous discussion. Since we now understand the multivibrator's operation, we might take a

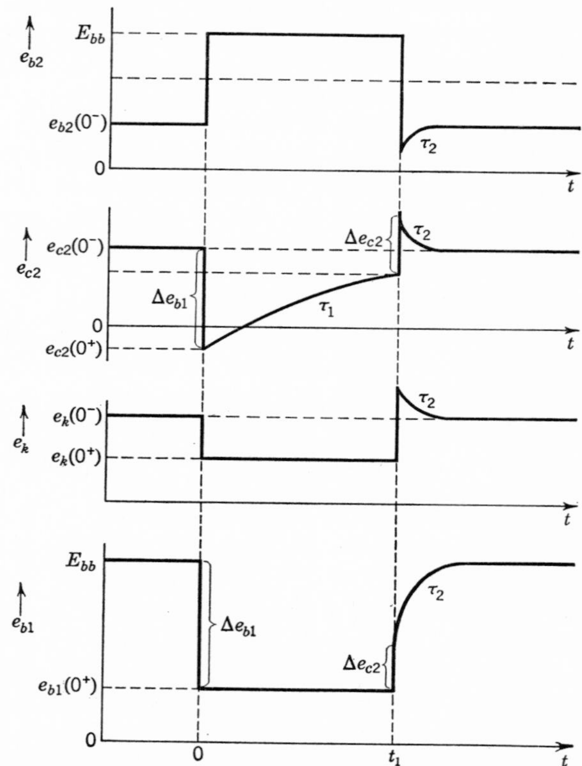

FIG. 10-14. Cathode-coupled multivibrator waveshapes—monostable operation.

second look at the terms previously ignored, with a view toward finding out how they would modify the original analysis.

One of the two terms affecting the pulse duration of the transistor multivibrator is the small voltage drop, about 0.1 or 0.2 volt, that actually appears between the base and emitter of the conducting transistor. This voltage could be included in the transistor models by inserting a small battery in the base emitter circuit. If the transistor switches to well below cutoff and starts charging toward E_{bb}, it seems completely reasonable to neglect 0.1 volt compared with the total base voltage change of 5 to 20 volts or more. However, near the lower limit of mode 12 and the upper limit of mode 32, the transistor is driven only slightly below cutoff and the resultant error in the pulse duration will be quite large. The generated pulse will always be shorter than the calculated pulse, thus introducing additional curvature in these regions of Fig. 10-7.

The second factor, which also tends to reduce the pulse duration, is the temperature-dependent I_{c0}. This, the reverse collector-to-base current, contributes an additional charging component to C while T_2 remains cut off. And of course faster charging means that the pulse will be shorter than expected. I_{c0} may be 5 μa or less at 20°C, but it increases exponentially with temperature, even reaching 50 to 100 μa at the elevated ambient temperatures often encountered. As long as the normal charging current through R remains much larger than I_{c0}, the temperature effects are minimized. Thus another reason appears for not operating under modes $n1$, where R is, of necessity, quite large. Furthermore, some form of temperature compensation is usually employed in transistor circuits.

The extreme curvature of the plate characteristics at low values of plate current leads to the tube's turning on at a lower grid voltage than that given by the piecewise-linear model. Consequently the charging exponential is interrupted sooner and the generated pulse will always be shorter than calculated. A larger plate drop is necessary to ensure driving the other tube into cutoff, and therefore the lower limit of mode 12 will occur at a higher setting of x and the upper limit of mode 32 at a lower setting of x. The difference from the ideal would be appreciable for low-μ tubes but would become negligible when high-μ tubes are employed.

The second-order effects are primarily discussed to show that where physical and theoretical results disagree, a closer look at our original assumptions, or at the active elements themselves, will often explain the source of discrepancy. Practical circuits always have adjustments for timing. Since 5 or 10 per cent accurate components and 20 to 50 per cent tolerance in tube and transistor parameters are what the designer must cope with, exact design is neither possible nor desirable. Thus a rapid, simple, approximate treatment is often more satisfactory than an exact analysis, provided that the answers obtained are reasonable.

PROBLEMS

10-1. The emitter-coupled circuit of Fig. 10-1 employs the following components: $R_1 = R_2 = 2$ K, $R_3 = 1$ K, $R = 50$ K, $C = 1\ \mu$f, $\beta = 50$, and $E_{bb} = 5$ volts.

(*a*) For $xE_{bb} = 0.75$ volt, plot to scale the waveshapes seen at both collectors, at the base of T_2, and at the common emitter.

(*b*) Repeat part *a* for xE_{bb} = 1.5 volts. Superimpose these plots on the waveshapes drawn for part *a*.

10-2. We wish to adjust the multivibrator of Prob. 10-1 so that it will generate a 2-volt 10-msec pulse at the collector of T_2. This should be the maximum possible pulse width which can be produced by this circuit.

(*a*) Specify the new values of R_3, *x*, and *C* needed to satisfy these conditions.

(*b*) Sketch the waveshape appearing at the base of T_2.

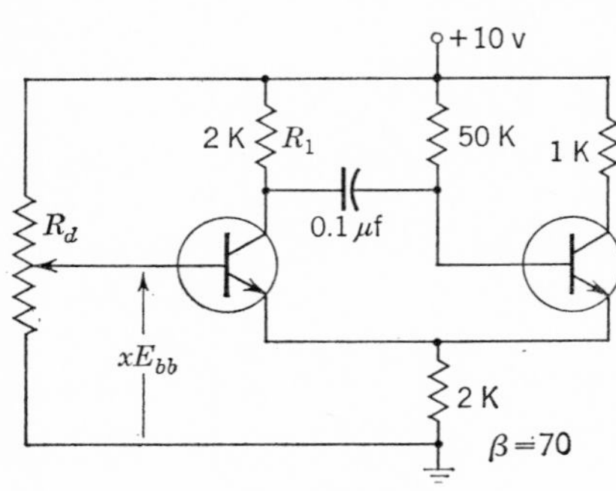

FIG. 10-15

10-3. (*a*) Calculate the limits on *x*, separating the various modes of operation for the multivibrator of Fig. 10-15. Select a value of *x* that lies halfway between the extremes of mode 12, and calculate the pulse duration and amplitude at the collector of T_2 (assume R_d small).

(*b*) Solve for the setting of *x* that will produce a pulse of the same duration but in mode 32. Plot the collector waveshape to scale on the same graph as in part *a*.

10-4. Design an emitter-coupled multivibrator that will generate at its maximum setting, a 10-msec pulse. This circuit should switch directly from mode 12 to mode 32 and must operate in mode 12 over the widest possible range of *x*. Base your design on a transistor having β = 50 and E_{bb} = 5 volts. Set R_3 = 1 K. Specify the range of *x* for both operating modes. Sketch the various circuit waveshapes produced when the multivibrator generates its 10-msec pulse.

10-5. (*a*) The multivibrator of Fig. 10-15 is controlled by a 6-volt battery in place of the potentiometer. E_{bb} suddenly drops by 5 per cent, from 10 to 9.5 volts. What effect will this have on the pulse duration?

(*b*) If this same control voltage is derived by setting the potentiometer at x = 0.6, by how much will the pulse width change when E_{bb} is reduced by 5 per cent?

(*c*) Repeat parts *a* and *b* if a 2,000-ohm resistor is inserted in series with the base of T_1.

10-6. (*a*) Show three methods of triggering the multivibrator of Fig. 10-15. Discuss the required source impedance of the signal generator and the means of coupling the pulse into the circuit.

(*b*) If a pulse is applied through a diode to the common-emitter terminal, calculate the required amplitude at x = 0.2, 0.4, 0.6.

10-7. (*a*) The emitter-coupled multivibrator shown in Fig. 10-15 must be adjusted, by changing R_1, to generate the longest possible pulse. If x = 0.4, find the required value of R_1 and the width of the pulse produced.

(*b*) With R_1 = 1 K and with *x* set to give the maximum possible swing at the collector of T_1, sketch and label fully the waveshape at the collector of T_1.

(*c*) Sketch and label the waveshapes at both collectors when x = 0.33 and when R_1 = 1 K.

10-8. (*a*) Plot the collector voltage swing of T_2 as a function of the potentiometer setting for the multivibrator described in the text in Example 10-1. Label all modes of operation.

(*b*) Repeat the plot, on the same graph, for the collector voltage of T_1.

10-9. The multivibrator whose characteristics are plotted in curve 1 of Fig. 10-7 is used in a special instrument to measure small linear displacements. This information is contained in the width of the pulse produced once the multivibrator is triggered with a read-out pulse. For the transducer we employ a small capacity, replacing C in Fig. 10-1, whose effective plate spacing is varied by the shaft displacement (Fig. 10-16). Assume that the minimum value of C is 1,000 $\mu\mu$f for $d = 10^{-4}$ cm and that its maximum value is 10,000 $\mu\mu$f for $d = 10^{-5}$ cm. Moreover, to prevent arc-over, E_{bb} is reduced to 2 volts.

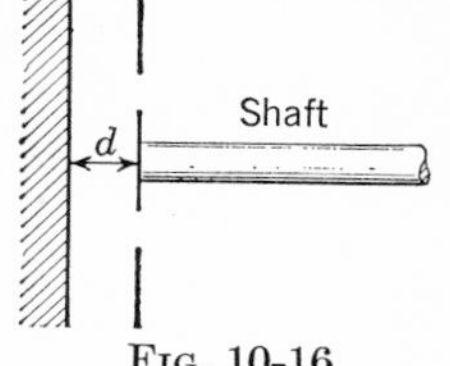

FIG. 10-16

(a) When $x = 0.3$, calculate the range of pulse widths generated as the rod is displaced.

(b) An angular rotation θ of $\pm 3°$ varies x between the limits of 0.2 to 0.4 from its nominal value of 0.3. Under these conditions, express the pulse duration t as a function of d and θ.

$$t_1 = f(d,\theta)$$

Evaluate all constants. Assume a linear variation of t_1 with respect to both d and θ. Is this assumption justified?

10-10. (a) Verify the bounds of each mode for the multivibrator discussed in the text in Example 10-2. Assume that R_s remains constant at 2,500 ohms. Is this approximation justified?

(b) Prove that the x boundary between mode 22 and mode 32 is independent of the potentiometer employed for control.

10-11. In the circuit of Fig. 10-15, R_d is a 5,000-ohm control. Plot the waveshapes at each transistor element, to scale, when $x = 0.5$. How does the pulse duration compare with the one generated when R_d is very small?

10-12. The equation

$$y = \ln \frac{4 - 5x}{1 - x} \qquad 0 < x < 0.75$$

defines the operating path of a circuit.

(a) For what value of x is y most nearly a linear function of x?

(b) If x is varied by ± 0.05 about this point, what is the nonlinearity of y?

(c) What is the NL of y if x varies by ± 0.05 about the point $x = \frac{1}{2}$? (Define the NL of y as the maximum variation in y from a straight line drawn between its bounded end points divided by the change in y between the same two end points.)

10-13. (a) Derive the limits of Eq. (10-28).

(b) Find the numerical values of x that delineate the modes of operation of the multivibrator discussed in Sec. 10-4. Tabulate, under each mode, the normal and the switched state of each transistor. Are any modes of operation monostable? Explain.

10-14. Repeat the calculations for the sample problem given in Sec. 10-4 when x is increased to 0.5. Make all reasonable approximations.

10-15. Determine the amplitude and duration of the output taken at the plate of T_2 in Fig. 10-12 if $x = \frac{1}{2}$, $R_1 = R_2 = 10$ K, $R_3 = 5$ K, $R = 500$ K, $C = 1{,}000$ $\mu\mu$f, $r_p = 20$ K, $\mu = 40$, and $E_{bb} = 300$ volts.

10-16. (a) Find the minimum and maximum values of E_1 that still permit the circuit of Fig. 10-17 to function as a monostable multivibrator.

(b) With E_1 adjusted to 5 volts below its maximum point, sketch and label the waveshapes produced at e_{b1}, e_{b2}, e_k, and e_{c2} when a trigger is applied at $t = 0$.

(c) In which modes would the source impedance of E_1 affect the pulse duration? Explain your answer.

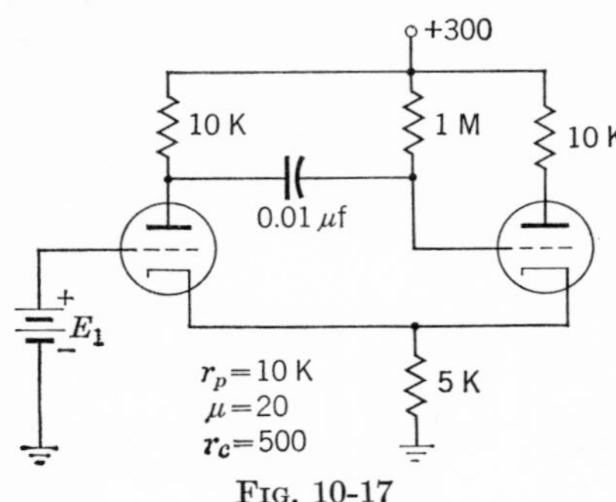

FIG. 10-17

10-17. The circuit of Fig. 10-17 is modified by returning the timing resistor to ground instead of to E_{bb} and by increasing the capacity to 2 μf. Solve for the response at all pertinent elements after a trigger is injected, if $E_1 = 50$ volts. Does this modification improve or degrade the operation? Explain.

10-18. The transistor multivibrator of Fig. 10-18a is designed to operate at very low voltages. Consequently its small emitter base drop must be taken into account in calculating the time duration. Furthermore, the temperature-dependent I_{c0} increases from 1 μa at 20°C to 20 μa at 100°C. Calculate the nominal pulse duration and amplitude at the collector of T_2 (at 0°C). By how much will the pulse vary over the expected temperature range? For your calculations use the transistor model of Fig. 10-18b.

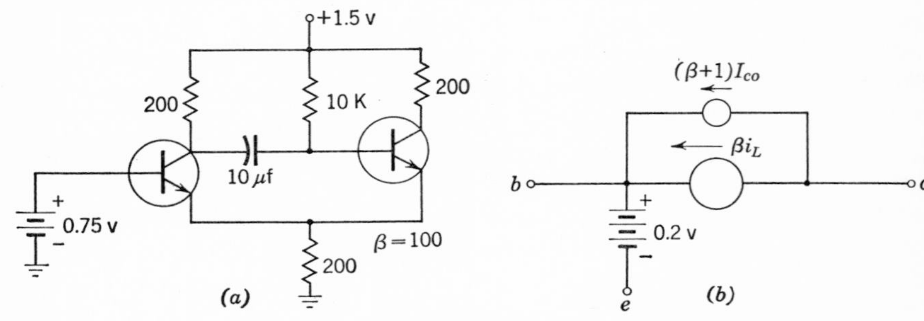

FIG. 10-18

BIBLIOGRAPHY

Chance, B., M. H. Johnson, and R. H. Phillip: Precision Delay Multivibrator for Range Measurements, *MIT Rad. Labs. Rept.* 63-2.

Clarke, K. K., and M. V. Joyce: "Transistor Circuit Analysis," Addison-Wesley Publishing Company, Reading, Mass., in press.

Glegg, K.: Cathode-coupled Multivibrator Operation, *Proc. IRE,* vol. 38, no. 6, pp. 655–657, 1950.

Millman, J., and H. Taub: "Pulse and Digital Circuits," McGraw-Hill Book Company, Inc., New York, 1956.

Reintjes, J. F., and G. T. Coate: "Principles of Radar," 3d ed., McGraw-Hill Book Company, Inc., New York, 1952.

Schmitt, O. H.: A Thermionic Trigger, *J. Sci. Instr.*, vol. 15, p. 24, 1938.

CHAPTER 11

NEGATIVE-RESISTANCE SWITCHING CIRCUITS

A two-terminal active network that exhibits a negative-resistance driving-point impedance over a portion of its range may, together with an energy-storage element, be used as a switching circuit. Our initial discussion concerns a postulated ideal device in various circuit configurations. After considering several available active elements that are used for this type of switching, we shall modify the original argument to account for the frequency dependence of the nonideal active elements. A physical device differs markedly from an ideal one, and some of the latter results may even contradict the earlier conclusions. If the reader considers only the problem posed in each individual network, the arguments employed will be found to be consistent.

11-1. Basic Circuit Considerations. The regenerative circuits treated in Chaps. 9 and 10—bistable, monostable, and astable multivibrators—depended for their proper self-switching action on the charge stored in a capacitor (the single energy-storage element of the circuit) maintaining the tube or transistor cut off. Only after a sufficient amount of the stored energy had been dissipated did the active element reenter its active region; then, during recovery, the original stored energy was replenished through a positive source impedance. But in order to transfer the capacitor from a region of low potential energy (off) to one of high energy (recovery), the switch itself must contain an energy source. Thus a switching circuit might well be characterized as a device having two stable or quasi-stable states, i.e., the dissipative regions, and a single transition zone.

Any two-terminal device with these attributes will, when combined with a capacitor or inductance, function as a multivibrator. Figure 11-1 presents the idealized volt-ampere characteristic of one class of such devices. In regions I and III, the curve has a positive slope with a corresponding positive incremental resistance. These are the dissipative segments. Region II is the negative-resistance portion of the characteristic, and it is here that the switching of circuit states takes place.

Negative-resistance characteristics arise only through the use of active elements, which serve as the source of the available energy. Passive elements, by their very nature, are always dissipative. Yet no physical device can be expected to have an unlimited range of negative resistance; to do so implies an infinite source of energy. Therefore each negative slope will always be flanked by two regions of positive resistance.

Because the terminal voltage is a single-valued function of current, we classify the characteristic of Fig. 11-1 as a current-controlled nonlinear resistance (CNLR). On the other hand, any one of three values of current becomes possible upon excitation by an input voltage. The particular value that will flow is determined by the constraints imposed by the external circuit, with this very multivaluedness permitting the several different circuit states. Since only the current is unrestricted, in our switching circuit we must utilize an energy-storage element allowing instantaneous current changes during the switching process, i.e., a capacitor.

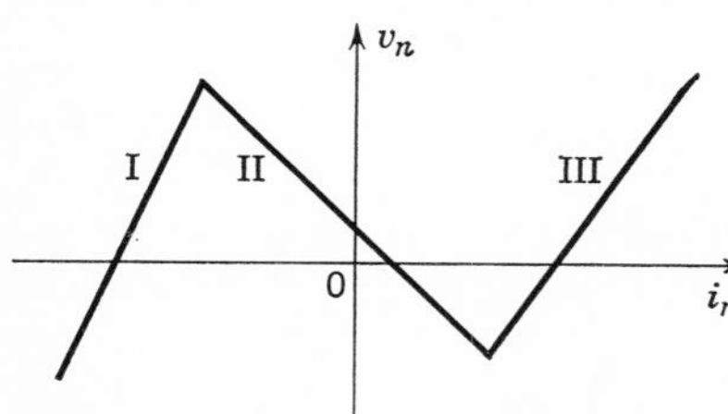

FIG. 11-1. Idealized-negative-resistance characteristic (current-controlled).

An alternative form of the nonlinear resistance, the dual of the above, also exists. Its voltage-controlled characteristic is illustrated by the sketch of Fig. 11-2 (VNLR). To complete the duality, an inductance would be used instead of the controlling capacitor to permit rapid terminal voltage changes.

Negative-resistance regions are exhibited by many devices. Current-controlled characteristics appear in point-contact transistors, in unijunction and avalanche diodes, and in gas tubes. For examples of the voltage-controlled nonlinear resistance (VNLR), we may refer to the screen characteristics of a tetrode or a pentode, to the tunnel diode, and to the *p-n-p-n* transistor. In addition, the use of feedback allows the production of almost any desired form of NLR. Generally voltage feedback furnishes the voltage-controlled characteristics and current feedback establishes those that are current-controlled.

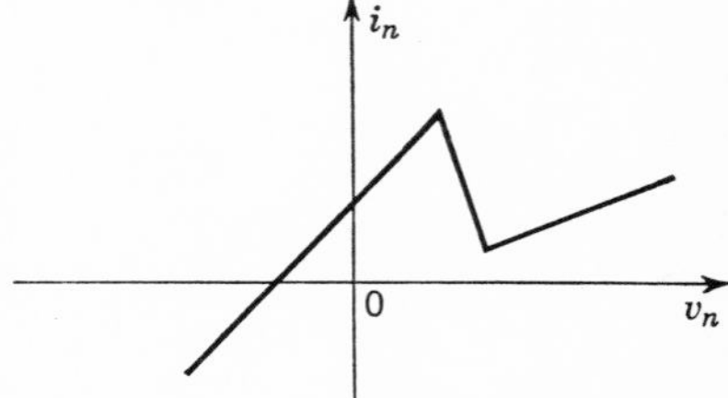

FIG. 11-2. Voltage-controlled nonlinear resistance.

Behavior of the two classes of NLR are similar enough so that any conclusions derived from the examination of one class may be applied to the other. Of course, caution as to the duality relationship must be observed while interpreting the results.

11-2. Basic Switching Circuits. The basic form of the switching circuit with which we shall be concerned is shown in Fig. 11-3. For the negative-resistance element, we will use the current-controlled characteristic previously given. In this circuit, the items of interest are the necessary conditions for stable operation at any one point and the mechanism of transition from one state to the other. We shall start the analysis by writing the single-node equation:

$$i_r = i_n + i_c = i_n + C\frac{dv_n}{dt} \tag{11-1}$$

and

$$V_{nn} - i_r R = v_n \tag{11-2}$$

Solving Eq. (11-2) for i_r and substituting the result into Eq. (11-1) yields

$$(V_{nn} - i_n R) - v_n = RC\frac{dv_n}{dt} \tag{11-3}$$

Let

$$\mathbf{v}_t \equiv RC\frac{dv_n}{dt} \tag{11-4}$$

However, $V_{nn} - i_n R$ is simply the static (d-c) load line which we can superimpose on the volt-ampere characteristic. The distance measured

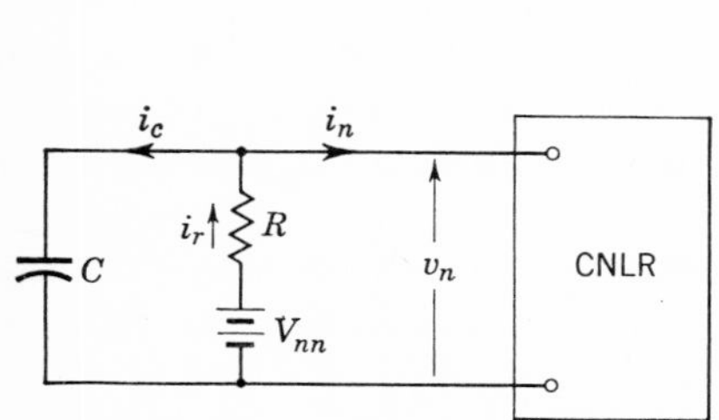

FIG. 11-3. Basic CNLR switching circuit.

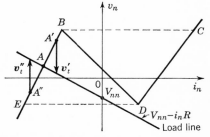

FIG. 11-4. Graphical solution of the circuit of Fig. 11-3.

from the known curve to the load line must be $\mathbf{v}_t$, and as shown in Fig. 11-4, it may be treated as a vector.

The steady-state operating point, the intersection of the load line and the characteristic, is stable if, and only if, any momentary perturbation will create the conditions forcing a return to the original point. Since the volt-ampere plot represents the locus of all possible behavior of the NLR, any disturbance will shift the operating point along it, say from A to A'. Equation (11-4) defines the vector $\mathbf{v}_t$, drawn from any point on the characteristics to the load line, as being proportional to the time rate of change of v_n. At point A', this vector is negative, indicating that the terminal voltage across the capacitor must decrease with time. If instead the initial disturbance were from A to A'', the vector would be positive, with the terminal voltage increasing with time toward point A.

Only at A itself is $\mathbf{v}_t$ zero, and only here do we have a stable operating point.

Operation as a Monostable Switching Circuit. A voltage pulse, applied in series with the bias supply, momentarily shifts the load line to the position indicated by the dashed line of Fig. 11-5. While the pulse is present, the shifted load line establishes a new stable point at F. But $\mathbf{v}_t$, as drawn from the original operating point A to the shifted load line, is positive, and therefore the terminal voltage increases toward point B. At the peak, $\mathbf{v}_t$ is still positive, forbidding travel down line segment BD. Operation must be restricted to the characteristics and must stabilize at point F. It can do so only if the operating point can transfer from segment EB to CD. The voltage across the capacitor may not change instantaneously, but the current can and does; it jumps from B to C.

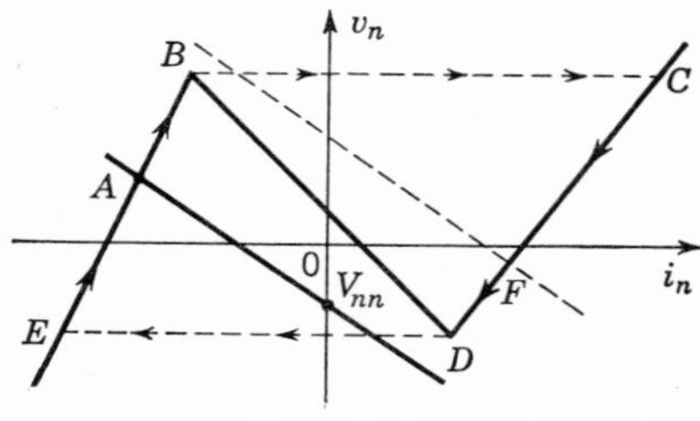

FIG. 11-5. Monostable operation.

Along line segment CF, $\mathbf{v}_t$ becomes negative. After the jump, the direction of the operating path is down toward point F.

Removal of the input trigger permits the load line to return to its original position. Even after it does so, the terminal voltage, constrained by the capacitor to change slowly, remains on segment CD and travels toward point D. At D, $\mathbf{v}_t$ is still negative, preventing the traverse up the line segment DB. A second jump in current is indicated, this time from D to E. Following this jump, $\mathbf{v}_t$ becomes positive, and the operating path is finally back toward the original stable point A.

In order to repeat the operating cycle, another trigger must be injected. The minimum-size pulse, for guaranteed triggering, is that value necessary to shift the load line so that it just clears the peak point B.

As an alternative method of triggering, we can inject a current impulse, having an area of K amp-sec, into the common node of Fig. 11-3. $K\delta(t)$ changes the voltage across the capacitor from the initial value of V_A to

$$v(0^+) = V_A + \frac{K}{C}$$

If $v(0^+)$ is greater than the peak voltage V_B, the operating point will switch to the appropriate voltage coordinate along the extension of line segment CD. Recovery proceeds as before, from the new initial value established by the applied impulse.

Since this system has one, and only one, stable condition, any disturbance, no matter how large, eventually results in the circuit returning to this point; it functions as a monostable device.

Bistable Operation. For operation as a bistable, the value of V_{nn} and the load resistance will have to be changed so that the circuit has the two stable points (A, G) indicated in Fig. 11-6. Upon first examination, H appears to be a third stable point, but once switching begins, the transition will always be from A to G for positive triggers and from G to A when a negative trigger is applied. The operating path is in the direction of the arrows. Regardless of how or where the triggers are injected, it is impossible to establish a transition path to point H.

A practical CNLR differs in important aspects from the ideal, and it is these very differences that preclude the establishment of point H as a third stable point (Sec. 11-8). In general, it is difficult to stabilize a system within its negative-resistance region; whenever there is an appreciable-size energy-storage element present, it becomes almost impossible to do so.

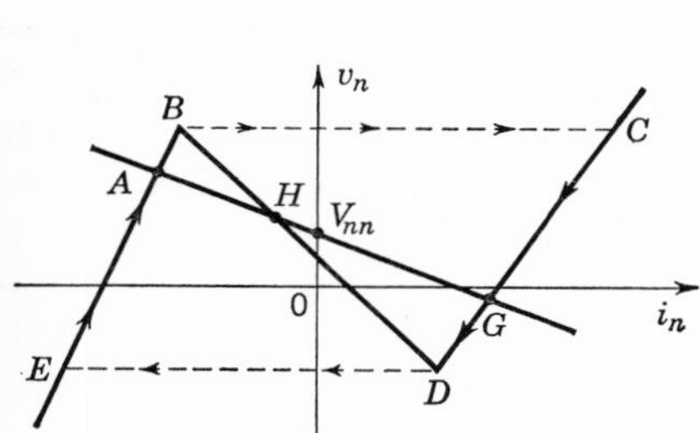

FIG. 11-6. Bistable operation.

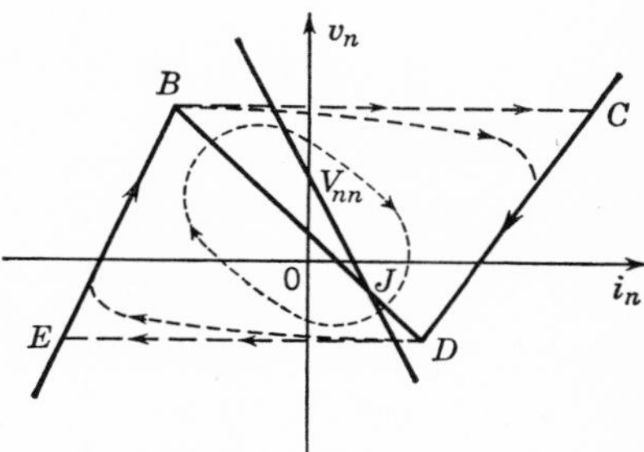

FIG. 11-7. Astable operation.

In effecting the change of state, the external trigger forces the operating point to move from its stable position to the peak of the curve, i.e., from A to B or from G to D. In sweeping through this distance, power proportional to the product of the changes in voltage and current will be dissipated, and this power must be supplied from the trigger source. We conclude that if the stable points are established closer to the peaks, the switching-power requirement imposed on the trigger generator will be much less severe.

The sequence of the multivibrator's behavior in switching from one stable point to the other is identical with that discussed for the monostable circuit.

Astable Operation. When the load line is so chosen that it intersects the volt-ampere characteristic only on the negative portion of the NLR, no stable point of operation exists. This case is illustrated in Fig. 11-7. A power balance, evaluated in the vicinity of the point of intersection J, would show that the energy supplied by the NLR is greater than that dissipated by the load resistor. The surplus energy, available for storage by the capacitor, results in a voltage build-up toward either point B or point D.

Once the peak is reached, the path of operation becomes $BCDE$, with the instantaneous current jumps taking place from B to C and D to E. We might observe that at all points on the characteristic, the value of $\mathbf{v}_t$ is such as to direct the time rate of voltage change toward the two peaks.

An alternative way of viewing the build-up phenomena is to recognize that in region II the negative resistance $-R_n$ and the load resistor R are in parallel. Surplus energy means that the parallel combination is still a negative resistance with the system's pole located at

$$p = -\frac{1}{C(R \parallel -R_n)} \tag{11-5}$$

This pole lies on the real axis in the right half of the complex plane. Obviously, the circuit is unstable, having an increasing exponential for its transient response. Terminal voltage builds up until limiting occurs when the operating point enters the positive-resistance region.

Instantaneous current jumps are forbidden in any physical CNLR circuit by the inductive component of the driving-point impedance. This modifies the path of operation, introducing the curvature shown by the dashed lines of Fig. 11-7. For very-low-frequency operation, the transition time is small enough so that the path approaches the ideal. But as the generated pulse duration decreases, the transition time becomes an appreciable portion of the total cycle and the locus constricts to the dashed curve sketched. At very high frequencies, the path may even turn into a small ellipse.

Stability of Ideal CNLR Switching Circuits. For absolute stability, i.e., the system's pole remaining on the left-hand half of the real axis, the parallel combination of the ideal negative resistance and the external load resistor must be positive.

$$R_p = \frac{R(-R_n)}{R + (-R_n)} > 0$$

In the particular circuit of Fig. 11-3, where the graphical solution is given by Fig. 11-7, this condition can be satisfied only when

$$R < |R_n| \tag{11-6}$$

If the load is a short circuit, then regardless of the value of R_n the parallel combination will always be positive. In addition, the now horizontal load line intersects the positive-resistance, as well as the negative-resistance, region of the CNLR and consequently establishes at least two stable operating points. Alternatively, an infinite-resistance load could intersect only the negative-resistance portion, and it would cause astable behavior in the presence of any external capacity. It thus seems logical to refer to the *ideal CNLR* as a short-circuit stable device. Other considerations will cause us to modify this conclusion for a physical CNLR, and reference should be made to Sec. 11-8, where the topic of stability is treated in much greater detail.

11-3. Calculation of Waveshapes. The calculation of the waveshapes of an ideal switching circuit (no parasitic energy-storage elements present) may be greatly simplified by representing each linear region of the NLR by a resistor in series with a battery. If we extend the straight lines of NLR until they reach the voltage axis, the point of intersection is the battery voltage and the slope of the line segment is the resistance value. Figure 11-8 shows the resultant equivalent circuit for region I. Since the instantaneous current jump carries the operating point through the negative-resistance region, only regions I and III need be considered.

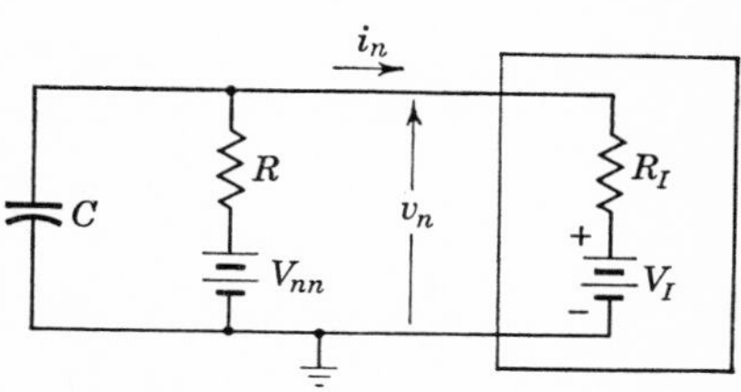

FIG. 11-8. Piecewise-linear circuit used for the calculation of waveshapes.

Within each region, the exponential terminal response has, as its single boundary condition, voltage continuity across the current jumps of the circuit. The problem resolves itself into finding the boundary values and the time constants holding within regions I and III.

At the instant that the operating point enters region I, the voltage across the capacitor is that of point E in Fig. 11-5, 11-6, or 11-7. It rises with a time constant τ_1 toward the steady-state voltage of the Thévenin equivalent circuit across its terminals V_1.

$$\tau_1 = C(R \parallel R_{\mathrm{I}}) \tag{11-7}$$

$$V_1 = \frac{RV_{\mathrm{I}} + R_{\mathrm{I}}V_{nn}}{R_{\mathrm{I}} + R} \tag{11-8}$$

This voltage [Eq. (11-8)] is simply the value of the intersection of the load line with the extension of the line segment defining region I. In the astable circuit, V_1 must always be larger than V_B; otherwise the output will never reach the voltage peak B. However, if the circuit is adjusted for bistable or monostable operation, and if it has a stable point along the segment EB, then V_1 will be the voltage at the stable point. Once this value is reached, sweep action ceases.

At the peak, $v_n = V_B$ and the operating point flips from B to C. Upon entering the new region (III), the circuit of Fig. 11-8 changes; R_{III} and V_{III} replace R_{I} and V_{I}. The terminal voltage immediately starts charging toward the new Thévenin equivalent voltage with a time constant τ_3.

$$V_3 = \frac{RV_{\text{III}} + R_{\text{III}}V_{nn}}{R_{\text{III}} + R} \qquad \tau_3 = C(R \parallel R_{\text{III}}) \tag{11-9}$$

Equation (11-9) defines the final value of any circuit having a stable point lying on line segment CD. For astable operation, $V_3 < V_D$. After reaching the peak, the operating path jumps to point E, and the cycle repeats.

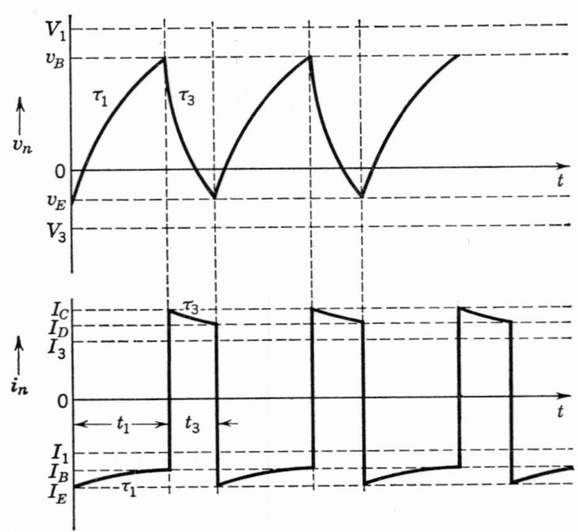

FIG. 11-9. Waveshapes produced in a CNLR switching circuit (astable operation).

The current values at the switching points are simply those given by NLR characteristic at points B, C, D, and E. In order to find the steady-state values, we must consider the circuit when the capacitor is fully charged and the full current flows into the NLR terminals. In region I,

$$I_1 = \frac{V_{nn} - V_{\text{I}}}{R_{\text{I}} + R} \tag{11-10}$$

and in region III,

$$I_3 = \frac{V_{nn} - V_{\text{III}}}{R_{\text{III}} + R} \tag{11-11}$$

These values also correspond to the point of intersection of the extended volt-ampere characteristic and the load line.

From the characteristic and from Eqs. (11-7) to (11-11), we have all the voltage and current values necessary to sketch the terminal waveshapes. Figure 11-9 shows the current and voltage waveshapes for an astable configuration, and Fig. 11-10*b* those appearing in the monostable circuit of Example 11-1.

The duration of the two portions of the generated waveshape, evaluated by substituting the appropriate voltage values into the general time equation, is

$$t_1 = \tau_1 \ln \frac{V_1 - V_E}{V_1 - V_B} \tag{11-12}$$

and

$$t_3 = \tau_3 \ln \frac{V_3 - V_B}{V_3 - V_E} \tag{11-13}$$

In some NLR devices we may exercise a measure of control over the shape of the volt-ampere characteristic. Adjusting the ratio of R_{I} to R_{III} determines the ratio of pulse width to pulse spacing. Furthermore, if R_{I} is made very much larger than R_{III} and if V_1 is very much larger than V_B, then the circuit becomes an almost linear sweep. Its fast recovery time is mainly dependent on R_{III}.

We see that the greater the degree of control over the characteristic, the more versatile the system. Not all devices allow for wide latitude of adjustment, but even in those that do not, the characteristics might be modified by external diodes biased for conduction at the desired voltage levels (Chap. 2).

Example 11-1. A CNLR having the volt-ampere characteristics given in Fig. 11-10*a* is used as a monostable pulse generator. Its external load consists of a 1-μf capacitor and a 2,000-ohm resistor in series with a 20-volt source, as shown in Fig. 11-3.

Only two sets of coordinates are unknown: (1) the location of the intersection of the load line with the line segment defining region III, i.e., the single stable point A; (2) the intersection of the load line with the extension of segment I, that is, V_1 and I_1. In order to find these points we first solve the graph for the three defining equations

Region I: $\quad v_{n\text{I}} = 110 + (5\text{ K})i_n$

Region III: $\quad v_{n\text{III}} = -12.5 + 250i_n$

Load line: $\quad v_{nL} = 20 - (2\text{ K})i_n$

By equating $v_{n\text{III}}$ to v_{nL}, we find that the stable point is located at

$$I_3 = 14.45 \text{ ma} \qquad \text{and} \qquad V_3 = -8.9 \text{ volts}$$

The other set of coordinates is

$$I_1 = -12.85 \text{ ma} \qquad \text{and} \qquad V_1 = 45.7 \text{ volts}$$

After the pulse is applied, the operating point jumps to point F, and i_n and v_n start charging toward I_1 and V_1. From Eq. (11-12), the time required to reach the peak is

$$t_1 = 1{,}430 \times 10^{-6} \ln \frac{45.7 + 10}{45.7 - 10} = 636\ \mu\text{sec}$$

where $\tau_1 = (2\text{ K} \parallel 5\text{ K})1\ \mu\text{f} = 1{,}430\ \mu\text{sec}$.

Upon jumping to point C, the circuit recovers toward the stable point A with the time constant

$$\tau_3 = (2\text{ K} \parallel 250)1\ \mu\text{f} = 222\ \mu\text{sec}$$

Figure 11-10*b* shows the current and voltage waveshapes generated in this circuit. Note that the recovery portion of the wave is longer than the pulse duration and that the voltage rise is almost a linear sweep.

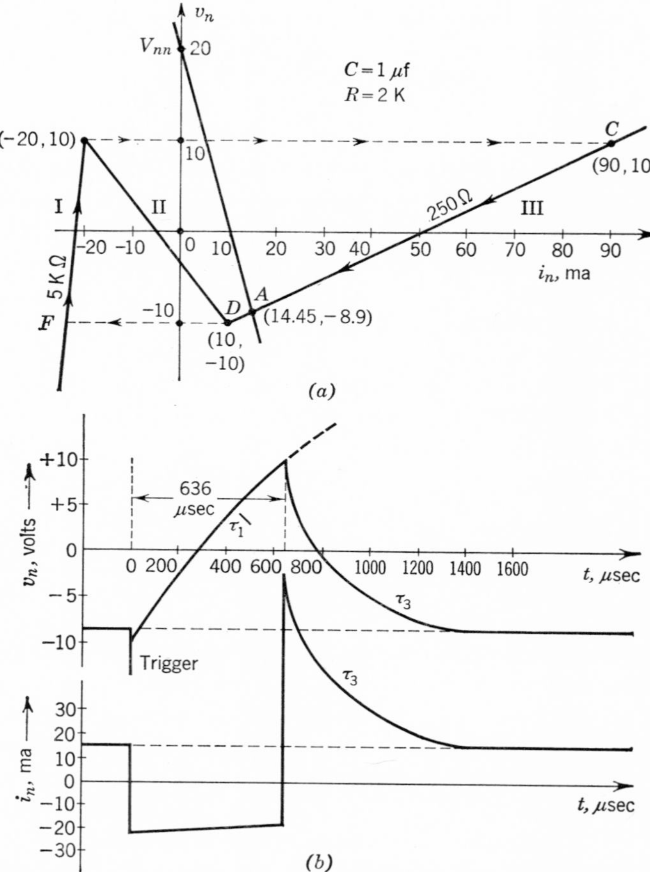

FIG. 11-10. Monostable operation. (*a*) CNLR characteristic and graphical construction for Example 11-1; (*b*) current and voltage waveshapes produced after triggering.

We might further note that the ratio of the recovery time to the pulse duration depends on the relative slopes of the two positive-resistance regions. For a fast pulse and a long recovery, the single stable point should be established in the high-resistance region. For a relatively fast recovery and a long sweep, the stable point must be placed in the low-resistance region, as it is in the above example.

11-4. Voltage-controlled NLR Switching Circuits. The basic switching circuit associated with the VNLR is simply the dual of the one discussed in Sec. 11-2. Figure 11-11 illustrates the resultant series switching circuit together with the graphical construction holding when adjusted for monostable operation.

By properly arranging the terms, we can write the input loop equation in a form that will present the steady-state solution as well as indicate the permissible time variation.

$$(V_{nn} - i_n R) - v_n = L\frac{di_n}{dt} = \mathbf{v}_t \tag{11-14}$$

It follows from Eq. (11-14) that the intersection of the load line $(V_{nn} - i_n R)$ with the characteristics v_n is the only possible stable operating point

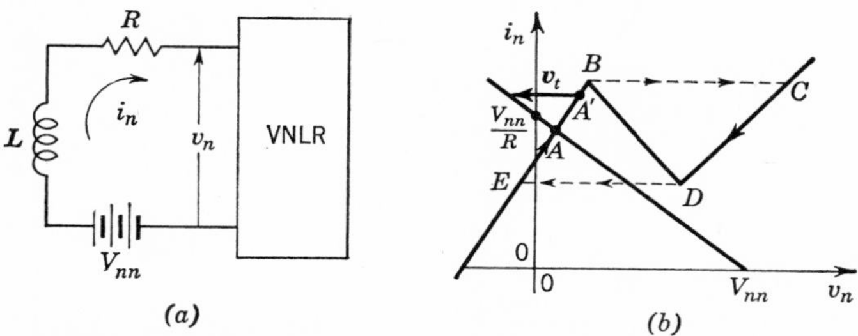

FIG. 11-11. (a) Basic VNLR switching circuit; (b) monostable path of operation.

$(di_n/dt = 0)$. Any perturbation from this point creates a time rate of change of current that forces the operating point back to the original stable point (point A in Fig. 11-11b). Thus the path of operation, location of the stable points, calculation of minimum trigger amplitude, and the calculation of circuit waveshapes are similar to those discussed for the CNLR. The major difference is that now the current is constrained to change slowly, but this only supports the duality relationship, i.e., the interchange of the circuit's voltage and current response.

The second important difference in the *ideal VNLR* concerns the condition which must be satisfied for absolute system stability. Here the external load appears in series with any internal incremental resistance. In order to prevent the system pole from migrating into the right half plane, the total series combination must remain positive.

$$R_s = R + (-R_n) > 0$$

or

$$R > R_n \tag{11-15}$$

This stability condition holds only for the ideal VNLR circuit. A practical device differs in important respects from the ideal, and as with the CNLR, the stability criterion will be reexamined in Sec. 11-8.

11-5. NLR Characteristics—Collector-to-base-coupled Monostable Multivibrator. As an example of how all single-energy-storage-element switching circuits may be treated from the viewpoint of their NLR characteristics, we shall now reexamine the collector-base-coupled monostable multivibrator of Chap. 9. Since the logical place to look for the negative resistance is across the energy-storage-element terminals, Fig. 11-12*a* shows the basic circuit with the timing capacitor omitted. In our analysis we shall make use of the equivalent circuit drawn in Fig. 11-12*b*. Both transistors are shown in their active region, and as each is driven into either cutoff or saturation, the model must be accordingly modified.

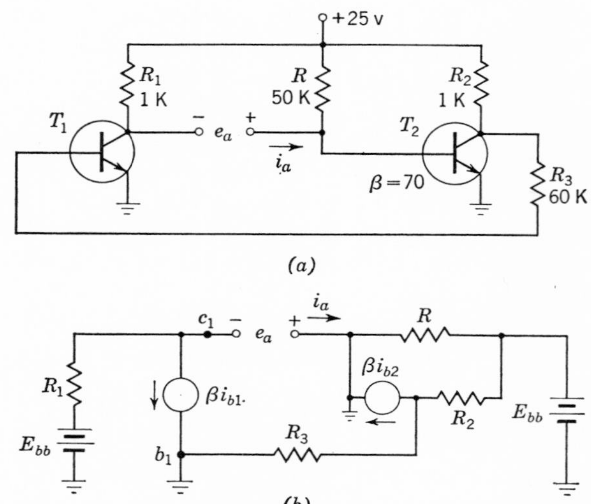

FIG. 11-12. (*a*) Monostable multivibrator; (*b*) equivalent circuit. The timing capacitor is normally connected across the driving-point terminals.

The circuit is initially adjusted so that in its normal state T_2 is fully on and T_1 is cut off. Even though the storage time of the saturated transistor limits the switching time, this configuration is considered because of its inherent simplicity. Further simplification arises from the following conditions:

1. β is very large; therefore $\beta + 1 \cong \beta$.
2. $R \gg R_2$, and $R_3 \gg R_2$.

Generally, three or four line segments are sufficient to define the complete voltage-ampere characteristic. In finding these segments attention should be focused on the controlling current, i_a. By starting from a high positive value of input current and considering the permissible change of state as the current decreases to, and below, zero, the possible operating regions are:

Region 1 T_2 saturated and T_1 off
Region 2 Both transistors in their active region
Region 3 T_2 active and T_1 saturated
Region 4 T_2 off and T_1 active
Region 5 T_2 off and T_1 saturated

At most, two of the last three regions can exist. Once T_1 saturates, the decreasing input current may still drive T_2 through its active to its cutoff region. Thus there is the possibility of operating over regions 3 and 5. On the other hand, if T_2 is driven into cutoff while T_1 is still active, the final bounding region will be number 4.

In each region, we shall solve for the equation of e_a as a function of i_a, in the form

$$e_a = E_i + R_i i_a \tag{11-16}$$

E_i is the voltage intercept found at $i_a = 0$, just as if the defined region remained invariant. R_i is the incremental driving-point resistance in the region under examination. A sequence of such straight lines presents, in a piecewise manner, the complete volt-ampere characteristic. In order to find the boundaries of the individual segments, we solve for the coordinates of the intersection of the appropriate two lines. We might also consider the physical limitations imposed by the active elements employed in establishing these bounds.

Region 1—T_2 Saturated and T_1 Off. Here $i_{b1} = 0$ and $e_{c2} = 0$, and hence

$$e_a = -E_{bb} + i_a R_1 \tag{11-17}$$

The lower limit of this region, where both T_1 and T_2 become active, occurs once

$$e_{c2} = E_{bb} - \beta i_{b2} R_2 = 0 \tag{11-18}$$

where

$$i_{b2} = \frac{E_{bb}}{R} + i_a \tag{11-19}$$

From Eqs. (11-18) and (11-19) we find that this zone is limited to

$$i_a > \frac{E_{bb}}{\beta R_2} - \frac{E_{bb}}{R}$$

And since $R < \beta R_2$, region 1 holds down to some negative value of i_a.

Region 2—T_1 and T_2 Active. From the solution of the circuit's loop equation, when i_{b2} is given by Eq. (11-18) and $i_{b1} = e_{c2}/R_3$,

$$e_a = -E_{bb}\left[1 - \frac{\beta R_1}{R_3}\left(1 - \frac{\beta R_2}{R}\right)\right] - \left(\beta^2 \frac{R_1 R_2}{R_3} - R_1\right) i_a \tag{11-20}$$

Note that once a transmission path involving the gain of both transistors exists, the slope of the volt-ampere characteristic becomes negative.

Here the positive feedback provides the required energy source. This negative-resistance region is bounded when T_2 turns off at $i_{b2} = 0$. And the corresponding constraints on i_a are

$$\frac{E_{bb}}{\beta R_2} - \frac{E_{bb}}{R} \geq i_a \geq -\frac{E_{bb}}{R} \tag{11-21}$$

Region 3—T_2 Active and T_1 Saturated. The conducting collector-base diode of T_1 and the emitter-base diode of T_2 now short-circuit the input terminals. The input equation becomes

$$e_a = 0 \tag{11-22}$$

Region 4—T_2 Off and T_1 Active. Under the conditions holding in this region,

$$i_{b1} \cong \frac{E_{bb}}{R_3}$$

and therefore

$$e_a = \beta E_{bb} \frac{R_1}{R_3} + i_a(R + R_1) \tag{11-23}$$

T_1 finally becomes saturated for

$$i_a = -E_{bb}\left(\frac{\beta}{R_3} - \frac{1}{R_1}\right)$$

Region 5—T_2 Off and T_1 Saturated. T_2 being an open circuit and T_1 a short circuit, the defining equation becomes

$$e_a = E_{bb} + i_a R \tag{11-24}$$

Example 11-2. In this problem we shall calculate and plot the characteristic for the typical transistor monostable multivibrator of Fig. 11-12*a*.

As the first step, the defining equation for each region is evaluated:

Region 1.	$e_a = -25 + (1\text{ K})i_a$	Eq. (11-17)
Region 2.	$e_a \cong -36.6 - (81\text{ K})i_a$	Eq. (11-20)
Region 3.	$e_a = 0$	Eq. (11-22)
Region 4.	$e_a = 29.2 + (51\text{ K})i_a$	Eq. (11-23)
Region 5.	$e_a = 25 + (50\text{ K})i_a$	Eq. (11-24)

By plotting the five straight lines, as in Fig. 11-13, we can determine the permissible circuit states. As the current decreases, we note that the segments traversed are 1, 2, 3, and 5. There is no possible way to reach line segment 4, and it therefore represents a forbidden mode of operation for this particular circuit.

One of the two remaining coordinates of interest is the location of the valley point. To find the intersection of lines 1 and 2 we equate (11-17) to (11-22), with the result

$$I_v = -\frac{36.5 - 25}{(81 + 1)\text{ K}} = -0.14\text{ ma}$$
$$V_v = -25.14\text{ volts}$$

The current intercept of region 5 is found from Eq. (11-24) by setting $e_a = 0$.

$$I_p = \frac{-25}{50\ \text{K}} = -0.5\ \text{ma}$$

All the resistors have been included in the base amplifier, and consequently the voltage axis is also the steady-state load line. The circuit remains at its single stable point ($i_a = 0$, $e_a = 25$ volts) until a trigger forces it into its unstable state. Transition is directly from region 1 to region 4. Here the slope is simply the timing resistance

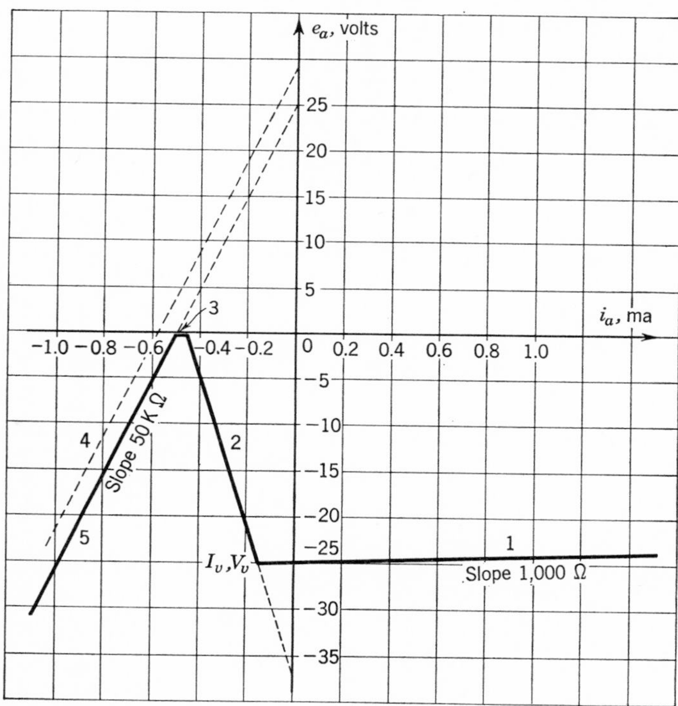

FIG. 11-13. CNLR characteristics of the collector-base-coupled monostable multivibrator of Example 11-2.

(50 K), and it is here that the output pulse is generated. When the circuit switches back to segment 1, it enters the low-resistance (1-K) recovery portion of the cycle.

Since the load line is the voltage axis, the time constants are the product of the slope of the line segment and the timing capacitor. Moreover, the steady-state charging voltage is the voltage intercept; the steady-state current must be zero. All the information necessary to calculate the voltage across, and current through, C is contained in the volt-ampere characteristic of Fig. 11-13.

11-6. Some Devices Possessing Current-controlled NLR Characteristics. *The Point-contact Transistor.* Illustrating, as it does, the complete range of problems which must be treated in applying a practical negative-resistance device to switching circuits, the point-contact transistor is the first device exhibiting CNLR characteristics with which we are concerned. This was not only the first semiconductor device in which a negative-resistance region was observed but also the first device which was extensively used in two-terminal switching circuits.

Positive current feedback from the collector back to the base, further emphasized by padding the base with a large series resistor, produces a negative driving-point impedance at either the emitter or collector terminals, with the most useful characteristic appearing at the emitter. The transistor circuit and its large-signal equivalent model are shown in Fig. 11-14.

First the low-frequency, static driving-point characteristic may be evaluated by examining the three possible regions of transistor operation,

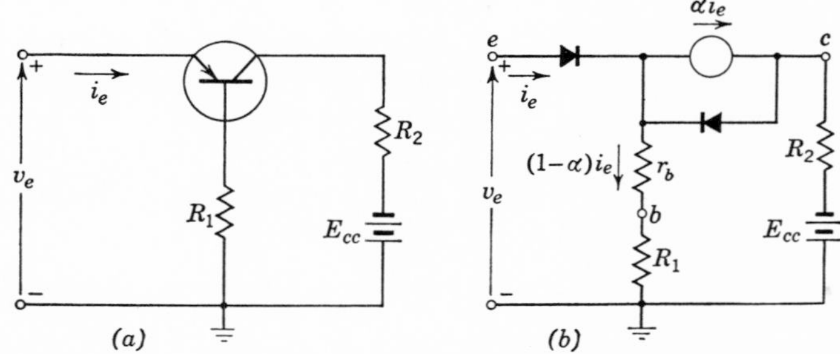

FIG. 11-14. (a) Point-contact transistor connected to develop a CNLR driving-point impedance; (b) large-signal T model.

cutoff, active, and saturated. Under cutoff conditions ($i_e < 0$) the circuit model would be modified by removing the current generator, by replacing the emitter diode with its reverse resistance r_{re}, and by replacing the collector diode by its large reverse resistance r_{rc}. From the reduced equivalent circuit, we find that the linear equation defining this region is

$$\begin{aligned} v_e &= i_e[r_{re} + (r_b + R_1) \parallel (r_{rc} + R_2)] - \frac{r_b + R_1}{r_b + r_{rc} + R_1 + R_2} E_{cc} \\ &\cong i_e r_{re} - V_p \end{aligned} \tag{11-25}$$

where $r_{re} \gg (r_b + R_1) \parallel (r_{rc} + R_2)$ and where the polarity of E_{cc} is taken into account (Fig. 11-14). The large value of r_{rc} appearing in the denominator usually makes the value of V_p close to, but slightly less than, zero.

In the active region, the emitter diode is forward-biased, and we might conveniently replace it by a short circuit. Also, $r_{rc} \gg (R_1 + R_2 + r_b)$, allowing the representation of D_c by an open circuit for the purpose of computing the input impedance. As a consequence, the driving-point equation becomes

$$v_e \cong i_e(1 - \alpha)(r_b + R_1) - V_p \tag{11-26}$$

where V_p is the voltage intercept at $i_e = 0$. Within this region the regeneration that develops the negative driving-point impedance is supplied by the greater-than-unity value of the emitter-to-collector current generator ($\alpha > 1$).

The final zone, complete transistor saturation, is characterized by heavy conduction through both diodes shown in Fig. 11-14*b*. For the defining equation we need only consider R_1, r_b, R_2, and E_{cc}.

$$v_e = [(r_b + R_1) \parallel R_2]i_e - \frac{r_b + R_1}{r_b + R_1 + R_2} E_{cc} \tag{11-27}$$

To find the coordinates of the valley point, i.e., the point separating the active from the saturation region, we simply solve Eqs. (11-26) and (11-27) simultaneously. But before beginning the calculation, even further simplification is possible. We are primarily interested in the negative-resistance portion of the characteristic, and in order to ensure an appreciable negative-resistance value, $R_1 \gg r_b$ [Eq. (11-26)]. If we also neglect the small value of V_p in Eq. (11-26), the location of the valley point will be given by

$$I_v \cong \frac{-E_{cc}}{R_1(1 - \alpha) - \alpha R_2} \qquad V_v \cong \frac{-R_1(1 - \alpha)E_{cc}}{R_1(1 - \alpha) - \alpha R_2} \tag{11-28}$$

One obvious design difficulty is that the valley-point coordinates are a function of the transistor α and vary rather widely between individual transistors. We can compensate by making R_1 adjustable.

Figure 11-15*a* shows the three regions of circuit behavior together with their particular resistance values. In a practical transistor, the nonlinear characteristics would introduce some curvature at both peaks.

The readily accessible additional elements of the device used to generate the CNLR characteristic permit the extraction of an output waveshape at a point well removed from the pulse timing network of R and C (Fig. 11-3). If the output is taken at the collector, with the circuit so adjusted that the critical timing occurs during the cutoff interval, then any loading of the collector will have only an extremely small second-order effect on the pulse duration.

Within the active region the proportionality between collector and emitter current is simply α. Outside this region, the transistor is either cut off, with the collector current dropping to its small I_{c0} value, or saturated, with the incremental current relationship now becoming

$$i_c \cong \frac{R_1}{R_1 + R_2} i_e \tag{11-29}$$

To this we would add the current contributions from the bias batteries, which of course depend on the particular circuit configuration. But since we already know the location of the valley point of i_e [Eq. (11-28)], the corresponding collector current is simply

$$I_{cv} = \alpha I_v$$

For current flow above this value, the slope of the transfer characteristic is given by Eq. (11-29). The information we now have yields the current transfer relationship shown in Fig. 11-15*b*.

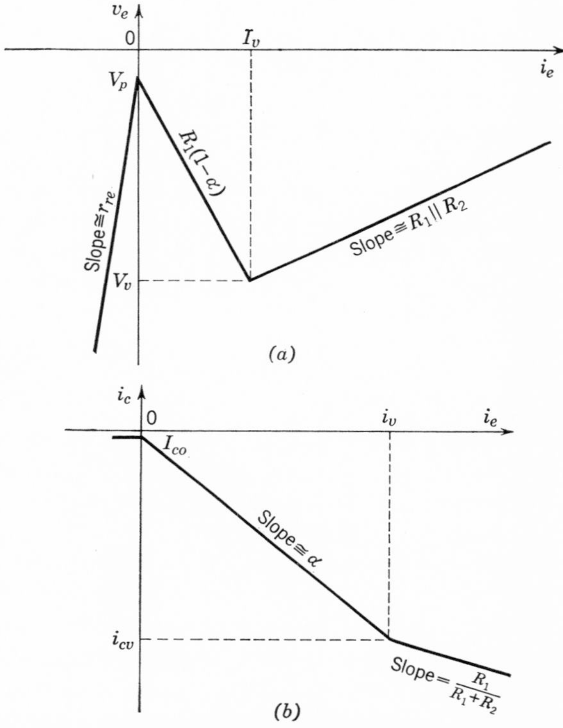

FIG. 11-15. (*a*) Point-contact-transistor CNLR driving-point characteristic and (*b*) emitter-collector current transfer characteristic.

Since the transistor switches through the active region very rapidly, when we evaluate the collector output waveshapes (both current and voltage), only the cutoff and saturation regions need be considered. This calculation will be left to the reader in his solution of individual problems. Furthermore, the additional elements permit the injection of the input trigger at the transistor base. By taking advantage of the amplification afforded within the switching transistor, the trigger requirements become much less severe. And under cutoff conditions the trigger source is also isolated from the timing circuit.

The p-n-p-n Junction Transistor. The *p-n-p-n* junction transistor also exhibits CNLR characteristics (Fig. 11-16), and like the point-contact transistor, it depends for its negative-resistance region on the positive current feedback from the output back to the base. In fact, within the

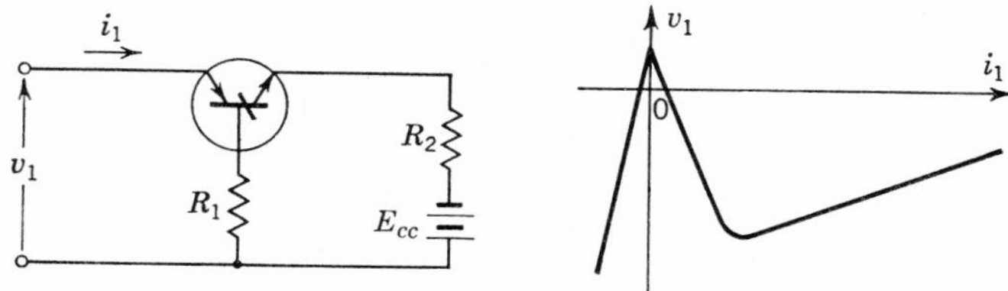

FIG. 11-16. *p-n-p-n* circuit and its CNLR characteristic.

point-contact transistor a *p-n* junction is established between the collector contact and the base, thus leading to a *p-n-p-n* structure. This similarity allows the immediate application of all results derived for the point-contact transistor to the new device.

We might alternatively represent the *p-n-p-n* transistor by a coupled configuration of two junction transistors, a *p-n-p* and an *n-p-n* (Fig. 11-17). When both are within their active regions, the collector current of T_1 is injected into the base of T_2, where it is amplified by the

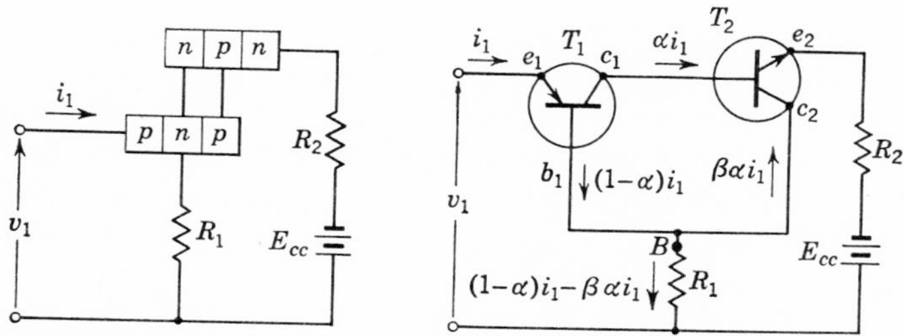

FIG. 11-17. The two-transistor equivalent configuration of the *p-n-p-n* circuit. Junction currents are indicated.

large base-collector amplification factor β. Finally, the collector of T_2, directly coupled to the base circuit of T_1, supplies the positive current feedback necessary to develop the negative input impedance. The approximate current flow in each branch of Fig. 11-17 is indicated in the interest of clarity. Note that the total composite base current is negative. By substituting the value of β, we find this current to be

$$i_B = i_{b1} - i_{c2} = [1 - (\alpha + \beta\alpha)]i_1 = (1 - \beta)i_1 \qquad (11\text{-}30)$$

Except that the larger amplification factor β replaces α, the current given by Eq. (11-30) is of the identical form as the current that would flow in the base circuit of the point-contact transistor (Fig. 11-14*b*). Thus the input impedance of this circuit, when it is in its active region, may be expressed as

$$R_{\text{in}} \cong (1 - \beta)R_1 \tag{11-31}$$

The cutoff frequency of this transistor can be made quite high, allowing satisfactory operation in switching circuits generating 1-μsec or smaller pulses.

The Unijunction Transistor. A silicon unijunction transistor consists of a bar of n material with a p emitter junction located somewhat above the center point of the bar (at the 60 to 75 per cent mark). Under the emitter cutoff condition, the conductive current flow through the high-resistivity silicon establishes a voltage drop from the emitter to base 1

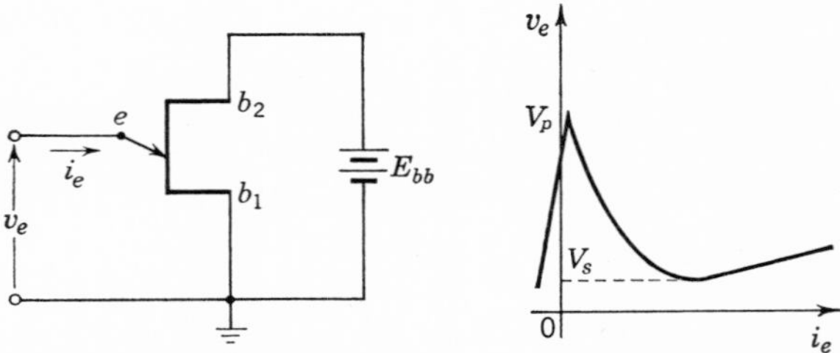

FIG. 11-18. Unijunction transistor circuit and input volt-ampere characteristic.

proportional to the spacing between these points. The emitter remains back-biased until the input driving voltage exceeds the conductive drop. Once the emitter begins conduction, the minority carriers injected into the n bar travel to base 1 and increase the charge density in this region; they effectively decrease the driving-voltage drop required for a given current flow. Consequently, a negative input resistance appears between the emitter and base 1 (Fig. 11-18).

An equivalent circuit for the unijunction transistor which explains, at least to a first approximation, the behavior of this device in its various operating regions is presented in Fig. 11-19. While it remains cut off, the effective input impedance is simply the reverse emitter diode resistance, about 500 K. But once the emitter voltage reaches the back-bias voltage ηE_{bb}, where

$$\eta = \frac{r_{b1}}{r_{b1} + r_{b2}} \qquad \text{and} \qquad V_p = \eta E_{bb}$$

the diode conducts. The defining equation now becomes

$$v_e = \eta E_{bb} + [r_e + (1 - \gamma)r_{b1} \parallel r_{b2}]i_e \tag{11-32}$$

If, in addition, account were taken of the small voltage drop (0.7 volt) appearing across the emitter junction, then the peak point of Fig. 11-18 would be shifted slightly up and to the right.

The current amplification factor γ varies with frequency in much the same manner as does α in the point-contact transistor. But γ further depends on the mobility of the majority and minority carriers, and therefore it will change with the current flow, from a value of approximately 3 at low current density to unity at saturation. As a result, the negative-resistance region is extremely nonlinear. In the model drawn in Fig. 11-19, all regions are linearized by assuming a constant γ.

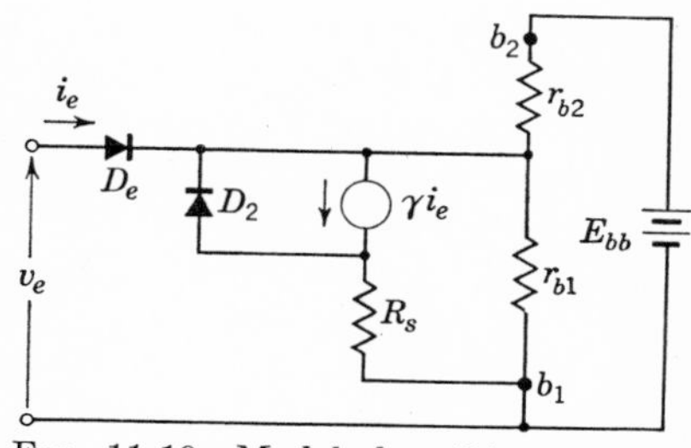

FIG. 11-19. Model describing the behavior of the unijunction transistor.

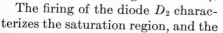

The firing of the diode D_2 characterizes the saturation region, and the full generator current γi_e flowing through it serves to maintain full conduction. Replacing D_2 by a short circuit permits the writing of the appropriate saturation-region equation:

$$v_e = V_s + (R_s \parallel r_{b1} \parallel r_{b2})i_e \tag{11-33}$$

where

$$V_s = \frac{R_s \parallel r_{b1}}{R_s \parallel r_{b1} + r_{b2}} E_{bb}$$

A large measure of control over the slopes and intercepts of the individual regions is afforded by the insertion of additional resistance in series with b_1 and b_2. Any resistance we add to b_1 has the most pronounced effect on the saturation region, and that included at b_2 mainly increases the magnitude of the negative input resistance.

Currently available unijunction transistors are limited to low-speed switching applications by their γ cutoff frequency of only 0.7 or 0.8 megacycle. The correspondingly large input inductive component of the input impedance (Sec. 11-8) will adversely affect the switching path even at low frequencies. Rather than the expected large instantaneous current jumps from the peak and valley, the path of operation becomes almost elliptic.

Avalanche-region Operation. Among the other devices exhibiting current-controlled negative-resistance regions are the space-charge diode and the avalanche-breakdown transistor. Their current multiplication depends on the high reverse voltage establishing an extremely high electric field intensity. This field dislodges valence electrons, and by creating additional electron-hole pairs, it increases the current density. Avalanche-region operation is widely used for very fast switching circuits since there is no inherent minority storage time. However, the negative-resistance region is quite narrow and the circuit will generate only a small-amplitude signal.

11-7. Some Devices Possessing Voltage-controlled Nonlinear Characteristics. The tetrode, one of the earliest devices found to exhibit voltage-controlled negative resistance, was the predecessor of many of the secondary-emission multiplier tubes in current use. Because the energy supplied to the external energy-storage elements often resulted in an undesirable oscillation, operation within this region of the plate volt-ampere characteristic was usually avoided. Realizing now its usefulness for switching and oscillator applications, and in order to round out our discussion of NLR devices, we shall discuss the tetrode along with several other voltage-controlled devices. Electrical-engineering literature refers

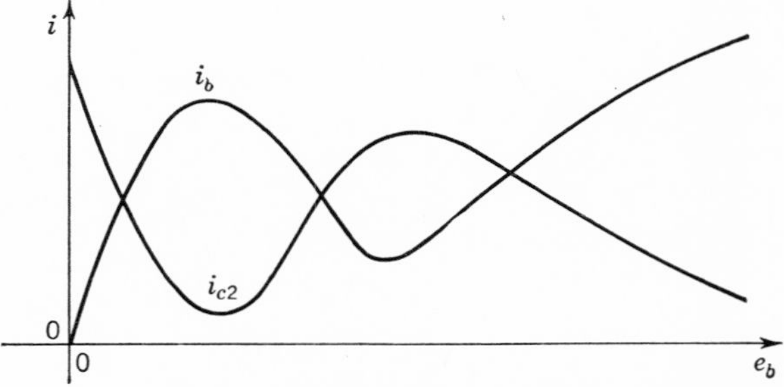

FIG. 11-20. Tetrode VNLR plate characteristic.

to the particular tetrodes used for their negative-resistance characteristics as dynatrons.

At very low values of plate voltage, the total cathode current flows to the screen, which is the tube element at the highest potential. As its voltage is raised, the plate receives an ever-increasing percentage of the total current flow. The electrons attracted to the plate strike it with more force, because of additional energy acquired as they are accelerated through the higher potential present. Eventually, their energy on impact becomes sufficient to cause emission of the valence electrons of the plate material. Since the screen is maintained at a constant potential, somewhat higher than that now appearing from plate to cathode, the secondary-emission electrons will travel from the plate back to the screen, causing the current at the plate to decrease, even though its voltage continues to increase (Fig. 11-20). Also present is the possibility that the plate current may become negative as a consequence of the large emission from the plate surface.

As the plate voltage continues rising, up to and even beyond the screen voltage, the secondary electrons begin returning to the plate.

Under these circumstances, the screen current falls as the rising current at the plate bounds the negative-resistance zone with the expected dissipative region.

Pentode VNLR Characteristic—The Transitron. A pentode may be so connected that it also will display a VNLR driving-point characteristic, but at its screen rather than at its plate (Fig. 11-21). At low values of screen voltage, the suppressor, highly negative with respect to the cathode, completely cuts off the plate current. The tube functions as a triode, and the total cathode current, which now flows to the screen, obeys Child's 3/2-power law. In this region, the screen resistance is identically that of the tube connected as a triode, r_{c2t}. As the screen voltage continues rising, the suppressor voltage $E_{c2} - E_3$ which must rise with it eventually reaches a point where it allows plate conduction. Any

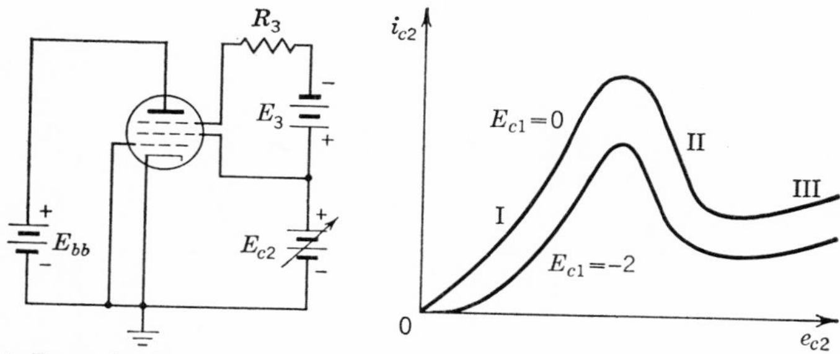

FIG. 11-21. Pentode circuit for VNLR transitron operation and resultant screen-circuit volt-ampere characteristic.

further rise in the screen voltage increases the total tube current, and simultaneously, through its effect on the suppressor, E_{c2} increases the percentage of the current flowing to the plate. Less current flows in the screen circuit, and the volt-ampere characteristic now exhibits a negative-resistance region.

Once the suppressor becomes positive and draws current, it saturates. The current flow through R_3 maintains the suppressor voltage at only a few volts positive with respect to the cathode. Above this point, the ratio of plate to screen current remains reasonably constant, and both now increase with the rising screen voltage. Since the conditions are identical with those treated for the phantastron in Sec. 6-9, the screen resistance in this region will be

$$r_{c2p} = r_{c2t}(1 + \rho)$$

where r_{c2t} = resistance in first region considered
ρ = ratio of plate to screen current

If we were now to turn back to the phantastron, which was discussed in Secs. 6-8 and 6-9, we would see that the switching action occurring in the screen circuit depends on its negative-resistance characteristic. Since the screen configuration is essentially of the form shown in Fig. 11-21, the normal load line should be selected for bistable operation. The two circuit states are (1) when the suppressor cuts off the plate (region I of Fig. 11-21) and (2) when the suppressor saturates (region III of Fig. 11-21). The normal position of the phantastron is in region I, requiring a positive pulse for switching. However, the circuit itself supplies the negative pulse necessary to switch the screen back from region III to region I. The presence of the varying control-grid signal means that the path of screen operation will be along the composite of several of the family of characteristic curves, instead of along a single curve.

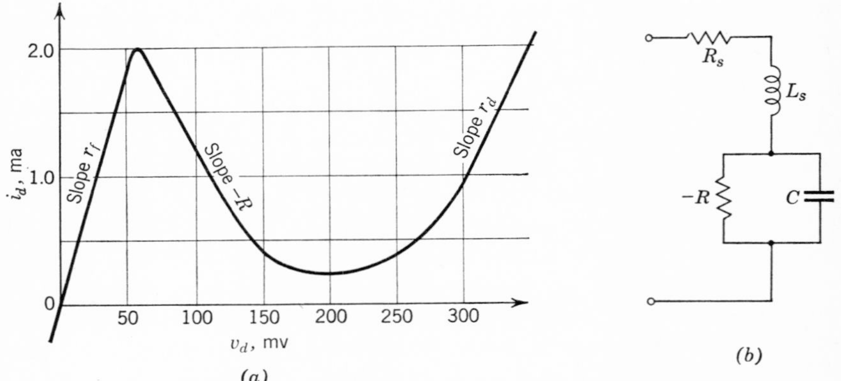

FIG. 11-22. (a) Tunnel-diode volt-ampere characteristic; (b) model holding in the negative-resistance region—L_s is due to lead inductance, R_s represents the lead resistance and ohmic losses in the semiconductor, and C is the junction capacity.

Tunnel Diode. The tunnel diode, which was discovered by Dr. L. Esaki in 1957, consists of an extremely thin *p-n* junction formed between two heavily doped regions (large amounts of added impurities) of a semiconductor. The shape of the volt-ampere characteristic (Fig. 11-22*a*), which exhibits a voltage-controlled negative-resistance region for small forward biases, can be explained from a consideration of the electron-wave propagation through the junction boundary. Because of the heavy doping there exist relatively large numbers of conduction electrons in the *n* material and a wide range of empty states in the *p* material. The electron wave propagates freely within each region but cannot tunnel through the potential barrier at the junction unless the energy level on one side is matched by an equivalent empty state on the other side. During the transition the electron wave is attenuated, while the energy is conserved. Thus the junction must be thin in order for the electron wave to have an appreciable probability of transmission.

When the diode is back-biased, the energy level of the electrons in the n material is lowered below that of the free electrons in the p material. The reverse current, which is completely due to tunneling, can increase without limit. In this region, the volt-ampere characteristic looks exactly like that of a conducting diode.

An applied positive bias increases the potential energy of the electrons in the n material. As a consequence the forward current will continue to increase until the complete range of free states in the p material is matched by the tunneling electron waves. Any further increase in the forward bias raises the energy level of the free electrons above that of the empty states and is, therefore, accompanied by a decrease in the terminal current. This is the negative-resistance zone. Eventually the increasing bias causes the injection of the minority carriers, the diode conducts in the normal manner, and the current again increases with increasing voltage.

The major advantage of the tunnel diode over all other negative-resistance devices is the high speed of the current transmission. The velocity of propagation approaches that of light. There is, however, a large capacity (20 to 60 $\mu\mu$f) associated with the junction as well as series resistance and lead inductance shown in Fig. 11-22*b*. These parasitic elements tend to slow the switching time. In spite of this, the large value of negative conductance permits the generation of pulses having rise times of less than 10^{-10} sec. Sinusoidal oscillation at frequencies in excess of 4,000 megacycles is also possible (see Chap. 15).

It should be noted that the negative-resistance region is quite narrow; the peak is normally located between 50 and 100 mv and the valley point at 150 to 500 mv. Thus, if the junction is designed for large peak currents, the negative-resistance value will be extremely low. For example, approximately -2 ohms is measured in the active region of a gallium arsenide tunnel diode having a peak current of 100 ma. When we examine a diode whose maximum current is less than 1 ma, we observe that the average negative resistance has increased to a few hundred ohms.

Since the impedance of the power supply is of the same order of magnitude as the negative resistance, it is extremely difficult to bias properly and to stabilize the very-low-resistance devices in their negative-resistance region. Even a small amount of lead inductance may lead to undesired switching or spurious oscillations.

A two-terminal tunnel diode does not afford the same flexibility in obtaining an isolated output as do the three-terminal active devices. Consequently care must be taken that the external load will not disturb the operation of the timing or switching circuits. In order to minimize possible interaction when multiple stages involving tunnel diodes are to be interconnected, some type of unilateral decoupling must be used. We may even be forced to associate a junction transistor with each tunnel-diode circuit. Because the actual rise is limited by the slowest stage, many of the advantages of the tunnel diode are negated. In some circumstances it becomes practical to employ fast-responding diodes to decouple the individual switching circuits. Diodes whose conduction is due to tunneling, but which do not exhibit negative resistance, are ideal for this purpose.

Point-contact and p-n-p-n Junction Transistor. A VNLR driving-point impedance will also be developed at the base of the point-contact transistor and at the base of its junction equivalent, the *p-n-p-n* transistor. Instead of merely discussing this device qualitatively, we shall define the complete circuit behavior by following our usual procedure of examining the operation with respect to the increasing independent variable, in this case v_1. When the drive voltage is highly negative, the transistor will be completely saturated. Since this condition is characterized by heavy conduction through both of the diodes in the model of Fig. 11-23, the input node equation, which is written by superposition, becomes

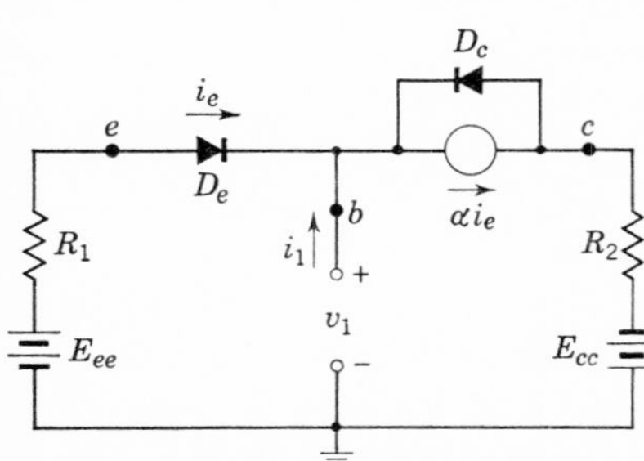

FIG. 11-23. Model for VNLR driving-point impedance of point-contact transistor.

$$i_1 = -E_{ee}G_1 + E_{cc}G_2 + v_1(G_1 + G_2) \tag{11-34}$$

where $G_1 = 1/R_1$ and $G_2 = 1/R_2$.

As v_1 rises and as the transistor enters its active region, the emitter current decreases with increasing driving voltage.

$$i_e = (E_{ee} - v_1)G_1$$

The input current contribution from E_{cc} that normally flows through r_{rc} will be small enough so that it can be ignored, thus allowing the following defining equation to be written for the active region:

$$i_1 = -(1 - \alpha)i_e = -(1 - \alpha)G_1(E_{ee} - v_1) \tag{11-35}$$

From Eq. (11-35) we conclude that $\alpha > 1$ is the only required criterion for a negative driving-point impedance at low frequencies.

When the *p-n-p-n* transistor is used in place of the point-contact transistor, β would replace α in Eq. (11-35).

Once the high positive value of v_1 cuts off the transistor ($v_1 > E_{ee}$), the circuit enters into its third region. With $r_{re} > R_1$ and $r_{rc} > R_2$, the input equation is of the same form as Eq. (11-34); only the conductance terms must be changed to conform to the new conditions.

$$i_1 = -E_{ee}g_{re} + E_{cc}g_{rc} + v_1(g_{re} + g_{rc}) \tag{11-36}$$

A plot of the three characteristic equations appears in Fig. 11-24.

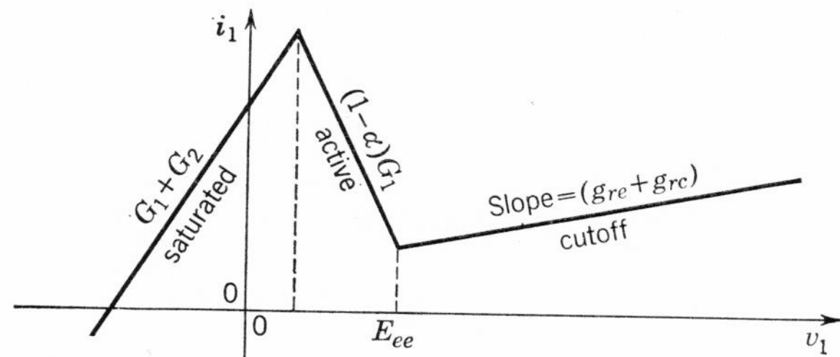

FIG. 11-24. Driving-point volt-ampere characteristic of point-contact transistor—base input.

11-8. Frequency Dependence of the Devices Exhibiting NLR Characteristics. Up to this point we have discussed only the static behavior of the various devices that exhibit negative-resistance regions. But to utilize these elements properly, their frequency limitations must also be known. Some of these were treated briefly in earlier chapters, e.g., the rise and fall times and the minority storage time of the solid-state devices. The major item which we must yet consider is the effect of frequency on the transistor parameters.

In each case, the negative input resistance developed in the active region depended on the current amplification of the active element employed. Equations (11-26), (11-31), and (11-32) defining the negative-resistance regions are all basically alike. Of course, the controlled-current-source parameter is α in one case and β or γ in the other two, but this is simply a detail dependent on the particular device considered. In all three, the term of interest is of the form

$$R_{\text{in}} = (1 - \alpha)R_1$$

where α is now used as a general current amplification factor.

The parameter most affected by frequency is this very amplification factor. Equation (11-37) expresses its approximate variation, and we note that α decreases at a rate of 6 db per octave as ω rises above the 3-db point ω_c.

$$\alpha(\omega) = \frac{\alpha_0}{1 + j\omega/\omega_c} \tag{11-37}$$

The α cutoff frequency f_c usually ranges from 100 kc to 2 megacycles in the unijunction and the *p-n-p-n* transistors, up to about 100 megacycles in point-contact and junction transistors that are specifically designed for high-frequency operation.

If we substitute Eq. (11-37) into the general negative-impedance term, the resultant expression becomes

$$Z_{\text{in}} \cong \left(1 - \frac{\alpha_0}{1 + j\omega/\omega_c}\right) R_1$$
$$= R_1\left(1 - \frac{\omega_c{}^2\alpha_0}{\omega_c{}^2 + \omega^2}\right) + j\omega\frac{\omega_c R_1 \alpha_0}{\omega_c{}^2 + \omega^2} \tag{11-38}$$

The first part of Eq. (11-38) represents the resistive portion of the input impedance, which will remain negative up to

$$\omega_h = \omega_c\sqrt{\alpha_0 - 1}$$

Above this frequency, the various transistors can no longer sustain their negative-resistance characteristics and are unable to supply any energy to the external load. It follows that switching operations would have to be restricted to the range of frequencies below ω_h.

The second term contributes an inductive component to the driving-point impedance. First of all, this prevents any instantaneous current jumps. Secondly, it may also resonate with the external capacity, generating an almost sinusoidal waveshape, provided that the circuit is biased within the active region.

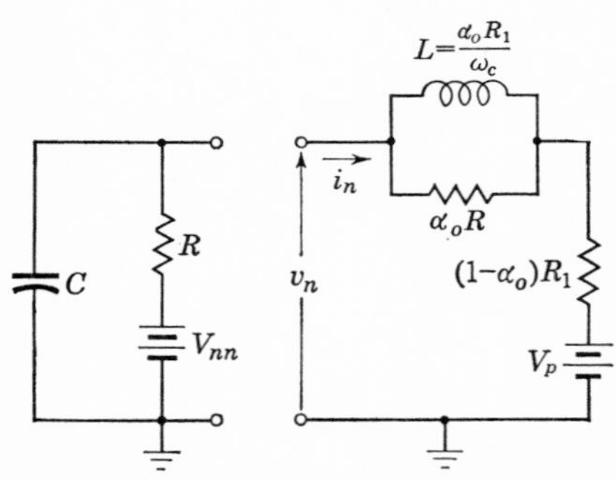

FIG. 11-25. Equivalent driving-point network of a CNLR in the active region and the external load.

Figure 11-25 shows an equivalent driving-point network which represents the incremental behavior of the device within its active region and which, of course, also satisfies Eq. (11-38). At low frequencies, the input inductance is effectively a short circuit, leaving only the negative-resistance term. At elevated frequencies the presence of the additional energy-storage term complicates the network and forces us into a reevaluation of the conditions to be satisfied for absolute circuit stability.

Stability of the Nonideal CNLR Circuits. The problem of stability can be neither considered nor defined without treating the complete circuit before us. Instability simply means that sufficient surplus energy exists in the system to produce an increasing exponential response in any energy-storage element present. But if the external network also contains dissipative elements, then their effect on the system may even change one having an energy surplus into one that is completely dissipative. The particular conditions necessary to ensure this happening are those that produce absolute stability and prevent any regenerative switching.

Consider, for example, the network (Fig. 11-25) that represents the input characteristic of the current-controlled devices of Sec. 11-6. The external load consists of a parallel combination of R and C together with a bias battery whose function is to set the intersection of the load line and the NLR characteristic within the proper region. In the following discussion we shall assume intersection of the negative resistance. Since the NLR is current-controlled, for stability the poles of the current function must not be allowed to lie in the right half plane. And this corresponds to restricting the zeros of the impedance function [Eq. (11-39)] to the left half plane.

$$Z(p) = (1 - \alpha_0)R_1 + \frac{pLR_1\alpha_0}{pL + \alpha_0 R_1} + \frac{R}{pRC + 1}$$
$$= \frac{R_1RCLp^2 + [(R_1 + R)L + CRR_1{}^2\alpha_0(1 - \alpha_0)]p + \alpha_0 R_1[R + R_1(1 - \alpha_0)]}{(pL + \alpha_0 R_1)(pRC + 1)} \qquad (11\text{-}39)$$

In order to guarantee this restriction, all the coefficients of the polynomial of the numerator of Eq. (11-39) should have the same sign. This leads to the two inequalities Eqs. (11-40) and (11-41), which we must satisfy to ensure absolute circuit stability.

$$R > -R_1(1 - \alpha_0) \qquad (11\text{-}40)$$
$$C < \frac{R_1 + R}{RR_1(\alpha_0 - 1)\omega_c} \qquad (11\text{-}41)$$

The value of L given in the model of Fig. 11-25 was substituted while solving for the condition expressed in Eq. (11-41).

When both inequalities hold, the system cannot operate as a switching circuit. Once C is larger than the minimum value given by Eq. (11-41), and if Eq. (11-40) is still satisfied, the circuit becomes free-running. At the bounding value of C, the zeros of the impedance function lie on the imaginary axis; for C less than this value, the zeros are in the left half plane and the system is stable. As C increases, the roots move into the right half plane toward the real axis (Fig. 11-26). If the zeros are complex conjugates lying close to the imaginary axis, the time response of the astable system is sinusoidal. This particular mode of operation will be discussed in Chaps. 14 and 15.

For bistable operation R must be less than the magnitude of the negative resistance; i.e., Eq. (11-40) must remain unsatisfied. The load line will now intersect the positive-resistance regions of the volt-ampere characteristics. Both zeros of the impedance function will always lie on the real axis, one in the right half plane and the other along the negative real axis. As C increases, both zeros move to the right, the negative root approaching zero as a limit and the positive root approaching

$$p_h = \omega_c(\alpha_0 - 1)$$

for large C. Thus the switching speed, through the negative-resistance region, is limited primarily by the frequency response of the active element employed.

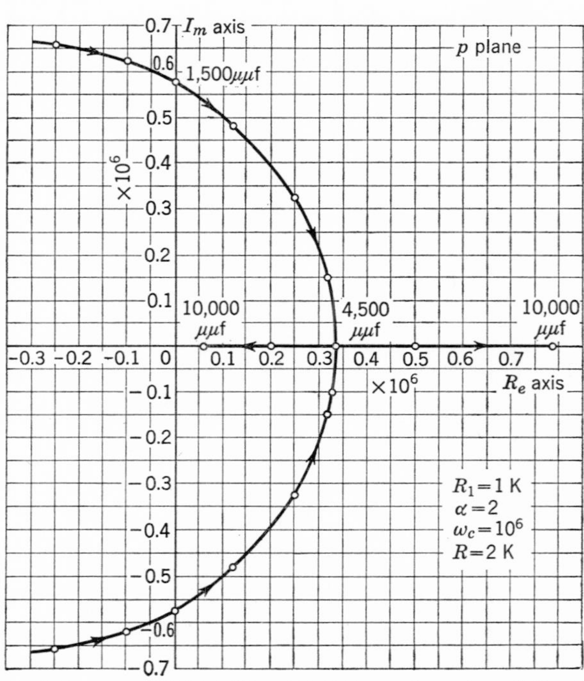

FIG. 11-26. Path of the zeros of $Z(p)$ [Eq. (11-39)] as a function of C. Specific circuit values are given above for astable operation.

The stability condition presented in Eq. (11-40) is exactly opposite to the condition found when we discussed the ideal NLR in the earlier portion of this chapter [Eq. (11-6)]. This does not really contradict the earlier discussion, since a short circuit or a low resistance across the input terminals of the equivalent network of Fig. 11-25 results, essentially, in the inductively controlled behavior of the VNLR (Fig. 11-11). Furthermore, when $\omega_c \to \infty$ or when $L = 0$, that is, when the circuit approaches the ideal, the stability conditions found from Eq. (11-39) will reduce to the single equation given in Eq. (11-6).

We conclude that a physical negative-resistance device cannot support a stable point within the negative-resistance region unless the two inequalities of Eqs. (11-40) and (11-41) are satisfied. Point H of Fig. 11-6 (the load-line intersection with the negative resistance) will, in general, be unstable. Away from the vicinity of this point, the system rapidly stabilizes at one of its two intersections in the completely dissipative regions.

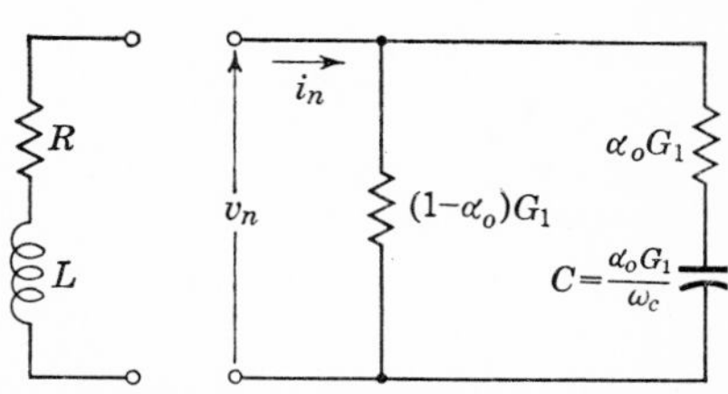

FIG. 11-27. Equivalent input network of the VNLR holding during the active region and the external load.

Stability conditions are seen to depend on the particular circuit configuration. In order to avoid ambiguity, it is much better to refer always to the device used in terms of its single-valuedness, i.e., current or voltage, rather than its conditions for stability. Furthermore, when any changes are made in the external circuit, the reader must re-solve for the conditions necessary to ensure absolute stability.

VNLR Stability. In Sec. 11-7 we saw that the basic form of the negative conductance developed in the active region was

$$Y_{\text{in}} = (1 - \alpha)G_1$$

This equation is of the identical form with the negative-impedance function derived for the CNLR devices. It follows, from Eq. (11-38), that the substitution of $\alpha(\omega)$ into the admittance term results in

$$Y_{\text{in}} = G_1\left(1 - \frac{\omega_c^2\alpha_0}{\omega_c^2 + \omega^2}\right) + j\omega\,\frac{\omega_c G_1\alpha_0}{\omega_c^2 + \omega^2} \tag{11-42}$$

Equation (11-42) yields the equivalent input network given in Fig. 11-27, which we note to be simply the dual of the network of Fig. 11-25.

To ensure that the poles of the controlling voltage function will not lie in the right half plane, the zeros of the admittance function must be restricted to the left half plane. The two required conditions for absolute system stability become

$$G > -G_1(1 - \alpha_0) \tag{11-43}$$

$$L < \frac{G_1 + G}{GG_1(\alpha_0 - 1)\omega_c} \tag{11-44}$$

Equations (11-43) and (11-44) are the duals of Eqs. (11-40) and (11-41) previously derived. And as before, when neither equation is satisfied, the load line also intersects the positive-resistance regions, thus establishing bistable circuit operation. Satisfaction of only Eq. (11-43) allows astable behavior for L larger than the minimum value of Eq. (11-44).

Just as with the CNLR, this circuit will also exhibit an almost sinusoidal oscillation for small values of L.

11-9. Improvement in Switching Time through the Use of a Nonlinear Load. Generally, if fast signals are to be generated, and if narrow pulses are used for triggering, operation within the saturation region of semiconductor devices must be avoided. The long time delay introduced by the minority-carrier storage precludes all but the slowest switching intervals. In order to accomplish this restriction, we rely on nonlinear load lines which are developed with the aid of appropriately biased diodes.

With one region forbidden us, both of the remaining circuit states must be used in a bistable; one stable point will be situated in the cutoff zone, and the other will lie in the negative-resistance region. A simple bistable circuit for high-speed switching, featuring this arrangement, is shown in Fig. 11-28. It makes use of a single external diode to insert

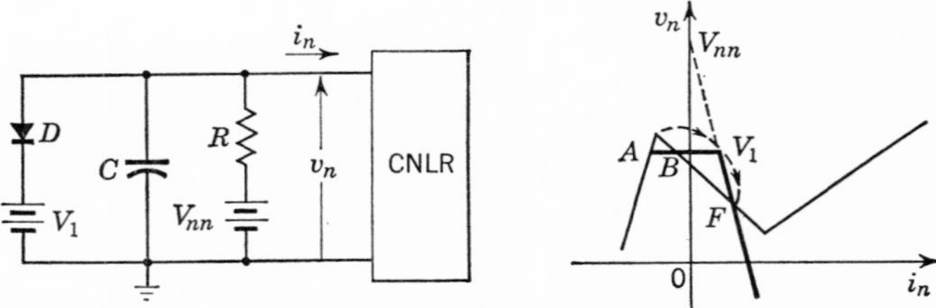

FIG. 11-28. Stabilization within the negative-resistance region—bistable operation.

the necessary break in the load line, ensuring that it intersects the volt-ampere characteristic only in these two regions.

The absolute stability of the point established in the completely dissipative cutoff region, by the diode's conduction (point A), is not open to question. But for a true bistable, we must justify the stability of point F, which lies on the negative-resistance portion of the characteristic. At this point the large load resistance R definitely satisfies one of the two stability conditions [Eq. (11-40)]. If the stray capacity is kept low enough, or if the parameters of the CNLR satisfy the second condition [Eq. (11-41)], or an equivalent condition if the device used is neither a point-contact nor a *p-n-p-n* transistor, then point F will also be absolutely stable. From Eq. (11-41) we see that the smaller the value of negative resistance, the larger the capacity that can be tolerated without changing the stable to an unstable point.

Switching in the circuit of Fig. 11-28 will always be from A to F and from F back to A. We depend on the combination of the stray capacity and the inductive component present in the driving-point impedance of the CNLR to slow the system response enough so that the path of operation will never enter the saturation region (see the dashed path of Fig. 11-28).

Astable-operation Stabilization. An alternative technique for preventing the transistor from being driven into saturation, illustrated in Fig. 11-29, is most widely applied in astable systems. This circuit configuration requires the insertion of a resistor R_2 in series with C to stabilize the intersection occurring in the negative-resistance region. Suppose that the charge stored in C back-biases the diode while the operating point is at A. Then the additional resistance increases the net circuit dissipation to a point where it will exceed the net energy supply.

In order to find the conditions which must be satisfied to stabilize point A when the diode is back-biased, we must solve the complete model of the system. Representing the CNLR by the model of Fig. 11-25,

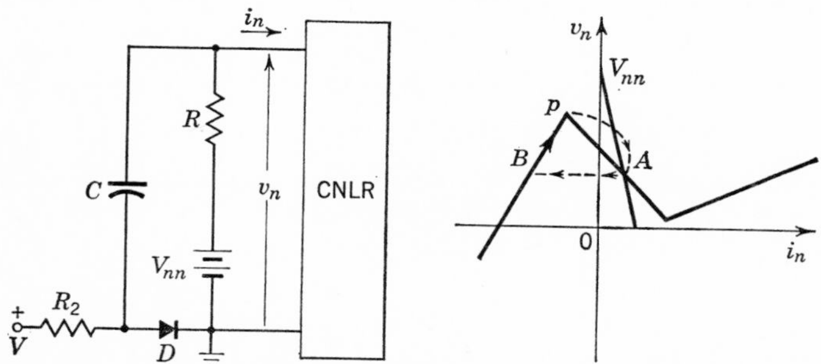

FIG. 11-29. Stabilization within the negative-resistance region—astable operation.

the two conditions which will ensure absolute circuit stability in the negative-resistance region are

$$R > -R_1(1 - \alpha_0)$$

$$R_2 > \frac{(\alpha_0 - 1)RR_1}{R_1(1 - \alpha_0) + R} - \frac{R_1 + R}{[R_1(1 - \alpha_0) + R]C\omega_c}$$

where the negative resistance is $R_1(1 - \alpha_0)$. The first condition is the same as expressed in Eq. (11-40). From the second condition we see that the smallest value of R_2 that will maintain the circuit stable, regardless of the value of C, is a resistance equal in magnitude to the parallel combination of R and $(1 - \alpha_0)R_1$. This makes the net resistance across the energy-storage element positive.

However, C eventually charges, and at the instant that the voltage at its lower terminal reaches zero, the diode again conducts. The circuit becomes astable, and the circuit flips clockwise to point B. As discussed in Sec. 11-3, the capacitor charges toward the Thévenin equivalent voltage across its terminals, eventually reaching the peak, V_p.

In this circuit, the voltage across the terminals of the CNLR can change instantaneously because this change will not appear across C but will be coupled by C to R_2. Any voltage drop, no matter how small, back-biases the diode. The operating point thus jumps from the peak to the now stable point A, and the diode is driven negative by this same voltage change. C again charges, with its bottom terminal rising from $-(V_p - V_A)$ toward V and with the approximate time constant

$$\tau_2 \cong (R_2 + R \parallel - R_n)C$$

It eventually reaches zero, the diode conducts, the circuit again becomes astable, and the cycle repeats. The approximate voltage waveshapes

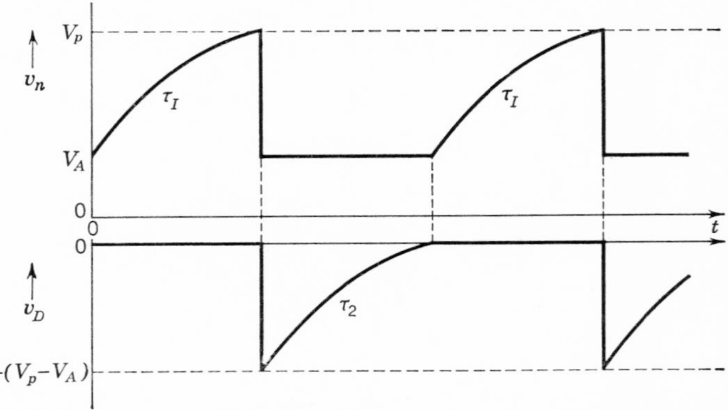

FIG. 11-30. Voltage waveshapes appearing at the input of CNLR and across the diode in the circuit of Fig. 11-30.

generated across the diode and at the input to the CNLR are sketched in Fig. 11-30.

An arrangement similar to that shown in Fig. 11-29 might also be used in a monostable circuit. In this case, returning R_2 to a small negative voltage $-V$, instead of to a large positive one, will keep the diode back-biased and guarantee the stability of point A. After an external trigger forces the diode into conduction, the circuit momentarily becomes free-running and switches clockwise into the cutoff zone. If the circuit parameters are properly adjusted, the capacitor charging current will maintain diode conduction during the complete interval that the operating point remains in this region.

Subsequent to reaching the peak value of the CNLR, any drop in voltage, coupled by C, will turn off the diode and reestablish point A as the single stable point. The operating point drops from the peak to point A, and the circuit recovers. Since the steady-state voltage across the diode is $-V$, the diode remains back-biased and the operating point finally stabilizes at A.

11-10. Negative-impedance Converters. The basic approach taken in developing negative-input characteristics, through the use of active elements, is illustrated by the two typical block diagrams of Fig. 11-31.

In the circuit of Fig. 11-31*a*, when we write the input node equation, assuming an ideal voltage amplifier,

$$i_1 = \frac{e_1 - A_V e_1}{Z_L}$$

we readily arrive at the recognized form of the Miller input impedance

$$Z_{\text{in}} = \frac{Z_L}{1 - A_V} \tag{11-45}$$

If the voltage amplification within the active region is greater than unity, then the input impedance becomes negative. Under the particular

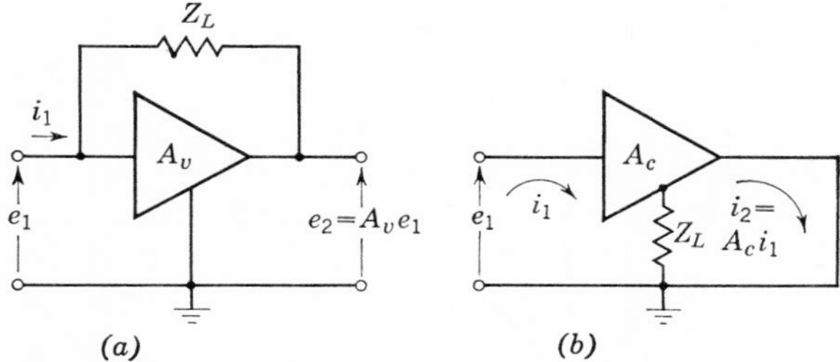

FIG. 11-31. Basic negative-impedance converters (NIC). (*a*) Voltage-controlled circuit; (*b*) current-controlled configuration.

conditions where A_V is set equal to +2, we obtain the following very convenient result:

$$Z_{\text{in}} = -Z_L \tag{11-46}$$

In general, A_V is a two-stage amplifier having definite frequency characteristics and the over-all response will not be in as simple a form as Eq. (11-46).

The simplest possible operation of the basic current-controlled circuit of Fig. 11-31*b* is where the complete input driving current flows through the short-circuited input of the ideal current amplifier. Under these circumstances the input loop equation is

$$e_1 = (i_1 - i_2)Z_L = i_1(1 - A_c)Z_L \tag{11-47}$$

and by making $A_c = 2$,

$$Z_{\text{in}} = \frac{e_1}{i_1} = -Z_L$$

However, if only a small percentage of the input current flows directly to the output, the load current becomes

$$i_L = Ki_1 - A_c i_1$$

And if this term is substituted into Eq. (11-47), the input impedance may be written

$$Z_{in} = (K - A_c)Z_L \tag{11-48}$$

where $K \leq 1$ and A_c is the forward current gain.

For example, in the *p-n-p-n* transistor, $A_c = \beta$. Consequently, when these terms are substituted into Eq. (11-47), the resultant expression is identical with that given in Eq. (11-31):

$$Z_{in} = (1 - \beta)Z_L$$

All the devices that were discussed in Secs. 11-6 and 11-7 could just as easily have been analyzed by converting their equivalent circuits into the appropriate block diagrams. By doing so we would have lost the insight that was gained in examining the actual device. The major role served by the block diagrams is to indicate the general conditions toward which we must design if we wish to develop negative-input characteristics.

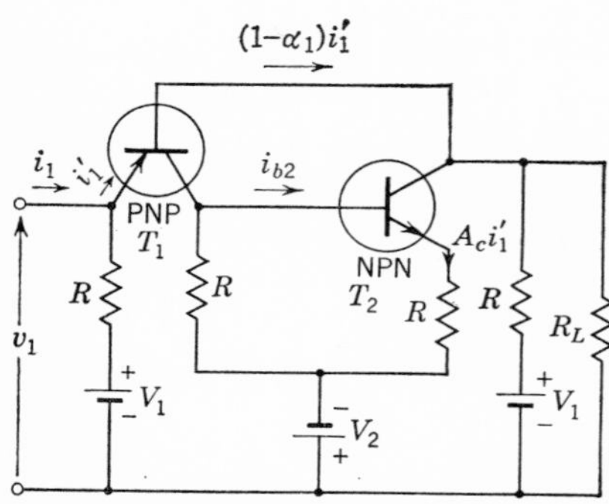

FIG. 11-32. A practical negative-impedance converter—current-controlled operation.

Consider, for example, the standard negative-impedance-converter (NIC) circuit of Fig. 11-32. Except for the additional bias resistors and batteries, it is of the identical configuration of the composite transistor circuit used to describe the behavior of the *p-n-p-n* transistor. Once we recognize that the output load is $R_L \parallel R$, we can also identify this circuit as a practical form of the basic impedance converter of Fig. 11-31*b*.

Only a small fraction of the input current flows directly to the output, and we must therefore evaluate both K and A_c in Eq. (11-48). The current through the direct transmission path is simply $(1 - \alpha_1)i_1'$, and since α_1 is very close to unity, this term becomes insignificant compared with i_1'. K in Eq. (11-48) may be taken as zero. Thus the input *p-n-p* stage acts as a simple current amplifier having a gain, from the emitter to the collector, of approximately unity.

The output current of T_1 divides between the collector load R and the input impedance to T_2 of $R(\beta_2 + 1)$:

$$i_{b2} = \frac{i_1'R}{(\beta_2 + 1)R + R}$$

and the current gain to the emitter of T_2 becomes

$$A_c = \frac{\beta_2}{\beta_2 + 2} \cong 1 \tag{11-49}$$

where the approximation holds for a high-gain transistor.

Substituting $K = 0$ and $A_c = 1$ into Eq. (11-48), we find the effective input impedance to be

$$Z'_{\text{in}} = -(R \parallel R_L)$$

But this is paralleled by the input resistance R, which cancels the negative term due to $-R$. The only remaining term is that dependent on the load R_L:

$$Z_{\text{in}} = -R_L \tag{11-50}$$

This same result can also be obtained by noting that the current flow through $R_L \parallel R$ is $-i'_1$. Since a short circuit exists through the emitter and base of T_1, the voltage drop across the load must be identically

$$v_1 = -i'_1(R_L \parallel R)$$

By taking into account the role of the input resistor R, the input impedance will be as given by Eq. (11-50).

Of course, here also the pure negative input resistance would exist only at very low frequencies. At the higher frequencies, the frequency dependence of α_1 and β_2 will introduce the additional inductive component shown in Fig. 11-25.

PROBLEMS

11-1. A certain CNLR with the characteristics given in Fig. 11-33 is used in the basic sweep of Fig. 11-3. The load resistance R is 4 K, and the external timing capacity is 2 μf. Plot the current and voltage waveshapes after the circuit is triggered if V_{nn} is as given below. In each case state the area of the current impulse which must be injected into the node to cause switching.

(a) $V_{nn} = 40$ volts.

(b) $V_{nn} = -40$ volts.

11-2. (a) What limits of load resistance will permit bistable operation of the CNLR of Fig. 11-33?

(b) The load resistance used with CNLR of Fig. 11-33 is 10 K. What ranges of V_{nn} permit operation as a monostable circuit?

(c) Repeat part b if the load resistance is now 2 K.

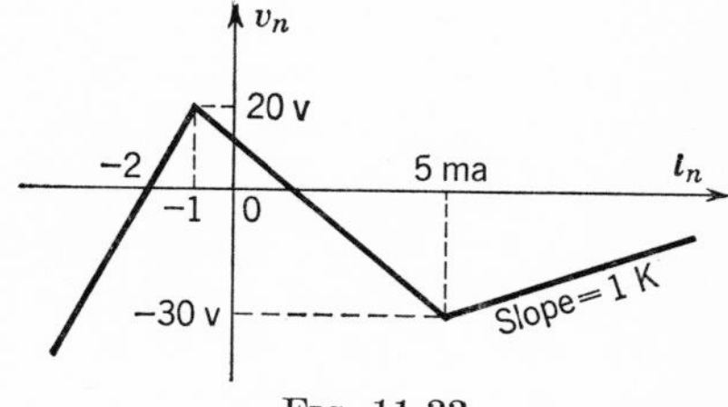

FIG. 11-33

11-3. A 5-μf capacitor is connected directly across the input terminals of the CNLR, which has the characteristics of Fig. 11-33. Sketch the current and voltage waveshapes, labeling them with respect to time constants, voltage and current values, and times.

11-4. At $t = 0$ the network N of Fig. 11-34 is activated by the voltage impulse indicated. Sketch i_n and v_n as functions of time, labeling clearly all break points and time constants.

11-5. (*a*) Give the range of external resistance that will make the circuit of Fig. 11-34 astable when the battery voltage is between the limits of $4 < V_{nn} < 10$ volts.

(*b*) Sketch the output waveshapes, labeling them completely, when $R = 10$ ohms and $V_{nn} = 10$ volts.

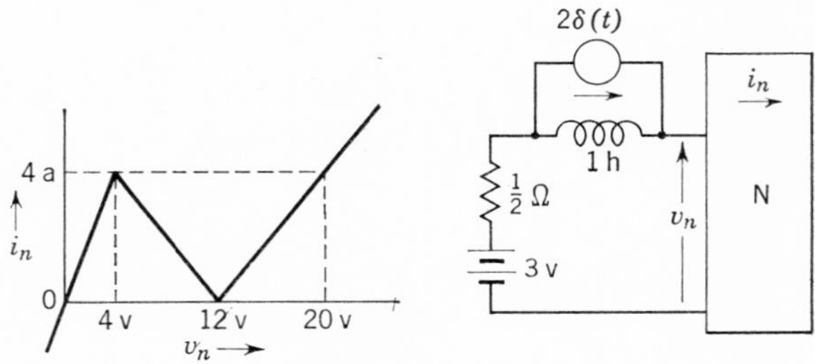

FIG. 11-34

11-6. Calculate and plot the CNLR characteristics seen when looking across C in the monostable circuit of Fig. 9-38 (Prob. 9-14).

11-7. Plot the CNLR characteristics for the circuit whose values are given in Fig. 11-12 when $R = 100$ K and $R_3 = 25$ K. All other parameters remain as before. Superimpose this plot on a copy of Fig. 11-13.

11-8. (*a*) Evaluate and plot the transfer characteristic, i.e., collector voltage of T_2 versus i_a, for the monostable multivibrator (Fig. 11-12) discussed in Example 11-2.

(*b*) Sketch one complete cycle of i_a after the circuit is triggered. Using the curve found in part *a*, draw to scale 1 cycle of e_{c2}.

11-9. Plot the volt-ampere characteristic for the multivibrator of Fig. 11-12 when R_3 is increased to 100 K. Compare your results with Fig. 11-13. Which regions are most affected by the increase in R_3? What does it do to the modes of operation?

11-10. Calculate and plot the volt-ampere characteristic seen across the inductance in the circuit of Fig. 11-35. Using this plot, sketch and label the inductive current i_L after a trigger is applied.

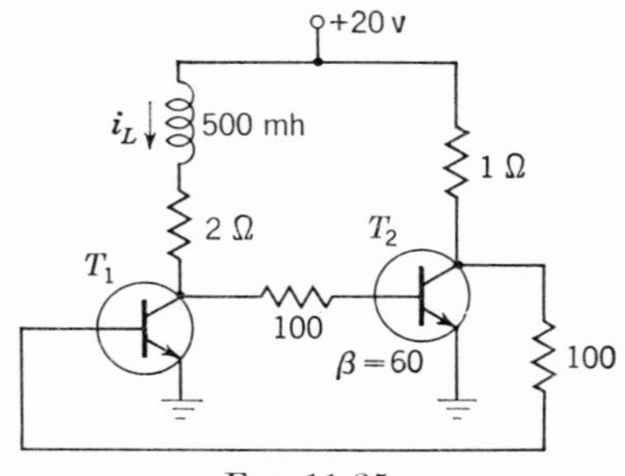

FIG. 11-35

11-11. The point-contact transistor of Fig. 11-14 has $\alpha = 1.2$, $r_b = 200$ ohms, and $r_{re} = 150$ K. Assume that the peak point of the input negative-resistance characteristic is located at the origin. Specify all circuit parameters necessary to set the valley point at -10 volts and 10 ma. Sketch the driving and transfer characteristics, labeling all slopes.

11-12. Plot the magnitude and phase of the input impedance of the point-contact transistor in its active region as a function of ω. $R_1 = 5$ K, $\alpha_0 = 1.5$, and $\omega_c = 10^6$.

11-13. Assume that the *p-n-p-n* transistor of Fig. 11-17 is composed of two individual units, each having $\alpha = 0.98$. In all other respects these transistors are ideal units. Plot the input volt-ampere and the v_{e2} versus i_1 characteristics of this device. Specify the break points when $R_1 = R_2 = 1$ K and $E = 10$ volts. Make all reasonable approximations in your calculations.

11-14. The unijunction transistor shown in Fig. 11-36*a* may be represented approximately by the volt-ampere characteristic of Fig. 11-36*b*. Sketch the waveforms of V_e and I_e as functions of time, labeling clearly all break points and time constants.

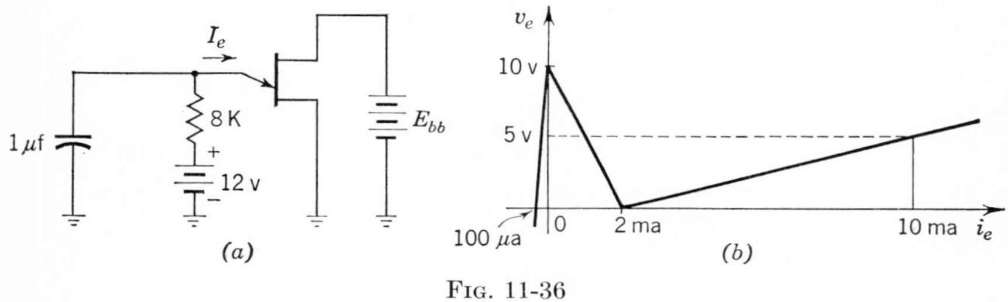

FIG. 11-36

11-15. The unijunction diode of Fig. 11-18 has the following parameters: $r_{b1} = 140$, $r_{b2} = 60$, $r_e = 30$, $\gamma = 2.5$, and $R_s = 10$ ohms. The back-biased input impedance is 50 K.

(*a*) Plot the input volt-ampere characteristics when $E_{bb} = 20$ volts.

(*b*) Repeat part *a* when a 2,000-ohm resistor is inserted in series with b_2 and a 1,000-ohm resistance in series with b_1.

11-16. The point-contact transistor of Prob. 11-11 is used in the configuration of Fig. 11-23. $R_1 = R_2 = 5$ K, and the reverse resistance of both the collector and base is 500 K.

(*a*) Find $E_{cc} = E_{ee}$ necessary to produce a current swing of 20 ma when the circuit operates as an astable device.

(*b*) The external conductance is twice the limiting value. What is the smallest battery in series with the inductance that will allow the circuit to free-run? What is the largest series battery?

(*c*) If the series inductance is 100 mh, what is the smallest cutoff frequency of the transistor for satisfactory operation? Where are the poles and zeros of $Y(p)$ located under this condition?

11-17. (*a*) Prove the equivalency of the driving-point network of Fig. 11-25.

(*b*) Derive Eq. (11-39) and verify Eqs. (11-40) and (11-41).

(*c*) Show that as $L \to 0$, the stability condition is satisfied by Eq. (11-6).

11-18. (*a*) The tunnel diode of Fig. 11-37*a* is connected to an external circuit consisting of a 10-mh inductance, a 1-ohm load resistance, and a 250-mv bias source. Approximate the characteristic by three line segments, and plot the terminal-voltage waveshape.

(*b*) If $R_s = 0.3$ ohm, $L_s = 2$ μh, and $C_s = 50$ μμf in the active-region model of Fig. 11-22, what is the highest frequency of operation?

(c) Express the absolute stability conditions for the general tunnel-diode model of Fig. 11-22b.

11-19. A tunnel diode having the characteristic of Fig. 11-37a is used as a coincidence gate. The circuit appears in Fig. 11-37b. Positive input pulses applied at e_1 and e_2 have an amplitude of 1.5 volts and a duration of 0.1 μsec. Plot the output voltage under the following conditions:

(a) $E_{bb} = 0$, e_1 or e_2 present.
(b) $E_{bb} = 0$, e_1 and e_2 simultaneously applied.
(c) $E_{bb} = 250$ mv, e_1 or e_2 present.
(d) $E_{bb} = 250$ mv, e_1 or e_2 simultaneously applied.

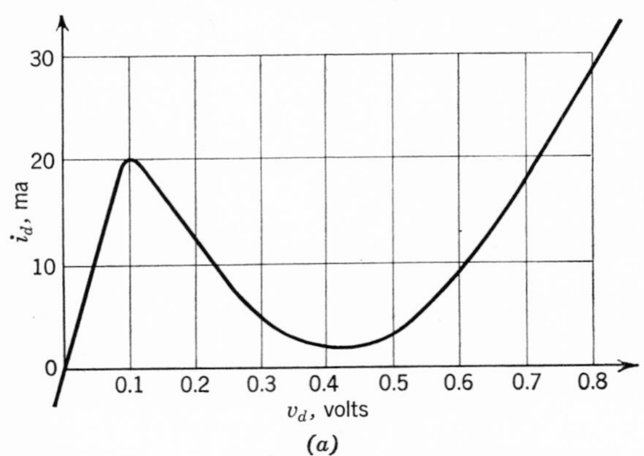

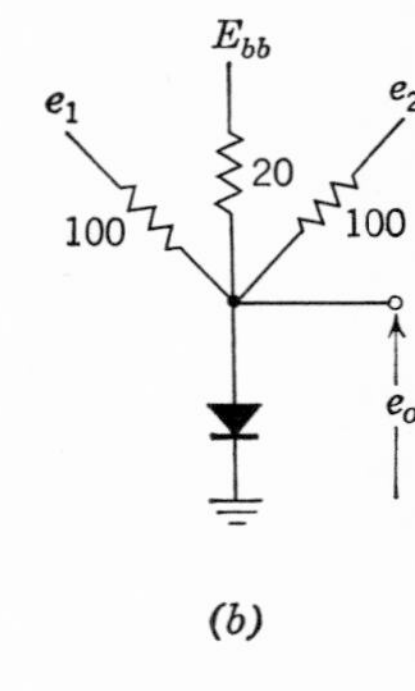

FIG. 11-37

11-20. Figure 11-38a shows a five-segmented approximation to a tunnel diode's volt-ampere characteristic. This particular device is employed in the switching cir-

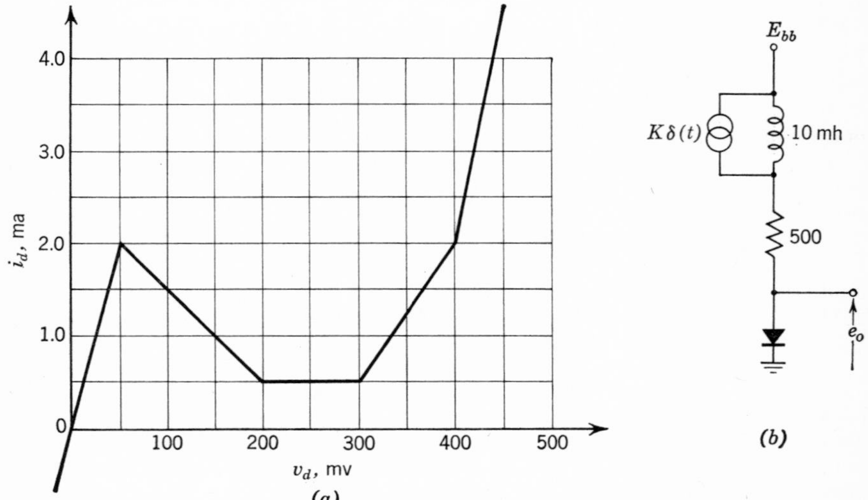

FIG. 11-38

cuit of Fig. 11-38*b*. A voltage impulse having an area K of 40×10^{-6} volt-sec is used for triggering. Sketch and label the output voltage for both positive and negative impulses under the following conditions:

(*a*) $E_{bb} = 0$.

(*b*) $E_{bb} = 1$ volt.

11-21. A train of 1-volt positive and negative pulses, 0.1 μsec wide and spaced 2 μsec apart, is applied to the circuit of Fig. 11-39. D_1 and D_2 are tunnel diodes whose volt-ampere characteristic is linearized in the manner shown. D_3 is a fast-acting decoupling diode and may be considered ideal for the purposes of this problem.

(*a*) Sketch and label the output voltage over a 10-μsec interval.

(*b*) Repeat part *a* when D_3 is removed and the coupling is directly through the 100-ohm resistor.

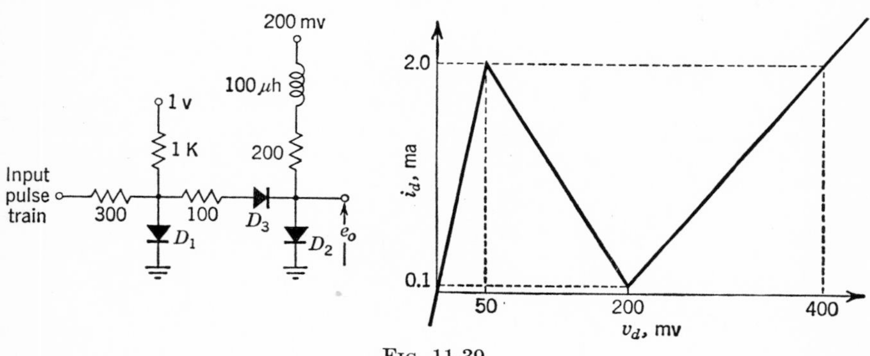

FIG. 11-39

11-22. The terminal characteristics of a certain CNLR are shown in Fig. 11-40. Also shown is the equivalent circuit for the device in its active region.

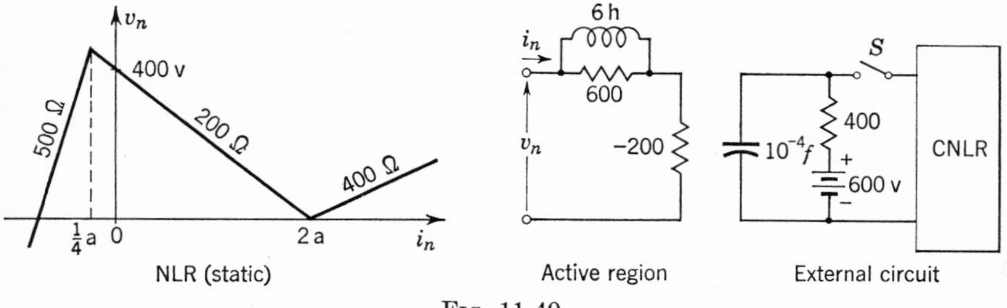

FIG. 11-40

(*a*) When the external network is connected by closing switches at $t = 0$, determine i_n as a function of time. (HINT: Solve for the poles of the network in its active region and also for the steady-state component of i_n; then write $i_n = i_{\text{transient}} + i_{ss}$ and evaluate the necessary arbitrary constant.)

(*b*) How does the circuit function if C is reduced by a factor of 2? If it is increased by a factor of 10? Give a qualitative answer and describe the expected terminal waveshape.

11-23. (*a*) Repeat Prob. 11-14 when the 1-μf timing element is shunted by a Zener diode which conducts for $V_e > 4$ volts (Fig. 11-28).

(*b*) To what value must C be reduced before point F becomes the second stable point?

11-24. Prove that the insertion of a resistor in series with C (as in Fig. 11-29) can make a normally unstable circuit stable. [HINT: Return to the driving-point network of Fig. 11-25 and find the conditions necessary to restrict the zeros of $Z(p)$ to the left-half plane when R_2 is in series with C. Compare these with the stability conditions given by Eqs. (11-40) and (11-41). Equation (11-40) is satisfied and (11-41) is not when R_2 is removed.]

11-25. In the negative-impedance converter of Fig. 11-32, $R_L = R = 10$ K, $V_1 = V_2 = 10$ volts, and $\beta_1 = \beta_2 = 50$. Calculate the input volt-ampere characteristic. Specify the slopes and intercepts of each line segment. Find the current transfer characteristics from the input to the load, R_L.

BIBLIOGRAPHY

Anderson, A. E.: Transistors in Switching Circuits, *Proc. IRE*, vol. 40, no. 11, pp. 1541–1548, 1952.

Beale, I. E. A., W. L. Stephenson, and E. Wolfendale: A Study of High Speed Avalanche Transistors, *Proc. IEE (London)*, pt. B, vol. 104, pp. 394–402, July, 1957.

Ebers, J. J.: Four-terminal p-n-p-n Transistors, *Proc. IRE*, vol. 40, no. 11, pp. 1361–1365, 1952.

Esaki, L.: Letter to the Editor, *Phys. Rev.*, vol. 109, pp. 603–604, Jan. 15, 1958.

Farley, B. G.: Dynamics of Transistor Negative Resistance Circuits, *Proc. IRE*, vol. 40, no. 11, 1497–1508, 1952.

Hall, R. N.: Tunnel Diodes, *IRE Trans. on Electron Devices*, vol. ED-7, pp. 1–9, January, 1960.

Lesk, I. A., and V. P. Mathis: The Double-base Diode: A New Semi-conducting Device, *IRE Conv. Record*, pt. 6, p. 2, 1953.

Linvill, J. G.: Transistor Negative Impedance Converters, *Proc. IRE*, vol. 41, no. 6, pp. 725–729, 1953.

Lo, A. W.: Transistor Trigger Circuits, *Proc. IRE*, vol. 40, no. 11, pp. 1531–1541, 1952.

Merrill, J. L.: Theory of the Negative Impedance Converter, *Bell System Tech. J.*, vol. 30, no. 1, pp. 88–109, 1951.

Shea, R. F.: "Transistor Circuit Engineering," John Wiley & Sons, Inc., New York, 1957.

Shockley, W., and J. F. Gibbons: Introduction to the Four-layer Diode, *Semiconductor Prods.*, January–February, 1958, pp. 9–13.

Suran, J. J., and E. Keonjian: A Semiconductor Diode Multivibrator, *Proc. IRE*, vol. 43, no. 7, pp. 814–820, 1955.

CHAPTER 12

THE BLOCKING OSCILLATOR

Most of the multivibrators discussed in Chaps. 9, 10, and 11 depended for their timing on the energy-storage element maintaining the tube or transistor off for the required interval. Because an active element is essentially an open circuit within its cutoff region, the output pulse is available only at a relatively high impedance level and with a low power content. Furthermore, stray capacity slows the fast rising and falling edges, preventing the generation of extremely narrow pulses. One method of overcoming these disadvantages is to time the pulse within the high-current low-impedance saturation region.

The blocking oscillator is one circuit which is so designed. Only a single active element is necessary, with a specially designed transformer used for timing as well as for phasing the regeneration. Because this deceptively simple circuit is so widely used, in computers, radar, television, etc., it will be treated in some detail. In doing so, we extend the approximation methods of analysis to multiple-energy-storage-element systems. We shall also be obliged to consider the problems posed when some of the passive components exhibit nonlinearity. No attempt will be made to obtain an exact solution, but the analysis will adequately explain the role of the various elements and the functioning of the circuit.

12-1. Some Introductory Remarks. Figure 12-1 shows one possible form of the blocking oscillator, a collector-emitter-coupled circuit, together with its general piecewise-linear representation. As possible alternative configurations, the transformer may couple either the collector or the emitter to the base. In brief, the sequence of monostable operation is the following. The transistor is initially back-biased, and in response to an externally applied trigger, it is forced into the active region. Provided that the transformer has the proper turns ratio and connections (introducing a sign change), the net loop gain will be positive and greater than unity. Regeneration drives the circuit into saturation. The transistor acts as a switch, which operates with a minimum amount of input energy and which connects E_{bb} across the primary of the transformer.

The full duration of the saturation interval is controlled, as is all timing, by the energy-storage elements present (in this circuit by the magnetizing inductance L_m and the coupling capacitor C). When generating long pulses, an evaluation of the width may be further complicated if the large current build-up in the magnetizing inductance L_m drives the transformer into saturation. For short pulses, the timing will be influenced by the rate of flux penetration into the core (Secs. 12-3, 13-2, and 13-3). The solution of the complete problem is quite complicated, involving as it does multiple modes of energy storage, core properties, and hysteresis.

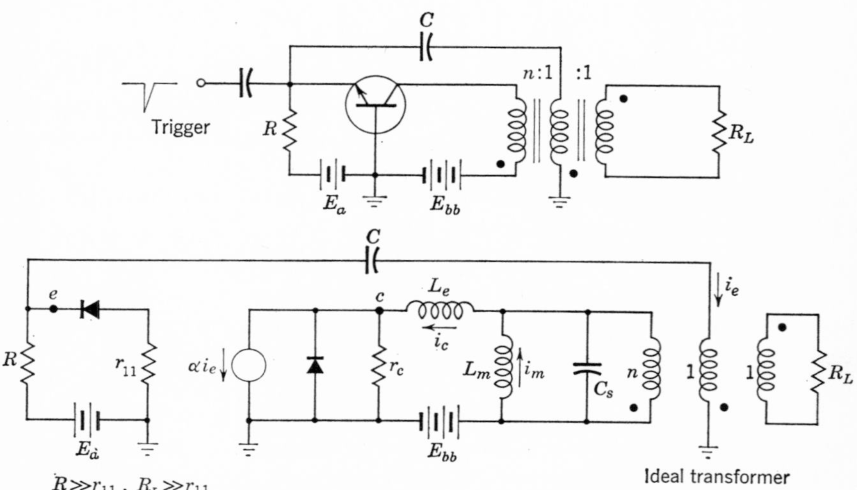

FIG. 12-1. Collector-emitter-coupled blocking oscillator and complete piecewise-linear model.

Eventually the circuit reenters the regenerative region and switches back off. The oscillator recovers and remains off until the next trigger is applied.

The blocking-oscillator transformer is a very important component, so critical, in fact, that the circuit is designed about its characteristics. By interleaving the coil windings and by using a high-permeability core material, the leakage inductance and stray capacity are minimized, and consequently so is the rise time. For example, a transformer designed to generate a 1-μsec pulse may have a nominal magnetizing inductance of 1.0 mh compared with a leakage inductance of only 20 to 50 μh. As it is quite small physically, the stray capacity would only be 10 $\mu\mu$f.

The transformer usually includes one or more tertiary windings which are used to couple the generated pulse to the isolated external circuit.

12-2. An Inductively Timed Blocking Oscillator. The following simplifications are now possible:

1. The input impedance of the transistor in the active and saturation regions is so very low that C_s will have a negligible effect on the rise time.
2. The coupling capacitor C is very large, and we may therefore assume that its terminal voltage remains constant over the entire pulse interval.
3. Both R and R_L are much greater than r_{11}.
4. The transformer core never saturates.

Using the above assumptions, the incremental model holding during the active region reduces to the one shown in Fig. 12-2*a*. The two node equations are

$$\left(\frac{1}{r_c} + \frac{1}{pL_e}\right) e_c - \frac{1}{pL_e} e_1 = -\alpha i_e \tag{12-1a}$$

$$-\frac{1}{pL_e} e_c + \left(\frac{1}{pL_e} + \frac{1}{n^2 r_{11}}\right) e_1 = 0 \tag{12-1b}$$

Substituting $i_e = -e_1/nr_{11}$, the solution of these equations yields the system's pole, which is located at

$$p \cong -\frac{r_c(1 - \alpha n)}{L_e} \tag{12-2}$$

From Eq. (12-2), we conclude that the condition which must be satisfied if the circuit is to be regenerative (a pole located in the right half plane) is

$$\alpha n > 1$$

and that this corresponds to a loop current gain greater than unity.

Before the circuit enters into its active region, the value of the collector voltage is E_{bb}; immediately after the pulse turns the transistor on, the collector drops to zero. The full supply voltage appears across L_e, and the transistor saturates rapidly at an extremely low current. To find the time required, we must know the starting point of the exponential build-up. But this depends on the energy content of the excitation pulse, and since, in general, it is unknown, the problem is not completely defined. For a rough order of magnitude, we can approximate the initial switching time by 2.2 time constants of the positive exponential of Eq. (12-2).

$$t_1 \cong 2.2 \frac{L_e}{(\alpha n - 1)r_c} \tag{12-3}$$

With a good pulse transformer Eq. (12-3) may even yield a time of less than 10^{-8} sec. The turn-on time of the transistor may be very much longer, and if it is, it will predominate—the solution of Eq. (12-3) will be totally without meaning.

Once the transistor saturates, the models of Fig. 12-2*b* and *c* will be used to define the collector and emitter current build-up. Because

$L_e \ll L_m$, the actual double-energy problem will be treated by the methods of Chap. 1, i.e., by assuming that the current build-up in L_e is complete before that of L_m starts. The waveshapes obtained from this approximation are sketched in Fig. 12-4.

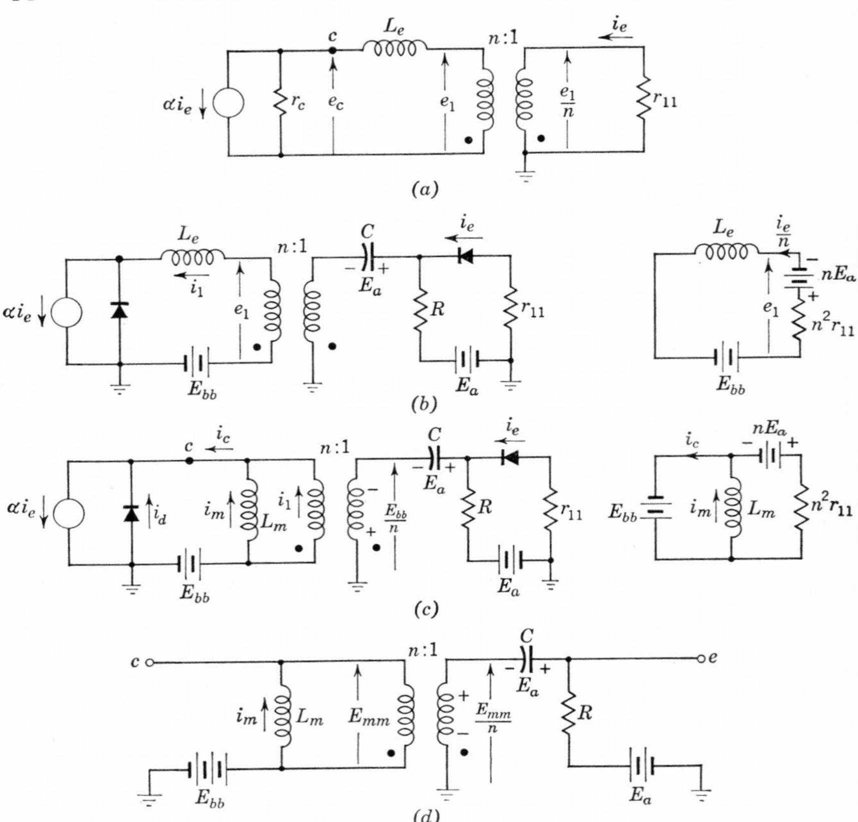

FIG. 12-2. Models holding for the various regions of blocking-oscillator operation—timing due to the transformer's magnetizing inductance. Waveshapes appear in Fig. 12-4. (a) Active-region incremental model; (b) models for the initial portion of the saturation region; (c) models for the final portion of the saturation region; (d) model for the recovery region.

The primary voltage exponentially approaches a peak value of $-E_{bb}$ with a time constant due to the leakage inductance and the input resistance of the transistor reflected through the ideal transformer.

$$\tau_2 = \frac{L_e}{n^2 r_{11}}$$

where r_{11} is the saturation value of the input resistance.

Since the voltage across C remains constant at E_a, the net drop across r_{11} will reach a peak of

$$E_{em} = E_a - \frac{E_{bb}}{n}$$

and the corresponding value of emitter current is given by

$$I_{em} = -\frac{E_{em}}{r_{11}} = \frac{1}{r_{11}}\left(\frac{E_{bb}}{n} - E_a\right) \tag{12-4}$$

For saturation $I_{em} > 0$, and therefore the circuit must be designed so that

$$\frac{E_{bb}}{n} > E_a$$

If this condition is not satisfied, the transistor will immediately switch back into its active region and no pulse will be generated.

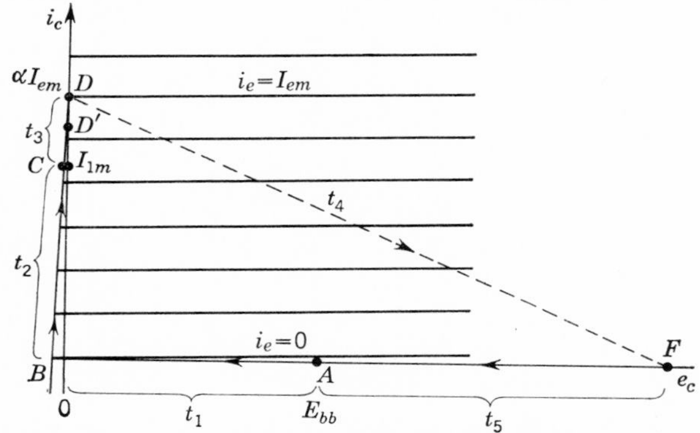

FIG. 12-3. Transistor collector volt-ampere characteristics—grounded-base connection—showing the path of operation of the blocking oscillator. The transition time between the various points is indicated.

The primary current, which flows into the collector, is related to the emitter current by the transformer turns ratio n.

$$I_{1m} = \frac{I_{em}}{n} \tag{12-5}$$

This segment of the path of operation lies between points B and C in Fig. 12-3. The time required for the rise, from 10 to 90 per cent of the final value, as defined in Eq. (1-32), is

$$t_2 = 2.2\tau_2 = 2.2\frac{L_e}{n^2 r_{11}} \tag{12-6}$$

Since r_{11} is quite small, in order to minimize the rise time, L_e must also be small.

Next the magnetizing current starts building up. If the small resistances of the conducting collector diode and the transformer primary are neglected, the model reduces to the one shown in Fig. 12-2*c*. The constant voltage across L_m produces a linearly increasing magnetizing current

$$i_m = \frac{E_{bb}}{L_m} t \tag{12-7}$$

which increases the total collector current, driving the operating point from *C* toward *D* in Fig. 12-3. When i_c finally reaches αI_{em}, the net collector diode current drops to zero and the transistor reenters its active region. Since the emitter current remains almost constant over the range of interest, from Eqs. (12-4), (12-5), and (12-7), we obtain

$$i_c = I_{1m} + i_m = \frac{1}{r_{11}n}\left(\frac{E_{bb}}{n} - E_a\right) + \frac{E_{bb}}{L_m} t \tag{12-8}$$

By setting i_c equal to αI_{em}, we find that the final portion of the pulse lasts for

$$t_3 = L_m \frac{n\alpha - 1}{n^2 r_{11}} \left(1 - \frac{nE_a}{E_{bb}}\right) \tag{12-9}$$

Because t_3 must be real for any combination of terms, Eq. (12-9) again proves that the conditions which must be satisfied for the proper circuit operation are $n\alpha > 1$ and $nE_a < E_{bb}$. In this mode, the segment defined by the linear current build-up in the magnetizing inductance constitutes the major portion of the desired pulse (that is, $t_3 \gg t_2$) and Eq. (12-9) essentially defines the complete pulse width.

The transistor switches back off in much the same manner as it turned on, and the circuit begins its recovery. As the current in L_m decays, the change in the direction of di_m/dt produces a large backswing of voltage which, coupled by the transformer, aids in back-biasing the emitter.

From the model of Fig. 12-2*d*, we see that the primary voltage would be given by the product of the peak value of the magnetizing current and the reflected resistance.

$$E_{mm} = I_{mm}n^2R = (\alpha I_{em} - I_{1m})n^2R \tag{12-10}$$

The collector voltage jumps from zero to

$$E_{cm} = E_{bb} + E_{mm}$$

with the emitter voltage going to

$$E_{em} = E_a + \frac{E_{mm}}{n}$$

Recovery toward the initial conditions is with the fast time constant

$$\tau_5 = \frac{L_m}{n^2R} \tag{12-11}$$

Instead of the current and voltage decaying monotonically toward the steady-state values, the magnetizing inductance may resonate with the stray capacity of the circuit, producing ringing in the output. The initial amplitude depends on the amount of energy previously stored in

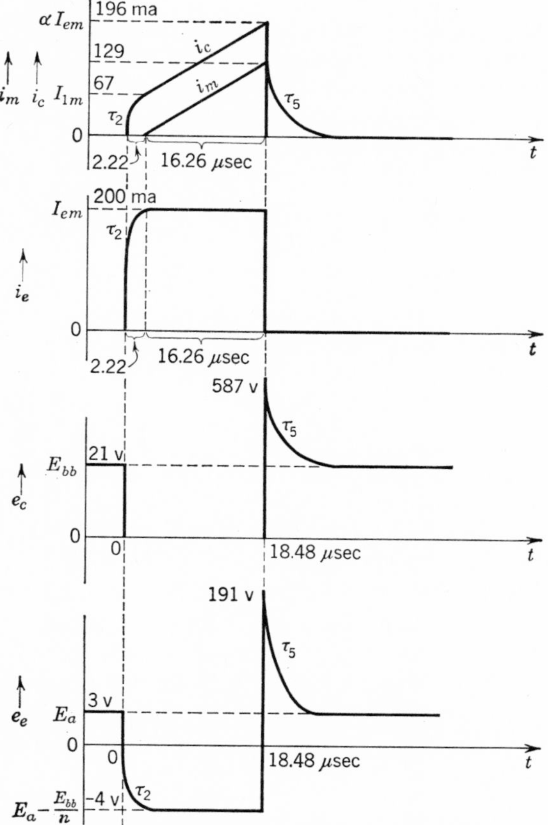

FIG. 12-4. Waveshapes produced in the inductively timed blocking oscillator. The values given are those found in Example 12-1.

the transformer. If the oscillations damp out slowly, the next change in polarity may force the transistor back into its active region, resulting in a second, undesired output pulse—the circuit would become astable.

Example 12-1. The blocking oscillator of Fig. 12-1 employs a transformer having $L_m = 2.5$ mh, $L_e = 100$ μh, $n = 3$, and $C_s = 20$ $\mu\mu$f. The transistor is characterized by

$r_{11} = 20$ ohms	$\alpha = 0.98$	turn-on time 0.1 μsec
$r_c = 1$ megohm		turn-off time 0.1 μsec

And the remaining parameters are $E_{bb} = 21$ volts, $E_a = 3$ volts, $R = 500$ ohms, $R_L = 5$ K, and $C = 10\ \mu$f. We wish to construct the various waveshapes encountered (Fig. 12-4).

From Eq. (12-3) the saturation time is given by

$$t_1 = 2.2 \frac{100\ \mu\text{h}}{(0.98 \times 3 - 1)10^6} \cong 10^{-10} \text{ sec}$$

but since the turn-on time is 0.1 μsec, this would be the proper value of t_1; the equation gives a solution that is a factor of 10^{-3} too small.

The emitter current next rises to

$$I_{em} = \tfrac{1}{20}(\tfrac{21}{3} - 3) = 200 \text{ ma}$$

with the time constant $\tau_2 = 0.556\ \mu$sec. At the end of this interval the collector current is only

$$I_{1m} = \frac{200 \text{ ma}}{3} = 67 \text{ ma}$$

In the saturation region the magnetizing current starts increasing as

$$i_m = \frac{20}{2.5 \text{ mh}} t$$

When this current builds up to the difference between αI_{em} and I_{1m}, the transistor turns off. Under the conditions of this problem, the transformer must tolerate 129 ma of magnetizing current without saturating. Thus t_3 is given by

$$[0.98(200) - 67]10^{-3} = \left(\frac{20}{2.5} \times 10^3\right) t_3$$

or $t_3 = 16.26\ \mu$sec.

The peak voltage developed across the primary is

$$E_{1m} = (196 - 67)10^{-3} \times 9 \times 500 = 566 \text{ volts}$$

Unless limited by the judicious use of diodes, as shown in Fig. 12-5, this extremely large voltage will destroy the transistor. The voltage at the emitter winding is only E_{1m}/n, or

$$E_{2m} = \tfrac{566}{3} = 188 \text{ volts}$$

Recovery is with the relatively fast time constant

$$\tau_5 = \frac{2.5 \times 10^{-3}}{9 \times 500} = 0.54\ \mu\text{sec}$$

Figure 12-5 shows how to prevent the saturation of the transistor as well as how to limit the excessive amplitude backswing. Zener diode D_S fires before the transistor can saturate and so sets a bottoming voltage of E_S volts. The saturation conditions are transferred from the collector diode to the Zener diode. Except that the primary voltage builds up to $E_{bb} - E_S$ volts instead of to E_{bb}, the solution of the circuit is identical with that previously discussed. Diode D_B conducts on the backswing if the terminal voltage exceeds E_B. Since it shunts the coil with its low forward resistance, the discharge time constant would be greatly increased. In the solution of the recovery interval, two time constants must be considered, the long one holding while D_B conducts and the fast one (Eq. 12-11) holding after the voltage decays below E_B.

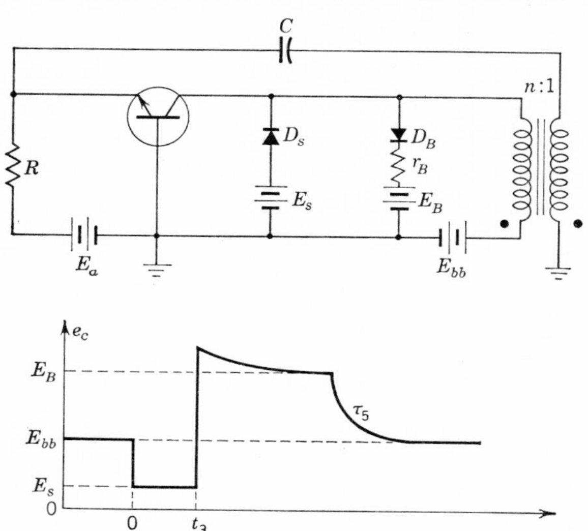

FIG. 12-5. Zener-diode limiting of the collector voltage of the blocking oscillator.

12-3. Transformer Core Properties and Saturation. The inductance of the blocking-oscillator transformer is proportional to the ratio of flux linkages and the current establishing this flux.

$$L = N \frac{d\Phi}{di} 10^{-8} \qquad \text{henrys} \tag{12-12}$$

At low frequencies or even at d-c, the relationship between the flux and the excitation is adequately expressed by the hysteresis curve (Fig. 12-6). Assuming ideal conditions, B is simply the flux per unit area and H is proportional to the ampere-turns per unit length. For large signals, $B = \mu H$, and hence the inductance is proportional to the permeability of the core. From the hysteresis loop of Fig. 12-6*a*, we can see that μ varies over rather wide limits as the core flux increases from zero to saturation.

If the hysteresis loop is approximated by the rectangular plot of Fig. 12-6*b*, we avoid the necessity of treating a circuit containing a continuously changing inductance. After lumping the core losses together with the external resistance, it can be assumed that

$$L = L_m \qquad |i| < |i_s|$$

and

$$L \cong L_s \qquad |i| > |i_s|$$

where i_s is the value of the coil current corresponding to the saturation magnetizing force H_s. The inductance in the saturation region approximates that of the coil in air; since $L_s \ll L_m$, it is often taken as zero.

Because it requires finite time for the applied excitation field H to propagate into the core and establish and align the randomly oriented magnetic domains, the above formulation is not completely correct. With a pulse excitation, the flux is initially only at the surface, and consequently the effective permeability is quite low. It increases as the field penetrates into the core. Even if the excitation is well above the saturation value, it may still take several microseconds to saturate a thin core. The penetration time may be long compared with the width of the pulse generated in the blocking oscillator, and consequently the assumption of a constant L_m is not valid.

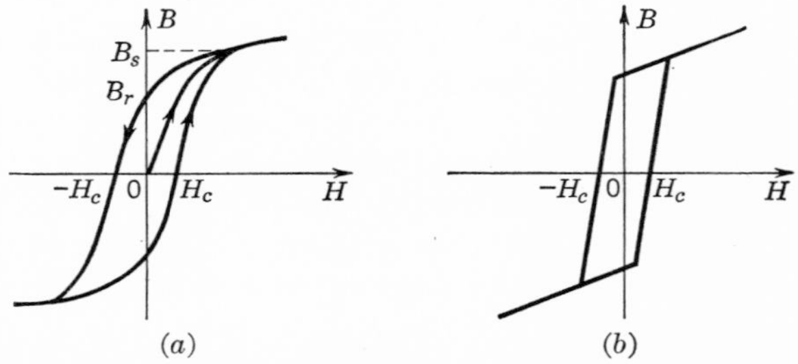

FIG. 12-6. Hysteresis curve and piecewise-linear representation.

In order to avoid this inconsistency, we would have to postulate a magnetizing inductance whose value increases with time from slightly above that of an air-core coil to a peak given by the steady-state core characteristics. A circuit element which exhibits a response of this nature is impossible to use in any simple approach to circuit analysis. We shall therefore continue to explain the blocking-oscillator operation on the basis of a fixed L_m and accept the resulting errors. However, the accuracy of calculations can be improved if the inductance value used is not that at direct current but rather that measured under pulsed conditions.

To summarize:

1. For pulse durations greater than several microseconds, the assumption of a constant L_m gives reasonably correct times.

2. When generating pulses of less than 1 or 2 μsec, the duration cannot be accurately calculated from any simple model. If a constant L_m is assumed, then the actual pulse will terminate sooner than calculated.

3. A finite time is required to saturate the core, and therefore this problem need be considered only when generating wide pulses.

Returning to the blocking oscillator, we shall now examine the operation when the core does saturate. Up to this point, the response will be identical with that discussed in Sec. 12-2. Since point C of Fig. 12-3 indicated the start of the magnetizing-current build-up, the saturation-current point D' would fall somewhere along line segment CD; for a high-permeability core, it might be quite close to the initial point. This is the termination point of the pulse; the lower the saturation value, the more it is foreshortened.

Once the transformer saturates, L_m drops to a very small value. The primary current increases rapidly, limited only by the total series resistance. At the same time, the secondary voltage falls, the emitter current drops, and the transistor again becomes active. As the stored energy dissipates, the left-hand branch of the hysteresis curve is traversed by the operating point. As a result, a large reverse voltage pulse appears at the collector. The time required for the decay depends on the nature of the transformer core. (This problem is treated in more detail in Chap. 13.) Because of the extremely nonlinear behavior, it is difficult to define the decay time in terms of the specific circuit parameters. In general, the manufacturer's specifications as to the rise and fall times and pulse width would be used in the circuit design.

12-4. Capacitively Timed Blocking Oscillator. The coupling capacitor C is now reduced in size until it alone will control the pulse duration. Instead of the increasing collector current bringing the transistor out of saturation, the decreasing emitter current, due to the charging of C, will now so serve. To simplify the following analysis, we shall assume, quite incorrectly, that the magnetizing current remains zero over the complete pulse interval. Moreover, since the Cr_{11} time constant is on the same order of magnitude as L_e/n^2r_{11}, the approximation that the initial build-up is complete before the timing element starts charging is no longer completely valid. We shall, however, assume that the peak values expressed in Eqs. (12-4) and (12-5) are still correct and shall begin our analysis from this point. By doing so, the nature of the reduction in the pulse duration may be seen most readily.

From the model of Fig. 12-7a, we can see that C charges from its initial value of E_a toward the Thévenin equivalent voltage

$$E_{Th} = \frac{E_{bb}}{n} + E_a \frac{r_{11}}{R + r_{11}} \cong \frac{E_{bb}}{n} + E_a \frac{r_{11}}{R} \tag{12-13}$$

The time constant is

$$\tau_3 = C(R \parallel r_{11}) \cong Cr_{11}$$

During this interval, the emitter current decays from its peak [Eq. (12-4)]

$$I_{em} = \frac{1}{r_{11}}\left(\frac{E_{bb}}{n} - E_a\right)$$

toward the steady-state value of

$$I_e(\infty) = -\frac{E_a}{r_{11} + R} \cong -\frac{E_a}{R}$$

The collector current will always be $1/n$ times as large. Consequently, because the transistor starts out saturated, it will remain so until I_e falls to zero.

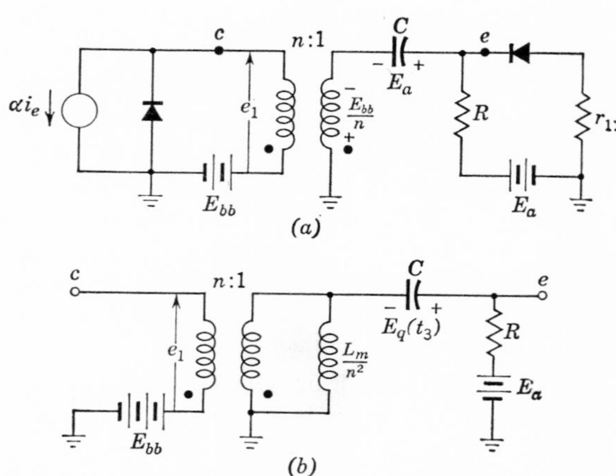

FIG. 12-7. Models holding for the capacitively timed blocking oscillator. (a) Model holding during the charging interval; (b) model defining the recovery period.

The duration of the unstable state, as found from the exponential charging equation, is given by

$$t_3 = \tau_3 \ln \frac{I_e(\infty) - I_{em}}{I_e(\infty)}$$

or by substituting the appropriate terms,

$$t_3 = Cr_{11} \ln \left[1 + \frac{R}{r_{11}} \left(\frac{E_{bb}}{nE_a} - 1\right)\right] \tag{12-14}$$

If $R \gg r_{11}$, this portion of the pulse will consist of virtually the complete exponential. To avoid the ambiguity arising when the switching point is close to the steady-state value, E_a might be made highly negative and R might be reduced.

At the termination of the pulse, the transistor switches off and the recovery model reduces to the one shown in Fig. 12-7*b*. Because the approximations made in the course of the above analysis neglected the energy storage in the transformer, the exact nature of the response over this portion of the cycle is somewhat difficult to define. One type of response would be expected when the secondary magnetizing inductance limits the rate of capacitor current flow, and yet another type where the transformer saturates rapidly. Regardless of the particular controlling element, the energy storage will almost always produce a large spike of voltage, and then either ringing (which must be suppressed) or an exponential decay back toward the original state. Waveshapes appearing at all elements, illustrating the type of recovery to be expected, appear in Fig. 12-8.

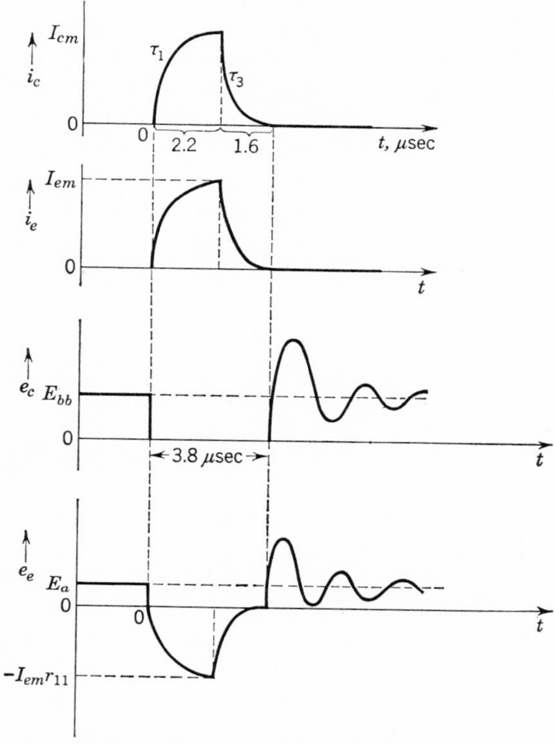

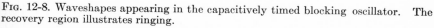

FIG. 12-8. Waveshapes appearing in the capacitively timed blocking oscillator. The recovery region illustrates ringing.

We shall now consider the change in the response of the blocking oscillator of Example 12-1 when C is reduced from 10 to 0.02 μf. From Eq. (12-14), the duration of the final portion of transistor saturation lasts for

$$t_3 = Cr_{11} \ln \left[1 + \frac{1{,}000}{40} (7 - 1) \right]$$

Since this is almost the complete exponential,

$$t_3 \cong 4Cr_{11} = 4(0.02 \times 10^{-6}) \times 20 = 1.6 \ \mu\text{sec}$$

The pulse width, under this condition, is approximately one-tenth the time calculated when L_m controlled the timing.

We should note that the maximum pulse duration is due to the current build-up in the magnetizing inductance. Either the charging of C or the saturation of the core can only reduce this time. Furthermore, the simultaneous magnetic-flux build-up means that the peak currents that are reached and the actual pulse duration will always be less than calculated on the basis of the idealizations made above. C is almost never used to control the pulse width, but it is used to time the interval between pulses in a free-running blocking oscillator (Sec. 12-5).

12-5. Astable Operation. As might be anticipated from the previous discussion of monostable and astable operation in Chaps. 10 and 11, shifting the quiescent operating point from the cutoff to the active region will make the blocking oscillator free-running. For example, the astable circuit of Fig. 12-9, except for the reversal of the emitter battery, is identical with the monostable circuit of Fig. 12-1.

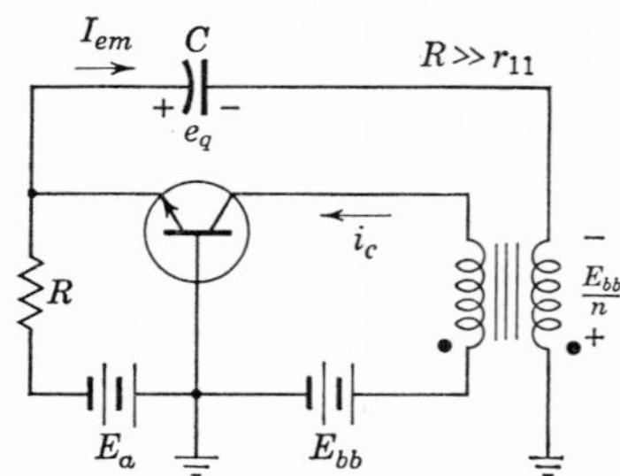

FIG. 12-9. An astable blocking oscillator—voltages shown for the saturated region.

During the pulse interval, the large emitter current charges C slightly positive. After the circuit switches off, then the accumulated charge maintains the emitter back-biased. Eventually the voltage from emitter to ground decays to zero and the circuit generates another pulse.

At the instant of switching on, the net charge in C must be zero. The voltage at the transformer secondary has not as yet built up to E_{bb}/n, and therefore the emitter state depends solely on the voltage across C. If this voltage were positive, the emitter would be back-biased, and if it were negative, the circuit would have switched on earlier. Except for the change in the initial condition, the operation of the blocking oscillator, during the pulse interval, is identical with that discussed in Secs. 12-2 and 12-3. The peak negative voltage across the emitter and the peak current flow are now given by

$$E_{em} = -\frac{E_{bb}}{n} \qquad I_{em} = \frac{E_{bb}}{nr_{11}} \tag{12-15}$$

For the purposes of computation we shall assume that this current remains constant over the complete pulse interval. Since I_{em} flows through C, it will produce a net voltage change of

$$\Delta E = \frac{1}{C} I_{em}\,\Delta t \tag{12-16}$$

where Δt is the width of the pulse [$\Delta t = t_2 + t_3$ as defined in Eqs. (12-6) and (12-9)]. The capacitor thus charges linearly from its initial value of zero to

$$E_{qm}(\Delta t) = +\Delta E$$

as shown in Fig. 12-10. In order to sustain a constant emitter current over the pulse interval, the change in the capacitor voltage must be small in comparison with the voltage across the transformer secondary.

$$|E_{qm}| \ll \frac{E_{bb}}{n} \tag{12-17}$$

Combining Eqs. (12-15), (12-16), and the inequality of Eq. (12-17), we can express one of the limiting conditions as

$$C \gg \frac{\Delta t}{r_{11}} \tag{12-18}$$

At the end of the pulse interval the transistor is driven hard off by the inductive backswing. After the initial recovery with the fast time

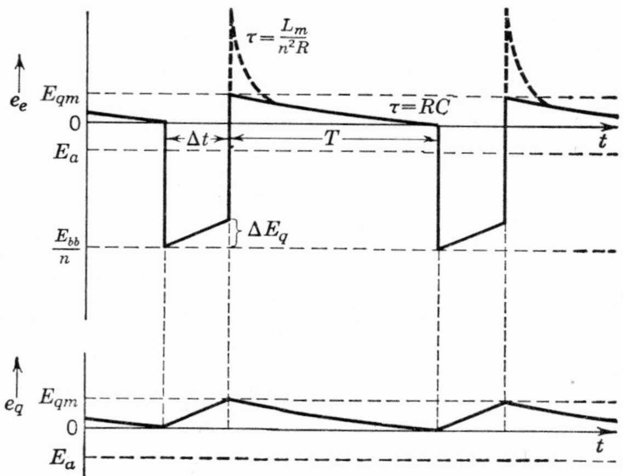

FIG. 12-10. Emitter and capacitor voltage waveshapes in the astable blocking oscillator.

constant, $\tau_5 = L_m/n^2R$, the charge in C will maintain the cutoff condition. As it discharges toward $-E_a$, with the relatively long time constant $\tau = RC$, the emitter voltage decays from $+E_{qm}$ to zero. Thus the duration of the interval between adjacent pulses is given by

$$T = RC \ln \frac{-E_a - E_{qm}}{-E_a} \tag{12-19}$$

And, for a given period, Eq. (12-19) determines the size of R.

The astable blocking oscillator is commonly used to generate trains of narrow pulses having relatively wide separation. The time defined in Eq. (12-19) very nearly represents the complete period of the generated signal.

As with all free-running circuits, the blocking oscillator may be synchronized to an external control signal. It must, of course, have a frequency and amplitude placing it within the regions of synchronization. Because the pulse is so very narrow when compared with the full period, the solution of the synchronization problem would be much closer to that found for the sawtooth sweep in Chap. 5 than to any regions which might be constructed for a multivibrator.

Example 12-2. In this problem we wish to calculate the values of C and R necessary to establish a pulse spacing of 2.5 msec. The blocking oscillator generates a 5-μsec pulse. The significant parameters for the recovery interval are $r_{11} = 40$ ohms, $E_{bb} = 20$ volts, $E_a = 1$ volt, $n = 2$, and $L_m = 2.5$ mh.

From the above parameters, Eq. (12-18) yields

$$C \gg \frac{5 \times 10^{-6}}{40} = 0.125\ \mu\text{f}$$

In order to keep its size within bounds, we shall choose $C = 2\ \mu$f. The peak voltage developed across it is

$$E_{qm} = \frac{1}{C}\frac{E_{bb}}{nr_{11}}\Delta t = 0.625 \text{ volt}$$

The remaining circuit component R is now found from Eq. (12-19).

$$R = \frac{T}{C \ln \dfrac{E_a + E_{qm}}{E_a}} = \frac{2.5 \times 10^{-3}}{2 \times 10^{-6} \ln 1.625} = 2{,}580 \text{ ohms}$$

As a final step we should verify that the voltage backswing due to the energy stored in the transformer will have damped out long before the transistor turns back on. This time constant is

$$\tau_5 = \frac{L_m}{n^2R} = \frac{2.5 \times 10^{-3}}{4 \times 2.58 \times 10^3} = 0.242\ \mu\text{sec}$$

and thus the backswing occupies an insignificant portion of the recovery interval. If a Zener diode was included, this might no longer be true.

12-6. A Vacuum-tube Blocking Oscillator. The circuit of Fig. 12-11 is probably the most difficult to analyze of all those used for pulse generation. Many words have been written purporting to detail its operation, but none of the papers or texts have been completely successful. The difficulties faced are many:

1. More than a single mode of energy storage is always operative.
2. The various parasitics must be included; they establish the switching time and thus place a lower limit on the pulse duration.
3. The tube operates in a region not previously defined, where its parameters change drastically from the small-signal operation. In this region the values of μ, r_p, and r_c are not even well known.

4. Because of the flux build-up and even possible core saturation, the timing inductance becomes a function of the magnetizing current and the pulse width (Sec. 12-3).

Difficult problems always have a peculiar fascination. In discussing them, one tends to go deeper and deeper until perspective is lost and the subject appears overly important. In an effort to avoid this pitfall, the following arguments are concerned with two rather limited goals:

1. The development of a tube model for the new region of operation
2. The construction of a set of reasonably consistent models and the extraction of some essential information when these models are inadequately defined

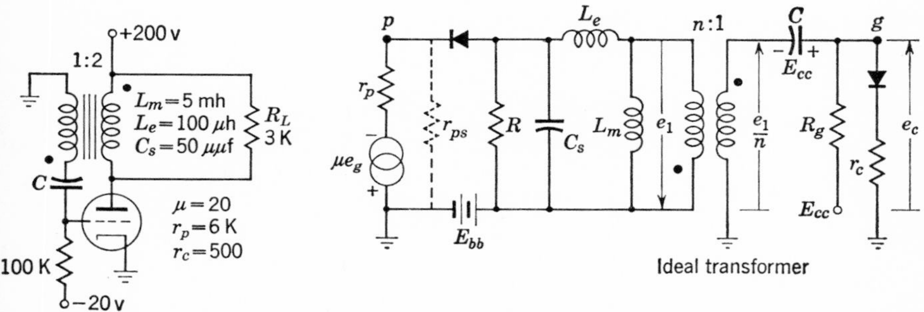

FIG. 12-11. A vacuum-tube monostable blocking oscillator and its general equivalent model—timing controlled solely by the transformer. Waveshapes produced are shown in Fig. 12-16.

Whenever the analysis becomes overly complicated or does not give promise of rewards commensurate with the work involved, it will immediately be dropped.

We shall assume that the reader has some knowledge of the waveshape produced (Fig. 12-16). Such an assumption is not unreasonable; the laboratory must always be a close adjunct to the paper work, especially when treating a complicated circuit. It is far easier to clear up fine points with a little laboratory work than from a model that is at best only an idealization.

The first step in the analysis of the vacuum-tube blocking oscillator is to define a new tube model. This becomes necessary because as the tube in the circuit of Fig. 12-13 switches on, the large plate drop, coupled by the transformer, drives the grid beyond the point at which the previously derived models hold. In fact, within the timing region, the grid voltage may even exceed that at the plate. When this happens, the grid loses control over the plate current. Any increase in the grid voltage increases the total cathode current up to the emission capabilities of the tube. But because the grid is at the highest potential, almost all the additional current flows to it; the plate current remains essentially constant. As can be seen in Fig. 12-12*a* and *b*, when $E_c > E_b$, the family of plate volt-ampere characteristics degenerates into a single curve. It follows directly that the plate-circuit response may be represented by a simple diode having the forward resistance r_{ps} (Fig. 12-13).

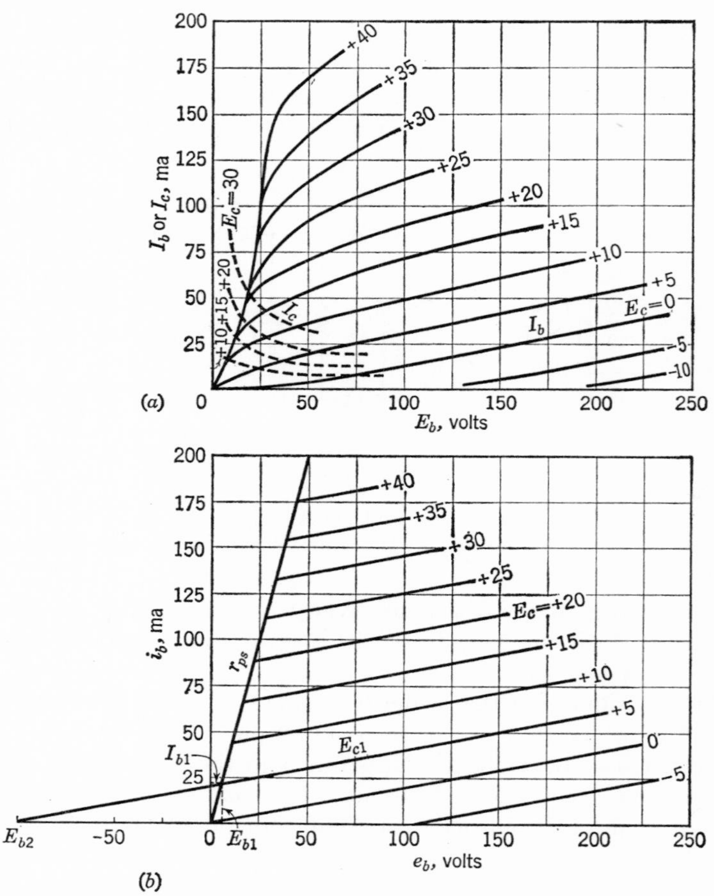

FIG. 12-12. Vacuum-tube positive grid characteristics and piecewise-linear representation (after 12AU7 characteristics).

The value of the plate resistance in the absolute saturation region of Fig. 12-12*b* is given by

$$r_{ps} = \frac{E_{b1}}{I_{b1}} = \frac{E_{c1}}{I_{b1}} \tag{12-20}$$

But the plate voltage intercept of the extended active-region characteristics through the point (E_{b1},I_{b1}) is

$$E_{b2} = -\mu E_{c1}$$

Thus, from the geometry, the plate resistance in the active region may be expressed as

$$r_p = \frac{E_{b1} - E_{b2}}{I_{b1}} = \frac{(\mu + 1)E_{c1}}{I_{b1}} \tag{12-21}$$

Comparing Eqs. (12-20) and (12-21) allows us to write the saturation resistance in terms of the active-region parameters.

$$r_{ps} = \frac{r_p}{\mu + 1} \tag{12-22}$$

The grid resistance used in the model of Fig. 12-13 must also be reduced to one-half or one-quarter of the value measured at the lower values of grid voltage. Furthermore, this resistance is extremely nonlinear. At very high values of voltage and current, the grid driving-point characteristic may even begin to approximate a constant voltage drop more closely than a pure resistance. In the interests of simplicity, however, we shall assume a constant resistance whose value would be found in the vicinity of $e_c \cong e_b$.

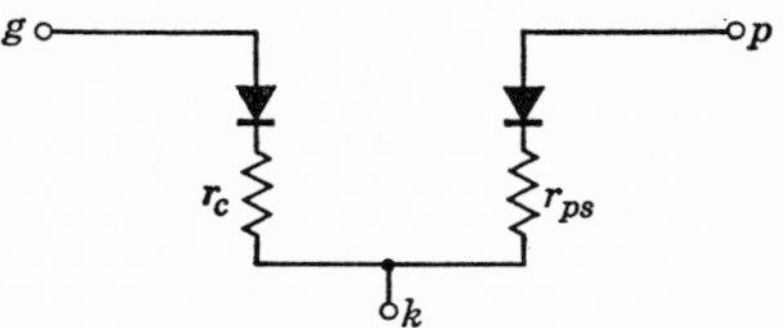

FIG. 12-13. Triode model for the absolute saturation region.

For the purposes of discussion, the operation of the vacuum-tube blocking oscillator of Fig. 12-11 may be divided into the same four regions found for the transistor circuit. These are characterized by:

I. Active region. The positive loop gain drives the tube into "absolute" saturation (that is, $e_c \geq e_b$).

II. Tube saturation region. Here the circuit voltages build up toward their peak values.

III. Timing. Current build-up in the transformer, core saturation, and/or the charging of C return the tube to the active region and terminate the pulse.

IV. Switching and recovery. The regeneration of the circuit turns the tube off, and the energy previously stored must now be dissipated. The output consists of a large voltage overshoot and either ringing or an exponential decay toward the initial conditions.

Of all the parasitic elements present, only the two of major significance, that is, L_e and C_s, will be included in the linearized models. The stray capacity, which is distributed throughout the circuit, may be lumped into a single element. But where should it be placed? If it is inserted from the grid to cathode or directly across the magnetizing inductance, nothing constrains the plate voltage; once the tube turns on, the full supply voltage appears across L_e and the plate immediately bottoms at zero. This will not occur in the physical circuit. If the model permits such a drop, the model is incorrect. To prevent the abrupt change in e_b, the stray capacity should be connected from the plate to cathode as shown in Fig. 12-11.

Without actually solving for the exact time response, we shall now discuss the basic behavior of the circuit and the role of the various parameters.

Region I. Initial Rise. The voltage swept through during the initial portion of the grid rise, from cutoff to zero, is a very small percentage of the total voltage change. Moreover, since the grid will not load the plate circuit, the loop gain will be much higher than that measured in the positive grid region. The rate of voltage change is very rapid, and the time contribution to the over-all pulse duration insignificant.

In the positive grid region, the nature of the response would be found from the model of Fig. 12-14*a*. Since

$$e_c = -\frac{e_1}{n} = -i_2 n r_c$$

the circuit poles would be given by the solution of the determinant

$$\begin{vmatrix} R + \dfrac{1}{pc_s} & Anr_c - \dfrac{1}{pc_s} \\ -\dfrac{1}{pc_s} & n^2 r_c + pL_e + \dfrac{1}{pc_s} \end{vmatrix} = 0$$

or

$$p^2 + \left(\frac{1}{RC_s} + \frac{n^2 r_c}{L_e}\right) p + \frac{R + n^2 r_c + nAr_c}{RL_eC_s} = 0 \qquad (12\text{-}23)$$

For proper switching, one pole must lie in the right half plane. With the values given in Fig. 12-11, the two poles are located at

$$p_1 = -7.43 \times 10^7 \qquad p_2 = 2.43 \times 10^7$$

In a relatively short time the effect of the negative exponential will have damped out. The time response is primarily due to the positive pole, and we may approximate the plate-voltage fall by

$$e_b \cong E_{bb}(2 - e^{p_2 t})$$

From the definition that the rise time is the time required to charge from 10 to 90 per cent of the bounding voltage,

$$t_1 = \frac{2.2}{p_2} = 0.091\ \mu\text{sec}$$

The negative pole, along with the additional parasitic elements not included in the model, will slow the rise by a factor of 1.5 or 2. Any increase in L_e or C_s would also adversely affect the switching time.

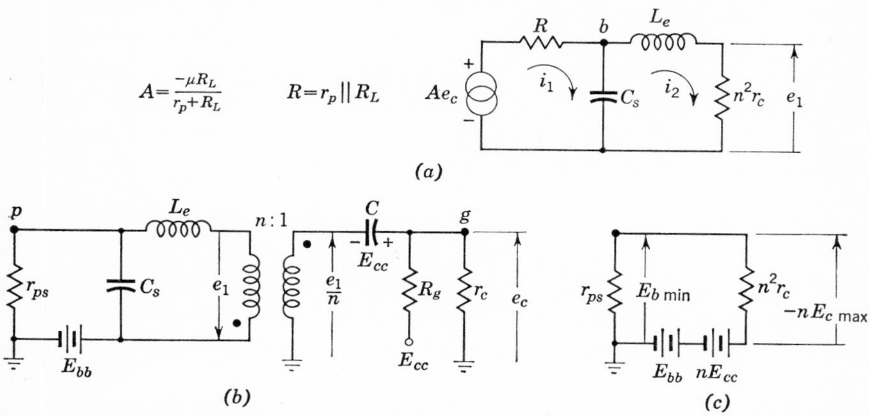

FIG. 12-14. Models holding for regions I and II of the vacuum-tube blocking oscillator of Fig. 12-11. (*a*) Incremental model holding within the active region; (*b*) model defining the rise in the saturation region; (*c*) model used to solve for $E_{b,\min}$ and $E_{c,\max}$.

This portion of the response is finally bounded when the grid rise and plate fall drive the tube into saturation. Reflecting the grid circuit voltages into the transformer primary results in

$$E_{bb} + nE_{cc} = e_b + e_L + ne_c$$

where e_L is the drop across the leakage inductance. Solving for

$$e_b = e_c = E_{b1}$$

we obtain

$$E_{b1} = \frac{E_{bb} + nE_{cc} - e_L}{n + 1} \tag{12-24}$$

Equation (12-24) cannot be solved until e_L is evaluated. But this is too difficult to do. The particular voltage at which the tube saturates is not crucial to the circuit operation. Because L_e is small, the voltage developed across it will not be large even at the boundary. Arbitrarily assuming $e_L = 10$ volts, the circuit used as an example yields

$$E_{b1} = \frac{200 - 40 - 10}{3} = 50 \text{ volts}$$

Region II. Final Current Build-up. After the tube saturates, the circuit model reduces to the one shown in Fig. 12-14*b*. Because R_L is very much larger than the 285-ohm plate saturation resistance, the 3,000-ohm external load may be neglected. The two poles in the left-hand plane are now located by the solution of

$$p^2 + \left(\frac{1}{r_{ps}C_s} + \frac{n^2 r_c}{L_e}\right)p + \frac{r_{ps} + n^2 r_c}{r_{ps}L_e C_s} = 0 \tag{12-25}$$

or at $\qquad p_1 = -9.51 \times 10^7 \qquad p_2 = -1.75 \times 10^7$

Charging continues from the boundary value of $E_{c1} = E_{b1}$ toward the steady-state conditions, which can be found from the model of Fig. 12-14*c*. The pole located closest to the origin is associated with the longest time response, and consequently the duration of this charging interval is approximately

$$t_2 \cong 4 \frac{1}{|p_2|} = 0.228 \ \mu\text{sec}$$

From Fig. 12-14*c* the peak voltages are given by

$$E_{b,\min} = \frac{r_{ps}}{r_{ps} + n^2 r_c}(E_{bb} + nE_{cc}) \tag{12-26a}$$

$$E_{c,\max} = \frac{nr_c}{r_{ps} + n^2 r_c}(E_{bb} + nE_{cc}) \tag{12-26b}$$

Solving these equations in the circuit used as an example, we find that the plate falls to 20 volts while the grid rises to +70 volts. In an actual circuit r_c would decrease markedly when the grid voltage greatly exceeds e_b. This lowers $E_{c,\max}$ and raises $E_{b,\min}$.

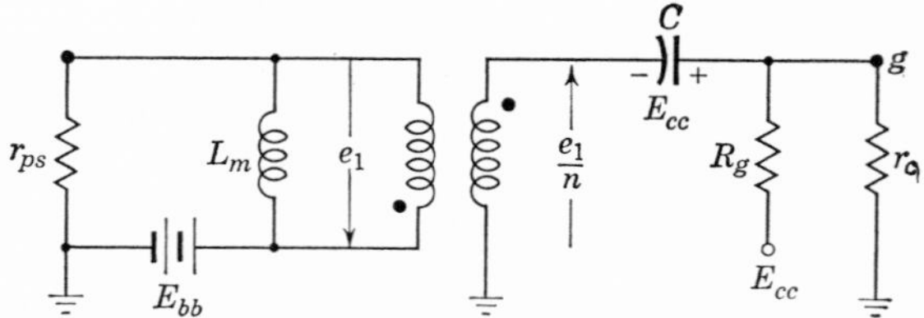

FIG. 12-15. Model holding over the timing region.

Region III. Pulse Timing. This, the most important region, is defined by the very simple model of Fig. 12-15. Note that because $L_m \gg L_e$, C_s is much less significant and may even be omitted. The magnetizing current begins increasing with the time constant

$$\tau = \frac{L_m}{r_{ps} \parallel n^2 r_c}$$

toward the steady-state value

$$I_{ss} = \frac{E_{bb}}{r_{ps}}$$

Meanwhile, the plate voltage rises from $E_{b,\min}$ toward E_{bb} and the grid decays back toward E_{cc}. The two charging equations are

$$e_b = E_{bb} - (E_{bb} - E_{b,\min})e^{-t/\tau} \tag{12-27a}$$
$$e_c = E_{cc} - (E_{cc} - E_{c,\max})e^{-t/\tau} \tag{12-27b}$$

Eventually the decay at the grid and the rise at the plate will permit the tube to reenter the active region. Solving Eqs. (12-27a) and (12-27b), the time elapsed until $e_b = E_{b2} = E_{c2}$ is

$$t_3 = \tau \ln \frac{E_{bb} - E_{cc} + E_{c,\max} - E_{b,\min}}{E_{bb} + E_{cc}} \tag{12-28}$$

The value of $E_{b2} = E_{c2}$ may be found by substituting the t_3 back into Eqs. (12-27) or by eliminating the exponential term between these two equations. The simplest expression for the boundary value becomes

$$E_{c2} = E_{b2} = \frac{E_{bb} + nE_{cc}}{n + 1} \tag{12-29}$$

We might observe that the 53 volts at which the circuit leaves the saturation region is slightly higher than the 50 volts at which it entered. The duration of the pulse is

$$t_3 = 20 \times 10^{-6} \ln (1 + 50/220) = 20 \times 10^{-6} \ln 1.227 = 4.08\ \mu\text{sec}$$

At the end of the pulse the magnetizing current has reached a peak of

$$I_m(t_3) = \frac{E_{bb}}{r_{ps}} (1 - e^{-t_3/\tau}) = 130 \text{ ma}$$

If the transformer cannot tolerate such a current without saturating, the pulse would terminate proportionately earlier.

In practical blocking oscillators, the high grid current which charges C increases the rate of the grid voltage decay. Switching will occur somewhat sooner than given by Eq. (12-29). This same charging is also used in the astable circuit to back-bias the tube during the interpulse period.

Region IV. Termination of the Pulse. Once the circuit again becomes active, regeneration drives the tube toward and even beyond cutoff. As long as the tube remains active, the poles defining the response will be given by Eq. (12-23). Below cutoff the time response is defined by the parallel R_L, L_m, and C_s circuit. Depending on the degree of damping, the output may be either an exponential decay or a damped sinusoid. The final decay is from a peak determined by the energy previously stored in L_m. The external damping R_L not only limits the backswing to a safe value, but also prevents the ringing that may cause a false retriggering of the circuit.

The magnetizing current of 130 ma flows through R_L after the tube is cut off. This results in a peak voltage at the plate of

$$E_{b,\max} = E_{bb} + I_m(t_3)R_L = 590 \text{ volts}$$

At the grid the maximum possible backswing is

$$E_{c,\min} = -20 - {}^{390}\!/_{2} = -215 \text{ volts}$$

The above calculation neglected the stray capacity, which will, of course, slow the switching and reduce the amplitude of the backswing.

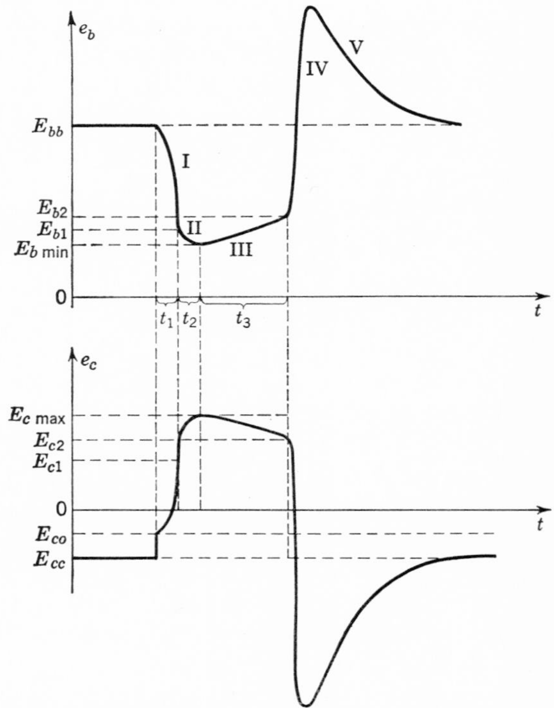

FIG. 12-16. Plate and grid waveshapes for the monostable blocking oscillator of Fig. 12-11.

12-7. Some Concluding Remarks. Even a small receiving tube, limited to 2 or 3 watts plate dissipation and 0.5 watt grid dissipation, is able to supply 50 or 100 watts of peak power over the narrow pulse interval. To ensure that the average power will not exceed the ratings, the blocking oscillator is normally operated with a duty cycle of 1 to 5 per cent (time on as compared with the total period). For pulses having a larger duty cycle, multivibrators would be used in preference to the blocking oscillator.

On the other hand, only a small amount of power is dissipated by the saturated transistor during the pulse. If large currents are switched in the collector circuit, then the peak collector dissipation is reached within the active region—during the turn-on and turn-off times. Larger duty cycles are possible without damaging the transistor. Usually the resistance inserted to limit the voltage backswing imposes much more severe restrictions on the duty cycle (long recovery time) than do the power considerations.

Of the many other modes of blocking-oscillator operation possible, one of the most common is where the transformer primary is designed to resonate with the stray capacity. The circuit operates as a tightly coupled tuned plate oscillator such as discussed in Chap. 14. This circuit is not really a relaxation oscillator, but it can still be analyzed by the methods discussed in this chapter, with, however, the active-region model defining the major portion of the response. The waveshapes appearing at the plate and grid would be portions of a sinusoid, although somewhat distorted by the changing grid resistance.

PROBLEMS

12-1. In Example 12-1 the stray capacity is increased until the circuit is on the verge of becoming oscillatory during recovery.

(*a*) Calculate the minimum value of C_s which will resonate with L_m.

(*b*) When C_s is ten times the minimum value, sketch the response in the recovery region. Pay particular attention to any retriggering of the blocking oscillator.

12-2. Figure 12-17 shows an emitter-collector-coupled blocking oscillator where *the period is independent of any power-supply variations.* Except for R_1 and R_2, all components are as given in Example 12-1.

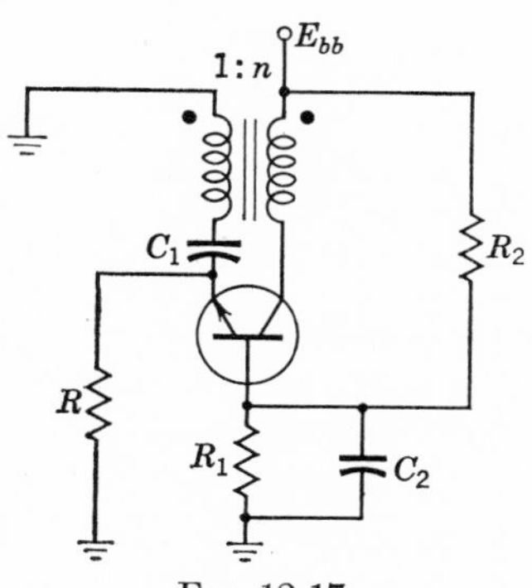

FIG. 12-17

(*a*) Prove or disprove the above statement.

(*b*) R_1 is 500 ohms, R_2 is adjustable, and C_2 is very large. Plot the peak value of emitter current and the pulse duration as functions of R_2. At what value will the circuit stop operating?

12-3. Figure 12-18 shows a collector-base-coupled blocking oscillator with the external load connected to a tertiary winding.

(*a*) What is the minimum value of n for guaranteed operation? Indicate the polarity of the transformer connections.

(*b*) Assume that the transformer turns ratio is ten times the bounding value. In addition, the ratio $L_m/L_e = 25:1$. Specify the transformer parameters for a 5-μsec pulse duration.

(*c*) Sketch and label the load current.

(*d*) Compare the advantages and disadvantages of this configuration with the circuit of Fig. 12-1.

12-4. Draw the circuit for an emitter-base-coupled blocking oscillator. Using the parameters of Fig. 12-18 with leakage and magnetizing inductance (referred to the emitter winding) of $L_m = 10$ mh, $L_e = 0.5$ mh, and $n = 3$ (base winding), calculate the pulse duration. Sketch and label the load current and the collector voltage waveshapes.

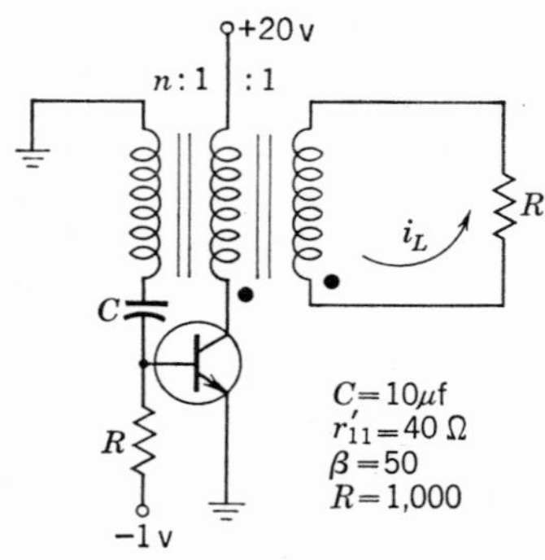

FIG. 12-18

12-5. The blocking oscillator of Example 12-1 is modified to the circuit of Fig. 12-5. Repeat the waveshape calculations if the bottoming value is 2 volts. The Zener diode chosen to limit the collector voltage conducts at 40 volts; in series with it, we insert a recovery resistance to limit the peak at the collector to 75 volts. How would the circuit respond if the Zener resistance is 10 ohms? 0 ohms?

12-6. Show three methods of triggering the blocking oscillator of Example 12-1. Use both current and voltage input pulses. Specify the pulse height, polarity, and order of magnitude of the source impedance. Does any one method chosen have overwhelming advantages? Explain.

12-7. The transformer of Example 12-1 is changed to one that saturates at 50 ma. Assume that L_m drops from 2.5 mh to 250 μh after saturation. Plot the new waveshape, paying particular attention to operation after saturation. Are all the assumptions made in the text still valid? What happens after the transistor turns off?

12-8. Figure 12-19 shows a blocking oscillator designed so that the pulse width can be controlled by a constant current injected into a tertiary winding. This current establishes a bias flux and thus influences the saturation point. Saturation occurs at a field strength of $50N \times 10^3$ amp-turns, where N is the number of turns in the collector winding. Specify the parameters (L_m, C, and R) that will permit the adjustment of the pulse duration from 5 to 50 μsec. Neglect the effect of L_e on the pulse width.

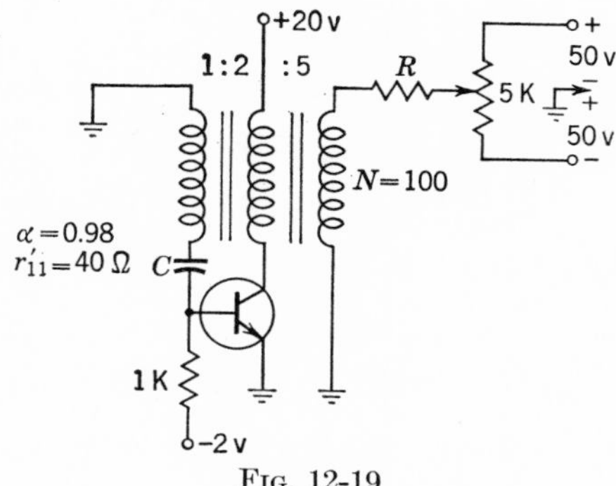

FIG. 12-19

12-9. (*a*) The circuit of Fig. 12-18 is made astable by reversing the base bias battery. In addition, $L_m = 5$ mh and $n = 0.2$. Calculate the value of C that will set the period at 6 msec. Neglect L_e in your calculations. Show the recovery portion of the collector waveshape and the capacitor current.

(*b*) By how much would the charging current reduce the pulse duration? Make all reasonable approximations in your calculations.

12-10. Repeat the calculations for the vacuum-tube oscillator discussed in the text when $C_s = 0$. Sketch the waveshapes and compare the times with those previously found. Plot the path of operation of these two cases on the volt-ampere characteristic and compare the location of significant points.

12-11. Can e_L in Eq. (12-25) be evaluated from the known conditions of the problem? If it can be, do so. If it cannot be, explain why not.

12-12. (*a*) Justify the approximations made in finding t_1 and t_2 in the text in Sec. 12-6.

(*b*) If these simplifications were not made, would it be possible to calculate the exact response? Explain.

12-13. (*a*) Find the value of R_L, in terms of the other circuit parameters, that will just prevent ringing in the recovery region (Fig. 12-11).

(*b*) Evaluate this resistance for the circuit discussed in the text. Calculate the backswing produced.

12-14. Sketch and label the plate-current, grid-current, and cathode-current waveshapes for the blocking oscillator of Sec. 12-6. Calculate the power dissipated in the tube over the pulse interval.

12-15. Plot the peak grid voltage; the minimum plate voltage; the peak grid, plate, and cathode currents; and the pulse duration as a function of the transformer turns ratio. Let $0.2 < n < 5$ and use the example given in the text as your circuit. The initial rise may be neglected in your calculations. Can any conclusions be drawn as to the "best" transformer?

12-16. An astable vacuum-tube blocking oscillator is shown in Fig. 12-20. Calculate the pulse duration and the period. Sketch and label 2 full cycles of the grid voltage waveshape.

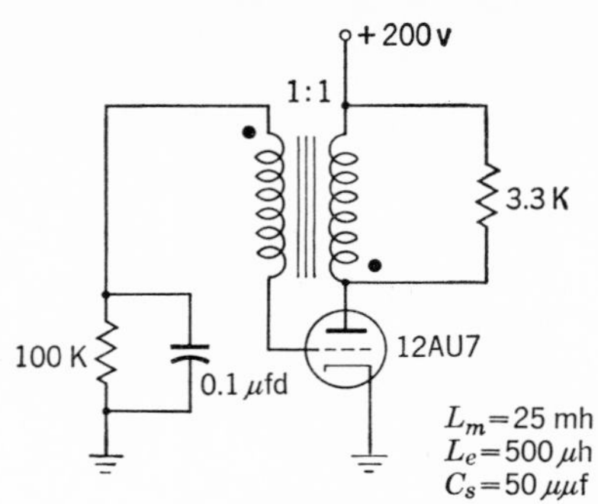

FIG. 12-20

BIBLIOGRAPHY

Benjamin, R.: Blocking Oscillators, *J. IEE (London)*, pt. IIIA, vol. 93, pp. 1159–1175, 1946.

The Blocking Oscillator, *Wireless World*, vol. 63, pp. 285–289, June, 1957.

Linvill, J. G., and R. H. Mattson: Junction Transistor Blocking Oscillator, *Proc. IRE*, vol. 43, no. 11, pp. 1632–1639, 1955.

Narud, J. A., and M. R. Aaron: Analysis and Design of a Transistor Blocking Oscillator Including Inherent Nonlinearities, *Bell System Tech. J.*, vol. 38, no. 3, pp. 785–852, 1959.

PART 4

MEMORY

CHAPTER 13

MAGNETIC AND DIELECTRIC DEVICES AS MEMORY AND SWITCHING ELEMENTS

In this chapter we shall be making use of just those properties of magnetic and dielectric materials that were so annoying in linear circuits. One of the more important is hysteresis, i.e., the dependency of the present state on the past excitation, the material's memory. The other characteristic, saturation, which allows several regions of operation, permits the use of these solid-state devices in controlled gates and other circuits previously restricted to diodes, tubes, and transistors. Not only are special materials used, but these are also treated to exaggerate the hysteresis and saturation regions before being fabricated into cores or capacitors. The behavior of magnetic materials has been studied much more extensively, and consequently there is a much wider range of properties available than can be found in the dielectric mediums. For this reason we shall concentrate mainly on those circuits making use of ferromagnetic devices. However, as this situation will most probably be rectified in the near future, the last sections of this chapter will consider certain ferroelectric devices and circuits.

13-1. Hysteresis—Characteristics of Memory. We must sometimes store the information contained in a sequence of pulses which are generated by a multivibrator or blocking oscillator and transmitted through various gates. In digital computers, rapid storage and read-out are essential for the solution of complex problems. Besides storing data and answers, the program controlling the sequence of the solution is fed into the memory banks. As each step is completed, the computer switches to the next memory location for further instructions.

Storage consists in switching a bistable device from its low to its high state, arbitrarily designated by 0 and 1. Thus a time sequence of pulses may contain almost any desired coded information. If a pulse is present, it would be indicated by 1, its absence noted by 0. For example, one particular five-digit word might be 10011. Each digit contains one bit of information, and each would have to be registered in a separate memory location. Upon the application of the appropriate read-out pulses, the excited memory units would switch from 1 to 0, with the previously stored information appearing as output pulses. Those in the 0 state remain undisturbed.

We shall now consider the particular characteristics required in the individual memory unit.

1. It should have at least two definitive, widely separated levels. Once excited from the lower to the higher, the memory element should maintain the new state after the initial storage pulse has disappeared. This precludes use of all nonlinear devices having continuous characteristics. We cannot identify the state of the diode (curve *a* in Fig. 13-1) by looking at the zero excitation point.

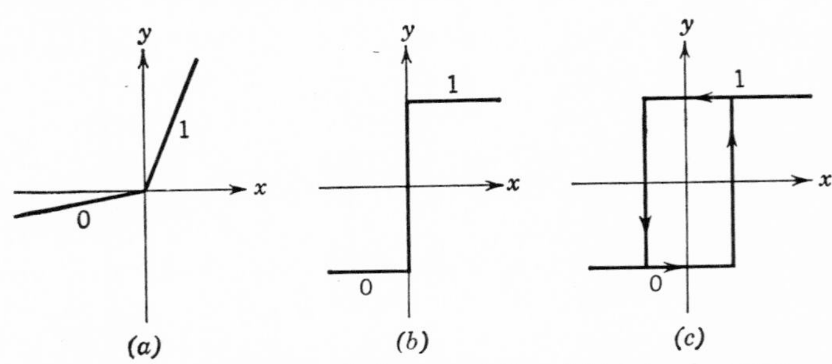

FIG. 13-1. Three typical characteristics of bistate elements.

2. Both the process of storage and read-out should require a finite amount of energy. If the device switches levels with an absolute minimum input, what is to prevent it from switching erratically in the presence of noise? The two states of curve *b* in Fig. 13-1 are interchangeable at zero excitation; a device having this characteristic would be unreliable for use as a memory element.

3. At any instant the state of the device must represent the past history of the system as well as the present excitation.

4. In general, storage and read-out should require different types of excitation. This is necessary because we do not want the memory to shift from 1 to 0 when a storage pulse is applied or to store a read-out pulse falsely by switching from 0 to 1. Such differentiation might be as simple as using positive and negative pulses for storage and read-out, respectively.

It follows directly from the above statements that hysteresis is essential in any device used for information storage (curve *c* in Fig. 13-1). It can be a natural property of the device, as in the ferromagnetic cores or in various ferroelectric dielectrics, or it can be simulated by the use of diodes and energy-storage elements, as discussed in Sec. 2-9. Bistable multivibrators, constructed either with tubes or transistors or with the two-terminal negative-resistance devices of Chap. 11, also exhibit hysteresis, and as we know, the state of these circuits is controlled by input triggers.

As an example, consider the multivibrator of Fig. 13-2. Assuming that it is initially in the 0 state (T_2 off and T_1 on), the voltage at the grid of T_1 is positive, limited primarily by the resistive loading of the conducting grid. R_1, R_3, and the positive grid resistance form a resistive summing network. T_1 cannot be turned off and T_2 on until the external input e_1 is negative enough to bring the grid voltage to below zero, i.e., to bring the operating point to point A in Fig. 13-2. Regeneration then causes the jump to point B. Even if e_1 is made more negative, it will have no further influence over e_2. When the input trigger is removed, the output finally stabilizes at point 1. The right-hand portion of the

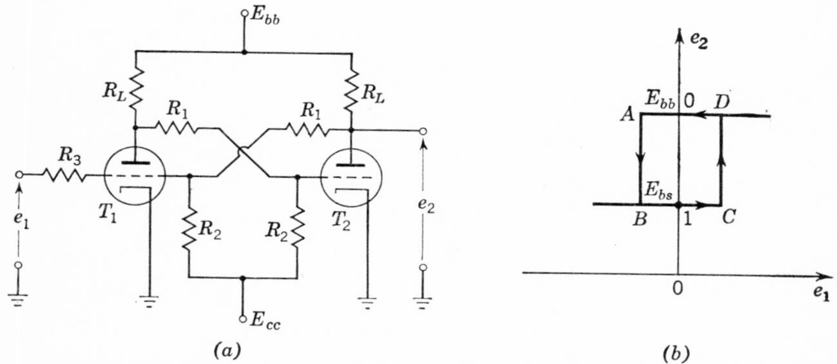

FIG. 13-2. Bistable multivibrator and input-output transfer characteristic illustrating hysteresis.

hysteresis curve is traced upon the application of a positive read-out pulse, which resets the multivibrator to state 0.

Among the disadvantages of multivibrators for use as memory elements is their large size. Even when using transistors, the sheer bulk of the units needed to store 10,000 or 20,000 bits of information would force us to turn to some other storage device. Furthermore, since each multivibrator always has one element conducting, a large bank of them requires an excessive amount of power. Any failure in the power supply would automatically erase the stored information. For the above reasons, the use of multivibrators is restricted to systems requiring only a small memory capacity and to subsidiary registers in the larger computers.

13-2. Ferromagnetic Properties. In order to explain, even cursorily, the salient features of the B-H curve of Fig. 13-3, we shall start with a microscopic region and increase our range until it encompasses the whole core. There exist, within the material, small domains where all the atomic magnetic moments are aligned in some preferred direction. At room temperature iron has six and nickel has eight easy directions of magnetization which are related to the crystal structure. Separating the domains are walls composed of atoms whose moments are skew to the principal direction. Since, from a macroscopic viewpoint, the distribution of magnetic moments is random, the material is normally unmagnetized.

An external field increases the area of those domains magnetized in its direction and causes the contraction of those that have other magnetic moments. As the excitation is increased, portions of the walls become

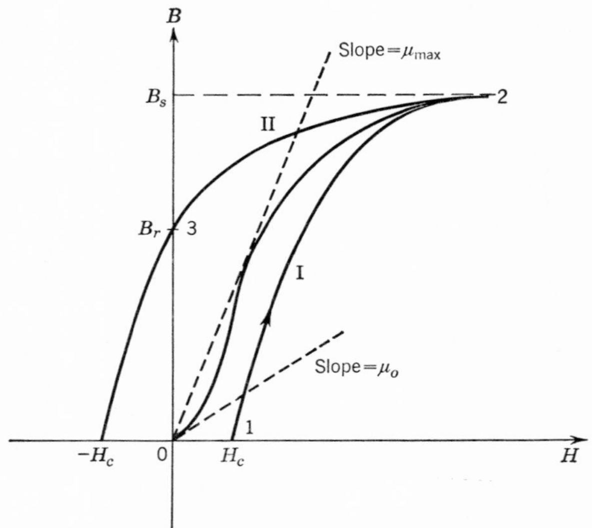

FIG. 13-3. Portion of the magnetization curve, showing some of the important constants of the material.

unstable, jumping to the direction of forced orientation. The finite field required to produce this change results in the hysteresis shown in Fig. 13-3. When all the atomic moments are essentially in alignment, we say that the material is saturated; it then supports a magnetic flux density B_s.

The presence of the external field is necessary to maintain the alignment of the magnetic domains. After the excitation is removed, they relax to the nearest easy direction of magnetization. Instead of the original random orientation, there now exists a component of flux in the direction of the applied field, and this is called the remanence B_r. To completely demagnetize the material, we must apply a reverse field that will overcome the internal coercive force H_c.

One important factor used to relate the field and flux is the magnetic permeability,

$$\mu = \frac{\Delta B}{\Delta H} \tag{13-1}$$

which is not a constant, but increases from a low value near the origin to a maximum near the peak of the magnetization curve, decreasing as the core finally saturates. Even though B_s, B_r, H_c, and σ (the volume conductivity) are also needed for a complete description, μ_{max} serves as a convenient measure of the magnetic quality. Those materials having a high permeability almost always have a narrow hysteresis loop. For example, iron, which has a maximum permeability of 5,000, requires a

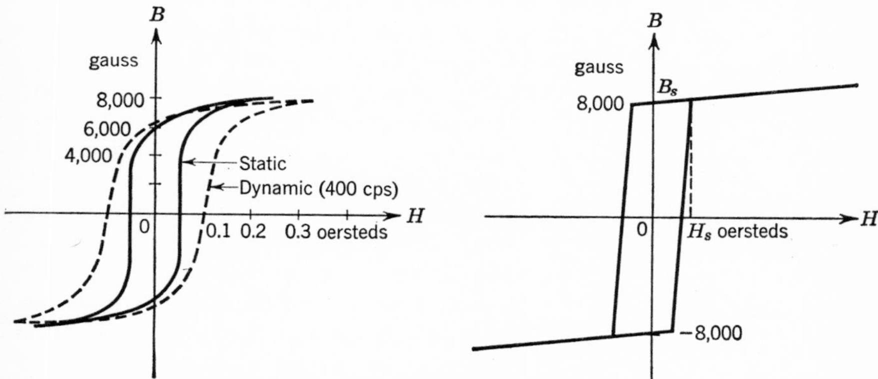

FIG. 13-4. Typical hysteresis curves and equivalent static piecewise-linear representation (4-79 Mo Permalloy).

magnetizing force of 3.2 oersteds to develop the saturation flux density of 16,000 gauss. A high-permeability alloy, such as Permalloy (79 per cent nickel, 17 per cent iron, and 4 per cent molybdenum), may have a maximum μ of 100,000 or higher. This material would saturate at a flux density of close to 8,000 gauss, when the field strength is approximately 0.1 oersted. It has a coercive force of 0.05 oersted and a retentivity of 6,000 gauss. Note that the hysteresis loop of this second sample (Fig. 13-4) begins to approach a rectangle, so much so that it becomes valid to approximate the curve in the piecewise-linear manner shown.

The above discussion was based on the response either to direct current or to relatively low frequencies where the flux in the core has time to build up to the maximum value permissible with the applied excitation. If the dynamic hysteresis loop were to be plotted by using a very-high-frequency excitation signal, then the area of loop, which represents the losses, would be greatly increased. This effect is noticeable even at 400 cycles (Fig. 13-4).

In pulse applications we are interested, not in the steady state, but in the much more complicated transient *B-H* response. With any suddenly applied magnetization force H_a, we should expect an immediate flux density B_a. It would not be present. The *H* field must produce the alignment of the magnetic domains before the flux given by the *B-H* curve can be sustained. In addition, the *H* field propagates from the surface into the core with a finite velocity. Initially, only the surface layer contributes, and therefore the effective μ is an extremely small percentage of the final value. It will, of course, increase as the flux builds up toward steady state.

Both the coercive force and the retentive field are structural properties, depending on such factors as grain orientation and microscopic imperfections, i.e., voids and inclusions. If, in working the magnetic alloy, the grain size is controlled and aligned to favor one easy direction of magnetization, μ_{max} can be greatly increased. One method used to produce almost square loop materials (Fig. 13-5) is to cool the hot-rolled sheet slowly in a hydrogen atmosphere with the magnetic field applied in the direction of rolling. The high permeability is measured only in the direction of grain orientation. To obtain the full advantage, the thin tapes produced are wound into toroidal cores. Deltamax (50 per cent nickel and 50 per cent iron), which has a maximum permeability of 70,000, has a squareness factor (B_r/B_s) of 0.98.

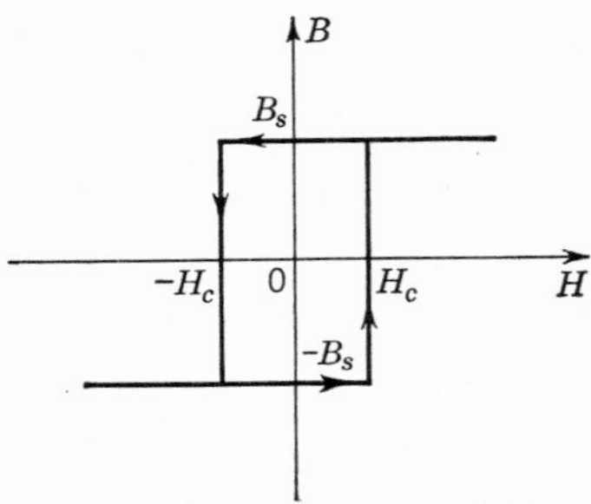

FIG. 13-5. Square hysteresis loop such as found in a tape-wound toroidal core of Deltamax.

Energy must be supplied to the excitation coil to overcome the losses involved in establishing and aligning the magnetic domains. The input per unit volume required to switch between two points on the hysteresis loop is given by

$$w = \oint_{H_1}^{H_2} H\, dB \tag{13-2}$$

The terminal characteristics of the coil depend on the amount of stored, and hence recoverable, energy. In switching from point 1 to 2 in Fig. 13-3, the net energy supplied is proportional to the area between branch I and the *B* axis. Once the excitation is removed, the operating point traverses segment II from point 2 to 3. Only the energy represented by the small area between branch II and the *B* axis is recoverable. The area of the hysteresis loop lying in the first quadrant represents the dissipated power, and consequently the resistive component of the terminal characteristic.

In square-loop materials (Fig. 13-5), all the supplied energy is dissipated and none can be recovered. We thus interpret the driving-point characteristic of the core as that of a nonlinear resistance. Since this case is of great interest, it will be considered in some detail below.

Ferrites. Some of the disadvantages of the thin-strip cores have been overcome by the use of various molded ceramic semiconductors. These materials, such as $NiO \cdot Fe_2O_3$ (nickel ferrite) or $MgO \cdot Fe_2O_3$ (magnesium ferrite), have a much lower electric conductivity and consequently lower losses. The nature of the material is such that the domain switching time would be much less than that of the tape cores. Even though the maximum permeability is small ($\mu_{max} = 1{,}000$), it is almost independent of frequency. The easily fabricated square-loop ferrite cores, of almost any desired configuration, are widely used in high-speed memory arrays and switching circuits.

13-3. Terminal Response of Cores. Before we can make use of cores in specific circuits, we must know their terminal response to various excitations. We have seen that this is a function of both the core geometry and the shape of the hysteresis loop. Because the general problem is quite complex, our discussion will concentrate on a square-loop core of relatively simple geometry. The core of Fig. 13-6 is constructed by winding a thin tape of grain-oriented magnetic material on a bobbin. By making the following assumptions the subsequent analysis will be greatly simplified.

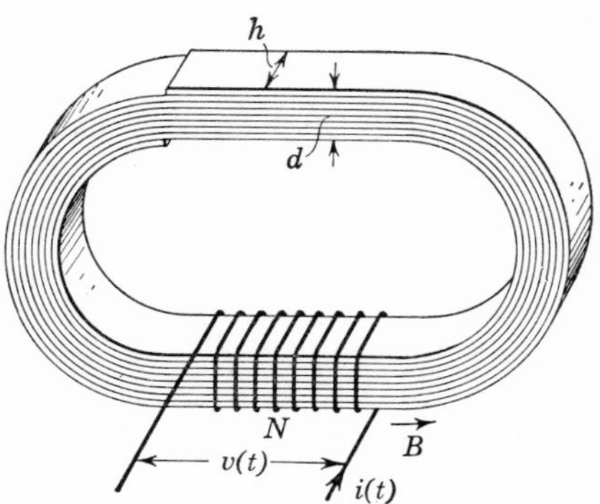

FIG. 13-6. Tape-wound core.

1. At every point the radius of curvature is large compared with the thickness d. In any small region the core may be treated as an infinitely long plane sheet and the geometry reduces to two dimensions.

2. The width h is much greater than the thickness d. Fringe effects may be ignored. Consequently the excitation can be assumed to be a current sheet flowing on the outer and inner surfaces of the core.

3. The hysteresis loop is perfectly rectangular. It follows that the core, which is initially magnetized to $-B_s$, switches to $+B_s$ as the H field propagates from the surface toward the center.

4. Because of the symmetry, the field will penetrate at equal rates from both the inside and outside of the core.

Once the magnetic field is established on the surface of the core, it creates the domain wall, which propagates toward the center, dividing the region having a flux density of $+B_s$ from that at $-B_s$. Throughout the complete material, the flux will have one of these two values. Only across the domain wall will there be any change of flux with respect to either time or space. Figure 13-7 illustrates the conditions in the core before the field penetrates to the center and completes the switch in the saturation direction.

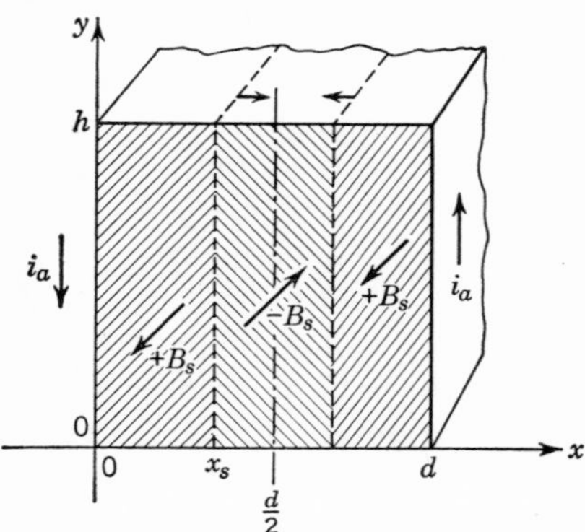

FIG. 13-7. Cross section of the core illustrating the flux penetration and the direction of the current flow.

Response to a Known Voltage Excitation. The terminal voltage response of the excitation coil is given by

$$v(t) = N \frac{d\Phi}{dt} = 2Nh \frac{d}{dt} \int_0^{d/2} B\, dx \tag{13-3}$$

But from Fig. 13-7, we see that

$$\int_0^{d/2} B\, dx = B_s x_s - B_s \left(\frac{d}{2} - x_s \right) \tag{13-4}$$

and consequently

$$v(t) = 4NhB_s \frac{dx_s}{dt} \tag{13-5}$$

Solving Eq. (13-5) yields the spacial variation of the domain wall in terms of the known voltage excitation.

$$x_s(t) = \frac{\int_0^t v(\tau)\, d\tau}{4NhB_s} \tag{13-6}$$

Saturation occurs when the domain wall reaches the center of the core. Setting $x_s = d/2$, we obtain

$$\int_0^{t_s} v(\tau)\, d\tau = 2NB_s hd = 2NB_s A \tag{13-7}$$

where A = cross-section area, m²
B_s = saturation flux density, webers/m²

Equation (13-7) states that the time required for the complete reversal of the core state depends on the volt-time area of the applied voltage signal. Regardless of waveshape, equal area signals will result in equal switching times. Or expressing this result in another way, under ideal conditions a volt-time area greater than that given by Eq. (13-7) cannot be sustained across the excitation coil.

In the special case where $v(t)$ is a constant V, Eq. (13-6) reduces to

$$x_s(t) = \frac{Vt}{4NhB_s}$$

and we can see that the domain wall propagates at a constant velocity from the surface to the center. The time required for complete saturation is

$$t_s = \frac{2NAB_s}{V} \tag{13-8}$$

In order to calculate the current flow, we turn to Maxwell's equations. Because of the simple geometry, they reduce to

$$\frac{\partial H}{\partial x} = -\sigma E \tag{13-9}$$

$$\frac{\partial E}{\partial x} = -\frac{\partial B}{\partial t} \tag{13-10}$$

where E = electric field intensity
σ = volume conductivity of the core material

From Eqs. (13-10), (13-4), and (13-5),

$$E(t) = -\frac{d}{dt}\int_0^{d/2} B\,dx = -2B_s\frac{dx_s}{dt} = -\frac{v(t)}{2Nh} \tag{13-11}$$

The presence of $E(t)$ results in an eddy-current flow in the excited portion of the core. This current may be considered as establishing a retarding field which limits the time rate of flux reversal.

B is constant everywhere except across the domain wall. Hence the spatial variation of the electric field must be zero everywhere except at $x = x_s$. In the center of the core, where the magnetic field has not as yet penetrated, $E(t)$ will be zero ($x > x_s$). For $x < x_s$, the electric field will be given by Eq. (13-11). Since E is constant with respect to x, H must decrease linearly from the surface value $H_a(t)$ to the coercive force H_c, at $x = x_s$. It follows that Eq. (13-9) may be rewritten as

$$\frac{H_a(t) - H_c}{x_s} = 2\sigma B_s\frac{dx_s}{dt} = \frac{\sigma v(t)}{2Nh} \tag{13-12}$$

where H equals Ni/l, amp-turns/m, in the mks system.

Substituting $B_s\,dx_s/dt$ and x_s, as given by Eqs. (13-5) and (13-6), into Eq. (13-12), we obtain the solution for the terminal current due to the known voltage excitation.

$$i_a(t) = \frac{\sigma l v(t)}{8N^3h^2B_s} \int_0^t v(\tau)\, d\tau + I_c \tag{13-13}$$

The first term in Eq. (13-13) is the total eddy-current flow in the core; the second term corresponds to the current needed to overcome the internal coercive force. We might note that the higher the conductivity of the ferromagnetic material, the greater the core loss. If the applied voltage is a constant, the current will increase linearly with time as shown in Fig. 13-8.

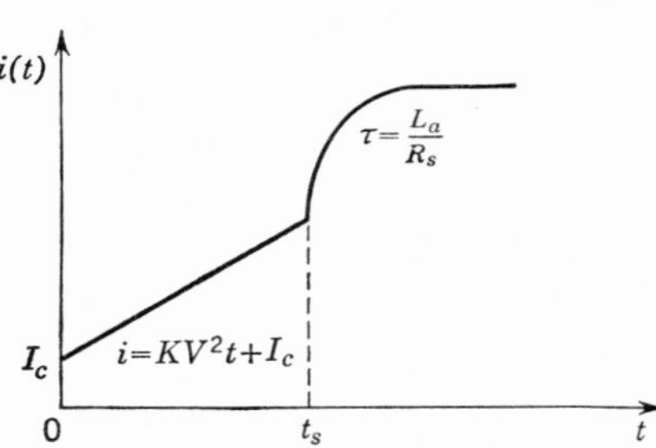

FIG. 13-8. Terminal current response of a square-loop core to a constant-voltage excitation.

$$i_a(t) = \frac{\sigma l}{8N^3h^2B_s} V^2 t + I_c$$

After the core saturates, the current will continue to increase, but at a rate controlled by the inductance of the driving coil in air, its winding resistance, and the internal resistance of the voltage source.

We might further note that the constant-current term in Eq. (13-13), due to the coercive force, may be treated as a separate bias generator in parallel with a postulated ideal core (zero-width hysteresis loop). This leads to the conclusion that the response of the core may be represented schematically by the models of Fig. 13-9.

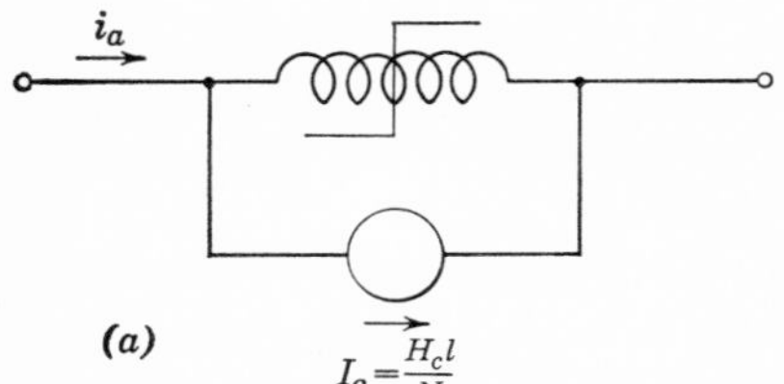

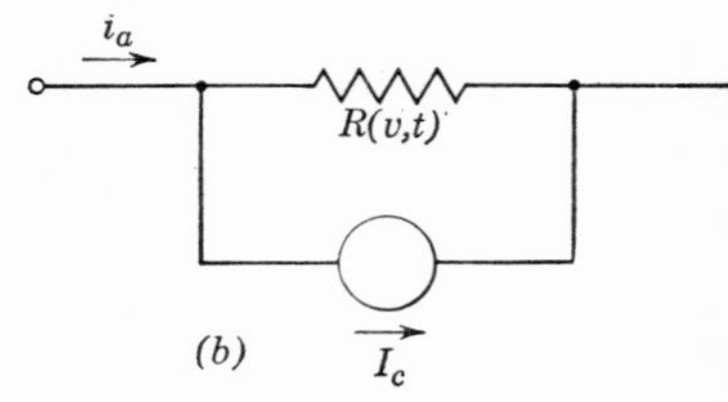

FIG. 13-9. Proposed equivalent model representations for the square-loop core.

Response to a Known Current Excitation. As our starting point, we shall solve Eq. (13-12) for the location of the domain wall in terms of the applied magnetic field.

$$x_s(t) = \sqrt{\frac{1}{\sigma B_s} \int_0^t [H_a(\tau) - H_c]\, d\tau} \tag{13-14}$$

Substituting $x_s(t)$ back into Eq. (13-12) yields

$$v(t) = \frac{2Nh[H_a(t) - H_c]\sqrt{B_s}}{\sqrt{\sigma \int_0^t [H_a(\tau) - H_c]\, d\tau}} \tag{13-15}$$

When the input is a constant current I_a, the terminal voltage and the saturation time are given by

$$v(t) = \sqrt{\frac{4h^2N^3B_s(I_a - I_c)}{\sigma l t}} \tag{13-16}$$

$$t_s = \frac{\sigma l B_s d^2}{4N(I_a - I_c)} \tag{13-17}$$

According to Eq. (13-16), the terminal voltage must be infinite at $t = 0$. This impossible solution is a result of the assumed ideal core characteristics. In practice, a finite time must elapse before the domain wall is established. Furthermore, the stray capacity present also limits the time rate of voltage build-up. The actual response will look like the dashed rather than the solid line of Fig. 13-10. After the core saturates at $t = t_s$, the two terminals should appear to be a short circuit and the voltage should drop to zero. However, the large series impedance of the current source together with the small air inductance of the driving coil actually produces the fast exponential decay shown.

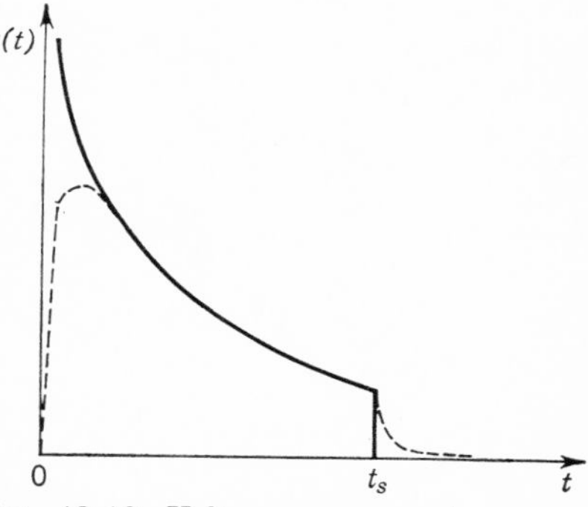

FIG. 13-10. Voltage response to a constant-current excitation of the core.

From Eq. (13-17), we can see that an external excitation of I_c would not allow the core to saturate until an infinite time had elapsed. The larger the excess of current over the internal bias value, the faster the core will switch between the two saturation values. Here also the coercive force may be treated as an external bias generator as shown in Fig. 13-9.

Response of an Externally Loaded Core. The voltage appearing across a load R connected to a secondary winding of N_2 turns is

$$v_R(t) = N_2 v(t)$$

where $v(t)$ is the terminal voltage developed across the excitation winding. An additional retarding field of

$$H_2(t) = \frac{N_2^2 v(t)}{Rl} \tag{13-18}$$

is produced by the current flow in R. $H_2(t)$ acts in the same direction as the internal coercive field, and it is simply added to H_c in all the integral and differential equations previously derived.

In the case where the applied voltage is a known function of time, the input current given by Eq. (13-13) would include, on the right-hand side, the term

$$i_R = \frac{N_2 v(t)}{R}$$

On the other hand, when a known current waveshape is used for excitation, the time-varying H_2 must be included inside the integral sign. The voltage response would have to be recalculated from Maxwell's equations. We would find that the smaller the effective load resistance, the larger the additional retarding field and the longer the time required to switch the core's state.

From an examination of the final response to both constant-voltage and constant-current excitation [Eqs. (13-13) and (13-16)], we see that the nonsaturated core might be approximated by a nonlinear resistance of the form

$$R_c = \frac{K}{tv(t)} \tag{13-19}$$

in parallel with the current generator I_c (Fig. 13-9). K has one value for constant-current excitation and yet another value when a step of voltage is applied.

The total resistance seen at the driving terminal is the parallel combination of the time-and-voltage-dependent core resistance R_c and the reflected load resistance.

$$R_{\text{in}} = R\left(\frac{N}{N_2}\right)^2 \parallel R_c \qquad \text{at } t = 0,\ R_c = \infty,\ R_{\text{in}} = \left(\frac{N}{N_2}\right)^2 R$$

The now finite resistance limits the initial value of the voltage. The parallel combination is always smaller than the input resistance of the unloaded core, and consequently the voltage produced by a constant-current drive will be less than that found in Eq. (13-16). In fact, if $R(N/N_2)^2 \ll R_c$ over the complete time and voltage range of interest, then the input resistance would remain essentially constant and a rectangular voltage pulse would be the result of a constant-current excitation. Since the switching time is controlled by the volt-time area [Eq. (13-7)], the external loading will have the adverse effect of increasing t_s.

To a good approximation, the ferromagnetic core can be considered to be a reasonably large resistance when it is unsaturated and a very small resistance (practically a short circuit) when saturated. It thus acts as a bivalued circuit element with, however, its switching action dependent on its own past history. If multiple windings are available, then the current flow in one can be used to control the terminal response at the others. For example, by alternately reflecting a high and a low resistance into the transmission path, the magnetic-circuit element can replace the diode bridge of Sec. 3-6 for use as a controlled gate (Fig. 13-16).

A Note on Units. The parameters of the ferromagnetic sample are usually expressed in the electromagnetic units (emu) of oersteds (H) and gauss (B). However, all equations used and derived are given in mks units. The important conversion factors are:

	Symbol	Emu	Mks
Magnetizing force..........	H	Oersteds $\times$ $10^3/4\pi$	Amp-turns/m
Flux....................	Φ	Maxwells $\times$ 10^{-8}	Webers
Flux density..............	B	Gauss $\times$ 10^{-4}	Webers/m^2
Permeability..............	μ	Gauss/oersted $\times$ $4\pi \times 10^{-7}$	Henrys/m

Example 13-1. In this example we shall compare the current response of two cores to an excitation of 20 volts. The first core is toroidally wound on a ½-in.-diameter form of 20 turns of 1-mil-thick 0.25-in.-wide Permalloy tape. The second core is a molded ceramic ferrite of the same size. Both cores have a 20-turn excitation winding.

	B_s, gauss	B_r, gauss	H_c, oersteds	ρ,* μohm-cm
Permalloy.........	8,000	7,200	0.07	55
Ferrite...........	4,500	3,400	0.18	10^5

*ρ is the volume resistivity, the reciprocal of the volume conductivity σ.

Solution. (*a*) The first step in the solution is the conversion of the mixed units given in the statement of the problem into the mks system, using the conversion factors given above. The parameters of Permalloy are $H_c = 5.56$ amp-turns/m, $B_s = 0.8$ weber, and $\rho = 55 \times 10^{-4}$ ohm-m. Expressing the dimensions in meters and substituting into the appropriate form of Eq. (13-13) results in

$$i_a(t) = 1.45 \times 10^3 t + 1.16 \times 10^{-2} \qquad \text{amp}$$

From Eq. (13-8) the saturation time of the Permalloy core is

$$t_s = 5.18 \ \mu\text{sec}$$

At the end of the switching interval the coil current has increased to

$$i_a(t_s) = 7.6 + 11.6 \text{ ma}$$

where the first term in the above expression is the eddy-current flow and the second is due to the coercive force. We might note that the low conductivity of the Permalloy sample results in relatively large eddy currents. This means that additional power is dissipated during the switching interval above and beyond that necessary to overcome the coercive force.

(*b*) We shall assume that the results derived for a tape-wound core apply equally well to the sintered ferrite core. They actually do not, but the answers obtained are on the correct order of magnitude and may be used for comparison. The solution of Eq. (13-13), for this sample, is

$$i_a(t) = 1.41t + 4.1 \times 10^{-2} \qquad \text{amp}$$

The ferrite core switches state in only 2.9 μsec. Hence the peak current flow becomes

$$i_a(t_s) = 4.1 \times 10^{-3} + 41 \text{ ma}$$

Because of the much higher resistivity of the ferrite sample, the eddy current of 4.1 μa is completely negligible. However, because of the large coercive force, the required driving current is still larger than that found for the Permalloy core.

13-4. Magnetic Counters. The basic magnetic counter of Fig. 13-11 consists of two components: the core itself where the count is registered by the change in the magnetic state and an energy-storage element which automatically resets the core after the required count has been entered. One of the more common applications of this circuit is as a binary, where one output pulse is produced for every two inputs. In this respect the magnetic counter behaves similarly to the vacuum-tube or transistor bistable circuits of Chap. 9. The circuit of Fig. 13-11 does offer one major advantage in that no power is required to sustain the excited state.

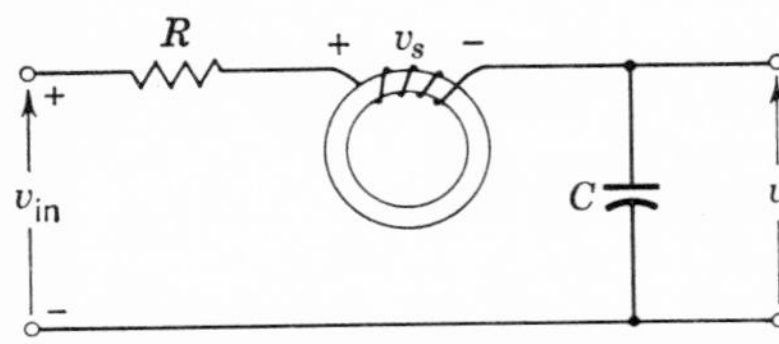

FIG. 13-11. Basic magnetic-core counter.

So that we may make use of the results of Sec. 13-3, we shall assume that the core is constructed of perfect square-loop material. In its unexcited condition, it is at $-B_s$; we shall call this state 0. A positive input pulse drives it toward $+B_s$ (state 1). The differential equation describing the response to the applied excitation is

$$v_{in} = Ri + \frac{1}{C}\int i\,dt + v_s \tag{13-20}$$

where v_s is the voltage drop across the coil.

In Sec. 13-3 we have seen that the core appears to be a very high resistance during the interval when it is switching from 0 to 1 or from 1 to 0. Since R is the small series combination of the input-source impedance and the winding resistance of the coil, almost the full excitation voltage will be developed across the driving coil. Equation (13-20) reduces to $v_{in} = v_s$. Hence the initial response is due to the known voltage excitation of the core and the current is given by Eq. (13-13). Until such time as the core saturates, the very small output may be approximated by

$$v_o(t) = \frac{1}{C}\int i\,dt$$

In the special case of a constant-amplitude pulse, this reduces to

$$v_o(t) = \frac{1}{C}(KV^2t^2 + I_ct) \tag{13-21}$$

where K is evaluated with the aid of Eq. (13-13).

The volt-time area of each input pulse $V\,\Delta t$ is adjusted so that the core state will not reverse completely. The first one primes the core, leaving it in the partially magnetized condition corresponding to point a in Fig. 13-12a. After the pulse terminates, the capacitor discharges through the high coil resistance. But since only a small amount of charge was stored when the pulse was present, the demagnetization path follows the dashed line in Fig. 13-12a from a to b.

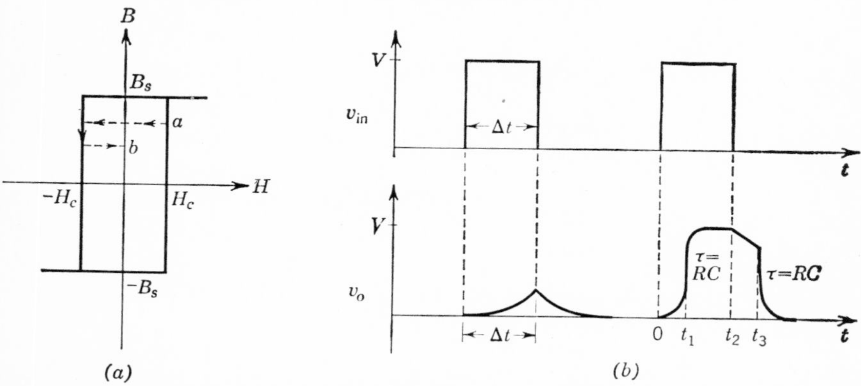

FIG. 13-12. Response of the counter of Fig. 13-11. (a) Hysteresis curve showing the partial demagnetization during the discharge of the first pulse; (b) excitation pulses and the resultant output.

The primed core also looks like a high resistance to the first portion of the second pulse. Consequently, in the interval from 0 to t_1 (Fig. 13-12b), the output will be given by Eq. (13-21). Once the core saturates at $+B_s$, its terminal response is that of a short circuit. The capacitor continues charging toward V with the small time constant RC. It is only here that a large amount of energy may be stored in C in a short time interval. It follows that R must be kept as small as possible. Otherwise the single output pulse, which represents the count of two (Fig. 13-12b), may never even reach V.

At the end of the second pulse, the core is left in state 1. But as the capacitor starts discharging from its peak voltage V, the reverse current flowing in the driving coil switches the core back to state **0**. Any energy remaining after the core resaturates at $-B_s$ is dissipated in the series resistance R. This portion of the cycle is identified by the double-segmented decay waveshape shown in Fig. 13-12b. The interval from

t_2 to t_3 represents the flux reversal, and the remaining portion shows the final discharge of C. To ensure the automatic reset after every second input, the energy stored in C must be greater than that dissipated in the core and the series resistance. Neglecting the small power loss in the series resistance, we obtain the necessary inequality

$$\tfrac{1}{2}CV^2 \geq 2B_sH_cAl$$

or

$$C \geq \frac{4B_sH_cAl}{V^2} \tag{13-22}$$

If Eq. (13-22) is not satisfied, then the discharge of C will not completely reset the core to state 0. The next applied pulse starts the switching process from a partially excited condition. It may even drive the core directly to state 1, leading to a false count at the output.

We conclude that the core in the magnetic counter acts as a controlled-series gate, with its bivalued state dependent on its own past history.

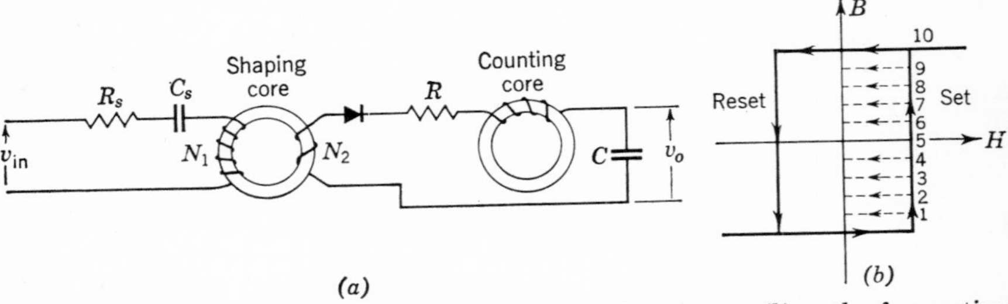

FIG. 13-13. (a) An arbitrary base counter using a pulse shaper; (b) path of operation followed in a scale-of-10 counter.

When unsaturated, it acts as a high series resistance which prevents the charging of the storage capacitor. After the core finally saturates, its resistance drops to zero, thus closing the charging path.

Counting to an Arbitrary Base. If the volt-time area of the input pulse is carefully controlled, then this same circuit may be used to count down by an arbitrary factor. Assuming that the minor hysteresis loops are also reasonably square, each input pulse shifts the core state in discrete jumps along the hysteresis curve, as shown in Fig. 13-13b. The final excitation produces saturation and resetting. For example, a scale-of-10 counter will result when each input pulse has a volt-time area that is slightly more than one-tenth of the total needed to reverse the saturation direction. The extra area of each pulse causes the core to saturate near the beginning of the tenth input and consequently permits the storage of the reset energy in C during the final count.

Provided that the input signal is larger than the minimum necessary to switch the core state, the volt-time area of the signal developed across a secondary winding will depend solely on the turns ratio and the core properties [Eq. (13-17)]. Only in the unsaturated condition does the ferromagnetic device act as a transformer; once it saturates, the driving voltage will be developed across the series resistance instead of across the low input impedance. This means that a second core may be used to shape the variable input pulses to a constant area. The charge stored in C_s in Fig. 13-13a serves to reset the shaping core after each pulse. The diode determines the polarity of those applied to the counting core; it prevents the reset pulse of the input core from registering as a negative count in the storage core.

Cascading Counters. In order to achieve higher counts than are possible with a single core, the output of one stage may be coupled to a second, and so on. Each core represents the appropriate binary or decimal place. Because of the difficulty in reading the counts corresponding to the unsaturated states of the core (numbers between 1 and 9), most cascaded counters use a binary rather than a decimal base.

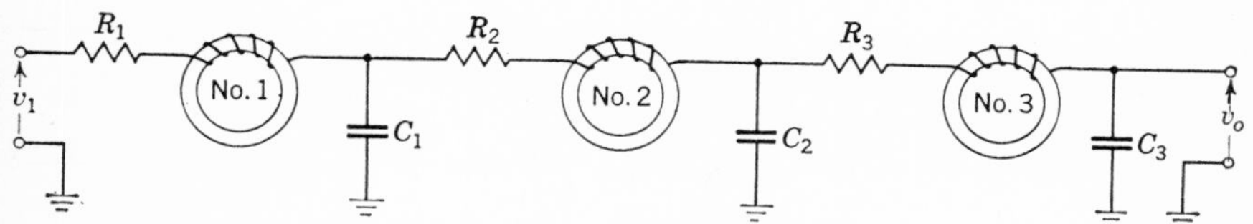

FIG. 13-14. Three-stage cascaded counter.

When several counters are directly coupled, as shown in Fig. 13-14, the single input must be able to supply the energy needed to reset all cores simultaneously. Consider the operation when the three cores are in state 1 (just below saturation) and the count is $1 \times 2^0 + 1 \times 2^1 + 1 \times 2^2$, reading from left to right. The eighth pulse saturates core 1, and as C_1 charges, core 2 saturates, and so on, until finally C_3 is also fully charged. Thus we see that the volt-time area of the input pulse must be able to change the state of all cores and that it must also supply the energy that will reset all three cores.

If more than two or three stages are cascaded, they may impose a severe load on the signal source. Consequently, an active regenerative circuit is usually included within the transmission path to decouple and to reshape the transmitted pulse. These circuits are discussed in Sec. 13-5.

Shift Registers. Suppose that we wish to store the digital word 10011. Since it is equivalent to

$$10011 = 1 \times 2^4 + 0 \times 2^3 + 0 \times 2^2 + 1 \times 2^1 + 1 \times 2^0$$

this word can be converted into a train of nineteen pulses, which would then be injected into five cascaded binary counters. But as this requires an additional step, it increases the possibility that an error may be introduced in the count. Moreover, if the word could be registered directly, less time would have to be allotted for storage.

When the five digits are simultaneously available, each can be steered directly to the appropriate core. This form of data processing, where only one pulse width is needed to register the information, is called parallel read-in.

On the other hand, the word 10011 may be presented in series as a time sequence (the serial input is pulse, pulse, blank, blank, pulse).

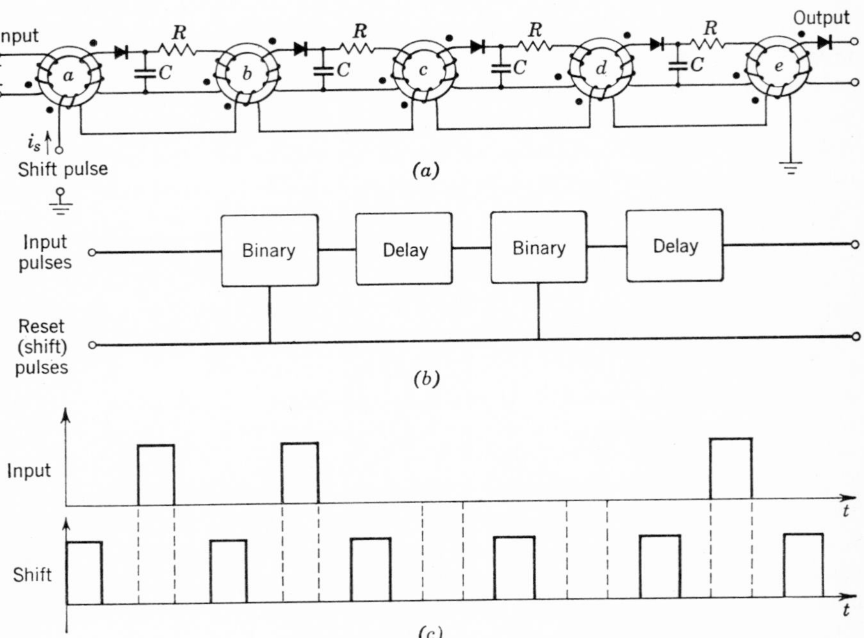

FIG. 13-15. (*a*) Magnetic-core shift register; (*b*) block diagram of any shift register; (*c*) time relationship between the input pulses (10011) and the shift pulses.

Separating each digit there is sufficient space to insert the pulses that control the switching of the shift register of Fig. 13-15*a*. The first digit, i.e., the one farthest to the right in the word to be stored, is inserted in the normal way into core *a*, changing its state from 0 to 1. The decoupling diode prevents the resulting negative output from switching the second core in the chain.

Before the next digit appears, we apply a separate shift pulse to all cores (Fig. 13-15*c*). Those that are in the primed state will be switched back to 0, while those already in the zero state will be unaffected. We see that the counter is set by the input and reset by the shift pulse. The positive voltage, which will now be developed across the output winding of the switched core, charges the storage element C. Its discharge, through R and the primary of core b, switches the second core to state 1. In order to prevent the shift pulse from interfering with the transferred digit, there must be a time delay in the forward transmission path. In the shift register of Fig. 13-15a, this delay is obtained by inserting a resistance in series with the driving coil of the core.

The next digit of the word, input digit 1, again changes the state of core a without influencing any other core. A shift pulse will now set the excited cores a and b back to zero. As both capacitors discharge, the two digits are transferred to the right, changing the states of cores b and c from 0 to 1.

The third digit of the input word is zero. After its application the state of the cores is 011– –, where the dashes represent the unknown states due to any previous excitation. A shift pulse transfers the core states to 0011–. Continuing the process of first switching the state of core a and then transferring the stored information to the right, the full word is finally registered.

Any other binary element that can be triggered on and off at two separate inputs, or with two different polarity pulses, can replace the magnetic cores in the register (Fig. 13-15b). Voltage- or current-controlled negative-resistance devices are ideally suited for use as memory elements in shift registers. If bistable multivibrators are used, a simple RC network can be used to delay the transfer until after the shift pulse terminates.

For read-out, five shift pulses will sequentially feed the stored digits to the output terminal. This process is identical with the normal shifting which transfers the input forward from core to core. In fact, as a new word is entered (starting with a shift rather than a digit pulse), the old word is automatically shifted out on the right.

One obvious disadvantage is that the stored word is erased as it is fed out for examination or use. However, if the shift register is formed into a closed loop, then the information fed out on the right can be automatically re-stored in the left-hand core. After the appropriate number of shift pulses are applied, the register again contains the original word.

A convenient means of closing the self-storage path is by way of a controlled gate such as shown in Fig. 13-16. This circuit makes use of the bivalued resistance properties of the core to interrupt or close the feedback path. During storage the gate is kept open (the gating core is in its active region) and the register functions normally. When reading out information temporarily stored, the gate is also left open. But if we desire more permanence, then the gate must be closed (core-saturated) during the intervals that the output pulses are produced. It is implicitly assumed that the amplitude of the transferred pulse will not change the state of the magnetic gate and that the reflected control signal will not register as a storage pulse.

Ring Counter. A closed-loop shift register can also be used as an arbitrary base counter. One and only one core (or binary) is set to state 1. Then as each succeeding input pulse is applied to the shift windings, the single stored digit is transferred sequentially around the loop. For example, of the 10 cores necessary in a decimal counter, initially only the zero core is excited. The first pulse transfers the single digit to core one, and so on. The tenth input switches the ninth core from 0 to 1 and resets the zero core to 1. This same voltage pulse may also be coupled to a second ring counter, which is used to indicate the next highest decimal place.

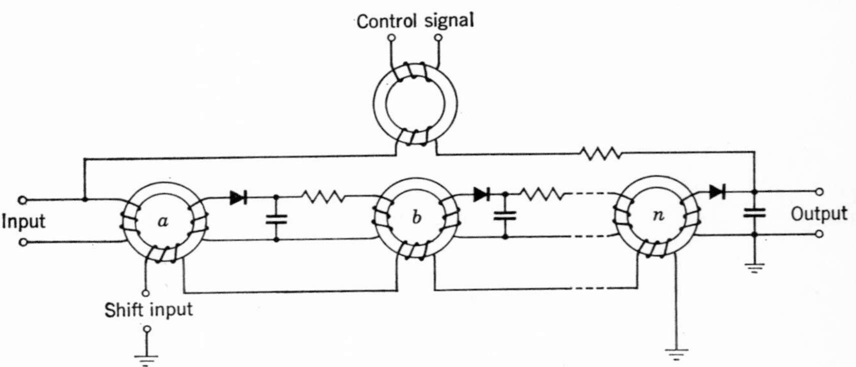

FIG. 13-16. Closed-loop shift register—a switched core used as a controlled gate.

It follows that the particular count registered is indicated by the number of the single excited core. If the volt-time area of the transfer pulse is carefully controlled, then the core can be switched from $-B_s$ to the verge of $+B_s$. In these circumstances the difference in the terminal resistance seen across an auxiliary winding readily identifies the location of the digit. In fact, if the current flow through the read-out winding is always less than I_c (so that it cannot influence the magnetization), then the individual core will act as a simple controlled gate, inserting a high resistance during the count and a low one at all other times. The gating process can, of course, be reversed by transferring a 0 rather than a 1 around the loop.

13-5. Core-transistor Counters and Registers. The number of stages which can be directly coupled in a counter or shift register is limited by the power capabilities of the pulse source. In the counter, the input must be able to switch all cores simultaneously. In the register, the shift pulse not only resets all cores but must also supply the energy that transfers the stored information to the right. And since the switching time depends on the excess of magnetizing current over the coercive force [Eq. (13-17)], the problem is further complicated when the counting speed becomes critical. For example, in order to switch a typical core in a 250-kc register, the 1-μsec shift pulse applied must have a peak power of almost 1 watt. The 330-ma pulse current will develop an average of 3 volts—and a peak which may be many times as large—across the shift coil. Under these conditions we can expect a single transistor amplifier to switch, at the most, three or four stages.

One obvious means of improving the response is to use an amplifier to decouple the individual cores. An even better way is by inserting a regenerative circuit between two cores; the output of the first core can be made to trigger the generation of a fast-rising high-power pulse for propagation in the forward direction.

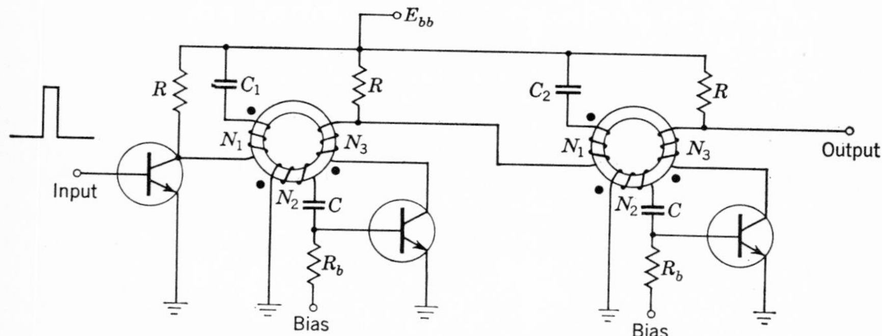

FIG. 13-17. Cascaded counter using a transistor blocking oscillator for regeneration and a core for storage. The input amplifier stage is also shown.

Figure 13-17 shows a counter which is a happy combination of a core and a transistor. This circuit employs a single core both as a memory (winding N_1) and as a transformer for the blocking oscillator. Besides the economy in using one rather than two cores, the sharing improves the response because the oscillator pulse also resets the counter. In the normal state the core is at 0 and the transistor is cut off by the external bias. The first pulse brings the core to the verge of saturation, and the second one saturates it and charges C_1. With the transformer connections shown, these input pulses act in a direction that keeps the transistor off.

After the termination of the second input, the voltage across N_1 reverses as C_1 starts discharging. This pulse, coupled to N_2, brings the transistor into its active region. And as the regenerative circuit goes through one complete cycle, the extra energy supplied by the collector current rapidly returns the core to state 0.

In the counter of Fig. 13-17, the functions of regeneration and storage are separately handled by the transistor and the core. The active element is operative only during the reset interval. At all other times, the passive core controls the circuit behavior. The capacitor only triggers the regenerative circuit; it does not have to supply the energy for reswitching. Hence the restrictions on C are much less severe, and this circuit will recover much faster than those depending only on the stored charge for reset.

From which point in the circuit shall we take the output? If the collector is chosen, all the transformed input pulses will also be coupled to the next stage. However, as these are of the opposite polarity to the pulse produced by the blocking oscillator, a series diode will prevent them from registering falsely at the next core. This diode may be eliminated if the output is taken at the junction of the collector resistor and the transformer winding, as shown in Fig. 13-17. Here the cutoff transistor effectively replaces the decoupling diode.

As an alternative, the output may be taken from a fourth winding on the core. Since the switching during recovery is between the two saturation levels, this pulse would have the stabilized volt-time area which is especially necessary when counting to a base other than 2. By properly choosing the turns ratio, the output volt-time area can be adjusted to any desired percentage of the reset pulse. This avoids the use of a separate core for shaping the counting pulses that are applied to the next stage.

If, instead, the fourth winding is used as an input for the shift pulses, then the train of cores and transistors will function as a shift register. When the core is in the zero state, the low impedance offered to the shift input will not permit the development of a pulse large enough to bring the transistor out of cutoff. After the information pulse primes the core, the opposite acting shift pulse can trigger the regenerative circuit. During reset, the previously stored information is transferred one position to the right.

13-6. Magnetic Memory Arrays. Figure 13-18 illustrates the arrangement of a compact large-capacity memory unit. We shall assume that each of the 25 small ferrite cores exhibits the ideal square-loop properties of Fig. 13-19. Before information is stored by changing its state, the individual core is saturated at $-B_s$. Three insulated leads thread the core: one passes through each row, a second through each column, and a third threads the complete array.

Suppose that we wish to switch the state of the single core 34, located at $x = 3$ and $y = 4$. Positive current pulses of amplitude I_a are simultaneously applied to row 3 and column 4. The total field in the core located at the intersection of the excited row and column (due to $2I_a$) must cause switching. However, as all other excited cores should remain

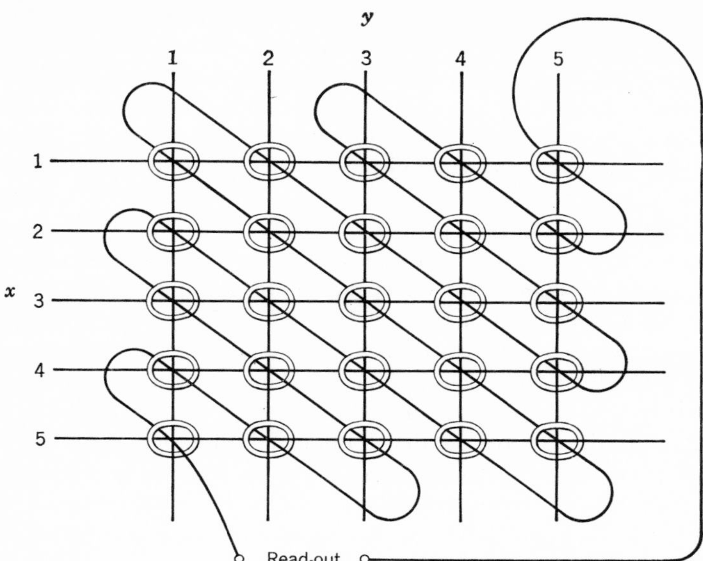

FIG. 13-18. A 5 × 5 magnetic-core coincident memory.

in their original state, the pulse amplitude must satisfy

$$\tfrac{1}{2}I_c < I_a < I_c \qquad (13\text{-}23)$$

Only core 34 is excited past H_c (to point $2H_a$ in Fig. 13-19). All the other cores in the row and column have a field strength of only H_a; after the termination of the pulse they relax back to the original state. Thus the injection of the two pulses carrying the address of the core switches its state and stores the individual digit. These pulses may be directed properly with the aid of auxiliary steering cores or diode gates.

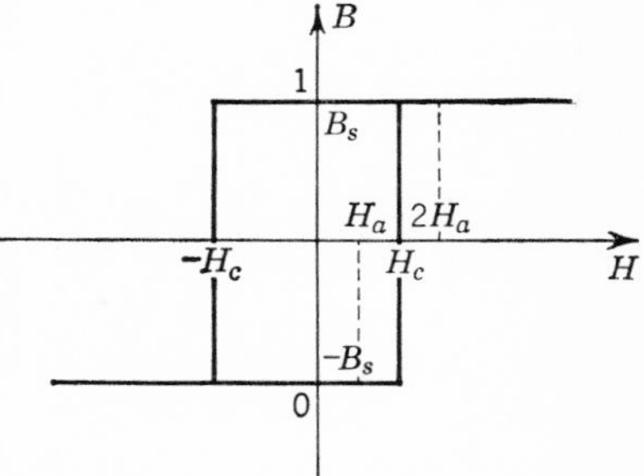

FIG. 13-19. Hysteresis loop showing excitation of switched and non-switched cores of the memory array of Fig. 13-18.

In order to read out the stored digit, the memory unit must be interrogated. To do so, negative current pulses $(-I_a)$ are injected into the appropriate row and column. If the core situated at the intersection is in an excited state, it will switch back to 0. The voltage developed during the transition appears at the terminals of the read-out winding which threads all cores (Fig. 13-18). Suppose that the particular core interrogated is in the zero state. In this case the low impedance presented would permit the development of only a very small output, which could not possibly be mistaken for a digit. Since only a single core is questioned at a time, there will not be any ambiguity as to the location of the output information.

We should note that the process of read-out is destructive; it erases the stored information. External circuitry has been devised which automatically resets the excited core. The presence of the output digit triggers the generation of a positive current pulse immediately after the termination of the negative interrogation signals. Nondestructive storage and read-out depending on special core geometries have also been devised, but a discussion of these is beyond the scope of this text.

Switching time in the array of Fig. 13-18 is on the order of 1 μsec. In order to reduce the access time, smaller cores must be used. But doing so increases the problem of wiring the large arrays needed. Instead of using individual cores, many high-speed memory units depend on switching small regions of ferrite or magnetic film. The conductors are first printed on an insulated sheet. At each "intersection" a small amount of ferrite or metallic film is deposited. Holes punched through the "core" region provide for the insertion of the read-out winding. With the small amount of magnetic materials used, switching times of 20 to 50 mμsec have been obtained. A further advantage is that this type of memory lends itself to the economical production techniques of automation.

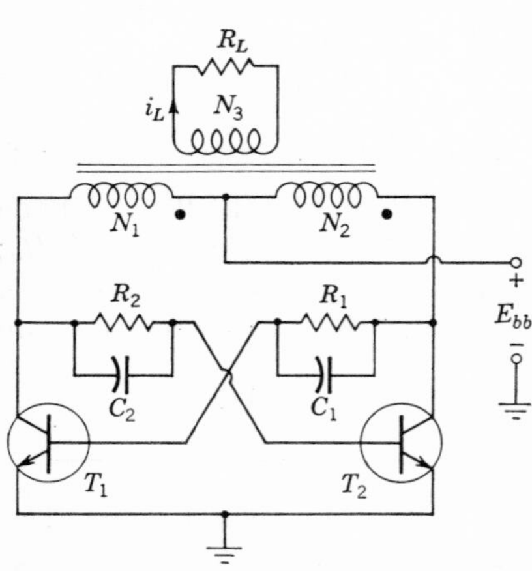

FIG. 13-20. Core-transistor multivibrator used as a d-c to d-c or a d-c to a-c converter.

13-7. Core-transistor Multivibrator. In Sec. 13-3 we have seen that the saturation time of a square-loop core, excited by a constant voltage, is very clearly defined. The abrupt change in the driving-point impedance, which marks the end of the flux build-up, permits the core to be used as the timing element in a monostable or an astable circuit.

Figure 13-20 shows a single-core multivibrator employing resistive coupling to complete the regenerative loop. In this circuit, the winding direction is such that when T_1 is saturated, the current through N_1 drives the core from $-B_s$ to $+B_s$. Current through the second winding N_2, due to saturation of T_2, resets the core state to $-B_s$. As in all astable multivibrators, the transistors furnish the greater-than-unity loop gain needed to switch between the two quasi-stable states. They become active only during the small switching interval corresponding to the saturation of the core. At all other times the individual transistor is either saturated or cut off.

We shall now detail the operation over one complete cycle, assuming, as the starting point, that T_1 is off, just turning on, and T_2 is on, just turning off. This is equivalent to saying that the core is on the verge of saturating at $-B_s$. As long as the flux is still changing, the full supply voltage will appear across the high driving-point impedance of N_2 and the collector voltage of T_2 will be approximately zero. Hence no current can flow into the base of T_1; it is cut off.

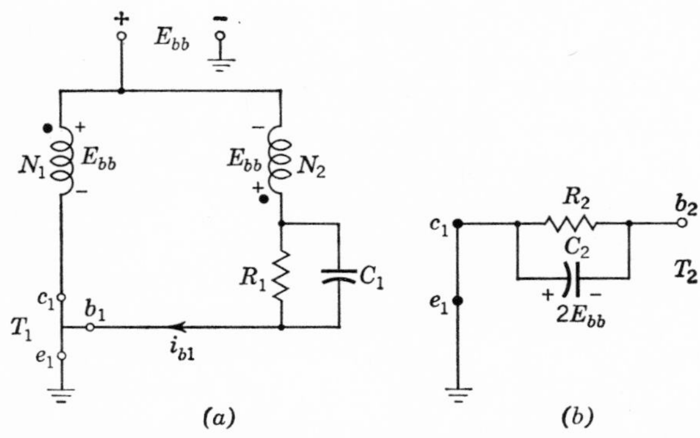

FIG. 13-21. Models holding during the change of flux density from $-B_s$ to B_s in the core of Fig. 13-20. (a) Saturated transistor T_1; (b) back-biasing of cutoff transistor T_2.

Once the core saturates, there is a marked decrease in the coil's driving-point impedance. Under these circumstances an appreciable voltage is developed across the collector-to-emitter saturation resistance of the series transistor T_2. Current can now flow into the base of the off transistor, and as T_1 turns on, the current through the winding N_1 starts the flux reversing. E_{bb} is connected across this winding, as shown in the model of Fig. 13-21*a*. The transformer action reverses the voltage across N_2. The resultant large increase in the base current of T_1 rapidly drives this transistor into saturation. At the same time, the drop in the collector voltage of T_1, coupled through the biasing and speed-up capacitor C_2, will turn T_2 off (Fig. 13-21*b*).

The time that T_1 remains saturated is controlled by the flux build-up in the core. If the small demagnetizing base current is neglected, then the core switching time, as given by Eq. (13-8), is

$$t_1 = \frac{2N_1AB_s}{E_{bb}}$$

After t_1 sec the core saturates at $+B_s$ and the circuit switches to its other quasi-stable state.

The charge stored in the speed-up capacitor aids in maintaining the base of the off transistor below zero, thus stabilizing the circuit's operation. From Fig. 13-21*a* we can see that as long as T_1 is saturated, C_1 is in series with the transformer winding N_2 and E_{bb}. When $N_1 = N_2$, C_1 will charge toward $2E_{bb}$. Meanwhile C_2 is discharging through R_2 as shown in Fig. 13-21*b*. The conditions which must be satisfied in order to sustain the base of the off transistor below zero for the full half cycle are

$$4\tau_2 > t_1 \qquad 4\tau_1 > t_2$$

where $\tau_2 = R_2C_2$ and $\tau_1 = R_1C_1$.

Suppose that C_2 is too small; will its discharge before the end of the half period cause the premature switching of this circuit? Since the base

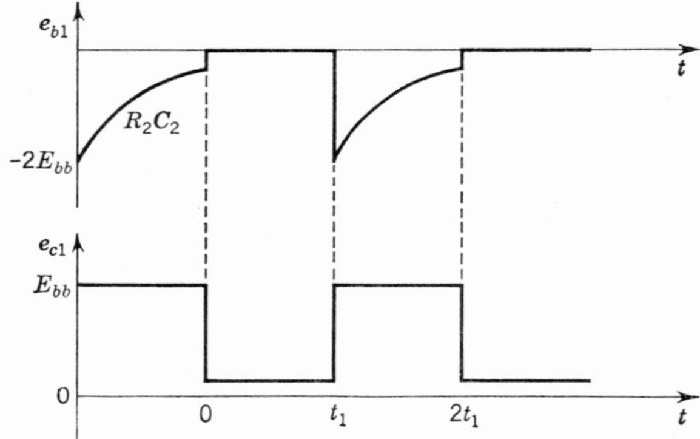

FIG. 13-22. Transistor collector and base waveshapes—circuit of Fig. 13-20.

of the off transistor T_2 is returned to the collector of the saturated one, T_1, only a very small base current can possibly flow into T_2. Its collector current, flowing in winding N_2, cannot institute regenerative switching. It only opposes the flux build-up due to the much larger current in N_1. We thus conclude that the core still controls the timing.

If the two timing coils are identical, this circuit will generate the square wave shown in Fig. 13-22. The frequency of oscillation will be given by

$$f = \frac{1}{2t_1} = \frac{E_{bb}}{4NAB_s} \tag{13-24}$$

when the transistor switching time is neglected. It is interesting to note that the square-wave frequency is linearly dependent on the supply voltage.

The output is usually obtained from a third winding; hence the transformer action not only affords isolation but also permits the amplitude to be scaled up or down.

Figure 13-23 shows another core-timed multivibrator, one which utilizes transformer rather than resistive coupling between the active elements. In this circuit, the voltages developed across the auxiliary windings N_1 and N_4 sustain the one transistor in cutoff and the other in saturation during the flux build-up interval. Consider the conditions when the saturated transistor T_1 connects E_{bb} across winding N_2. With the directions shown, winding N_1 supplies the saturation base current of T_1. The voltage appearing across N_4 back-biases T_2. These voltages are easily calculated once the turns ratios are known.

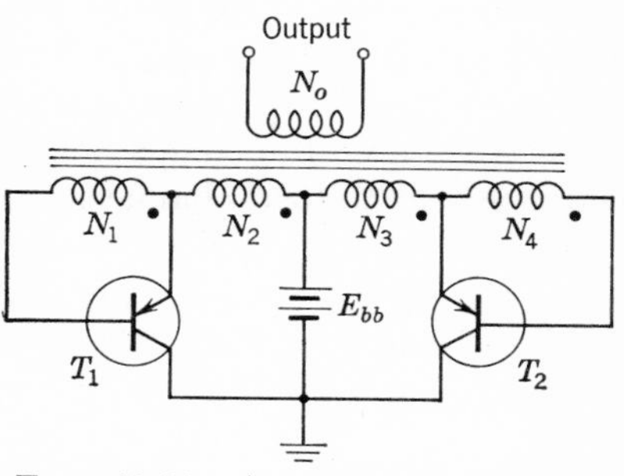

FIG. 13-23. A transformer-coupled core-transistor multivibrator.

The half cycle terminates when the saturation of the core permits the transistors to reenter their active regions. Any decrease in voltage across the driving coil is coupled by the transformer into the base of T_2, turning it on. Since the circuit is regenerative, switching continues until T_2 saturates and T_1 cuts off. The flux then starts reversing, and the cycle repeats.

These same circuits are widely used as d-c to a-c or as d-c to d-c converters. The primary peak-to-peak voltage of $2E_{bb}$ (measured from collector to collector) is first multiplied by the primary to secondary winding ratio n. If direct current is desired, the square wave, which is present at the output, must be rectified. Thus a 10-volt battery may be used to develop a 100-volt (or even higher) a-c or d-c output. Of course, the primary source impedance is multiplied by n^2 as it is reflected into the output circuit while the voltage is only increased by the factor n. Thus the I^2R losses increase faster than the voltage. This limits the permissible step-up ratio, especially when large amounts of power must be supplied to the load. In any case, power transistors having a very low saturation resistance should be chosen.

When this circuit is used as a d-c to a-c converter, the frequency of operation is usually the critical factor. It will even determine the transformer design, i.e., the turns ratio, cross-section area, and type of magnetic material employed. Since the frequency is inversely proportional to the product of the transformer parameters, the greater the turns ratio, the smaller the volume of iron needed. However, increasing the number of turns also increases the winding resistance and the losses; therefore some compromise must be selected.

On the other hand, when operating as a d-c to d-c converter, the higher the frequency of oscillation, the easier it is to filter any a-c components appearing in the output. As a further advantage, both the amount of transformer iron and turns needed decrease with increasing frequency. But if the frequency of operation becomes excessively high, the stray circuit capacity will adversely affect the waveshape. Since the transistor will remain active over a larger portion of the cycle, the effective source impedance also increases, resulting in poorer regulation with respect to load changes.

For example, a typical converter used in an automobile will operate from the 12-volt battery and will supply a maximum of 1 amp to the load at a nominal 120 volts and 60 cps. In this application the total primary resistance may be estimated at 0.1 ohm, 0.05 ohm due to the saturation of the power transistor and the other 0.05 ohm contributed by the winding and battery resistance. Since the transformer's turns ratio is 10:1, 10 ohms will be reflected into the output. At full current flow, the output drops to 110 volts. The primary voltage falls by the same percentage and causes a frequency shift down to 55 cps [Eq. (13-24)]. While this converter might be used to operate many small appliances, the frequency change under load would prevent its use for phonographs or other small constant-speed motors.

13-8. Properties of Ferroelectric Materials. Dielectrics are those substances where all charged particles are relatively tightly bound to the atomic nucleus or the molecular region. In the presence of an external field, these charges cannot move freely through the material to the surface as do the relatively loosely bound electrons in conductors. Instead, there will be a slight separation in the individual microscopic region; the positive charge moves in the direction of the **E** field, and the negative charge moves in the opposite direction. Hence the local effect on the field pattern is that of an elementary dipole, i.e., an associated positive and negative charge (q) separated by some small distance d (Fig. 13-24). In certain dielectrics these dipoles exist even before the external field is applied. But since they are randomly oriented, the material does not exhibit a net field of its own. It follows that the driving-point characteristics of the dielectric may be determined from the motion and alignment of the elementary dipoles under the influence of the applied field.

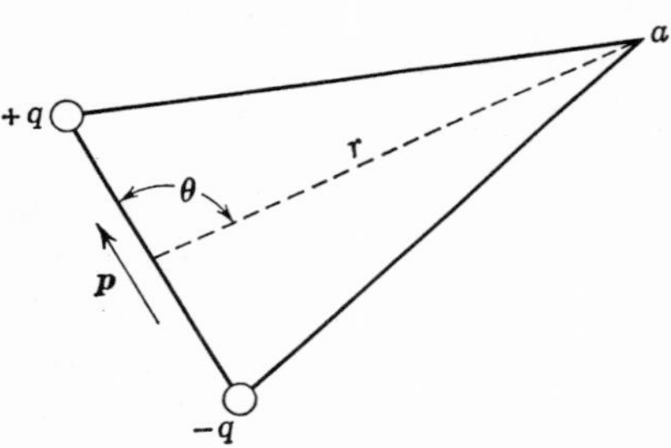

FIG. 13-24. Individual dipole.

Figure 13-24 shows an individual dipole from which the potential field at any point can be calculated. If the point is relatively far from the charge, the potential is given by

$$V_a = \frac{qd \cos \theta}{4\pi\epsilon_0 r^2} \qquad \text{volts} \tag{13-25}$$

where ϵ_0, the permittivity of free space, is equal to 8.85×10^{-12} farad/m in the mks system. The dipole moment is defined as

$$\mathbf{p} = q\mathbf{d}$$

and $\mathbf{p}$ is directed from the negative to the positive charge. This vector is called the polarization of the dipole. In any small volume, where there are n dipoles, the total polarization is the vector sum of the individual dipole moments. When they are all aligned, $\mathbf{P} = n\mathbf{p}$, and when they are in random array, $\mathbf{P} = 0$.

In order to express the terminal characteristics in simple terms, we define the displacement vector

$$\mathbf{D} = \epsilon_0\mathbf{E} + \mathbf{P} \tag{13-26}$$

The relationship between $\mathbf{P}$ and $\mathbf{E}$ is, in general, quite complex; for example, the polarization in a single direction in a crystal may depend on all three components of the applied field. However, for the ideal dielectric, we can assume the linear relationship

$$\mathbf{P} = \epsilon_0 k\mathbf{E} \tag{13-27}$$

which leads to

$$\mathbf{D} = \epsilon_0\epsilon_r\mathbf{E}$$

where $\epsilon_r = 1 + k$ is called the relative permittivity (or dielectric constant) of the medium. In the ferroelectric materials with which we shall be concerned, $k \gg 1$, and the electric displacement is almost exactly equal to the polarization.

One class of dielectrics can be defined as those materials where the polarization is produced solely by the external field. For these to be useful in capacitors, the relationship between $\mathbf{P}$ and $\mathbf{E}$ should be the linear one expressed in Eq. (13-27). If it is not, then the dielectric constant, and hence the capacity, will vary with the applied voltage.

Certain organic waxes exhibit a quasi-permanent residual polarization when they are solidified in the presence of an electric field. These are called electrets, and they are the closest electrostatic analogs to the permanent magnet currently existing.

In the third and, for our purposes, the most important class of dielectrics, the polarization is a nonlinear function of E. Here the material is characterized by spontaneous polarization, saturation, and hysteresis (Fig. 13-25). So as to recognize the duality with the magnetic materials, these dielectrics are unfortunately called ferroelectric. They contain no iron, nor is the duality complete.

Ferroelectricity was first observed in rochelle salts, $NaK(C_4H_4O_6)\cdot 4H_2O$, by J. Valasek, in 1921. The usable temperature range of this substance is only 40°C, and because of its complicated crystal structure, it develops ferroelectric properties in one direction only. Barium titanate, $BaTiO_3$, is much more useful since it is ferroelectric below its Curie point of 120°C. The crystal has a simple perovskite structure. Many other substances, such as triglycine sulfate and guanidine aluminum sulfate hexahydrate, also exhibit ferroelectric properties. Some of these other materials have squarer hysteresis loops, higher Curie temperatures, or better long-term storage properties than barium titanate.

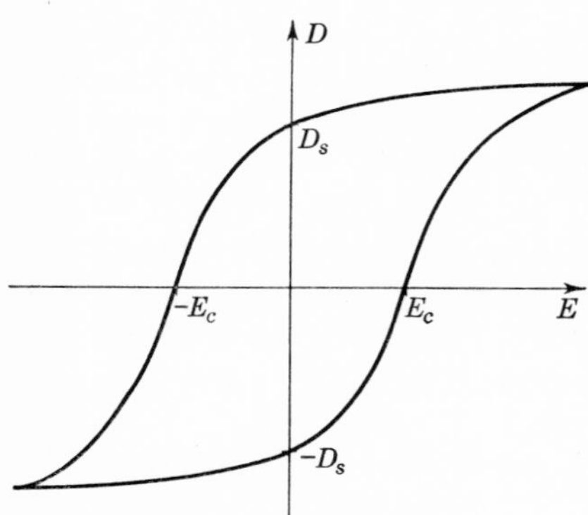

FIG. 13-25. Typical hysteresis loop of ferroelectric materials.

The switching behavior of the ferroelectric crystal has been extensively investigated with the aid of polarized light and optical examination. In the unsaturated sample, small domains are found where the net dipole moment is in one of the permissible directions. Studies with a thin plate

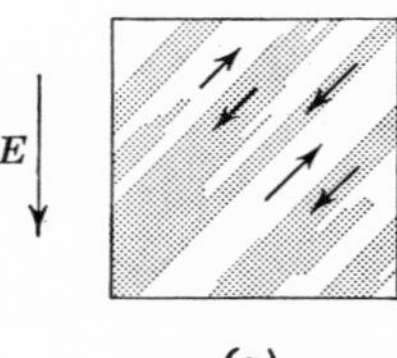

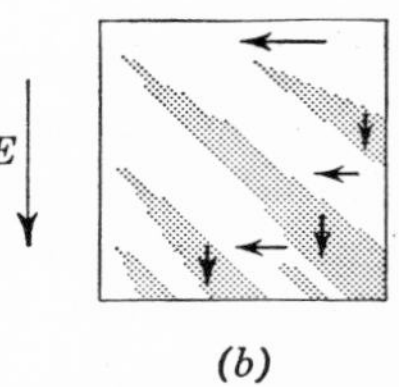

FIG. 13-26. Domain switching. (*a*) 180° domains showing the spike formation; (*b*) 90° domains showing the wedge formation. The shaded regions have been switched by the external field.

cut from a single crystal of barium titanate indicate that adjacent domains may have polarization directions either 180 or 90° apart. In the 180° domains, the application of a field $E > E_c$ causes the formation of spikes of new domains in the preferred direction (Fig. 13-26*a*). These then extend across the whole crystal. The 90° domains are reversed by the formation of wedges skewed to the cathode wall (Fig. 13-26*b*), which grow and spread sideways, eventually covering the entire region.

The number of both the 90 and 180° wedges formed, and hence the switching time, is a function of the excess of field strength over the internal coercive force.

13-9. Ferroelectric Terminal Characteristics. The practical form of the ferroelectric device is a thin wafer of barium titanate, or some other ferroelectric material, cut from a single crystal. The two electrodes must be carefully deposited on the flat surfaces because any air gap that exists will decrease the effective dielectric constant and seriously degrade the squareness of the observed hysteresis loop.

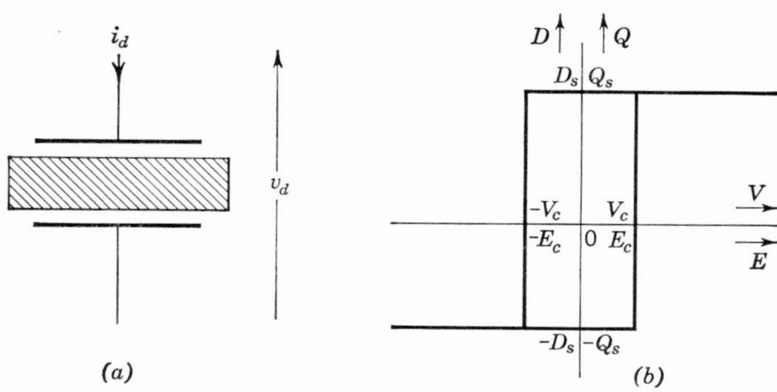

FIG. 13-27. (*a*) Schematic representation of a ferroelectric device; (*b*) ideal square-loop characteristics. Both the microscopic (E,D) and macroscopic (Q_s, V_s) coordinates are shown.

In a parallel-plate capacitor of thickness d and area A,

$$D = \frac{Q}{A} \qquad \text{and} \qquad E = \frac{V_a}{d} \tag{13-28}$$

where V_a is the terminal voltage. Furthermore, the charge flow is simply

$$Q = \int_0^t i\,dt$$

For a known current excitation, the time required to reverse the saturation direction of a perfect square-loop dielectric (Fig. 13-27) is given by

$$Q_{sw} = 2Q_s = \int_0^{t_s} i\,dt = 2D_sA \tag{13-29}$$

Equation (13-29) states that a fixed current-time area (charge) is required to switch the dielectric. Or, expressing the relationship of Eq. (13-29) in a more useful manner, the ferroelectric device acts as a series charge regulator. It permits only the fixed charge packet Q_{sw} to flow during the switching intervals. This equation should be compared with the equivalent relationship previously derived for the ferromagnetic core [Eq. (13-7)]. Under the special condition where the applied current is constant ($i = I_a$), the time required to switch from $-D_s$ to $+D_s$, or vice versa, is

$$t_s = \frac{2D_sA}{I_a}$$

During this interval the terminal voltage increases linearly with time, starting from the coercive value V_c.

After switching, the ideal ferroelectric device can no longer transfer any charge. Consequently, it seems reasonable to approximate the saturated response by an open circuit.

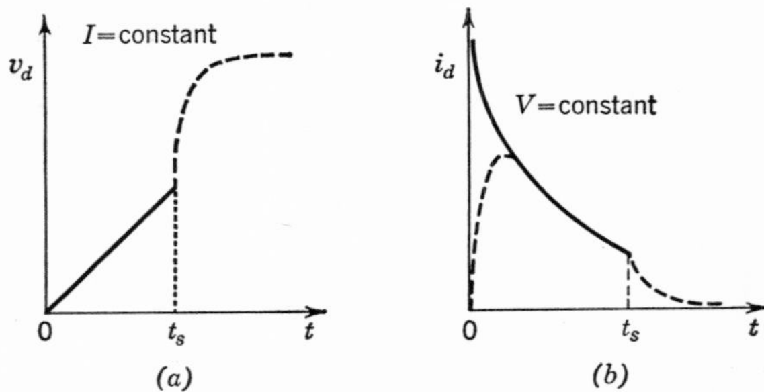

FIG. 13-28. Terminal response of ideal ferroelectric device. (a) Constant-current excitation; (b) constant-voltage excitation.

When a voltage excitation is applied, the switching time is found to be inversely proportional to the excess over the coercive force. For a constant voltage V_a, the relationship is

$$t_s = \frac{K}{V_a - V_c} \tag{13-30}$$

where K is a constant that depends on the geometry and properties of the ferroelectric medium. Equation (13-30) is exactly analogous to Eq. (13-17).

To a very good approximation the voltage and current response of the ferroelectric device during switching will look like the current and voltage response of the ferromagnetic core, respectively (Fig. 13-28). Where our concept of the core was a time-varying resistor decreasing from infinity as the core approached saturation, our model of the square-loop ferroelectric device is a resistance that increases from zero with time and current. It appears in series with a bucking voltage equal to the internal coercive force V_c. Sometimes the model of the ferroelectric element is further simplified, by neglecting the energy loss during switching, and it becomes a bivalued capacitor. In fact, when the termination of the excitation leaves the ferroelectric element unsaturated, its incremental response is most like that of a large capacitor. Since the relative dielectric constant drops from several hundred down to unity as the material saturates, the capacity is reduced to that of the two deposited electrodes in free space.

The widely used ferroelectric material barium titanate has a coercive field strength of 1,500 volts/cm. Only by using extremely thin slabs (0.033 to 0.167 mm) can the coercive voltage V_c be kept between 5 and 25 volts. Over the transition interval the average resistance of the ferroelectric element ranges between 100 and 1,000 ohms. Because of the large remnant polarization, 22×10^{-6} coulomb/cm², a large charge packet is transferred during switching, even from quite small elements.

13-10. The Ferroelectric Counter. The principle of charge monitoring is employed in the counter of Fig. 13-29. As the input square-loop

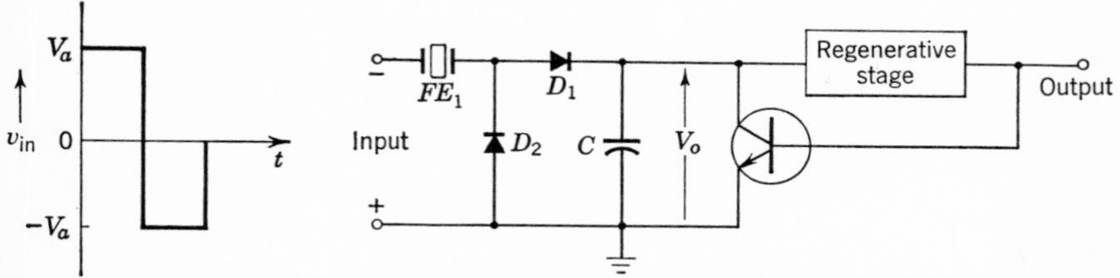

FIG. 13-29. Ferroelectric counter.

ferroelectric element (FE_1) is switched from negative to positive saturation by the leading portion of the input pulse, a charge packet of $2Q_s$ flows through D_1 into the storage element C. This increases the output voltage by the definitive increment

$$\Delta V_o = \frac{2Q_s}{C} \tag{13-31}$$

The negative portion of the input pulse resets FE_1 to negative saturation with D_2 establishing the current path. During this part of the cycle the back-biased diode D_1 prevents the discharge of the previously stored count.

Note that the input pulses must be properly shaped. They must have positive peaks greater than $V_c + V_o$, as well as a duration greater than the switching interval. The negative peak can be smaller, but its magnitude must still exceed V_c. Otherwise the ferroelectric device will not switch and reswitch between the two saturation limits and will not meter the full charge packet to the storage capacitor.

During the final count the change in the output voltage brings the regenerative circuit into conduction. For example, the final change of ΔV_o volts may be used to trigger a monostable multivibrator or a blocking oscillator which propagates a single count in the forward direction into the next stage. This same pulse will turn on the shunting transistor, discharge C, and reset the counter.

The switching action of the counter can be greatly improved by the simple modification shown in Fig. 13-30, i.e., the replacement of C by a second ferroelectric element. Each input pulse will be shaped into a charge packet of $2Q_1$ by FE_1. This charge also flows into FE_2 and starts it switching from $-Q_{s2}$ toward $+Q_{s2}$. If the second element is larger, n charge packets (or input pulses) will be needed to saturate FE_2. Until such time as it does saturate, the ferroelectric element appears

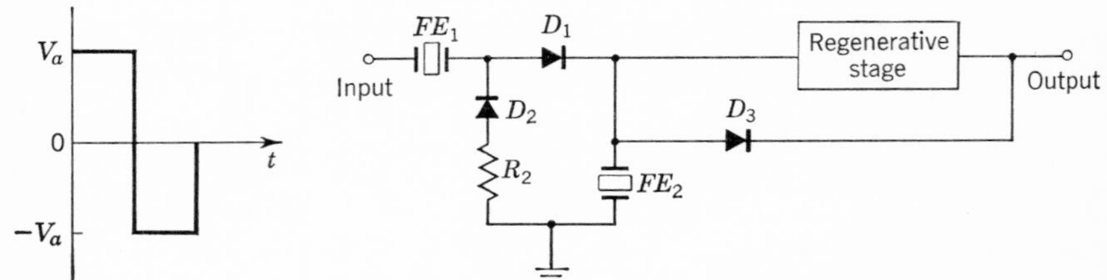

FIG. 13-30. Improved ferroelectric counter.

to be a low impedance and only a very limited voltage can be developed across it.

If FE_2 becomes saturated during the nth input, then it may be replaced by a very high impedance for the remaining portion of the pulse. The full excitation will appear across the output storage element, and instead of depending on identifying the small charge of ΔV_o volts, the large voltage jump presents a definitive trigger to the regenerative stage. With the modification of Fig. 13-30 this counter can accurately register many more counts than possible with the simpler circuit. Furthermore, since the count is registered by a change in the state of the element and not by the storage of charge, it will be less affected by leakage resistance. Counters having rates as low as one per day and counting ratios as high as 30:1 or 40:1 have been successfully operated.

In order to reset the storage element, a negative pulse can be applied through a diode from some point in the regenerative stage. However, unless resistance is inserted in series with D_2, the two input diodes would act as a short circuit, preventing the resetting of FE_2. Current will also flow into FE_1 during the reset interval, but this only aids its recovery toward negative saturation.

Example 13-2. Another interesting application of the pulse area shaping by the ferroelectric and ferromagnetic devices is the tachometer shown in Fig. 13-31. The sharp input pulses obtained from the distributor in a six-cylinder 2-cycle engine are assumed shaped to switch and reset the charge-metering ferroelectric element. Their amplitude and duration will, of course, be erratic. When switching from negative to positive polarization, the input element delivers a charge packet of 20×10^{-6} coulomb. We wish the highly damped d-c voltmeter reading of 5 volts to correspond to a speed of 5,000 rpm.

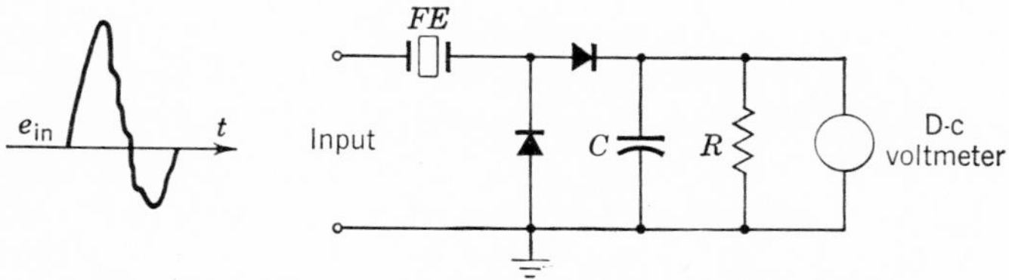

FIG. 13-31. A ferroelectric tachometer (Example 13-2).

Three input pulses are generated on each revolution. Hence the minimum spacing between the individual inputs, which occurs at the maximum velocity, is

$$T_m = \frac{60 \text{ sec}}{3 \times 5{,}000} = 4 \text{ msec}$$

So that the storage capacitor can discharge completely between the adjacent pulses, the output time constant must be much less than T_m. Assuming that the charging time is insignificant and that $T > 4\tau$, the average voltage read on the d-c meter is given by

$$V_{\text{d-c}} = \frac{1}{T}\int_0^T \Delta V\, e^{-t/\tau}\, dt = \frac{\Delta V\, \tau}{T}$$

where ΔV is the peak output voltage due to the metered charge packet. Note that the output RC circuit provides a d-c voltage inversely proportional to the spacing between the pulses and directly proportional to the motor rpm.

At 5,000 rpm,

$$\Delta V\, \tau = \frac{Q_{sw}}{C} RC = 20 \text{ volt-msec}$$

Thus $R = 1{,}000$ ohms. Setting $\tau = 500$ μsec yields $C = 0.5$ μf. Since $\Delta V = 40$ volts and $V_c = 10$ volts, for proper switching the peak positive input must be greater than 50 volts. The diode allows satisfactory resetting with negative peaks greater than 10 volts.

13-11. Coincident Memory Arrays. The ferroelectric element is somewhat more difficult to use in a memory matrix than the ferromagnetic core. Since only two electrodes are available, these must be used not only for storage and interrogation but also for read-out. It is not possible to place a third electrode at the memory position, as it was to thread the complete core array with a third winding. Consequently various ingenious circuits have been devised to obtain the output digit.

Consider the memory plate of Fig. 13-32, where the x and y direction leads are printed at right angles on the opposite faces of the ferroelectric plate. The intersections are the memory positions, and they may be treated as individual ferroelectric elements. In order to obtain the coincident switching, voltage inputs must be applied to the two leads.

To store a digit in a particular location, that memory element is switched from negative to positive polarization by applying a positive pulse to the y_i row and a negative one to the x_j column. Each pulse must have an amplitude falling within the limits

$$\tfrac{1}{2}V_c < |V_a| < V_c$$

and a duration sufficient to cause switching.

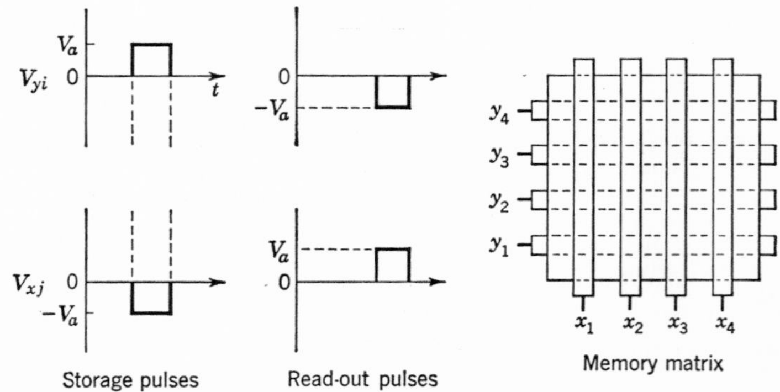

FIG. 13-32. A ferroelectric memory matrix.

It is quite simple to reset the memory element from 1 to 0. If it contains a stored digit, pulses of the polarity opposite to those used for storage will sum at the intersection and reverse the polarization. All other positions remain unaffected. But how may the digit be registered after interrogation? The switching process results in the transfer of a charge pocket which must somehow be monitored. In one method, shown in Fig. 13-33*a*, a resistor is connected in the ground return of either the x or y pulse generator. The current flow during storage will cause a negative voltage to appear across the resistor. During reset, the opposite polarity signal is developed. The two output pulses are easily distinguished, and if desired, a shunting diode may be incorporated to eliminate the unwanted negative pulse.

Figure 13-33*b* illustrates a somewhat superior method of producing an output after interrogation. All the x leads (or y leads) are threaded through a single read-out core. The current flow during the transfer of the metered charge packet induces a pulse into the output winding. One polarity output is produced on storage, and the opposite on reset; the diode shown selects the correct signal.

One major disadvantage of the ferroelectric memory matrix is that the state of the particular element is affected by single-voltage pulses of less than the coercive force. In barium titanate it was discovered that multiple queries in any one row caused the partial depolarization of all memory positions subjected to the half-voltage pulse. After several hundred interrogations the polarization may even be reduced to half of the saturation value. It has been found, however, that crystals of other materials, such as triglycine sulfate, appear to have more nearly

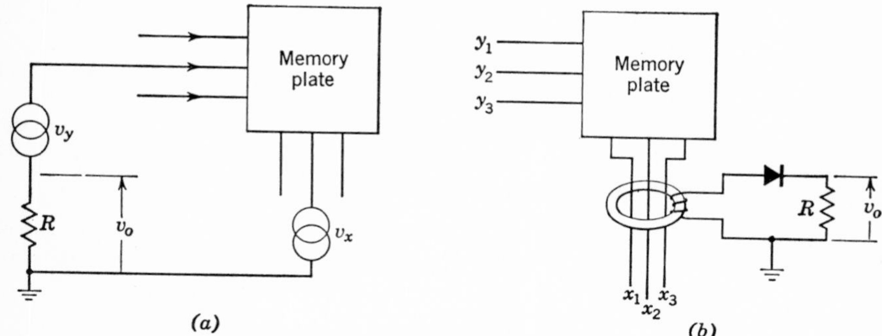

FIG. 13-33. Two methods of monitoring the read-out pulse.

ideal characteristics. As these sustain full polarization under repeated questioning, they will no doubt be used in practical memory banks.

PROBLEMS

13-1. A square-cross-section Permalloy core measuring ¼ in. on a side has an effective magnetic path length of 6 in. It is excited by a 10-volt peak-to-peak square wave applied across a 20-turn winding.

(*a*) What is the minimum-duration square wave needed to drive the core between its two saturation limits?

(*b*) Plot the spatial penetration of the field and the current build-up as a function of time when the duration of the half period is twice as long as that found in part *a*.

In the course of the calculations assume a source impedance of 10 ohms and winding resistance of 1 ohm where necessary to keep the solution within bounds.

13-2. Plot the spatial variation and current build-up for the core of Prob. 13-1 for the following excitations. After the core saturates, the current is limited by the 100-ohm series resistance; this resistance may be neglected during the interval that the core remains unsaturated.

(*a*) A 50-volt peak-to-peak 30-μsec-period sine wave.

(*b*) A 50-volt peak-to-peak 30-μsec-duration sawtooth.

(*c*) A 50-volt peak-to-peak 30-μsec-period triangular wave.

13-3. Consider the two models shown in Fig. 13-34 which have been suggested to approximate the core response during the switching interval. In order to see the

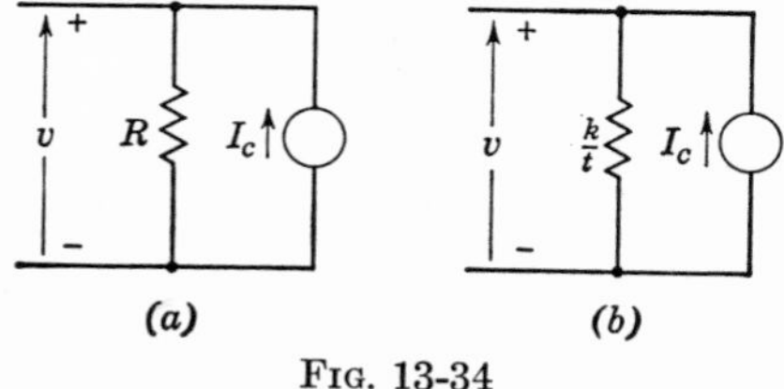

FIG. 13-34

advantages and disadvantages of these representations, we shall compare the exact and approximate response to a known voltage excitation.

(*a*) Calculate the model constants (R, k, and I_c) for the Permalloy core of Example 13-1. The current at $t = t_s$ of both models should agree with that given in the text for constant-voltage excitation.

(*b*) Plot on the same graph the exact and the model current response to a voltage ramp which increases at the rate of 5 volts/μsec. It drives the core from negative to positive saturation.

Which model gives the best representation? Is there any modification of the model which will result in a closer correlation? Explain.

13-4. Plot the incremental driving-point resistance as a function of time for the two cores described in Example 13-1. Will this resistance change with excitation? In your answer consider the response to a voltage ramp, which increases at a rate of 10 volts/μsec.

13-5. Find an equivalent resistance for each of the cores of Example 13-1 that will yield equal power dissipation over the switching interval. Treat the following two cases and compare the results.

(*a*) Constant-voltage excitation (20 volts).

(*b*) Constant-current excitation ($I = 10I_c$).

13-6. Repeat Prob. 13-1 when the core is excited by a square wave of current having a peak-to-peak value five times as large as the coercive force. In this case plot the terminal voltage response and the location of the domain boundary with respect to time.

13-7. Calculate and sketch the voltage response of the core of Prob. 13-1 to the following current excitations. The core is initially at negative saturation, and each signal reverses the flux direction.

(*a*) A current ramp which increases at the rate of 20 ma/μsec.

(*b*) A single cycle of a sine wave having a peak-to-peak amplitude of 50 ma and a duration of 5 μsec.

13-8. (*a*) Solve for the expression of the voltage response to a unit step of current when the core is loaded across a secondary winding N_2 with a resistor R.

(*b*) Plot the response of the Permalloy core of Example 13-1 to a 20-ma unit step. The external loading consists of 2,000 ohms across a 10-turn winding.

(*c*) Repeat part *b* when the load resistance is decreased to 100 ohms.

13-9. In the counter of Fig. 13-11 the ferrite core is wound with 20 turns; it has an effective radius of 3.0 cm and a square cross section of 1.0 cm on a side (its parameters are those given in the text). $C = 0.001$ μf, and $R = 500$ ohms.

(*a*) Specify the range of the volt-time areas of the input pulses for which this counter will count down by the ratio 4:1. What is the minimum spacing between these pulses?

(*b*) Repeat for a counting ratio of 8:1.

(*c*) Sketch and label the output when the core is excited by a train of 20-volt 5-μsec-wide pulses. These are widely spaced compared with the recovery time of the core.

13-10. A ferrite core having a radius of 0.5 in., $d = 0.2$ in., and $h = 0.3$ in. is used as the memory element in the simple counter of Fig. 13-11. One output pulse should be produced for every three of the 25-volt 10-μsec input pulses. During the two priming inputs, the output must remain below 5 volts.

(*a*) Specify the minimum value of C that will properly reset the core on the termination of the count.

(*b*) Using twice the minimum value of C, specify the range of core turns for which this counter will work. (The RC time constant is 1 μsec.)

(c) Sketch and label the output voltage when C is twice the minimum value and when N lies in the center of the acceptable range.

13-11. Two identical ferrite cores having the dimensions given in Prob. 13-10 are used in the scale-of-10 counter of Fig. 13-35. Complete the design by specifying C_s

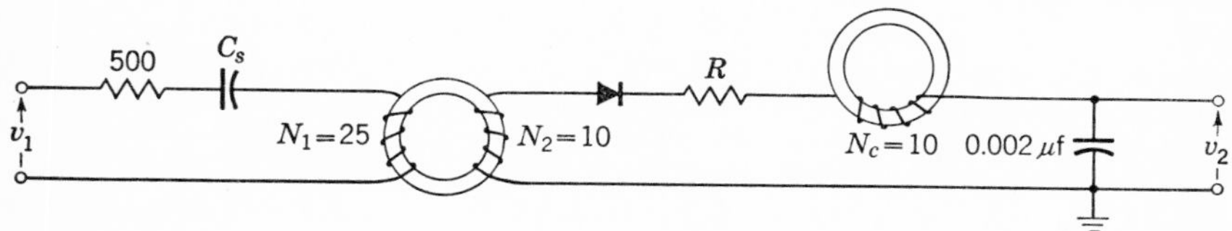

FIG. 13-35

needed to reset the input core. Calculate the minimum input volt-time area and the pulse spacing necessary for proper counting. Discuss the circuit modification necessary to ensure the automatic reset of the counting core.

13-12. (a) Draw the circuit of a transistor multivibrator shift register, indicating where and how to inject the input and the shift pulses. Show three stages. Indicate the time delay between the stages.

(b) Repeat part a when a tunnel diode is used as the memory element. Pay particular attention to the coupling network and to the method of injecting the input and the shift pulses.

(c) Neon bulbs which fire at 100 volts, which have a conduction drop of 75 volts, and which require 0.5 ma to sustain conduction might be used to indicate the count in a core decade ring counter. Explain how they would be incorporated into the circuit.

(d) Exercise your ingenuity to see if it is possible to ensure the reset of the core ring counter, regardless of the stored digit, by the injection of a single pulse. If necessary, the basic circuit may be modified.

13-13. Figure 13-36 shows a magnetic core AND gate incorporating automatic reset. Each coil consists of 5 turns wound on the single ferrite core (radius of 3 cm and with a cross section measuring 1 cm by 1 cm).

(a) Sketch the output voltage when 1-msec current pulses, having an amplitude equal to $0.4I_c$, are simultaneously applied to two inputs; to three inputs.

(b) If $C = 0.001$ μf, what is the minimum pulse width that will ensure the automatic reset of the core? The loss in R may be neglected in the calculation.

(c) How might this circuit be converted into an OR gate?

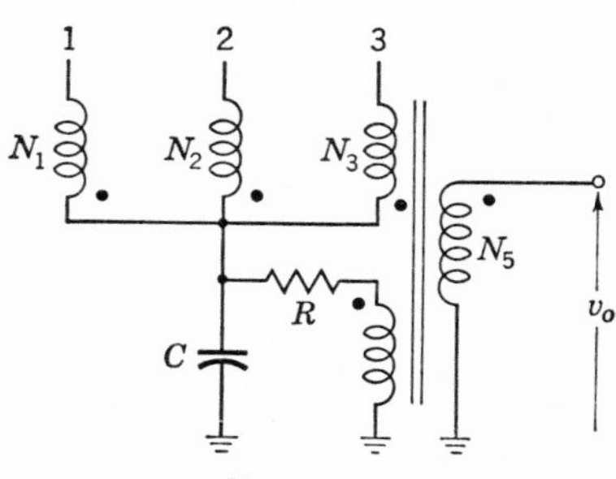

FIG. 13-36

13-14. The transistor-core multivibrator of Fig. 13-20 is used as a d-c to d-c converter producing 150 volts from the 20-volt source. It operates at approximately 1,000 cps, which simplifies the filtering at the output of the full-wave bridge rectifier. Each of the 10-turn primary windings has 0.01 ohm resistance. The saturation resistance of the transistor is 0.02 ohm, and at the boundary between the active and saturation regions, β may be taken as 5. Grain-oriented silicon steel, having the following parameters, is used for the square cross-section core: $B_s = 2$ webers, $H_c = 12$ amp-turns/m, $\rho = 40 \times 10^{-4}$ ohm-m, and $l = 0.3$ m.

(*a*) Calculate the maximum value of R and the minimum value of C necessary to sustain one transistor off and the other one on over the full half cycle.

(*b*) What cross-section area is needed for the core to operate at 1,000 cps?

(*c*) Calculate the total power dissipated in the converter when the external load current is 150 ma. How much power is dissipated under no-load conditions?

(*d*) Sketch and label the current and voltage waveshapes at the base and collector, under loaded conditions.

13-15. A silicon-steel core, having the characteristics given in Prob. 13-14, is used in the multivibrator of Fig. 13-23. For this circuit the cross section measures 2 cm on a side and the magnetic path is 20 cm long. The primary consists of four windings of 5, 15, 10, and 5 turns, which are connected to the base and collector of the first transistor and to the collector and base of the second transistor, respectively. The secondary is a single 50-turn winding.

Sketch and label the collector and base current and the output voltage waveshapes when $E_{bb} = 20$ volts. Assume a base-to-emitter resistance of 0.02 ohm for your calculations.

13-16. (*a*) Plot the potential as a function of θ far from an individual dipole. Assume that r is constant and equal to $50d$.

(*b*) On the same graph as in part *a* plot the constant potential distance r as a function of θ. The absolute value of the potential should be equal to the maximum value found in part *a*.

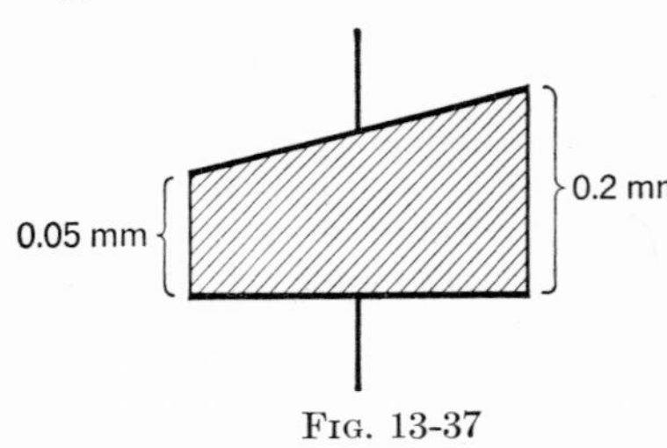

FIG. 13-37

13-17. The incremental capacity of the wedge-shaped ferroelectric element shown in Fig. 13-37 is a function of the applied direct current. Calculate this capacity variation, neglecting any fringe effects. The dielectric used has $\epsilon_r = 2{,}000$ and $E_c = 1{,}500$ volts/cm, and its cross-section area is 0.25 cm. (HINT: First show that the capacity of a large-area parallel-plate capacitor is $C = \epsilon_0\epsilon_r A/d$.) How will the resonant frequency of a tank circuit, using this element, vary with the d-c voltage?

13-18. (*a*) Prove that the charge packet flowing during the switching interval in a ferroelectric element is equal to the charge transferred in a parallel-plate capacitor of the same dimensions as it charges from $-V_c$ to V_c.

(*b*) The ferroelectric element FE_1 described in Prob. 13-19 is charged from a 20-volt source through a 5,000-ohm resistor. After saturating, ϵ_r drops to unity. Plot the current and voltage response. Calculate the approximate time-varying resistor

$$R(t) = At + B$$

that will result in equal charge flow over the switching interval. Furthermore, the terminal voltage at $t = t_s$ should be equal to V_c.

13-19. The counter of Fig. 13-38 is excited by two input sources, each connected to the single storage capacitor through a separate charge-metering element. FE_1 consists of a 0.03-mm-thick slab having an effective surface area of 0.02 cm², while FE_2 is twice as thick and has only half the electrode area. The ferroelectric material has a coercive field strength of 2,000 volts/cm and a remnant polarization of 8×10^{-6} coulomb/cm². We may further assume that the constant in the switching equation (13-30) is $K = 10$ volt-μsec.

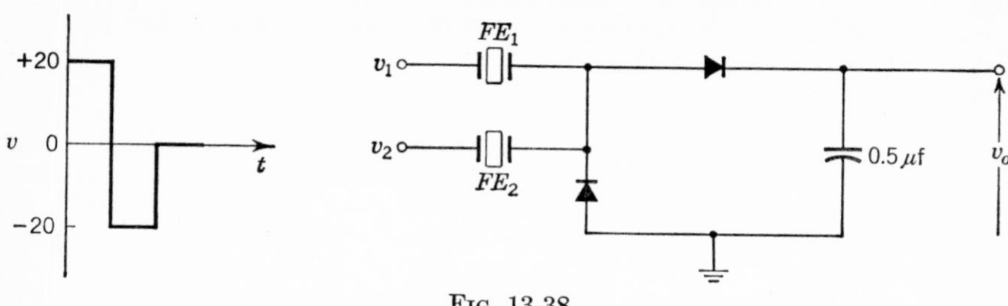

Fig. 13-38

Sketch the output voltage, giving all significant values, if the shaped 20-volt-peak 20-μsec-wide pulses are applied at the two inputs at

$$e_1 \text{ at } t = 0, 10, 20, 30, \ldots \text{ msec}$$
$$e_2 \text{ at } t = 5, 15, 25, 35, \ldots \text{ msec}$$

13-20. Figure 13-39 shows a monostable multivibrator where the duration of the quasi-stable state is controlled by the switching time of a ferroelectric element. In order to simplify the calculations it will be represented by a 0.005-μf capacitor which decreases by a factor of 1,000 after saturating at ±5 volts. Sketch and label the voltage at the collector of T_1 and at the collector and base of T_2 after a pulse is injected into the base of T_1. Does this type of timing offer any advantage over that obtained from a simple capacitor?

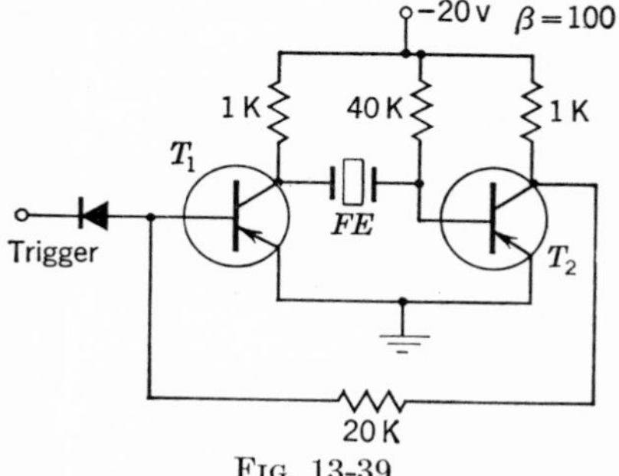

Fig. 13-39

13-21. Show that the circuit of Fig. 13-39 can be modified so that it can make use of a ferromagnetic core to control the timing. If the core of Prob. 13-10 is employed, sketch and label the important waveshapes.

BIBLIOGRAPHY

Bates, L. F.: "Modern Magnetism," 3d ed., Cambridge University Press, New York, 1951.

Chen, Kan, and A. J. Schiewe: A Single Transistor Magnetic Coupled Oscillator, *Trans. AIEE*, pt. I, *Communs. and Electronics*, vol. 75, pp. 396–399, September, 1956.

Chen, T. C., and A. Papoulis: Domain Theory in Core Switching, *Proc. Symposium on Role of Solid State Phenomena, Polytech. Inst. Brooklyn*, April, 1957; also in *Proc. IRE*, vol. 46, no. 5, pp. 839–849, 1958.

Collins, H. W.: Magnetic Amplifier Control of Switching Transistors, *Trans. AIEE*, pt. I, *Communs. and Electronics*, vol. 75, pp. 585–589, November, 1956.

Dekker, A. J.: "Electrical Engineering Materials," Prentice-Hall, Inc., Englewood Cliffs, N.J., 1959.

Katz, H. W.: "Solid State Magnetic and Dielectric Devices," John Wiley & Sons, Inc., New York, 1959.

Little, C. A.: Dynamic Behavior of Domain Walls $BaTiO_3$, *Phys. Rev.*, vol. 98, no. 4, pp. 978–984, 1955.

Menyuk, N.: Magnetic Materials for Digital Computer Components, *J. Appl. Phys.*, vol. 26, no. 6, pp. 692–697, 1955.

Meyerhoff, A. J., and R. M. Tillman: A High-speed Two-winding Transistor-magnetic-core Oscillator, *IRE Trans. on Circuit Theory*, vol. CT-4, no. 3, pp. 228–236, 1957.

Rajchman, J. A.: A Myriabit Core Matrix Memory, *Proc. IRE*, vol. 41, no. 10, pp. 1407–1421, 1953.

———: A Survey of Magnetic and Other Solid-state Devices for the Manipulation of Information, *IRE Trans. on Circuit Theory*, vol. CT-4, no. 3, pp. 210–225, September, 1957.

Royer, G. H.: A Switching Transistor D-C to A-C Converter Having an Output Frequency Proportional to the D-C Input Voltage, *Trans. AIEE*, pt. I, *Communs. and Electronics*, vol. 74, pp. 322–326, July, 1955.

Rozner, R., and P. Pengelly: Transistors and Cores in Counting Circuits, *Electronic Eng.*, vol. 31, pp. 272–274, May, 1959.

Sands, E. A.: An Analysis of Magnetic Shift Register Operation, *Proc. IRE*, vol. 41, no. 8, pp. 993–999, 1953.

Storm, H. F.: "Magnetic Amplifiers," John Wiley & Sons, Inc., New York, 1955.

Von Hippel, A.: "Dielectric Materials and Applications," John Wiley & Sons, Inc., New York, 1954.

Wolfe, R. M.: Counting Circuits Employing Ferroelectric Devices, *IRE Trans. on Circuit Theory*, vol. CT-4, no. 3, pp. 226–228, 1957.

PART 5

OSCILLATIONS

CHAPTER 14

ALMOST SINUSOIDAL OSCILLATIONS—THE LINEAR APPROXIMATION

The earlier chapters of the text showed how the generation of many periodic waveshapes (rectangular pulses and linear sweeps) was predicated on driving the active elements of the circuit far into their saturation and/or cutoff regions. The timing function depended upon the nonactive regions of the system, with the active zone simply supplying the energy necessary for switching between the two exponential timing regions.

As we start discussing the generation of almost sinusoidal signals, it should be pointed out that the nonlinearity of the system will now play a subsidiary role. The basic timing is due to a frequency-determining network, with the amplifier simply setting the necessary conditions for oscillation. To avoid distorting the output signal, the degree of nonlinearity must be small, and consequently most of the subsequent discussion can concern itself with the linear approximation of the sinusoidal oscillator.

14-1. Basic Feedback Oscillators. Figure 14-1 presents the basic configuration of a feedback oscillator as a block diagram. Even though each of the three essentials shown is not completely isolated, it is convenient to think of them as separate entities. It is especially helpful to segregate the complete nonlinearity so that it can be given individual attention. The remaining elements in the circuit may then be treated by the standard methods of linear analysis.

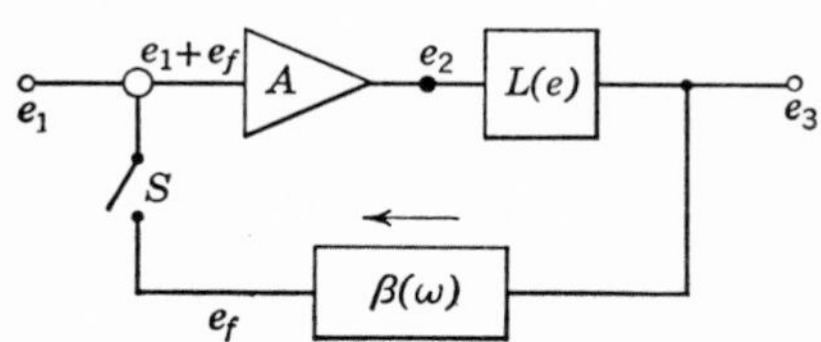

FIG. 14-1. Basic-feedback-oscillator configuration showing the ideal amplifier A, the amplitude limiter $L(e)$, and the frequency-determining network $\beta(\omega)$.

The behavior of the circuit of Fig. 14-1 is defined by two equations, one for the forward transmission and the other giving the feedback voltage.

$$e_3 = (e_1 + e_f)AL \qquad e_f = \beta e_3$$

From these equations, we find that the over-all closed-loop gain is

$$G = \frac{e_3}{e_1} = \frac{AL}{1 - \beta AL} \tag{14-1}$$

For self-sustained oscillations, there must be an output without any external excitation. This becomes possible only when the denominator of Eq. (14-1) vanishes. It follows that the frequency and amplitude of oscillation must satisfy

$$1 - \beta(\omega)AL(e) = 0 \tag{14-2}$$

where βAL is simply the open-loop transmission (i.e., the switch in Fig. 14-1 is open). Equation (14-2) implies that the feedback must be regenerative.

Limiting is often accomplished by driving one or more of the amplifier's active elements into their saturation or cutoff regions for a portion of the cycle. Alternatively, an amplitude-controlled resistor or other passive nonlinear element may be included as part of the amplifier or in the frequency-determining network. If a gross nonlinearity is permitted, the limiter will distort the signal and the output will be far from sinusoidal.

For small signals no limiting will occur and $L(e)$ will take on its maximum value of unity. It follows that if $A\beta > 1$ in the small-signal region, the amplitude will build up until the limiter stabilizes the system at an output level that satisfies Eq. (14-2). Thus, in the active region, the threshold loop transmission that permits self-sustained oscillation is

$$\beta A_t = 1$$

This equation is called the Barkhausen criterion for oscillation.

Unity loop gain at a single frequency is a necessary but not a sufficient condition for self-sustained oscillations. If the network characteristics are such that the net phase shift is zero at several frequencies, then the criterion for oscillation can be arrived at only from an examination of the complete amplitude and phase portrait of the system. Nyquist stated that the polar plot of $A\beta$ for $-\infty < \omega < \infty$ must encircle the point $1 + j0$ for oscillation. However, for many of the simpler configurations, the Barkhausen condition will be both necessary and sufficient. Below we shall consider circuits that are known to oscillate and that can be analyzed on the basis of their having unity loop gain.

To ensure our objective, the generation of a sinusoidal signal, the frequency should be primarily determined by a network whose characteristics can be rigidly controlled. This network must contain at least two energy-storage elements so that the system response [Eq. (14-2)] will have the necessary pair of complex conjugate roots which give the natural frequency of oscillation. For simplicity, A may be assumed to be a constant, with its frequency dependence lumped together with that of β.

Since A in Eq. (14-2) now represents the gain of an ideal amplifier, it will be a pure number having a sign corresponding to the stages of amplification (minus for an odd number and plus for an even number). β represents the transmission characteristics of the frequency-selective network and will therefore be a function of ω. To satisfy Eq. (14-2) the imaginary part of βA must vanish. Since the complete frequency variation is included in the β network, the imaginary part depends only on β. Consequently the frequency at which

$$\text{Im } \beta = 0 \tag{14-3}$$

will be the approximate frequency of oscillation.

At the oscillation frequency, the remaining portion of Eq. (14-2), that is, Re (βA), must be identically equal to unity. The value of gain that will just ensure the sinusoidal oscillations will be given by

$$A_t\beta(\omega_0) = 1$$

or

$$A_t = \frac{1}{\beta(\omega_0)} \tag{14-4}$$

This value of threshold gain is measured with the amplifier output loaded by the input impedance of the β network. The open-circuit gain must, of course, be somewhat larger.

Equations (14-3) and (14-4), taken together, state that the over-all loop gain must be unity and the over-all phase shift must be zero at the frequency of oscillation.

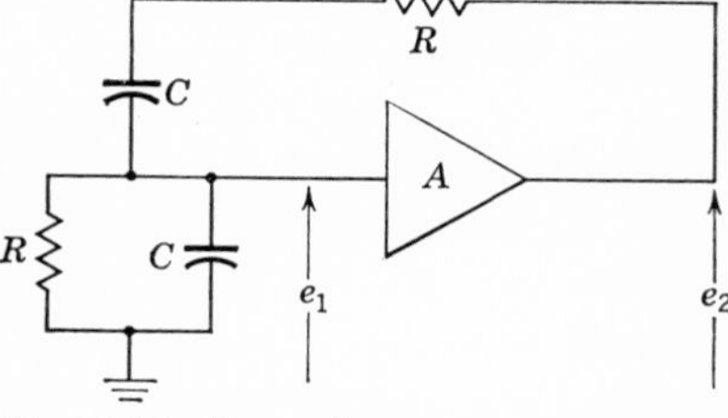

FIG. 14-2. Example of a feedback oscillator.

Consider the circuit of Fig. 14-2, where we shall assume that the amplifier is adjusted so that it will just sustain the oscillations. The frequency-determining network is characterized by

$$\beta(p) = \frac{e_1}{e_3} = \frac{\dfrac{R}{pCR + 1}}{R + \dfrac{1}{pC} + \dfrac{R}{pCR + 1}} = \frac{1}{3 + pCR + \dfrac{1}{pCR}} \tag{14-5}$$

Substituting $j\omega$ for p results in

$$\beta = \frac{1}{3 + j(\omega/\omega_0 - \omega_0/\omega)} \tag{14-6}$$

where $\omega_0 = 1/CR$. The imaginary portion of the denominator of Eq. (14-6) vanishes at

$$\omega = \omega_0 = \frac{1}{CR}$$

At this frequency $\beta = 1/3$, and from Eq. (14-4) we find that the gain necessary to sustain oscillation is $A_t = 3$. To achieve this positive gain, the amplifier must contain an even number of stages.

Because they determine the nature of the transient response, it is interesting to examine the location of the roots of $1 - \beta A$, and hence the poles of the complete feedback system as a function of A. The roots of the circuit of Fig. 14-2 are found by substituting Eq. (14-5) into $1 - \beta A = 0$. This leads to

$$p^2 + \frac{3 - A}{CR} p + \left(\frac{1}{CR}\right)^2 = 0 \qquad (14\text{-}7)$$

Equation (14-7) has two roots which traverse the path shown in Fig. 14-3. As A increases from 0 to 1, they first coalesce at $-1/CR$ on the negative real axis and then separate along the semicircular paths shown, finally reaching $\pm j/CR$ on the imaginary axis for $A = 3$. This condition corresponds to the threshold of oscillation, with the location of the complex conjugate roots giving the frequency.

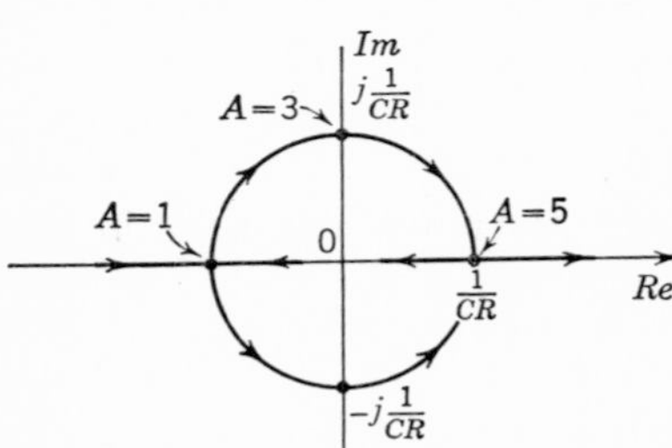

FIG. 14-3. Migration of the roots of Eq. (14-7) as a function of A. The arrows indicate increasing gain.

When the system has two distinct complex conjugate roots, i.e., for A between the limits $1 < A < 5$, the transient response will be given by

$$e(t) = Ke^{\alpha t} \cos (\omega_1 t + \phi)$$

And the two roots are located at

$$p_{1,2} = \alpha \pm j\omega_1$$

where $\omega_0 = \sqrt{\alpha^2 + \omega_1^2}$. For small values of α, the natural frequency is almost ω_0.

If A is less than 3, then the real part of the root will be negative and any oscillatory response will damp out. The degree of damping depends on the distance from the poles to the imaginary axis and hence on the value of A.

Once the poles move into the right half plane, the real part forces an increasing exponential build-up. But the voltage is bounded by the limiter; the output eventually stabilizes at a peak amplitude that makes the average gain over the cycle equal to 3. At the peaks of the sine wave, the limiter reduces the loop gain, driving the system poles from the right- into the left-half plane. The amplitude decays, the circuit reenters the active region, and the roots move back into the right half plane.

If the poles are initially close to the imaginary axis, then the build-up will be quite slow and small changes in the root location will have but little influence over any single cycle of the sine wave. When they are located far into the right half plane, the exponential build-up makes itself felt during each cycle; the waveform will include a greater degree of distortion. Even with a small gain margin over the threshold value, the location of the roots will be such that the oscillator will generate a signal of slightly different frequency than that calculated on the basis of the borderline behavior.

The oscillator will be self-starting only if initially the poles lie in the right half plane. It follows that the necessary gain must be somewhat in excess at A_t. Any infinitesimal distribution will cause an amplitude build-up until the limiter stabilizes the output. The threshold gain sustains existing oscillations, but does not provide a margin for build-up. Excess gain will also stabilize the circuit in that any slight reduction in A will not stop the oscillations when $A > A_t$ but will cause them to damp out when the circuit operates marginally.

If the amplifier gain ever becomes large enough to drive the roots onto the positive real axis, that is, $A > 5$, the system response will no longer be oscillatory. The exponential build-up will lead to a relaxation phenomenon similar to that found for the astable multivibrator.

14-2. Characteristics of Some *RC* and *LR* Frequency-determining Networks. The self-starting oscillator drives itself into limiting and in the process distorts the sinusoidal output signal. Harmonics, introduced by the limiter, may be treated as additional signals injected within the feedback loop. Each harmonic term will also be affected by the feedback present; it will be acted upon by the factor

$$H_n = \frac{1}{1 - A\beta_n} \tag{14-8}$$

where β_n is the feedback factor evaluated at the particular harmonic under investigation.

Since we wish to maintain an almost sinusoidal output, we should ensure that the amplitude of the harmonics produced in the limiter will be small compared with the fundamental. Each distortion term is further modified by H_n. With a properly designed network, the feedback will change from positive to negative as the loop excitation frequency increases from ω_0 to $2\omega_0$. The magnitude of H_n will become less than unity at the second-harmonic and even smaller at the higher-harmonic frequencies. Thus the nature of the existing feedback is changed and is used to reduce the amount of distortion.

The more selective the network, the greater the degree of limiting which can be tolerated without excessively distorting the final sinusoidal output. Consequently $|H_2|$ serves as a measure of the network's quality for oscillator application. For consistency it will always be evaluated under threshold conditions, instead of using the slightly larger value of the actual small-signal gain. The best network, all other things being equal, is the one having the lowest value of H_2.

The output signal, which is of the form

$$e_3 = E_1 \cos (\omega_0 t + \phi_1) + \sum_{n=2}^{\infty} H_n E_n \cos (n\omega_0 t + \phi_n) \tag{14-9}$$

is transmitted back to the input through the β network. Each term is also multiplied by β_n, resulting in an effective driving signal of

$$e_1 = \beta_1 E_1 \cos (\omega_0 t + \phi_1) + \sum_{n=2}^{\infty} \beta_n H_n E_n \cos (n\omega_0 t + \phi_n)$$

In order to have a true basis of comparison as to the relative amplitudes of the distortion components at the input and at the output, it is advisable to use the normalized input harmonic factor

$$K_n = \frac{\beta_n H_n}{\beta_1} \tag{14-10}$$

Equation (14-10) accounts for the relative attenuation of the fundamental component which would be ignored if $\beta_n H_n$ were chosen instead as the figure of merit. When $|K_n| = |H_n|$, the relative harmonic contents of the input and output are equal. In any specific circuit the best signal, i.e., the most nearly sinusoidal, will appear at the output for $|K_n| > |H_n|$ and at the input for $|K_n| < |H_n|$.

Phase-shift Network. One network commonly used in the so-called "phase-shift oscillator," which we must therefore name "the phase-shift network," appears in Fig. 14-4*a*. Either the three series branches (Z_1) will be energy-storage elements L or C and the shunt branches (Z_2) resistors, or vice versa. In general, all series branches and all parallel branches are composed of equal elements; however, this is not an essential condition. Satisfactory oscillators have been constructed with widely unbalanced sections and with networks of more than three sections.

From Fig. 14-4*a*, the network transfer characteristics can be found to be

$$\beta = \frac{e_f}{e_3} = \frac{1}{(Z_1/Z_2)^3 + 5(Z_1/Z_2)^2 + 6Z_1/Z_2 + 1} \tag{14-11}$$

Since either Z_1 or Z_2, but not both, is an energy-storage element, the

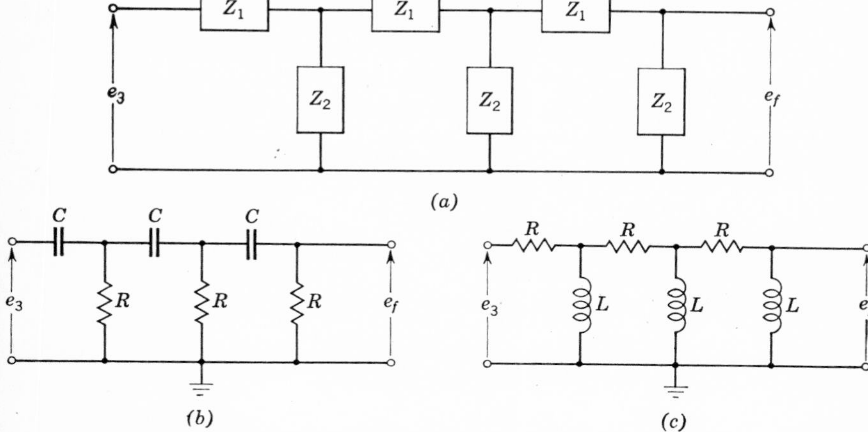

FIG. 14-4. (*a*) Basic "phase-shift network"; (*b* and *c*) two specific examples.

odd-power terms in the denominator of Eq. (14-11) contribute the imaginary part of $\beta(\omega)$. For it to vanish

$$\left(\frac{Z_1}{Z_2}\right)^3 + 6\frac{Z_1}{Z_2} = 0 \tag{14-12}$$

In the specific case of the RC network of Fig. 14-4*b*, $Z_1 = 1/j\omega C$ and $Z_2 = R$; substituting these values into Eq. (14-12) yields

$$\omega_0 = \frac{1}{\sqrt{6}\,CR} \tag{14-13}$$

As the elements in the network change, so will the form of the equation defining ω_0.

By either substituting the value of ω_0 from Eq. (14-13) into Eq. (14-11) or by making the simpler substitution of

$$\left(\frac{Z_1}{Z_2}\right)^2 = -6$$

from Eq. (14-12) into Eq. (14-11) and by noting that the odd powers of Z_1/Z_2 have vanished, the threshold value of β becomes

$$\beta(\omega_0) = \beta_1 = -\tfrac{1}{29}$$

Thus the amplifier must have a minimum gain of -29 for sustained oscillations. With this particular type of network, the required gain is independent of the elements comprising Z_1 and Z_2. Any other RC or LR combination will give the same value of gain but a different operating frequency and network input impedance. Since the necessary gain is negative, a single or an odd number of stages are required. Figure 14-5 illustrates one possible circuit.

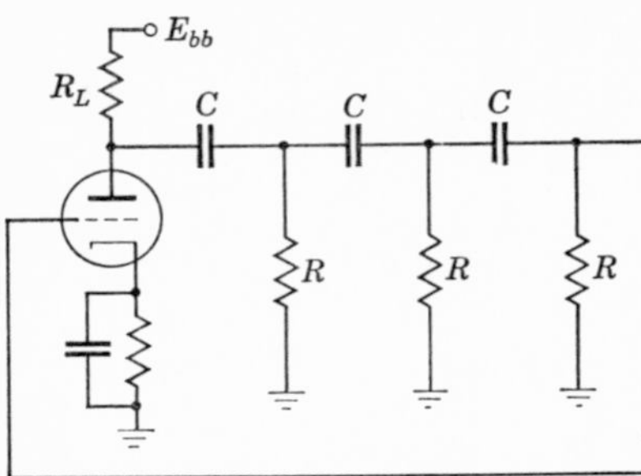

FIG. 14-5. A single-tube phase-shift oscillator.

In order to evaluate $|H_2|$ and $|K_2|$ for the RC network of Fig. 14-4b, β_n may be expressed as

$$\beta_n = \frac{1}{1 - 30/n^2 - j(6\sqrt{6}/n)(1 - 1/n^2)}$$

where n represents the order of the harmonic. Taking $A_t = -29$ and substituting into Eqs. (14-8) and (14-10) yields

$$|H_2| = 0.368$$
$$|K_2| = 1.25$$

For this network, the waveshape containing the smallest amount of harmonics appears at the amplifier output. If the positions of R and C are interchanged, this will no longer be true; the best signal would now appear at the input to the base amplifier.

Variation of the oscillator frequency over the widest frequency range requires the simultaneous adjustment of three similar elements. In the network of Fig. 14-4b, any changes in R will also change the driving-point impedance. This may load the base amplifier to a point where oscillations can no longer be sustained. If C is varied, then we face the problem of tracking three independent variable capacitors. Because of these difficulties, the phase-shift network is generally used for a fixed-frequency oscillator. Here only minor calibration adjustments are needed, and they may be made by means of a single small trimmer capacitor or padding resistor.

The Wien Bridge. The simple RC network used as an example in Fig. 14-2 exhibits extremely poor selectivity. Any second-harmonic components introduced are not only not reduced, but are actually increased in amplitude. In this network $|H_2| = 2.24$ and $|K_2| = 2$.

But all is not yet lost. We can convert the simple network into a null balance bridge (Fig. 14-6) and exchange necessary loop gain for selectivity. In the bridge

$$e_f = e_2 - e_3$$

but $e_2/e_1 = \beta$ of the simple network of Fig. 14-2 [Eq. (14-6)]. The resistor combination R_1 and R_2 is adjusted to satisfy the condition

$$\frac{e_3}{e_1} = \frac{R_2}{R_1 + R_2} = \frac{1}{3} - \frac{1}{\delta}$$

Thus the over-all β' of the bridge of Fig. 14-6 may be expressed as

$$\beta' = \frac{e_f}{e_1} = \beta - \left(\frac{1}{3} - \frac{1}{\delta}\right) \qquad (14\text{-}14)$$

where

$$\beta = \frac{1}{3 + j(\omega/\omega_0 - \omega_0/\omega)}$$

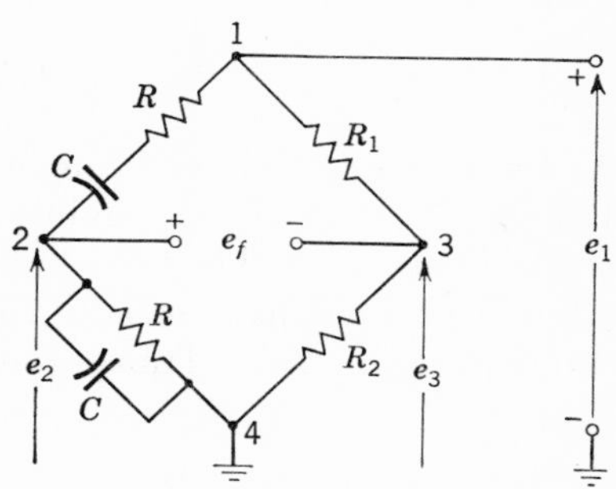

FIG. 14-6. A Wien-bridge frequency-selective network.

The amplitude and phase response of β' are plotted in Fig. 14-21. At the resonant frequency of the system ($\omega_0 = 1/CR$), β' reduces to

$$\beta' = \frac{1}{\delta}$$

and the threshold gain A_t is equal to δ. The term $1/\delta$ may be considered as the degree of bridge unbalance; when $\delta = \infty$, the bridge is perfectly balanced at ω_0, and when $\delta = 3$, the circuit reduces to the simple network of Fig. 14-2. If follows that the greater the degree of balance, the larger the necessary loop gain to sustain oscillations. At perfect balance, an infinite gain is required; with any physical amplifier, the circuit cannot oscillate.

The improvement in selectivity may best be seen by substituting β' given by Eq. (14-14) and $A_t = \delta$ into the expression for H_n [Eq. (14-8)]. The result is

$$H'_n = \frac{3}{\delta(1 - 3\beta_n)} \qquad (14\text{-}15)$$

where β_n is the transmission factor of the RC network at the harmonic frequency. Taking the ratio of H'_n for the bridge to H_n found for the completely unbalanced case ($\delta = 3$) shows the dependence of the selectivity on δ.

$$\frac{H'_n}{H_n} = \frac{3/[\delta(1 - 3\beta_n)]}{1/(1 - 3\beta_n)} = \frac{3}{\delta} \qquad (14\text{-}16)$$

From Eq. (14-16) we conclude that the percentage of second harmonics present at the output is reduced in proportion to the increase in required amplifier gain. With a two-stage amplifier having a gain of 300, the value of $|H'_2|$ is only 0.0224, a hundredfold reduction from the unbalanced case.

At the output of the bridge, i.e., at e_f in Fig. 14-6, the improvement in selectivity is not as impressive. K'_n may be expressed by

$$K'_n = \frac{\beta'_n}{\beta'_1} H'_n = \frac{3 - \delta(1 - 3\beta_n)}{\delta(1 - 3\beta_n)} \tag{14-17}$$

As δ gets large, the magnitude of Eq. (14-17) approaches unity as a limit. For other than very large gains, $|K'_n|$ will always be slightly above unity.

To incorporate the Wien bridge into an oscillator, we need two isolated input terminals, usually the grid and cathode of the input tube as shown in Fig. 14-7. Transformer coupling may also be used to convert

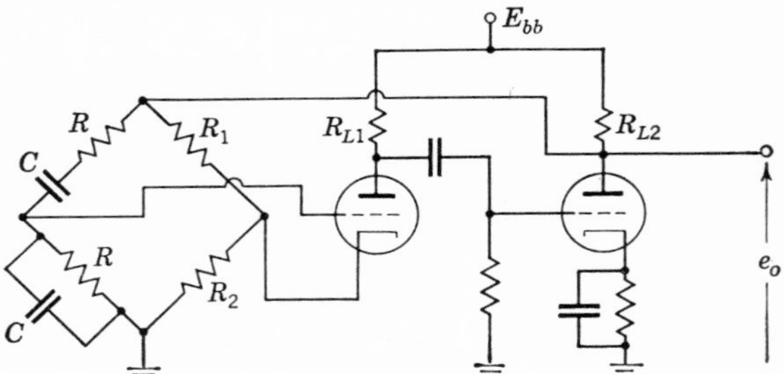

FIG. 14-7. A Wien-bridge oscillator.

the double-ended network output to a single-ended amplifier input. With a transistor amplifier, a transformer would almost always be used to avoid loading the bridge by the low-impedance input.

In this circuit, we see that positive feedback for regeneration is supplied through the RC branches to the grid of the input tube. The pure resistive path introduces a negative-feedback voltage into the cathode. The combination of both terms controls the operation of the circuit. At ω_0 the positive feedback predominates, and at the harmonics the net negative feedback reduces the distortion components.

The basic circuit of Fig. 14-7 is used in many commercial wide-range audio oscillators of from 10 cps to 200 kc or even higher. To adjust the frequency, usually both resistors are changed by steps and C is changed smoothly as a fine control. We can also do the reverse—switch C in steps and vary R continuously. Both arrangements perform satisfactorily.

Other Null Networks. Almost any three-terminal null network may be used as the frequency-determining pair of branches in a bridge. The other two arms are composed of resistors adjusted for the proper degree of unbalance.

All arguments employed with respect to the Wien bridge will also apply to these other networks, provided that care is taken as to the direction of the unbalance. For some networks the greatest reduction in harmonic content comes when δ is positive, as in the Wien bridge, and for others δ must be negative. Depending on the network and the sign of

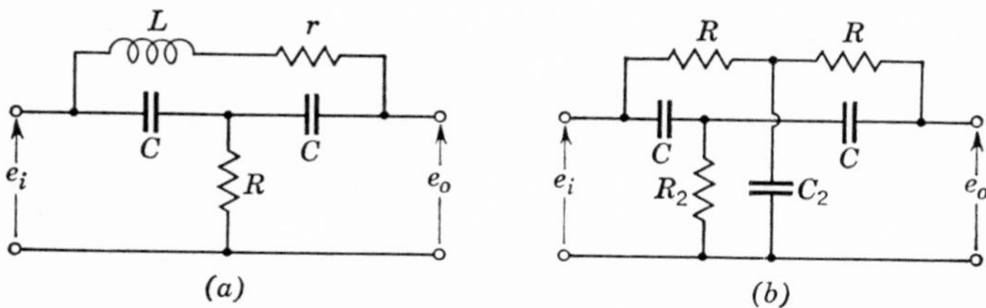

FIG. 14-8. Two null networks. (a) Bridged-T network; (b) twin-T network.

unbalance at ω_0, in some cases the resistive branches must be used for the positive feedback, and in others the reactive branches so serve.

Figure 14-8 shows two networks which give zero transmission at their null frequency. The feedback factors and further defining relationships are tabulated in Table 14-1. A plot of the amplitude and phase response

TABLE 14-1

Network	Transfer function	Defining terms
Bridged-T.	$\beta = \dfrac{1}{1 - j\dfrac{2}{Q_0}\dfrac{\omega\omega_0}{\omega^2 - \omega_0^2}}$	$\omega_0 = \dfrac{2}{LC}$ $Q_0 = \dfrac{\omega_0 L}{r}$ $R = \dfrac{L}{2rC}$
Twin-T.	$\beta = \dfrac{1}{1 - j2\dfrac{k+1}{\sqrt{k}}\dfrac{\omega\omega_0}{\omega^2 - \omega_0^2}}$	$\omega_0^2 = \dfrac{1}{2RR_2C^2}$ $k = \dfrac{R}{2R_2} = 2\dfrac{C}{C_2}$

appears in Fig. 14-21. At the oscillation frequency there cannot be any feedback through the reactive elements and the necessary positive feedback must be supplied through the resistive path. The basic circuit configuration needed to satisfy this condition is shown in Fig. 14-9. Here the value of β' may be expressed as

$$\beta' = \frac{R_2}{R_1 + R_2} - \beta$$

and at the null point, the required threshold gain is

$$A_t = 1 + \frac{R_1}{R_2}$$

As in the Wien bridge, when A_t is large, the harmonic content of the output will be small.

To adjust the frequency of these two networks, we must vary three elements simultaneously. The difficulty that this entails makes these networks best suited for fixed-frequency operation. For the same degree of unbalance, the bridged-T circuit will usually give the cleanest waveshape. However, since it is more difficult and expensive to obtain a high-quality inductance than it is to find extremely good resistors and capacitors, the twin-T network might be preferred.

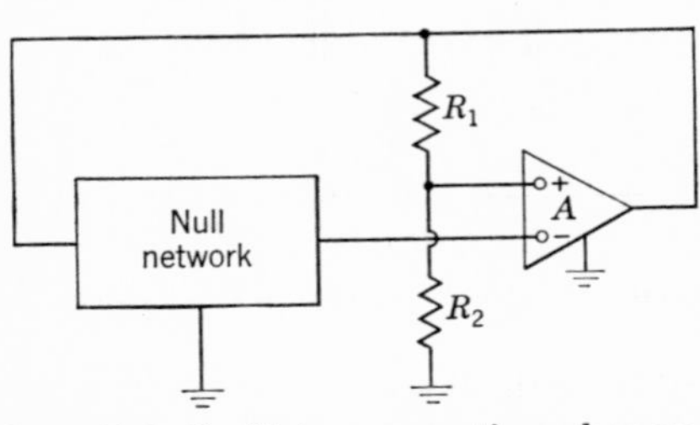

FIG. 14-9. Oscillator connection when using a null network for frequency determination.

14-3. Transistor Feedback Oscillators. The relatively low base input impedance of the transistor often prevents its direct substitution for the high-input-impedance vacuum tube in the various oscillator circuits previously discussed. Even after scaling down the resistors and increasing the capacity in the frequency-determining network, the heavy loading makes it more difficult to establish the necessary unity loop gain. For example, if the phase-shift network of Fig. 14-4 were connected directly between the collector and base of a suitably biased transistor, the output of this network would be heavily loaded by the input impedance of the transistor. Even though it is possible to sustain oscillations, the frequency would be extremely dependent on the transistor parameters —a relatively unsatisfactory situation. In order to solve this problem, many transistor oscillators resort to some form of impedance matching between the output of the feedback network and the input voltage-amplifier stage.

Figure 14-10 shows a transistor phase-shift oscillator which employs an emitter follower as the impedance transforming stage. It presents a high input impedance across the output of the frequency-determining network and a low output impedance for coupling to the input of the amplifier stage. By using this additional transistor, it now becomes possible to make $R \ll (1 + \beta)R_5$ and still keep the input impedance of the phase-shift network large compared with the collector load R_3 of T_1. The emitter follower has effectively isolated the elements controlling the frequency from the remainder of the circuit.

Since at the frequency of oscillation the attenuation from e_2 to e_1 is $-1/29$, the base amplifier must have a minimum loaded gain ($A = e_2/e_1$) of -29 to sustain the oscillation. Generally, the open-circuit (unloaded) voltage gain of T_2 would have to be from 20 to 50 per cent higher.

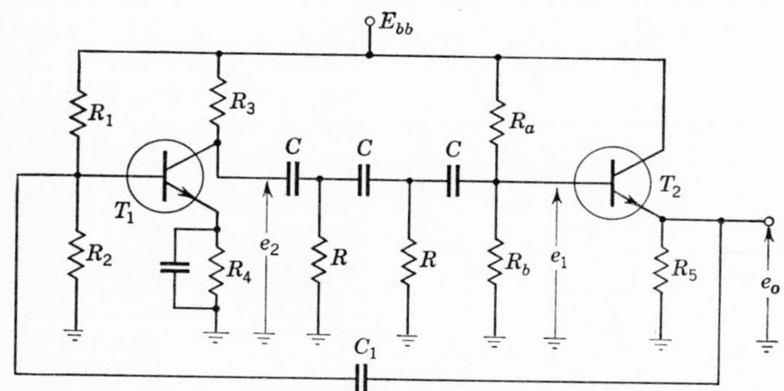

FIG. 14-10. A transistor phase-shift oscillator: T_1 is the voltage amplifier, and T_2 an emitter follower used for decoupling. The phase-shift network consists of three identical RC sections where $R_a \| R_b = R$.

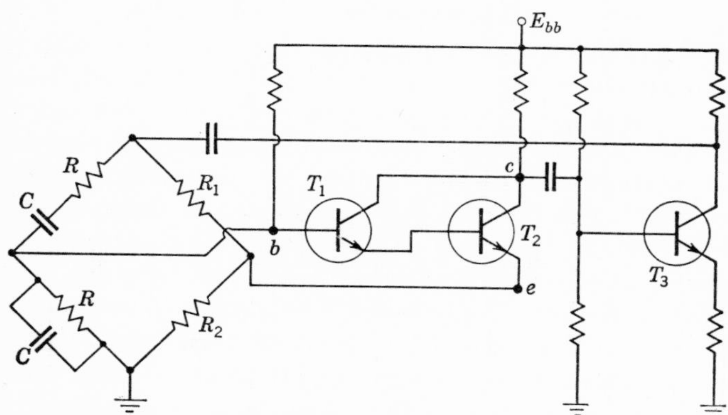

FIG. 14-11. A transistor Wien-bridge oscillator using a composite transistor input stage.

A second method of increasing the effective input impedance is illustrated by the Wien-bridge oscillator of Fig. 14-11. A composite transistor, which was discussed in Sec. 7-4, is used as the input stage of the base amplifier. The two transistors T_1 and T_2, taken together, have a base-to-emitter input impedance that is approximately $(1 + \beta)$ times as large as that of a single transistor. Provided that reasonable values of resistors are chosen for the bridge arms, the input characteristics of the composite transistor will not adversely affect the selectivity of the bridge. In order to decouple the bridge from the high-impedance collector as well as to have a low-impedance point from which to take the output, we could also insert an emitter follower after T_3. All the results of the discussion of the Wien bridge in Sec. 14-2 are directly applicable to this circuit.

Current-controlled Oscillations. If the transistor is used in its natural mode, with the appropriate form of feedback, then the oscillations produced may be said to be current-controlled. The basic circuit configuration is shown in Fig. 14-12. Except that i replaces e, it is identical with the voltage-controlled block diagram of Fig. 14-1. To avoid confusion between the voltage and current-feedback factors and with the forward-current-amplification factor of the transistor, we shall designate the current feedback by $T(\omega)$. This term is defined by

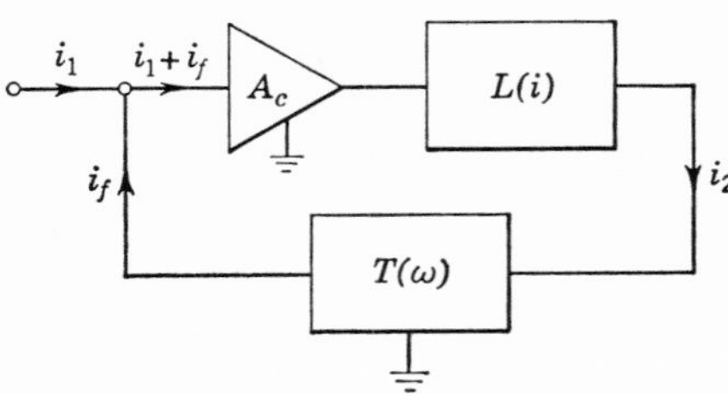

FIG. 14-12. Basic current-controlled oscillator: current amplifier A_c, limiter $L(i)$, and frequency-determining network $T(\omega)$.

$$i_f = T(\omega)i_2$$

and as before, the complete frequency dependence of the system is assigned to $T(\omega)$.

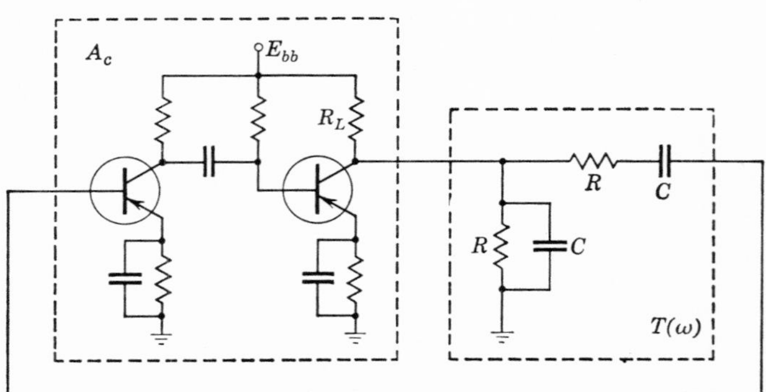

FIG. 14-13. An example of a current-controlled oscillator.

The conditions for self-sustained oscillations ($i_1 = 0$) may be written by analogy with Eq. (14-2).

$$1 - T(\omega)A_cL(i) = 0 \tag{14-18}$$

Equation (14-18) states that the net loop current gain must be unity at the frequency and amplitude of oscillations.

Figure 14-13 illustrates a circuit that is the current-controlled equivalent of the simple oscillator of Fig. 14-2. By assuming that the load impedance of the final stage is large compared with the input impedance of the network, the full output current will flow into $T(\omega)$. If this assumption is not justified, the current will divide proportionally between R_L and the network and R_L will influence the oscillation frequency.

For the ideal case,

$$T(\omega) = \frac{1}{3 + j(\omega/\omega_0 - \omega_0/\omega)}$$

where $\omega_0 = 1/RC$. [Compare this equation with Eq. (14-6).] The frequency of oscillation is ω_0, and the threshold current gain must be 3.

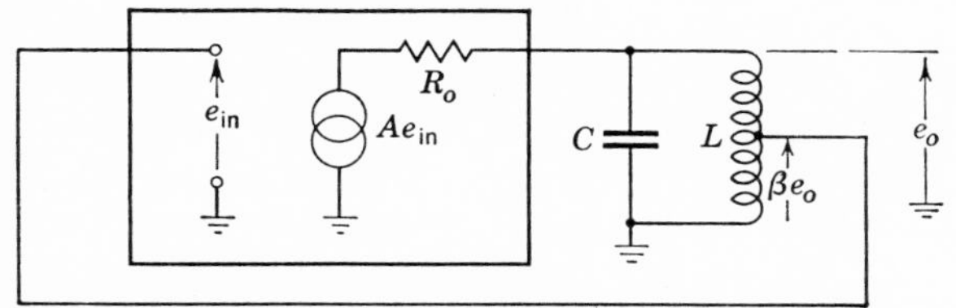

FIG. 14-14. An oscillator using a tuned circuit as a selective network.

The only conditions which we must impose on the various RC and RL networks, which may be used for feedback, are that $T(\omega)$ must give a clearly defined oscillation frequency and good harmonic rejection. Also, to avoid coloring the network response, the associated current amplifier should approach the ideal, i.e., a zero input impedance, a high output impedance, and constant gain over the frequency range of interest.

14-4. Tuned-circuit Oscillators. At frequencies above 50 kc, it becomes practical to use a high-Q tuned circuit for frequency selection. Because such a network is resistive only at its resonant frequency and is reactive everywhere else, the oscillation condition of zero net phase shift can be satisfied only at this particular frequency. Figure 14-14 illustrates how a portion of the developed voltage may be fed back to the input of the base amplifier by tapping the tank circuit. Other methods of feedback are also in use, and some of these will be discussed below.

Even if the excitation current is rich in harmonics, the low impedance of the tank, everywhere but at its resonant frequency, will not permit the development of other than an almost pure sinusoidal voltage. The feedback will further improve the selectivity, and consequently we shall not be particularly concerned with the harmonic response. We are, however, quite interested in generating a signal whose frequency will not be affected by external factors.

Almost all tuned-circuit oscillators may be represented by the basic circuits of Fig. 14-15*a* and *b*, where, in order to achieve the proper phase relationship with a single-stage amplifier, the tap of the tuned circuit is grounded. For simplicity, the biasing and power supplies have been omitted. In any specific circuit these connections would depend on the nature of the three impedance elements.

We might note that the network of Fig. 14-15 includes two modes of feedback, a direct transmission path from the plate (collector) to the grid (base) through Z_3 and the mutual coupling linking the input and output loops. Some oscillators use purely capacitive elements for Z_1 and Z_2, and in others two isolated coils are used. When we treat these cases, M

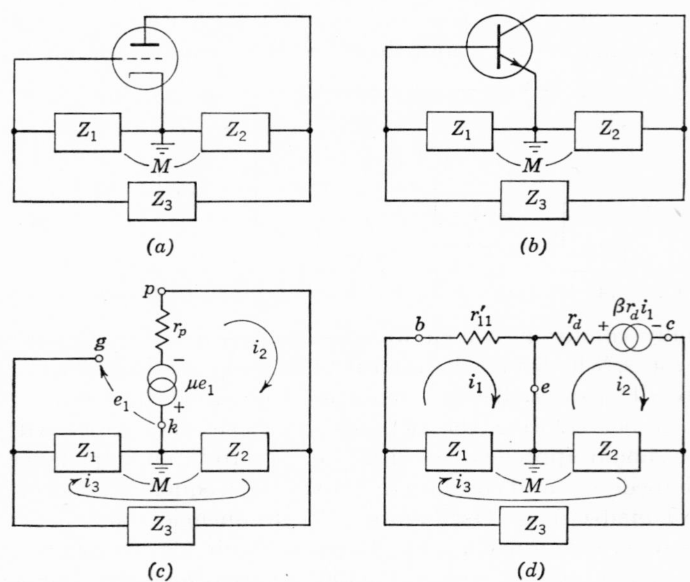

FIG. 14-15. Basic tuned-oscillator circuits. (a) Using a vacuum tube; (b) using a transistor; (c) vacuum-tube model; (d) transistor model.

would not appear. However, many of the more commonly used circuits do contain coupled coils, and therefore M must be included in any general treatment. Figure 14-15 also shows the various models with which we shall be concerned in the analysis of this type of oscillator. In the interests of simplicity, the small reverse-voltage-transmission term has been omitted from the transistor model. If this term ever becomes significant, it can always be included by inserting a voltage generator $h_{re}v_{ce}$ in series with r'_{11}.

Since the single tube or transistor introduces an effective phase shift of 180°, there must be an additional 180° contributed by the network, composed of Z_1, Z_2, and Z_3. These models may, of course, be treated as before by evaluating $A\beta$, where A is the gain when the output is loaded by the input impedance of the feedback network and β is the transmission from the plate (collector) to the grid (base).

By observing that the criteria for self-sustained oscillation are inherent in the vanishing of $1 - \beta(\omega)A$ or $1 - T(\omega)A_c$ in Eqs. (14-2) and (14-18), we can consider an alternative method of obtaining these criteria. The nature of the over-all response of any system may be found by solving a set of mesh or node equations. This response is undefined when the system determinant vanishes. Thus, by writing the loop equations, or where appropriate the node equations, finding the system determinant, and setting it equal to zero, we satisfy

$$1 - \beta(\omega)A = 0 \qquad \text{or} \qquad 1 - T(\omega)A_c = 0$$

The vanishing of the imaginary part of the determinant gives the frequency of oscillation. From the real part, we obtain the circuit conditions which must be satisfied if the oscillator is to be self-starting.

Vacuum-tube Tuned Oscillators. For the vacuum-tube circuit of Fig. 14-15c, the two loop equations are

$$\begin{aligned} (r_p + Z_2)i_2 - (Z_2 + Z_m)i_3 &= -\mu e_1 \\ -(Z_2 + Z_m)i_2 + (Z_1 + Z_2 + Z_3 + 2Z_m)i_3 &= 0 \end{aligned} \tag{14-19}$$

One additional defining equation is needed before the set of equations in (14-19) can be solved. The control voltage must be expressed in terms of the loop currents.

$$e_1 = -Z_m i_2 + (Z_m + Z_1)i_3 \tag{14-20}$$

Substituting Eq. (14-20) into Eq. (14-19) and collecting terms yields the system determinant,

$$\Delta = \begin{vmatrix} r_p + Z_2 - \mu Z_m & -(Z_2 + Z_m - \mu Z_m - \mu Z_1) \\ -(Z_2 + Z_m) & Z_1 + Z_2 + Z_3 + 2Z_m \end{vmatrix} \tag{14-21}$$

If we initially assume that the impedance elements are purely reactive ($Z_i = jX_i$), then the imaginary portion of the determinant will contain only odd powers of X_i. The sign of the reactance is assigned to the element (plus for inductance and minus for capacity). It follows that the frequency of oscillation will be given by

$$\text{Im}\,\Delta = r_p(X_1 + X_2 + X_3 + 2X_m) = 0 \tag{14-22}$$

Equation (14-22) can be satisfied only when the sign associated with one reactance is opposite to that associated with the other two. We shall see below [Eq. (14-23)] that Z_1 and Z_2 must be that same type of element to satisfy the gain condition. Thus if Z_1 and Z_2 are inductive at the oscillation frequency, Z_3 must be capacitive, and vice versa.

Since the sum of the loop reactances vanishes in Eq. (14-22), the real part of the determinant of Eq. (14-21) may be expressed as

$$\text{Re}\,\Delta = \mu(X_1 + X_m)(X_2 + X_m) - (X_2 + X_m)^2$$

By setting this equal to zero, we find that the threshold condition for self-starting is

$$\mu \geq \frac{X_2 + X_m}{X_1 + X_m} \tag{14-23}$$

Equation (14-23) can be satisfied only when Z_1 and Z_2 are the same type of component: either both are capacitive or both are inductive. If they are not the same, the feedback would be negative rather than positive.

Unless the ratio of impedances is somewhat less than μ, the over-all loop gain will not be greater than unity and the oscillator will not be self-starting. Furthermore, with threshold operation, the system is very sensitive to changes in the parameters of the active element. On the other hand, if this ratio becomes much less than μ, the limiting may introduce an excessive amount of harmonics, with a corresponding deterioration of the waveform. To avoid both problems and to have some latitude for component tolerances, at least one of the elements determining the threshold point should be made adjustable.

The following possibilities arise where the major mode of feedback is through X_3 and the mutual coupling either does not exist at all or is purely incidental.

1. Colpitts oscillator (Fig. 14-16*a*)
   X_1 and X_2 are capacitors.
   X_3 is an inductance.
   $X_m = 0$.
2. Hartley oscillator (Fig. 14-16*b*)
   $X_1 + X_2 + 2X_m$ is a single tapped coil.
   X_3 is a capacitor.
3. Tuned-plate tuned-grid oscillator (Fig. 14-16*c*)
   X_1 and X_2 are tuned circuits adjusted to be somewhat inductively tuned slightly below ω_0.
   X_3 is the stray grid-to-plate capacity.
   $X_m = 0$.

When the major mode of coupling is through the mutual inductance and X_3 represents the insignificant parasitic coupling, the following two circuits are also feasible:

4. Tuned-plate oscillator (Fig. 14-16*d*)
   X_2 is a tuned circuit in the plate loop.
   X_1 is the grid coil.
   $2X_m$ is the mutual coupling between the two coils.
5. Tuned-grid oscillator
   Virtually identical with the tuned-plate oscillator except that the tuned circuit is moved into the grid loop.

Various hybrid oscillators combining significant features of the five listed above are also in use. The above tabulation only indicates the range of possibilities; it makes no attempt to exhaust them.

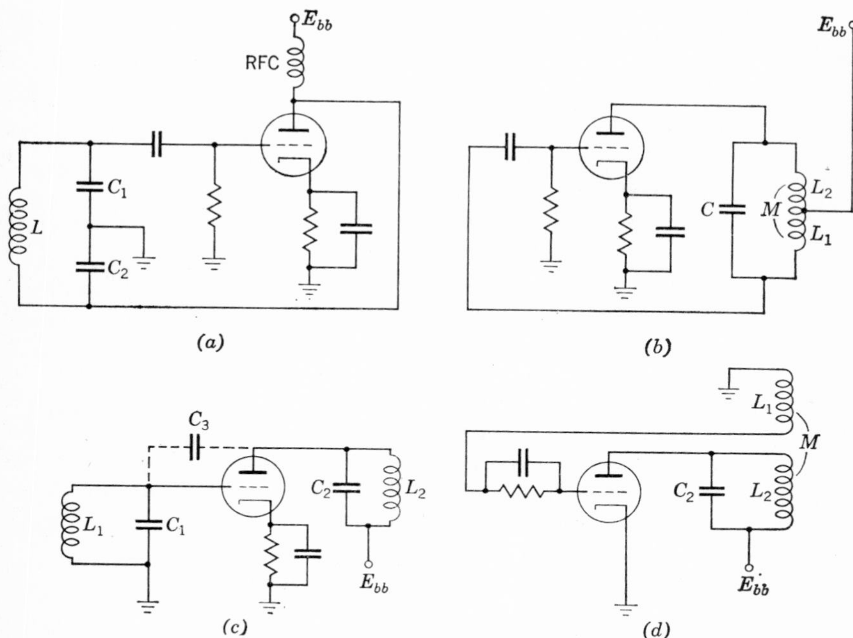

FIG. 14-16. Some practical vacuum-tube tuned oscillators. (a) Colpitts circuit; (b) Hartley circuit; (c) tuned-plate tuned-grid; (d) tuned-plate oscillator. The various components not labeled are used for bias and decoupling and would be chosen to have a negligible influence on the frequency of oscillation.

In the Colpitts oscillator of Fig. 14-16*a*, the frequency of oscillation as found from Eq. (14-22) is

$$\omega_{0C} = \sqrt{\frac{1}{LC_T}}$$

where $C_T = C_1C_2/C_1 + C_2$. For self-starting, $\mu \geq C_1/C_2$ [from Eq. (14-23)]. The Hartley circuit (Fig. 14-16*b*) oscillates at

$$\omega_{0H} = \sqrt{\frac{1}{C_3(L_1 + L_2 + 2M)}}$$

and here
$$\mu \geq \frac{L_2 + M}{L_1 + M}$$

In both circuits the frequency of oscillation is simply the resonant frequency of the *LC* combination. The capacitive term in the Colpitts equation is the series combination of C_1 and C_2. If the tube has a reasonably large gain, $C_2 \ll C_1$ and $C_T \cong C_2$. In the Hartley circuit, the inductive term is the total tank inductance and, with a high-gain tube, $L_2 \gg L_1$.

The Hartley and the two single tuned-circuit oscillators (circuits 2, 4, and 5 above) are best suited for variable-frequency operation. In these, the frequency may be changed by varying a single capacitor. Moreover, this adjustment will not affect the conditions for self-starting operation, which depends on the mutual coupling between two coils and on the location of the coil tap. In the other oscillators either two LC circuits must be retuned or two capacitors must be simultaneously tracked.

If the tank elements are dissipative, or if they are loaded by the external circuit when coupling to the next stage, then the associated resistance will change both the frequency of oscillation and the conditions for self-starting. Provisions for retuning and for adjusting the amount of feedback allow us to compensate for these changes. There is no point in calculating the new condition for threshold operation. It is, however, of some interest to recalculate the frequency of oscillation. By doing this we shall see that the circuit dissipation also makes the frequency dependent on the parameters of the active element.

Example 14-1. Let us consider, for example, the basic Colpitts oscillator of Fig, 14-16*a*, where the nominal unloaded frequency is $\omega_0 = 10^7$ radians/sec. The tube used has $\mu = 20$ and $r_p = 5$ K. The tank is so designed that $Q\sqrt{L/C_T} = 25$ K and, in addition, its loaded $Q = 25$.

From the above conditions, the tank components are found to be $C_T = 100\ \mu\mu$f and $L = 100\ \mu$h. To ensure self-starting and to allow for changes in the tube parameters we shall satisfy

$$\mu \cong 2\frac{C_1}{C_2}$$

instead of the threshold condition. Solving yields $C_2 = 110\ \mu\mu$f and $C_1 = 1{,}100\ \mu\mu$f. The final parameter—the equivalent series coil resistance—is

$$r = \frac{10^7 L}{Q} = \frac{10^7 \times 10^{-4}}{25} = 40 \text{ ohms}$$

By substituting $Z_3 = r + j\omega L$, $Z_1 = -j/\omega C_1$, and $Z_2 = -j/\omega C_2$ into Eq. (14-21) and collecting the imaginary terms, the frequency of oscillation is found from

$$r_p\left(\omega L - \frac{C_1 + C_2}{\omega C_1 C_2}\right) - \frac{r}{\omega C_2} = 0$$

The frequency becomes

$$\omega_0' = \sqrt{\frac{C_1 + C_2}{LC_1C_2}\left(1 + \frac{C_1}{C_1 + C_2}\right)\frac{r}{r_p}}$$

$$= \sqrt{10^{14}\left(1 + \frac{1{,}100}{1{,}210}\right)\frac{40}{5{,}000}} = 10^7\sqrt{1.00727}$$

or the frequency increases by approximately 0.36 per cent over its nominal value as a direct result of the resistive loading of the tank. The conditions for self-starting will also change; this calculation is left as an exercise for the reader.

Unless $r_p \gg r$, the circuit would be quite sensitive to the changes in r_p occurring during the life of the tube or when replacing tubes. Any resistive loading of the tuned circuit would effectively increase r and would also change the frequency of oscillation. External loading may be minimized by using an amplifier to decouple the final load from the oscillator stage and by loosely coupling this stage to the tank.

Transistor Tuned Oscillators. From the defining equations for the transistor model of Fig. 14-15*d*, the over-all system determinant is found to be

$$\Delta = \begin{vmatrix} r'_{11} + Z_1 & Z_m & -(Z_1 + Z_m) \\ \beta r_d + Z_m & r_d + Z_2 & -(Z_2 + Z_m) \\ -(Z_1 + Z_m) & -(Z_2 + Z_m) & Z_1 + Z_2 + Z_3 + 2Z_m \end{vmatrix} \tag{14-24}$$

When the impedances are all purely reactive, the imaginary part of the determinant will reduce to

$$r_d r'_{11}(X_1 + X_2 + X_3 + 2X_m) - X_3(X_1X_2 - X_m{}^2) = 0 \tag{14-25}$$

where the reactance term includes an associated sign. We might note that the first part of Eq. (14-25) contains the total series impedance of the self-resonant circuit composed of the three reactive elements. The last portion is a correction term due to the nature of the external loading of the tank. In general, we shall have to minimize the influence of these external factors if the oscillator is to have good frequency stability.

The significant portion of the frequency-determining equation is identical with that found for the vacuum-tube circuit. As discussed above, the nature of Z_3 must be opposite to Z_1 and Z_2. Consequently the possible circuit variations are those previously tabulated.

By assuming that the actual frequency of oscillation is very close to the natural frequency of the tank, the term

$$X_1 + X_2 + X_3 + 2X_m \cong 0$$

and the determinant may be simplified before solving for the condition for self-starting. It shall be found by setting the real part of the remaining terms equal to zero.

$$r'_{11}(X_2 + X_m)^2 + r_d(X_1 + X_m)^2 - \beta r_d(X_1 + X_m)(X_2 + X_m) = 0 \tag{14-26}$$

Because the second term on the left-hand side is relatively insignificant, Eq. (14-26) may be further simplified. The resulting criterion for self-starting oscillations becomes

$$\frac{X_2 + X_m}{X_1 + X_m} \le \frac{\beta r_d}{r'_{11}} = \frac{r_c}{r'_{11}} \tag{14-27}$$

To justify the use of this equation, we shall solve Eq. (14-27) for $(X_1 + X_m)$ and substitute back into the original expression.

$$r'_{11}(X_2 + X_m)^2 + \frac{(r'_{11})^2}{\beta^2 r_d}(X_2 + X_m)^2 - r'_{11}(X_2 + X_m)^2 = 0$$

The neglected second term is only $r'_{11}/\beta^2 r_d$ times as large as the first term. Since r'_{11} is the small input impedance, $\beta^2 r_d \gg r'_{11}$ and the condition expressed in Eq. (14-27) is essentially correct.

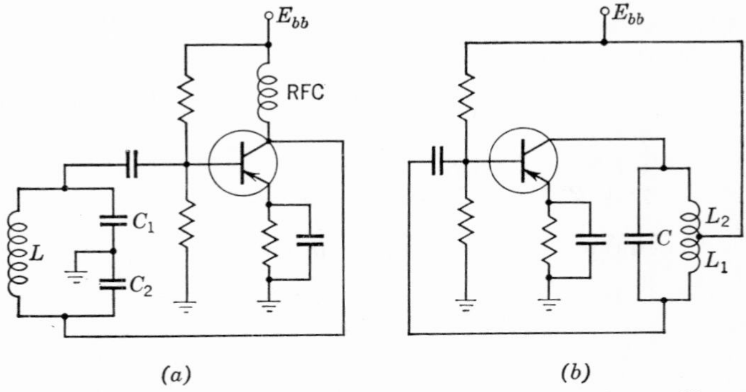

FIG. 14-17. (a) Transistor Colpitts oscillator; (b) Hartley oscillator.

From Eqs. (14-25) and (14-27) the frequency and gain requirements of the Colpitts oscillator of Fig. 14-17a are

$$\omega_{0C} = \sqrt{\frac{C_1 + C_2}{LC_1C_2} + \frac{1}{C_1C_2r_dr'_{11}}}$$

where $\sqrt{(C_1 + C_2)/LC_1C_2}$ is the resonant frequency of the unloaded tank. For self-starting, the Colpitts oscillator must be adjusted so that

$$\frac{r_c}{r'_{11}} \geq \frac{C_1}{C_2}$$

The Hartley circuit of Fig. 14-16b oscillates at

$$\omega_{0H} = \frac{1}{\sqrt{C(L_1 + L_2 + 2M) - \dfrac{L_1L_2 - M^2}{r_dr'_{11}}}}$$

and for self-starting,

$$\frac{r_c}{r'_{11}} \geq \frac{L_2 + M}{L_1 + M}$$

In both cases the resistive loading of the tuned circuit causes a small change in frequency from the nominal resonant point. This can be minimized by maximizing the $r_d r'_{11}$ product and by properly choosing the ratio of L to C. Furthermore, by using tightly coupled coils in the Hartley circuit, the numerator of the correction term will be reduced; with unity coupling it will reach zero and the circuit will oscillate exactly at ω_0.

Crystal Oscillators. A suitably clamped quartz crystal may be made to resonate by exciting it with an electrical signal of the proper frequency. The mechanical oscillations are fixed by the relative dimensions of the crystal, and the damping depends on the characteristics of the mounting. As the damping factor can be made quite small, the electromechanical Q will be proportionately large; expected values are between 1,000 and 50,000. To use the crystal in a fixed-frequency oscillator, we simply substitute it for one of the reactances in the basic tuned-oscillator configuration of Fig. 14-15.

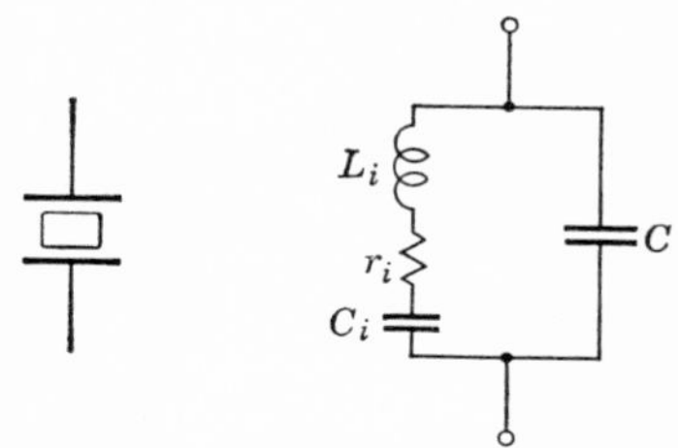

FIG. 14-18. Equivalent electrical circuit of a quartz crystal.

Sinusoidal oscillation is possible at one of the two modes of electromechanical resonance corresponding to the electrical resonances of the equivalent circuit of Fig. 14-18. The parallel-resonant mode depends on the mass factor L_i and the capacity of the mounting plates using the crystal as a dielectric, C. At this frequency, the terminal impedance is purely resistive and is extremely large. In its other mode, the mass and spring constant of the crystal, L_i and C_i, are series-resonant. Here the crystal is essentially a short circuit. Since the dissipation term r_i is small, the network appears reactive everywhere but at these two frequencies. Many crystals are cut to have several resonant points, and these might be incorporated into the electrical model by adding, in parallel, additional $L_i r_i C_i$ series arms.

Even though the frequency of oscillation is essentially that of the crystal, minor adjustments are possible, without reducing the Q. By adding series capacity or inductance the frequency can be changed by a few parts in a million. For wider ranges, the variable-frequency circuits would be used instead.

Two crystal-controlled oscillators are shown in Fig. 14-19. In the Pierce circuit, the crystal controls the amount of feedback applied. At its series-resonant frequency, the low impedance presented increases the amount of feedback to a point where oscillations can be sustained. Since the grid circuit is capacitive, the crystal must be slightly inductive for the proper phase of the feedback signal. To satisfy the conditions found above, the plate tank would also be tuned somewhat capacitively. To all other frequencies the crystal presents an extremely high reactance.

It thus reduces the loop gain well below the threshold value. Furthermore the net phase shift of the feedback voltage will no longer be the 180° needed for oscillation.

The second circuit of Fig. 14-19, the transistor oscillator, is a tuned-input tuned-output circuit with capacitive feedback. Here the output

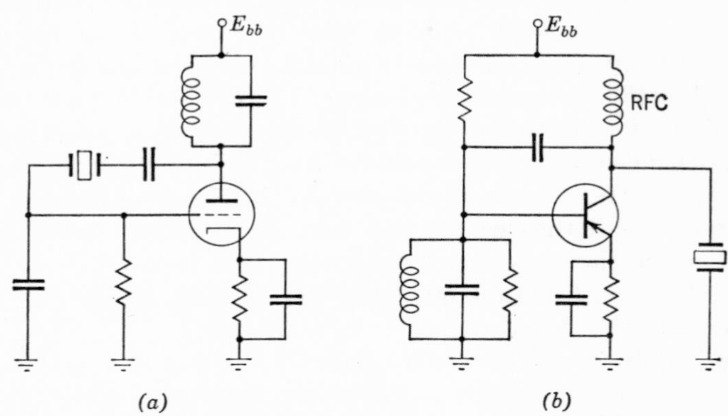

FIG. 14-19. (*a*) A Pierce oscillator using the crystal as a series-resonant mode; (*b*) a transistor oscillator where the crystal operates as a parallel-resonant circuit.

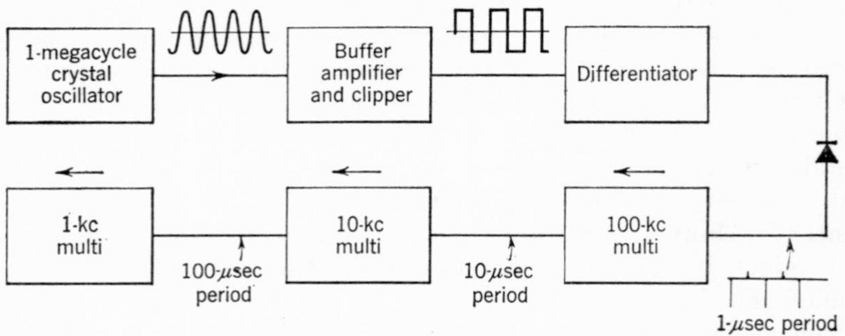

FIG. 14-20. A crystal-oscillator-controlled system designed for precise timing measurements.

will be developed when the crystal is a high impedance, i.e., at its parallel-resonant frequency. At all other frequencies the small reactance presented will load the amplifier and will also cause the feedback voltage to be in quadrature to that needed for oscillation.

Crystal-controlled oscillators are widely used as frequency standards. By amplifying, clipping, and finally differentiating a 1-megacycle sinusoid, we derive a train of negative pulses spaced 1 μsec apart. As shown in Fig. 14-20, these are next applied as a trigger source to synchronize an astable multivibrator normally operating at 100 kc. The 10-μsec-period pulse train may be further divided down by the other multivibrators shown. From this chain we derive pulse outputs spaced by 10 μsec, 100 μsec, 1 msec, etc. Since the base frequency can be maintained to within 1 part in 10^9, this system has been used for highly precise timing.

14-5. Frequency Stabilization. All oscillators are to some degree susceptible to frequency changes caused by the resistive loading of the selective network. If the loading were to remain constant, then the initial calibration of the instrument would correct for the deviation from the nominal tank resonance frequency. Unfortunately some of the dissipative elements may be expected to change with time, sometimes in one direction and sometimes erratically. All the circuit components contribute to this drift; even slight changes in the power-supply voltage will shift the operating point and thus affect the parameters of the active element. Therefore any oscillator which is designed as a precise frequency standard should be compensated with respect to all such variations.

We implicitly assume that the nature of the elements comprising the selective network is such that they themselves are completely stable with respect to aging and ambient-temperature variations.

Since it would be identical with detuning the tank, we are also neglecting the effects of any reactive loading of the tuned circuit. Some reactance would always appear across a portion, or across the complete tuned circuit, because of the interelectrode and stray capacity associated with the tube and the transistor. Choosing a large tuning capacity would, of course, make the frequency much less dependent on any changes in the parasitic-circuit elements.

Our first objective, then, is to eliminate, as far as possible, any other factors producing a frequency shift away from ω_0. Even though special provisions may be made in each individual circuit, such as using tightly coupled coils in the Hartley oscillator, in Sec. 14-4 we saw that the performance of all oscillators will be materially improved by minimizing the external loading of the network. First, a buffer amplifier may be used to decouple the oscillator from the varying output load, and second, since the harmonics produced in the limiter are reflected as additional loading, the circuit can be adjusted close to the threshold of oscillation. Finally, we should investigate the mechanism of frequency instability with a view toward selecting the circuit which best suits our particular needs.

Stabilization Factor. The frequency of oscillation is identically that frequency at which the net phase shift around the amplifier and feedback loop is zero. Since the feedback network contains reactive elements, the insertion of any resistance will change the phase response and also the null frequency. For example, assume that a change in one parameter, external to the tuned circuit, produces a net phase shift of 5° at the nominal frequency of oscillation f_0. For sustained oscillations, the remainder of the circuit must contribute the complementary shift of $-5°$. If the normal rate of phase variation in the vicinity of f_0 is $-10°$ per 1,000 cycles, then a frequency increase of only 500 cycles will reestablish the condition of zero net phase shift. The new frequency of oscillation would be $f_0 + 500$. From this simple example, we conclude that the highest degree of stability would correspond to the most rapid change of phase with frequency.

If, in an oscillator, we can find one set of elements whose phase varies most rapidly with frequency, then these elements would have the most pronounced effect on the over-all frequency stability. This will, in general, be the frequency-selective network. As a measure of frequency stability, we define the normalized sensitivity factor

$$S_f \equiv \frac{\Delta\phi}{\Delta\omega/\omega_0} \tag{14-28}$$

The larger the value of S_f, the more stable the oscillator with respect to all changes in the circuit which may produce an undesirable frequency shift. When, in the limit, S_f becomes infinite, the frequency of oscillation is completely independent of all other sections of the system.

Figure 14-21*a* is a plot of the phase behavior of a Wien bridge. In the vicinity of its null frequency, the response is similar to that seen in all other unbalanced null networks (Fig. 14-21*b*). For this particular example, the phase of β', as found from Eq. (14-14), is

$$\phi = \tan^{-1}\frac{3-\delta}{9}\left(\frac{\omega}{\omega_0} - \frac{\omega_0}{\omega}\right) - \tan^{-1}\frac{1}{3}\left(\frac{\omega}{\omega_0} - \frac{\omega_0}{\omega}\right) \tag{14-29}$$

This is plotted as a function of ω/ω_0 for three different degrees of unbalance. One of the three is the completely unbalanced bridge ($\delta = 3$). It is readily apparent that S_f reaches a maximum at ω_0 and that the closer the bridge is to balance, the larger its value. Differentiating Eq. (14-29) with respect to ω and multiplying by ω_0 yields

$$S_f = \omega_0\frac{d\phi}{d\omega} = \frac{\frac{3-\delta}{9}\left[1 + \left(\frac{\omega_0}{\omega}\right)^2\right]}{1 + \left(\frac{3-\delta}{9}\right)^2\left(\frac{\omega}{\omega_0} - \frac{\omega_0}{\omega}\right)^2} - \frac{\frac{1}{3}\left[1 + \left(\frac{\omega_0}{\omega}\right)^2\right]}{1 + \frac{1}{9}\left(\frac{\omega}{\omega_0} - \frac{\omega_0}{\omega}\right)^2}$$

Since $\delta \geq 3$, both terms will have the same sign and each will reach its maximum at $\omega = \omega_0$. Evaluating S_f at this frequency,

$$S_{f_0} = -\tfrac{2}{9}\delta \tag{14-30}$$

The minus sign indicates the direction of the phase change with frequency.

Equation (14-30) shows that the bridge improves the circuit stability in proportion to its degree of balance. We might note that previously we had shown that this same condition was necessary for the optimum harmonic rejection [Eq. (14-16)].

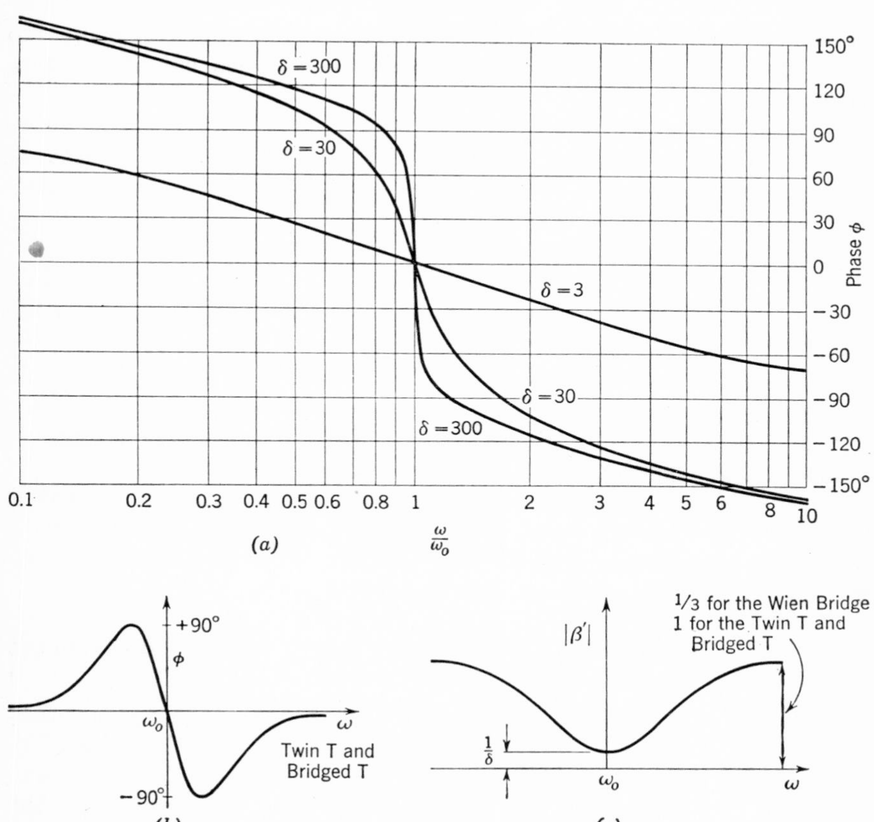

FIG. 14-21. Amplitude and phase characteristics of null networks. (*a*) Phase response of the Wien bridge; (*b*) the phase response of unbalanced bridge using a twin-T or a bridged-T network for one pair of arms; (*c*) the general amplitude response of the null networks.

Unless a sharp null is exhibited by the network, the phase changes relatively slowly in the vicinity of ω_0. The curve for $\delta = 3$ in Fig. 14-21*a* illustrates a variation of this nature. Since this curve represents the behavior of a completely unbalanced bridge, it also typifies the response of such *RC* and *RL* circuits as the phase-shift oscillator.

The phase response of a tuned-circuit oscillator is related to the circulating current through the three reactive components Z_1, Z_2, and

Z_3. Near ω_0 the relative phase of the feedback voltage, which is developed at the active-elements input, may be approximated as

$$\phi = \tan^{-1} Q_0 \left(\frac{\omega}{\omega_0} - \frac{\omega_0}{\omega} \right) \tag{14-31}$$

If this were to be plotted, we would have a family of curves similar to those drawn for the Wien bridge. After all, a tuned circuit is also a

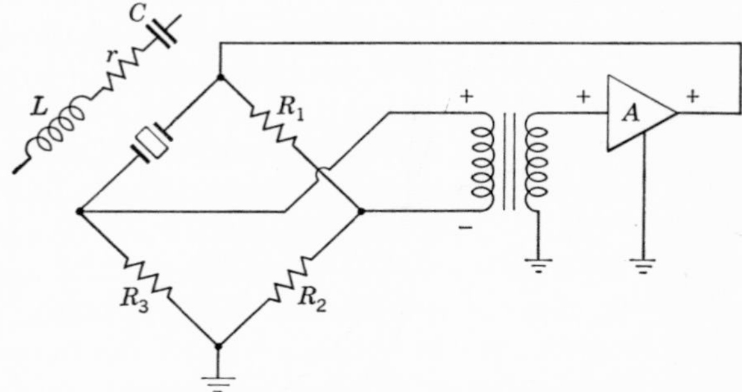

FIG. 14-22. Meacham-bridge oscillator.

null network. The phase starts at 90°, reaches the 180° necessary for the positive feedback at ω_0, and then continues increasing toward 270° at the higher frequencies. The frequency-sensitivity factor of this phase response, evaluated at ω_0, is

$$S_{f_0} = 2Q$$

For optimum stability we should use a high-Q circuit and should set the oscillation frequency as close to ω_0 as possible. An extremely good choice for one of the elements is a crystal which will give a frequency-stability factor of 10^3 to 10^5. With a normal tuned circuit, the best that can be expected is about 10^2.

For an extremely precise frequency standard we can combine the improvement found in a high-Q crystal-controlled oscillator with the selectivity multiplication of an almost balanced bridge. The Meacham oscillator of Fig. 14-22 has the highest stability of any circuit yet devised. The bridge nulls at exactly the series-resonant frequency of the crystal. At this frequency the crystal appears completely resistive, which makes the bridge easy to balance. By using a small degree of unbalance $(1/\delta)$ and approximately equal resistance arms, the stability factor will be

$$S_{f_0} = 2\delta Q$$

and for $Q_0 = 10^5$, stabilization up to 1 part in 10^8 is possible. This means that if the amplifier introduces a phase shift of 0.1 radian (a relatively large value), the frequency would change by only 1 part in 10^9.

Reactive Stabilization. Llewellyn showed that it is possible to stabilize an oscillator by inserting reactances in series with the terminals of the active element or in series with the applied load. The theory behind such stabilization is that the tank circuit appears resistive at its own resonant frequency and that only the need to compensate for the additional loop phase angles causes the frequency to shift. Now if the external resistance sees a completely resistive internal impedance, it would not affect the phase of the system; it would only increase the loading and the gain required for threshold operation. At many points in the circuit the two-terminal impedance has a reactive part. When this is loaded, the complete phase response of the system changes. By inserting in series with the external load a reactance of the opposite type to that originally seen, it is possible to tune the subsidiary loop and thus reduce the net phase shift to zero. The load now sees a pure resistance, and the frequency becomes independent of the load and of load variations.

The nature of this stabilizing reactance depends on the terminal at which it is introduced and on the configuration of the over-all network. It is also possible, by inserting a single reactance at an appropriate point, to compensate for the loading at several different parts of the network. But in general, compensation elements would have to be inserted in series with each of the resistive components of the external circuit.

As an example, we shall insert such a reactance in series with the base in the Hartley transistor oscillator described in Sec. 14-4. For simplicity, the mutual coupling will be taken as zero. Furthermore, since the stabilization will return the frequency to ω_0, the series impedance of the tank will also be zero. The simplified system determinant will now be

$$\Delta = \begin{vmatrix} r'_{11} + Z_s + Z_1 & 0 & -Z_1 \\ \beta r_d & Z_2 + r_d & -Z_2 \\ -Z_1 & -Z_2 & 0 \end{vmatrix}$$

where Z_s represents the stabilizing reactance. Setting the imaginary part equal to zero (when all impedances are purely reactive) yields

$$X_sX_2^2 + X_1X_2^2 + X_1^2X_2 = 0$$

and this equation enables us to find the value of X_s.

$$X_s = -X_1\left(1 + \frac{X_1}{X_2}\right)$$

But if the active element employed in the oscillator has a high gain, then, from Eq. (14-27), we see that $1 \gg X_1/X_2$ and the stabilizing reactance

$$X_s \cong -X_1 \tag{14-32}$$

The element to be inserted in series with r'_{11} is a capacitor whose reactance at ω_0 is given in Eq. (14-32).

In order to obtain an order of magnitude for C_s, consider a circuit where $C = 250\ \mu\mu\text{f}$, $L_1 = 10\ \mu\text{h}$, $L_2 = 990\ \mu\text{h}$, and $\omega_0 = 2 \times 10^6$. Substituting into the expression for X_s yields

$$C_s = \frac{1}{\omega_0^2 L_1} = \frac{1}{4 \times 10^{+12} \times 10 \times 10^{-6}} = 0.025\ \mu\text{f}$$

This value is quite feasible, and it would appear in the circuit as an input coupling capacitor. Note that C_s depends on the frequency and on the value of L_1. For variable-frequency oscillators, stabilization of this nature is obviously impractical.

14-6. Amplitude of Oscillations. The exponential build-up of the self-starting oscillator will continue as long as the average gain over the cycle is greater than the threshold value. Eventually, the amplitude of the output sinusoid is limited as its peaks force the instantaneous operating point into the nonlinear regions. As a crude first-order approximation, we can say that the output will be equal to the linear capabilities of the system. Since this depends on the nature and point of application of the nonlinearities, we shall now examine several of the amplitude-limiting schemes used in practical oscillations. Fortunately, the exact signal level is much less significant than the exact frequency, and therefore we can justify relatively gross approximations in treating this problem.

1. *Active-element Limiting.* The first case considered is where the amplitude is limited by the tube (transistor) being driven into saturation and/or cutoff. We shall make the following assumptions as to the oscillator behavior.

1. The gain is adjusted to slightly beyond the threshold value so that the output is not excessively distorted.

2. The selectivity of the frequency-determining network will greatly reduce the amplitude of the harmonics produced, and consequently there will be an almost pure sinusoid present at one point at least.

Since the response is sinusoidal at one point in the closed system, the oscillator behavior may be simulated by opening the loop at this point and exciting the open circuit from an external sinusoidal source of the same frequency. For example, in the Colpitts oscillator of Fig. 14-23*a*, the loop has been opened at the grid. To avoid changing the over-all response, the network must be loaded by the impedance it normally sees. The sinusoidal driving signal must also be injected through a source impedance of the appropriate magnitude.

In our effort to describe the nonlinear behavior of the oscillator, without having to account for the different impedances presented by the tank at its various harmonic frequencies, we shall assume that the plate load is a constant equal to the resistance of the tank at resonance. This incorrect assumption can be justified only by noting that, in an almost sinusoidal oscillator, the fundamental component is the predominant term. Any error resulting will be insignificant if the totality of the

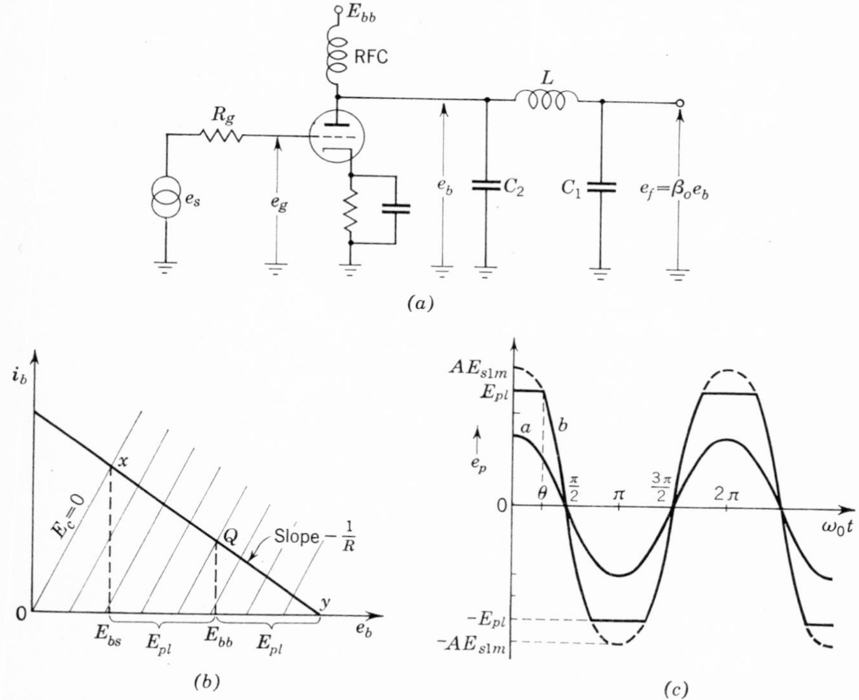

FIG. 14-23. (a) Open-circuit Colpitts oscillator; (b) plate-circuit operating path at the fundamental frequency; (c) plate waveshapes for two values of drive, assuming a constant-resistance plate load.

harmonics calculated on the basis of a constant-resistance load remains small. But this is the same as saying that the net gain in the small-signal region should be adjusted to slightly beyond the threshold value.

By solving Fig. 14-23 we find that the effective input resistance of the unloaded high-Q tuned circuit at resonance may be expressed as

$$R_{\text{in}_0} = R = \left(\frac{C_1}{C_1 + C_2}\right)^2 Q \sqrt{\frac{L}{C_T}} \tag{14-33}$$

From the self-starting condition for this oscillator, $C_1 < \mu C_2$, we see that C_2 is the smaller capacity; when $\mu > 10$, it will completely predominate. Thus the nominal resistance of the tank at resonance reduces to

$$R = Q\sqrt{\frac{L}{C_2}}$$

Using the equivalent load resistance R, the path of operation of the base amplifier is constructed (Fig. 14-23b) and the bounds of the linear region delineated.

For an input excitation of

$$e_s = E_{s1m} \cos \omega_0 t$$

the output remains sinusoidal up to the linear capabilities of the tube (point x or y in Fig. 14-23b and the corresponding point W in Fig. 14-24). Above this value the output is clipped by the nonlinearity as shown in Fig. 14-23c. In reality, the tank cannot sustain such a waveshape, but from it we can determine the approximate amplitude of the fundamental component of the tank voltage. Equation (14-34) may be used:

$$E_{p1m} = \frac{1}{\pi}\int_0^{2\pi} e_p \cos \omega_0 t \, d\omega_0 t \tag{14-34}$$

where e_p is the time-varying component of the plate voltage. When the output is not readily expressed in the form of an analytic function, the fundamental will be found by a graphical integration or by a schedule method.

Suppose, for instance, that the tube is biased so that the plate operating path is symmetrical about E_{bb}. One clipping point is at the $E_c = 0$ line, while the other corresponds to cutoff. If we further assume that the limiting in both regions is ideal, then the approximate waveshapes with which we are concerned are shown in Fig. 14-23c. From Fig. 14-23b, the peak signal in the linear region of operation is

$$E_{pl} = E_{bb} - E_{bs} = A(E_{s1m})_l = \frac{R}{2r_p + R} E_{bb} \tag{14-35}$$

where $A = -\mu R/(r_p + R)$. In a transistor oscillator biased in the center of its active region $E_{pl} \cong E_{bb}$.

Because of the symmetry exhibited by the signal of Fig. 14-23c, Eq. (14-34) reduces to

$$\begin{aligned} E_{p1m} &= \frac{4}{\pi}\int_0^{\theta} E_{pl} \cos \omega_0 t \, d\omega_0 t + \frac{4}{\pi}\int_{\theta}^{\pi/2} A E_{s1m} \cos^2 \omega_0 t \, d\omega_0 t \\ &= \frac{4}{\pi} E_{pl}\left[\sin\theta + \frac{AE_{s1m}}{2E_{pl}}\left(\frac{\pi - 2\theta}{2} - \sin 2\theta\right)\right] \end{aligned} \tag{14-36}$$

where $$\theta = \cos^{-1}\frac{E_{pl}}{AE_{s1m}}$$

The function describing the amplitude response of the oscillator, that is, E_{p1m} versus E_{s1m}, may now be plotted (curve a in Fig. 14-24). This same describing function is often obtained experimentally, by measuring the output as the input excitation is increased. At each point on the curve the ratio of E_{p1m}/E_{s1m} is the average gain of the base amplifier over 1 cycle of the fundamental. Since the criterion for the stable oscillation is satisfied when the gain is equal to $1/\beta_0$, by superimposing a line having

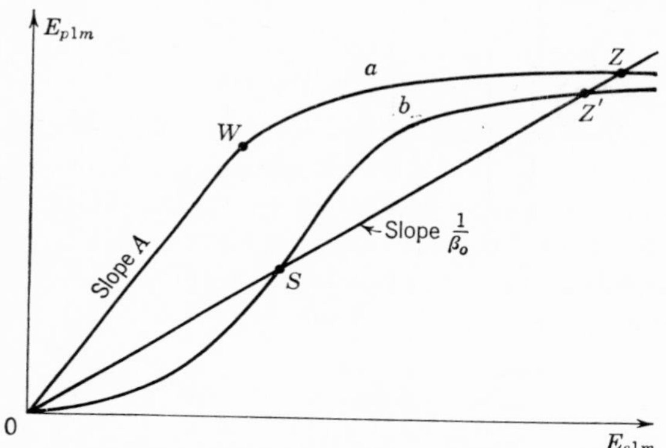

FIG. 14-24. Curve a, describing function for the oscillator of Fig. 14-23; curve b, describing function of a non-self-starting oscillator.

this slope and by locating its intersection with the describing function, we find the amplitude satisfying

$$A_{av} = \frac{E_{p1mz}}{E_{s1mz}} = \frac{1}{\beta_0}$$

When the small-signal gain is only slightly greater than the threshold value, point Z will fall close to the upper limit of the linear range of the circuit. Thus the area between the $1/\beta_0$ line and the describing function gives a qualitative measure of the harmonic content of the output; if the area is small, the signal will be an acceptable sinusoid; if it is large, the output will be somewhat distorted. That Z of Fig. 14-24 is the sole stable point may be verified by considering the response to a small change in the input excitation. If the input is momentarily reduced, then the new value of loop gain becomes greater than unity, indicating that the signal must now increase with time. Above point Z, the average loop gain is less than the minimum value needed to sustain the oscillations and they begin decreasing toward the stable value.

Curve b in Fig. 14-24 illustrates the shape of a describing function of a non-self-starting oscillator. This might be the circuit of Fig. 14-23 when the tube is biased on the verge of cutoff instead of in the center of its linear region. At small-signal levels the average gain is less than $1/\beta_0$

and the circuit is unable to sustain oscillations. However, if some external excitation forces the operating point past S, the oscillatory criterion is satisfied and the amplitude will continue to increase toward point Z'.

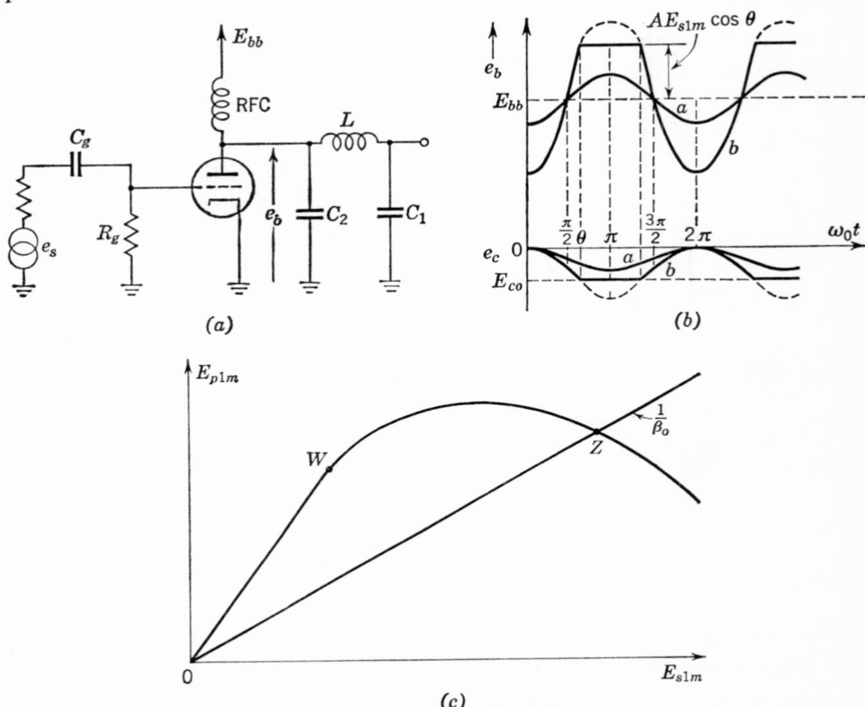

FIG. 14-25. (a) Grid-bias-limited Colpitts oscillator; (b) plate waveshapes for small a and large b excitation; (c) describing function for a circuit with bias limiting.

Nonsymmetrical clipping of the sinusoid will produce an additional d-c component in the plate current. It would be found from

$$I_{\text{dc}} = \frac{1}{2\pi} \int_0^{2\pi} \frac{e_p}{R} \, d\omega t$$

and since I_{dc} flows through R_K, the bias would change slightly. The resultant shift in the transfer characteristics might have to be considered when constructing the describing function. This shift is in the direction of more symmetrical operation, and it therefore aids in reducing the harmonics present in the output.

2. *Bias Limiting.* The general circuit response is similar to that considered in case 1, except that the bias is derived by the grid current charging of C_g (Fig. 14-25a). The only difference in the analysis is that

the input sinusoid would be clamped at zero by the energy-storage element included in the input lead. Consequently the position of the load line shifts with the driving-signal amplitude. The locus of the minimum plate voltage is the $E_c = 0$ line. As illustrated in Fig. 14-25*b*, until such time as the grid is driven below cutoff, the output voltage will vary symmetrically about E_{bb}.

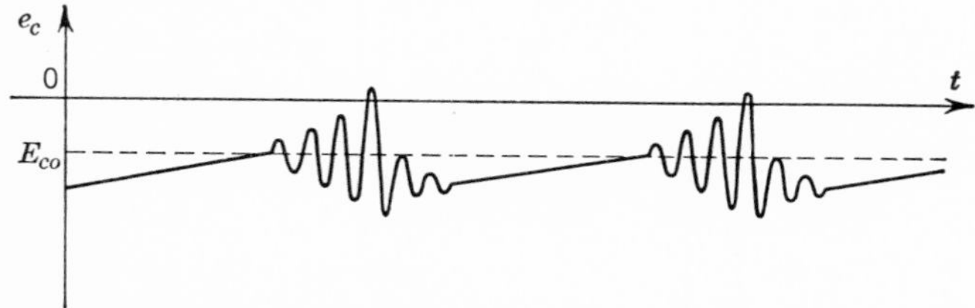

FIG. 14-26. Intermittent oscillation in a grid-bias-limited oscillator.

E_{p1m} is readily evaluated once θ is defined. From the clamped grid-circuit waveshape of Fig. 14-25*b*,

$$e_c = -E_{s1m} + E_{s1m} \cos \omega_0 t$$

Hence θ is given by

$$\theta = \cos^{-1}\left(1 + \frac{E_{co}}{E_{s1m}}\right)$$

where

$$E_{co} = -\frac{E_{bb} + AE_{s1m} \cos \theta}{\mu}$$

For this type of limiting, the amplitude would also be found from the describing function of the system (Fig. 14-25*c*). Of particular interest is that the output can reach a maximum and then decrease with an increasing input. When the output amplitude is stabilized on the decreasing segment of the describing function, the circuit is prone to intermittent oscillations, or "squegging." On the positive peaks the large pulses of grid current charge the input capacitor. If the net charge accumulated in C_g on the positive peaks is greater than the energy dissipated in R_g over the remaining portion of the sinusoid, the bias voltage will build up to a point where it cuts off the tube. The larger the net charge accumulating, the fewer the number of cycles contained in the oscillation interval. As the oscillations damp out (Fig. 14-26), C_g recovers toward zero, with the long time constant C_gR_g. The tube eventually turns on, and the cycle repeats. Reducing the time constant will often allow the circuit to oscillate properly.

3. *Feedback Limiting.* In this case, a passive nonlinear element is included in the feedback network at a point where it can change the magnitude of β but where it will not affect the null frequency. For

example, in the Wien-bridge oscillator of Fig. 14-27, the degree of bridge unbalance is controlled by the thermal characteristics of the tungsten lamp, which is used as one of the resistive arms. Its resistance increases with temperature, and hence with the voltage applied across the branch and across the bridge (Fig. 14-28). Normally the bridge is slightly unbalanced ($\beta' = 1/\delta$), adjusted so that the amplifier can just sustain the given amplitude of oscillation. Any increase in the output voltage will increase the resistance of the lamp and bring the bridge into closer balance, thus increasing δ. The loop gain will drop below unity, and the oscillations will start damping out. Any decrease in the output would establish the conditions necessary for an amplitude build-up. We conclude that this form of resistive limiting maintains a constant output amplitude with a high degree of stability. The normal operating condition is now given by

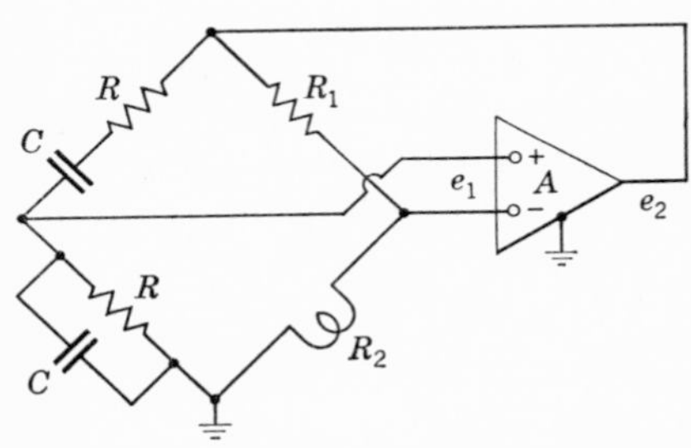

FIG. 14-27. Amplitude-controlled Wien-bridge oscillator.

$$A\beta'(e,\omega) = 1 \tag{14-37}$$

where A is simply the gain constant of the system. At ω_0 this reduces to

$$\frac{A}{\delta(e)} = 1$$

and the particular voltage e satisfying this equation is the oscillation amplitude. Since the limiting process readjusts the β' of the network, this oscillator will always operate under the threshold condition expressed in Eq. (14-37). Moreover, as the amplifier is never driven into its nonlinear region, the output will be almost completely free of harmonic distortion.

The lamp has thermal inertia, and consequently it will only respond to the mean value of the voltage applied over some small time interval. A standard small bulb, operating in the range of 600 to 1000°K, far below the temperature used for illumination, has a thermal time constant between 20 and 75 msec. The mass of the filament and the construction of the bulb are the determining factors; the smaller the nominal power rating of the lamp, the shorter the time constant. With respect to any single cycle, the tungsten lamp may be treated as a fixed resistance. At the lower audio frequencies where the period is comparable to the thermal time constant (below 20 cps), the change in resistance over the individual cycle distorts the output sinusoid and sets a lower frequency limit for this method of amplitude limiting.

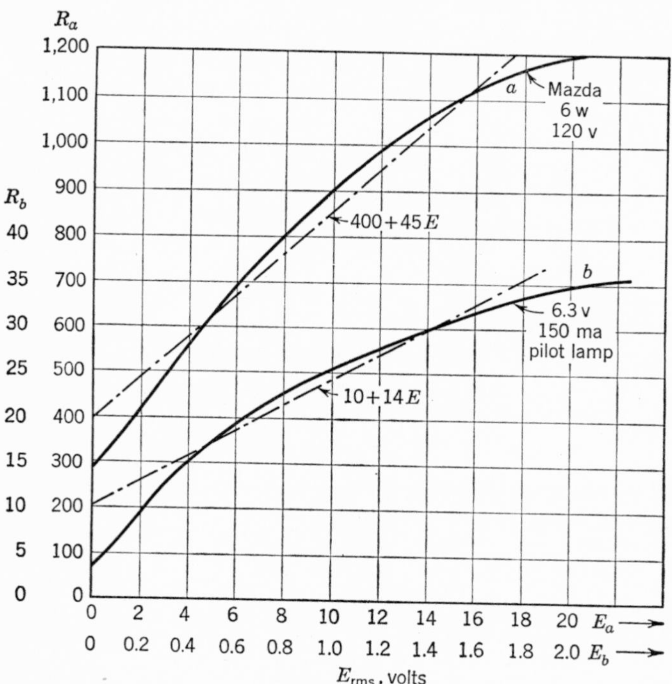

FIG. 14-28. Resistance characteristics of two typical tungsten lamps and their linear approximations.

Example 14-2. Let us consider the design of the amplitude-limited bridge of Fig. 14-27. The circuit contains an amplifier which has a nominal gain of 300 and a dynamic range of 120 volts peak to peak. The 6-watt Mazda lamp of Fig. 14-28 will be used for amplitude limiting.

To allow some latitude for variations in the amplifier response, we shall limit the output sinusoid to 30 volts rms. With the large gain available, the bridge will be almost completely balanced. For threshold operation $\delta_t = A_t = 300$, leading to

$$\frac{R_2}{R_1 + R_2} = \frac{1}{3} - \frac{1}{\delta} = \frac{1}{3} - \frac{1}{300} = 0.330$$

The voltage across the lamp is

$$E_{R2} = 0.33E_2 = 9.9 \text{ volts}$$

Since a high degree of quality control cannot be expected in a device made for illumination and not originally designed as a control element, the actual lamp characteristics will vary over very wide limits. Any reasonable approximation will serve for design purposes; for simplicity we shall use a straight line. Within the range of interest ($2 < E < 18$), the Mazda lamp will have a resistance variation given by

$$R_2 \cong 400 + 45E$$

At 9.9 volts across the lamp, the effective resistance is 845 ohms. Substituting into the bridge arm equation,

$$R_1 = \frac{1.0 - 0.33}{0.33} R_2 = 1{,}706 \text{ ohms}$$

R_1 would be made somewhat adjustable to allow for variation in the lamp resistance.

We shall now assume that the bridge is balanced as calculated above and that the amplifier gain decreases by 33 per cent because of the aging of the tubes. To sustain the oscillations, R_2 must also change until it satisfies

$$\frac{R_2'}{R_2' + R_1} = \frac{1}{3} - \frac{1}{200} = 0.3283$$

Thus R_2 becomes

$$R_2' = (1 - 0.0076)R_2 = 838.6 \text{ ohms}$$

The decrease of 0.76 per cent in the lamp resistance corresponds to a new lamp voltage of

$$E'_{R2} = 9.755 \text{ volts}$$

The new stable output is 29.71 volts. A gain reduction of 33 per cent is accompanied by an amplitude change of only 1.0 per cent. Consequently, this method of limiting also ensures amplitude stability. At the new output, the oscillator again operates under threshold conditions.

The technique of limiting by automatically controlling the feedback has also been applied to the Meacham bridge (Fig. 14-22), where the lamp replaces R_2, and to several tuned-circuit oscillators, where a resistance bridge containing lamps might be used for feedback. Figure 14-29 illustrates an amplitude-controlled bridge used to separate the feedback control from the frequency-selective network. Limiting may be assigned solely to the bridge. Other tuned circuits have used small lamps in series with the coil to control the effective Q of the tank.

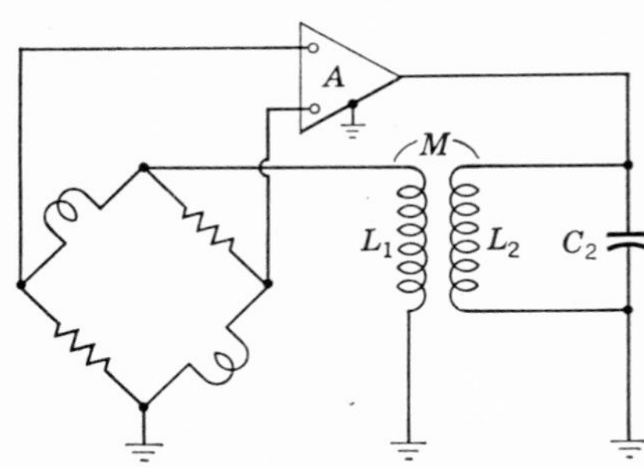

FIG. 14-29. Bridge-controlled feedback oscillator.

Besides tungsten lamps, most semiconductor materials (e.g., carbon, silicon, and germanium) and many compounds, such as silicon carbide, exhibit temperature-sensitive resistance properties. All these have been used for amplitude limiting. But since the semiconductor thermistors have a negative temperature coefficient of resistance, in contrast to the positive one of the pure metals, they will be used to replace the complementary arm of the bridge. In the Wien-bridge circuit of Fig. 14-27, the thermistor would substitute for R_1 instead of R_2. Thermistors are fabricated in a much wider range of resistance, and rate of resistance variation with temperature, than can be expected from a tungsten filament. Operating as they do at a lower temperature (300 to 375°K), they are extremely sensitive to changes in the ambient. For acceptable amplitude stability some form of temperature compensation would be necessary.

4. *Automatic Gain Control.* Threshold operation of the oscillator may also be ensured by using the output amplitude to control the gain of the base amplifier. With many active elements it is possible to find some d-c voltage or current which will determine the magnitude of the forward transmission. For example, in a pentode the grid-to-plate transconductance is a function of the suppressor voltage. Remote-control tubes are designed with a gain that decreases with the control-grid bias. In a tetrode junction transistor the value of β may be adjusted within relatively wide limits by injecting a bias current into the second base connection. And in all tubes and transistors, the small-signal gain varies widely with the quiescent point when operating close to cutoff.

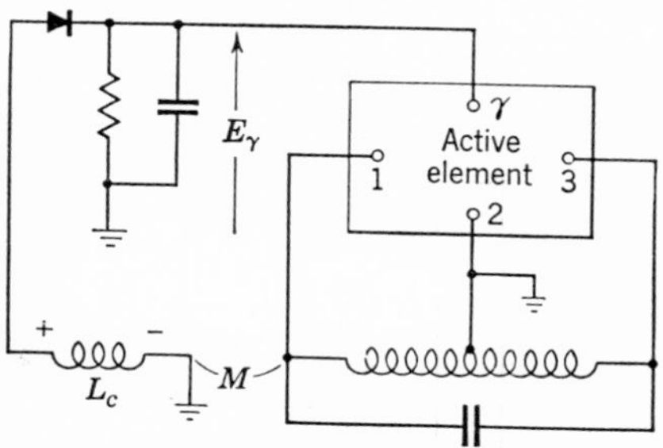

FIG. 14-30. Basic automatic-gain-control oscillator—Hartley circuit.

By deriving the gain-control voltage from the oscillator output, any increase in the amplitude will create the conditions that will automatically reduce the gain and the signal. The response to a decrease in the output would be just the opposite. This action is similar to the thermally adjusted bridge previously discussed. To avoid distorting the individual cycle, the sinusoidal output is rectified and applied through a relatively long time constant to the gain-control element. Therefore the amplitude-defining equation may be written

$$A(E)\beta_0 = 1$$

where E is the d-c control signal.

Consider the general problem posed in Fig. 14-30, where the control terminal is indicated by γ. The output of the oscillator is coupled through the extra coil winding, rectified, and applied to this terminal. As shown, the gain is assumed to decrease with any increase in E_γ (or with an increase in the oscillation amplitude). For example, the linear approximation of the transconductance may be expressed as

$$g_m = g_{m0} - KE_\gamma \tag{14-38}$$

where K is a positive constant. If g_m were to increase with E_γ, then the control loop would be regenerative instead of degenerative and the output amplitude would increase until the active element limits.

At any particular amplitude, the threshold of oscillation, as given by Eq. (14-23), is

$$\mu = r_p g_m = \frac{L_2 + M}{L_1 + M}$$

Taking the various coupling factors and amplitude transformations into

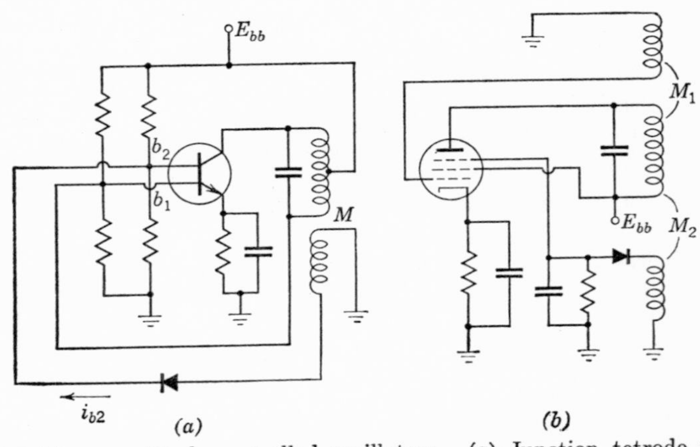

FIG. 14-31. Two amplitude-controlled oscillators. (a) Junction tetrode transistor circuit—Hartley oscillator. The control current is injected into the second base ($\beta = \beta_0 - Ki_{b2}$). (b) A pentode tuned-plate oscillator where the suppressor is used to control the effective transconductance.

account, this condition may be expressed as

$$g_{m0}r_p - K'E_0 = \frac{L_2 + M}{L_1 + M}$$

E_0 is the peak value of the sinusoidal output and will be found from the solution of this equation.

Figure 14-31 shows two oscillators using automatic gain control to maintain the threshold operation. The first one is a transistor oscillator where the gain-control current is injected into the second base connection. Variations in β over a range of 20:1 have been measured for control-current variations between 0 and 2 ma. In the second circuit, the control signal is fed to the suppressor. An alternative arrangement, where the roles of the suppressor and the control grid are interchanged, has also been used; the greater effectiveness of the control grid in varying the gain of the tube would further improve the amplitude stability.

In all the amplitude-controlled circuits, the variation of the controlled source with respect to the variable bias is difficult to express in general terms and will have to be evaluated in each individual case. Because the range of operation is severely restricted, a few measurements are usually sufficient. The best region in which to operate is the one where the variation of the controlling element with voltage is most pronounced. Even though satisfactory limiting has been obtained by this method, the selectivity multiplication of the bridge makes it superior when the output amplitude must be maintained constant. For an extremely high degree of stability, both methods of limiting may be incorporated in a single circuit.

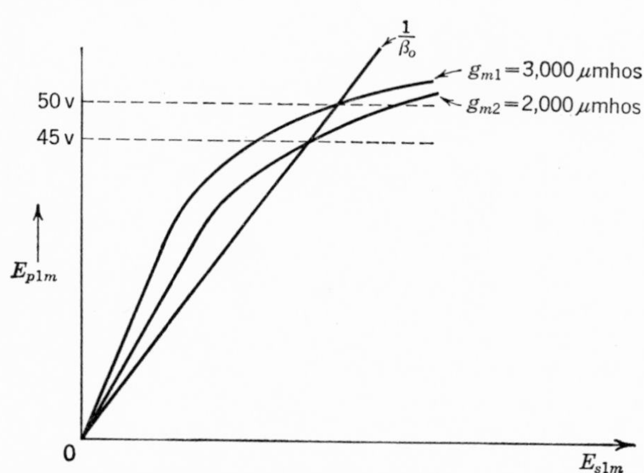

FIG. 14-32. Amplitude stability illustrated by describing functions.

14-7. Amplitude Stability. As a second figure of merit for the oscillator, we might define a normalized amplitude stability factor

$$S_E^x = \frac{dx/x}{dE/E} \tag{14-39}$$

where x is the variable having the most pronounced effect on the amplitude. We interpret S_E^x as meaning that a 10 per cent change in x produces only a $10/S_E^x$ per cent change in the amplitude of oscillation.

In those circuits where the limiting depends on the nonlinearity of the active elements, S_E^x may be found graphically by plotting a family of describing functions for various values of x. This process is illustrated in Fig. 14-32, where the variable of interest is the g_m of the tube. At the intersection with the $1/\beta_0$ line, the stability factor would be given by

$$S_E^{g_m} \cong \frac{\Delta g_m/g_{m\,\text{av}}}{\Delta E/E_{\text{av}}} = \frac{(g_{m1} - g_{m2})/(g_{m1} + g_{m2})}{(E_1 - E_2)/(E_1 + E_2)}$$

For the values shown in Fig. 14-32,

$$S_E^{g_m} = 3.8$$

If the amount of feedback were to be increased, then the stable point of operation would fall on the more nearly horizontal portion of the describing function and the stability would improve. However, under these conditions, the harmonic content of the output would also increase, and as this represents a loading on the frequency-selective network, the frequency stability would be adversely affected.

In the automatically stabilized circuits, such as the Wien-bridge oscillator of Fig. 14-27, any change in the base gain is compensated for by controlling the degree of bridge unbalance. Since A is always equal to δ, the stability factor of interest is S_E^δ. For the Wien bridge

$$\frac{R_0 + KE}{R_0 + KE + R_1} = \frac{1}{3} - \frac{1}{\delta} \tag{14-40}$$

By taking the differential, there results

$$\frac{R_1 K}{(R_1 + R_0 + KE)^2}\, dE = \frac{1}{\delta^2}\, d\delta \tag{14-41}$$

But from Eq. (14-40),

$$\frac{R_1}{R_1 + R_0 + KE} = \frac{2}{3} + \frac{1}{\delta} \tag{14-42}$$

Since $\delta \gg 1$, the result of substituting Eq. (14-42) into Eq. (14-41) and of solving for the stability factor is

$$S_E^\delta = \frac{2}{3}\, \delta\, \frac{KE}{R_1 + R_0 + KE} \tag{14-43}$$

As the rate of the resistance variation with voltage K increases, S_E^δ will approach $2\delta/3$ as an upper limit. Thus the amplitude stability is directly proportional to the amplifier gain and to the degree of bridge unbalance. Maximizing Eq. (14-43) by using a high-gain base amplifier also optimizes the frequency stability [Eq. (14-30)] and the harmonic rejection ratio [Eq. (14-16)].

For the particular values used in Example 14-2, $\delta = 300$, the amplitude stabilization becomes

$$S_E^\delta = 35.3$$

This is many times the stability that could be obtained in the pure-resistance bridge unless the signal is distorted beyond recognition by the limiting in the tube.

The automatic-gain-control circuit (Fig. 14-30) has a stability factor directly proportional to the rate of change of g_m with the control voltage. Since

$$g_m = g_{m0} - K'E_\gamma$$

$$S_E^{g_m} = -K'\,\frac{E_\gamma}{g_m}$$

For optimum stability a tube whose element has the most pronounced control over the transconductance should be chosen. Moreover, if the signal were to be amplified before applying it for control, the stability factor could be increased to almost any desired value.

PROBLEMS

14-1. (*a*) Find the frequency and necessary gain for sustained oscillation if the phase-shift network of Fig. 14-5 consists of four equal RC sections instead of three.

(*b*) Evaluate $|H_2|$ and $|K_2|$ for this network. Compare the answers with the harmonic coefficients found for the three-section network.

(*c*) Can the conditions for oscillation be satisfied with a two-section network? Explain your answer.

14-2. (*a*) The network of Fig. 14-4*c* is used in the phase-shift circuit. Calculate the necessary amplifier gain, the frequency of oscillation, and the two harmonic factors.

(*b*) Repeat part *a* if R and L are interchanged.

14-3. The frequency of the phase-shift oscillator of Fig. 14-5 is to be controlled by varying only one of the three series capacitors over the range $0.1C \leq C_a \leq 10C$. In which section should this capacity be placed if the range of frequency variation is to be maximized? What are the two bounding values of ω, expressed in terms of $\omega_0 = 1/(\sqrt{6}\,RC)$?

14-4. Calculate the input impedance of the three-RC-section phase-shift network at ω_0. Under what conditions will it be invariant as the null frequency is changed? What is the oscillation frequency when the output impedance of the amplifier is equal to R? What is the new value of the threshold gain?

14-5. Verify Eqs. (14-15) and (14-17). Find H_n and K_n for the Wien bridge for $2 \leq n \leq 5$. (Let $\delta = 300$.)

14-6. The base amplifier of Fig. 14-7 has an unloaded gain of 200 and an output impedance of 5,000 ohms. It employs, for the input stage, a tube having $\mu = 20$, $r_p = 10$ K, and a plate load of 5 K. If $\omega_0 = 10^4$ and $R_2 = 10$ K, specify the remaining parameters of the bridge. What is the actual value of δ? Make all reasonable approximations in the course of your solution and take into account the loading of the amplifier by the bridge and the loading of the bridge by the amplifier.

14-7. Repeat Prob. 14-6 when the bridge is decoupled from the output stage of the base amplifier by means of a cathode follower. Its output impedance should be taken as 400 ohms.

14-8. Calculate the oscillation frequency of the circuit of Fig. 14-13 when $R_L \gg R$. What are the harmonic-rejection factors? Plot the locus of the system's poles as A_c increases from zero.

14-9. In the circuit of Fig. 14-33, what is the minimum value of β for sustained oscillations? At what frequency does this circuit operate?

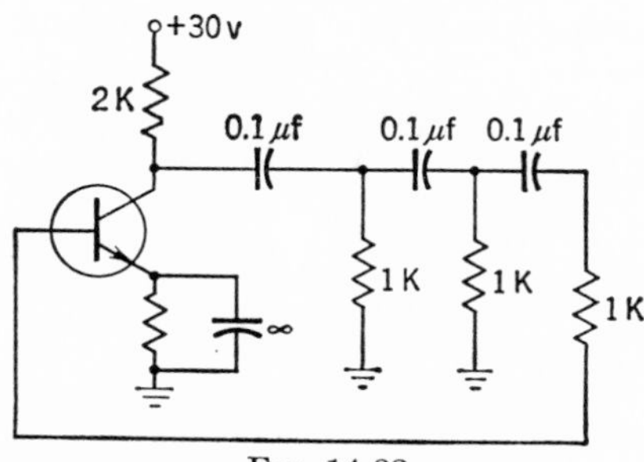

FIG. 14-33

14-10. A vacuum-tube tuned-plate oscillator (Fig. 14-16d) has a plate tank circuit consisting of a 10-mh coil and 100-$\mu\mu$f capacitor. The grid coil is 5 mh, and the mutual inductance is only 1 mh.

(a) Specify the frequency and the minimum value of μ for oscillations.

(b) If the plate tank circuit has $Q_0 = 50$ and if $r_p = 5$ K, how would the frequency change? Under this condition, what is the minimum value of g_m needed for proper operation?

14-11. Consider the following two cases of the general feedback problem posed in Fig. 14-15a. All elements are assumed to be purely reactive.

(a) When there is no mutual coupling between X_1 and X_2.

(b) When there is mutual coupling but Z_3 is an open circuit.

Under these conditions, calculate separately the gain and the feedback factor and solve for the frequency of oscillation. If a high-μ tube is used, what simplifications may be made in evaluating β_0 for the Colpitts and for the tuned-plate oscillator?

14-12. A tube having $\mu = 20$ and $r_p = 10$ K is used in a Hartley oscillator where the two coils are completely isolated ($M = 0$). It is to be tuned over a range of 500 to 1,500 kc by using a capacitor that varies from 300 $\mu\mu$f down to 30 $\mu\mu$f. If the Q of the complete coil is 20 at 1 megacycle, specify the two inductances that will permit oscillation over the complete range of frequencies. Be sure to check the end points and to account for the loading effect of the tank resistance.

14-13. Verify Eqs. (14-25) and (14-27) and the frequency and self-starting conditions given in the text for the Hartley and Colpitts transistor oscillators.

14-14. A transistor used for a Colpitts oscillator has $r'_{11} = 500$, $r_c = 1$ megohm, and $\beta = 50$. The nominal frequency of oscillation is $\omega_0 = 10^6$. Plot the deviation from ω_0 as a function of the tank impedance. Assume Q_0 remains constant. Take a range of tank impedances from 1 K to 1 megohm. Under what conditions will the frequency of oscillation be least susceptible to changes in the external loading?

14-15. Figure 14-34 shows a three-phase transistor oscillator where the three secondaries are symmetrically loaded.

(a) Calculate the frequency of oscillation, assuming threshold operation.

(b) What is the maximum load that can be applied at the secondary without causing the cessation of oscillation?

(c) Calculate the frequency-stability factor and the harmonic-rejection factor $|H_2|$.

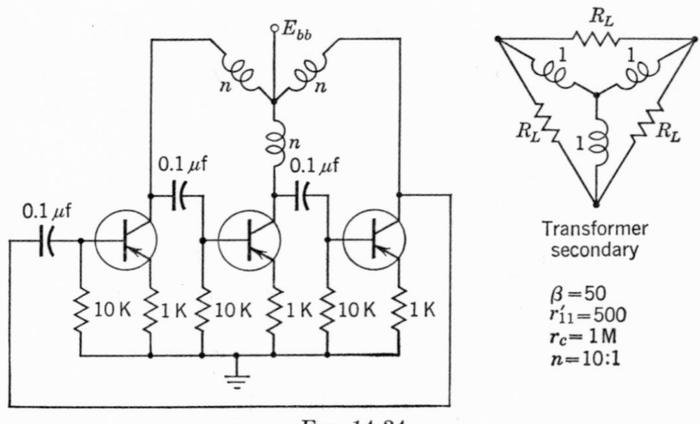

FIG. 14-34

14-16. Compare the frequency-stability factor of the phase-shift oscillator of Figs. 14-5 and 14-10 when the frequency-determining network consists of three sections to one where four *RC* sections are used.

14-17. (*a*) Verify the frequency-stability factor for the Meacham bridge.

(*b*) Two identical crystals are used in this bridge instead of one. The second one replaces R_2 in Fig. 14-22. If each has $Q = 10^5$ and the degree of bridge unbalance is $\delta = 100$, what is the new frequency-stability factor? The nominal resonant frequency of the crystal is 10^6 cps, and the change in the amplifier phase shift may reach a maximum of 10°; what is the effective change in frequency?

14-18. Find the frequency-stability factor for the transistor current-controlled oscillator of Fig. 14-33.

14-19. A Hartley oscillator is adjusted for threshold operation at $f_0 = 1$ megacycle, using $C = 250$ $\mu\mu$f. As the g_m of the active element changes, the tap on the coil is accordingly changed to maintain the oscillations. Assume that there is 10 $\mu\mu$f of stray capacity from the input to the output of the active element; we wish to minimize the effect of the stray reactance on the frequency of oscillation. Should a device with a low or high value of transconductance be used? Explain your answer and justify it fully by comparing two circuits, one which uses a tube having $\mu = 100$ and $r_p = 50$ K and the other a transistor where $r'_{11} = 500$ ohms, $\beta = 100$, and $r_d =$ 100 K. Which device would make a more stable oscillator?

14-20. A transistor used in a Colpitts oscillator has the following parameters: $r_{11} = 20$, $r_c = 2$ megohms, and $\alpha = 0.98$. The oscillator uses a 50-mh coil to set the nominal frequency of $\omega_0 = 5 \times 10^5$ radians/sec. We can expect stray capacity of 5 $\mu\mu$f between the base and collector connections.

(*a*) If the circuit is initially adjusted so that the loop gain is twice the threshold value, by how much will the frequency shift as a result of the stray capacity?

(*b*) Repeat part *a* for a transistor having $\alpha = 0.99$. The nominal gain is again twice the threshold value.

(*c*) If the tank has a loaded $Q = 20$ and if the phase of the base amplifier is 10°, by how many cycles would the frequency shift from ω_0? Compare the answer with that obtained in parts *a* and *b*.

14-21. The tuned circuit in the Colpitts oscillator of Prob. 14-20 has a Q of 20. Without accounting for the effects of the stray capacity, calculate the reactance which would have to be inserted into the base lead in order to return the frequency of oscillation to ω_0. Repeat the calculations for a stabilizing reactance placed in series with the emitter.

14-22. Would it be feasible to minimize the effect of stray capacity by means of a stabilizing reactance? Explain and justify your answer by considering the vacuum-tube Hartley circuit of Fig. 14-16*b*.

14-23. Given the Colpitts oscillator of Fig. 14-23 adjusted to 25 per cent above the threshold value of gain. The parameters of interest are $E_{bb} = 150$ volts, $r_p =$ 20 K, $\mu = 50$. The tank circuit has a loaded $Q = 20$ and an input impedance of 30 K at its resonant frequency of 10^6 cps. R_k is chosen to give a symmetrical transfer characteristic.

Verify Eqs. (14-35) and (14-36).

Plot the describing function by first finding the maximum value of the fundamental component of plate voltage in the linear region; next the output when the cosinusoidal signal is clipped from -15 to $+15°$; and then when it is clipped from -30 to $+30°$; etc. Represent the describing function by a sequence of straight lines connecting these points. Find the approximate amplitude of oscillation. Calculate S_E^R at the operating point.

14-24. Repeat Prob. 14-23 when the limiting is controlled by the assumed perfect grid circuit clamping.

14-25. A transistor tuned-collector, tuned-base oscillator, operating at 10^5 cps, has an effective collector-circuit tank impedance of 5 K. $E_{bb} = 20$ volts, $r'_{11} = 100$, and $\beta = 100$. The circuit is adjusted to 50 per cent beyond the threshold. The bias is derived by assumed ideal base-circuit clamping.

(*a*) Approximate and plot the describing function and find the amplitude of oscillation.

(*b*) Evaluate $S_E^{g_m}$ at the operating point.

14-26. Design an amplitude-regulated Meacham-bridge transistor oscillator using the 6.3-volt pilot lamp of Fig. 14-28 as the control element. The peak amplitude across the bridge should be 3 volts. The crystal, at its series-resonant frequency, may be replaced by a 20-ohm resistor. Specify all the elements of the bridge and draw the basic amplifier indicating the various elements used for impedance matching.

14-27. Find the output amplitude of a Wien-bridge oscillator where the bridge is initially unbalanced by a factor $\delta = 100$ and where the amplitude-control element is a thermistor having the approximate characteristics $R \cong 10{,}000 - 250E$ ohms. The associated pure-resistance bridge arm is 3,000 ohms.

14-28. Repeat Prob. 14-27 if the remaining resistance arm is replaced by a tungsten lamp having the approximate characteristics $R' \cong 1{,}000 + 100E$. Thus two temperature-dependent elements are used in the bridge. Evaluate S_E^{δ}.

14-29. Evaluate the amplitude-stability factor of the Meacham bridge of Prob. 14-26. What combination of arm resistances would maximize this factor? (The bulb may be changed if necessary.)

BIBLIOGRAPHY

Anderson, F. B.: Seven-league Oscillator, *Proc. IRE*, vol. 39, no. 8, pp. 881–890, 1951.

Bode, H. W.: "Network Analysis and Feedback Amplifier Design," D. Van Nostrand Company, Inc., Princeton, N.J., 1945.

Bollman, J. H., and J. G. Kreer, Jr.: Application of Thermistors to Control Networks, *Proc. IRE*, vol. 38, no. 1, pp. 20–26, 1950.

Bothwell, F. E.: Nyquist Diagrams and the Routh-Hurwitz Stability Criterion, *Proc. IRE*, vol. 38, no. 11, pp. 1345–1348, 1950.

Chance, B., et al.: "Waveforms," Massachusetts Institute of Technology Radiation Laboratory Series, vol. 19, McGraw-Hill Book Company, Inc., New York, 1949.

Edson, W. A.: "Vacuum-tube Oscillators," John Wiley & Sons, Inc., New York, 1953.

Ginzton, E. L., and L. M. Hollingsworth: Phase-shift Oscillators, *Proc. IRE*, vol. 29, no. 1, pp. 43–49, 1941; also corrections, vol. 32, no. 10, p. 641, 1944.

Hooper, D. E., and A. E. Jackets: Current Derived Resistance-Capacitance Oscillators Using Junction Transistors, *Electronic Eng.*, vol. 28, pp. 333–337, August, 1956.

Keonjian, E.: Variable Frequency Transistor Oscillators, *Elec. Eng.*, vol. 74, no. 8, pp. 672–675, 1955.

Llewellyn, F. B.: Constant-frequency Oscillators, *Proc. IRE*, vol. 19, no. 12, pp. 2063–2094, 1931.

Meacham, L. A.: The Bridge Stabilized Oscillator, *Bell System Tech. J.*, vol. 17, pp. 574–590, 1938; also *Proc. IRE*, vol. 26, no. 10, pp. 1278–1294, 1938.

Nyquist, H.: Regeneration Theory, *Bell System Tech. J.*, vol. 11, pp. 126–147, 1932.

CHAPTER 15

NEGATIVE-RESISTANCE OSCILLATORS

The energy needed to sustain oscillations can be supplied by shunting the dissipative tuned network with the negative driving-point resistance of an active element. The solution of this problem is well defined, and from it we can draw some general conclusions as to the behavior of even those circuits where it is difficult to isolate the two terminals across which the negative impedance is developed. This chapter serves not only as an extension of the previous techniques, but also as an introduction to the difficult problems posed by nonlinear differential equations.

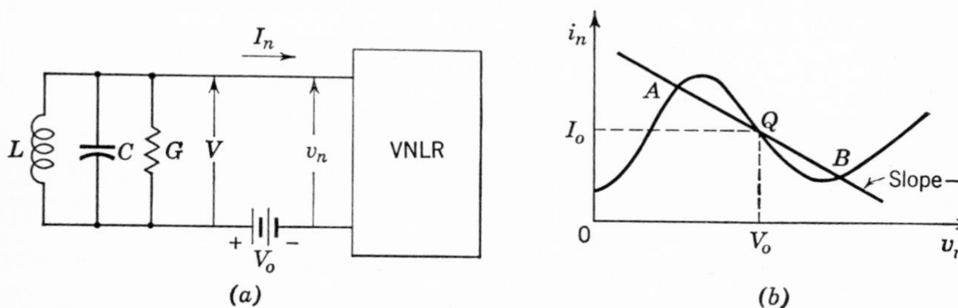

FIG. 15-1. (a) Basic negative-resistance oscillator; (b) typical volt-ampere characteristic with superimposed conductive load line.

15-1. Basic Circuit Considerations. The response of the voltage-controlled circuit of Fig.. 15-1a, with which we are initially concerned, is defined by the single node equation

$$C\frac{dV}{dt} + GV + \frac{1}{L}\int V\,dt + I_n = 0 \tag{15-1}$$

where the bottom of the GLC circuit is taken as the reference node. Since

$$V = v_n - V_o \qquad \text{and} \qquad I_n = I_o + i_n(t)$$

by differentiating Eq. (15-1) and collecting terms, the time-varying response will be given by the solution of

$$\frac{d^2v_n}{dt^2} + \frac{1}{C}\left(G\frac{dv_n}{dt} + \frac{di_n}{dt}\right) + \frac{v_n}{LC} = 0 \tag{15-2}$$

For small-signal operation,

$$\frac{di_n}{dt} = \frac{di_n}{dv_n}\frac{dv_n}{dt} = g\frac{dv_n}{dt}$$

where g is the incremental conductance of the VNLR measured at the Q point of the volt-ampere characteristic (point Q in Fig. 15-1b). With the above substitution, the basic incremental defining equation may finally be written as a quasi-linear differential equation:

$$\ddot{v}_n + \frac{1}{C}(G + g)\dot{v}_n + \frac{1}{LC}v_n = 0 \tag{15-3}$$

The linearization of the differential equation, which results from the implied assumption of a constant value of g, will not be valid once the signal amplitude carries the operating path into the dissipative regions of the volt-ampere characteristics. To find the amplitude of oscillation, the nonlinear differential equation of the system must be solved. Before treating this more difficult problem, we shall find the necessary and sufficient conditions for the circuit of Fig. 15-1 to sustain almost sinusoidal oscillations from the quasi-linear equation.

Equation (15-3) has two roots, which are located at

$$\begin{aligned} p_{1,2} &= -\frac{1}{2C}(G + g) \pm j\sqrt{\frac{1}{LC} - \frac{1}{4C^2}(G + g)^2} \\ &= \alpha \pm j\omega \end{aligned} \tag{15-4}$$

These roots determine the nature of the time-varying response of the negative-resistance oscillator, and therefore we shall investigate their location as a function of g. In order to have a growing transient, $\alpha \geq 0$, which corresponds to

$$G < -g \tag{15-5}$$

Equation (15-5) can be satisfied only when the conductive load intersects both the dissipative and the negative conductance portion of the characteristic. If there is only a single intersection on the negative portion of the curve, the response will decay instead of increasing with time.

The second restriction which must be imposed on the roots, if the response is to be oscillatory, is that ω must be real. From Eq. (15-4),

$$\frac{4C}{L} > (G + g)^2 \tag{15-6}$$

The boundaries delineating the inequality of Eq. (15-6) are two straight lines, which satisfy

$$-G + \frac{4C}{L} \geq g \geq -G - \frac{4C}{L}$$

These regions are shown in Fig. 15-2. We are interested in only that portion of the plane below the $g = -G$ line, because it is here that a self-excited signal is generated, and we are primarily concerned with the narrow segment defining the sinusoidal oscillatory response.

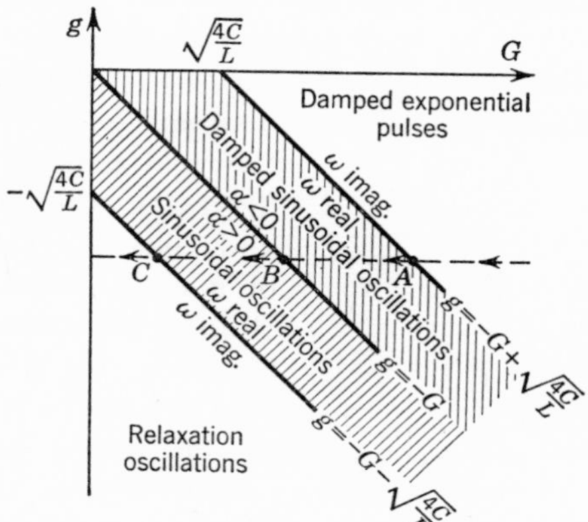

FIG. 15-2. Modes of operation of the circuit of Fig. 15-1 as a function of the external and internal conductances.

At the threshold of sustained oscillations, i.e., when $G = -g$, the external conductance is tangent, at the Q point, to the volt-ampere characteristic and the negative conductance of the active element exactly cancels the positive conductance of the tuned circuit. The purely imaginary poles are located at

$$p_{1,2} = \pm j \frac{1}{\sqrt{LC}}$$

For any other value of the external conductance lying in the oscillatory zone, the load line also intersects the positive-resistance regions, and as the oscillations build up, these segments will limit the amplitude to a finite value.

When G is small compared with the magnitude of the negative conductance, ω becomes imaginary and the circuit operates as an astable multivibrator. In the relaxation region, the response is similar to that discussed in Chap. 11, where the second energy-storage element appeared as part of the driving-point impedance of the active element instead of as part of the external load. To return the operating point to the sinusoidal oscillation region, we can load down the tuned circuit and hence reduce its effective Q.

We might further note that as $\sqrt{L/C}$ is increased, the width of the oscillatory region shrinks. A circuit operating properly under load may switch into the relaxation zone once the load is removed. Since the design of the tank controls the width of the oscillatory region, by minimizing $\sqrt{L/C}$, the performance of the oscillator becomes much less critical.

The possible modes of system operation may also be explained by following the migration of the system's poles as G is reduced toward zero (as along the dashed line of Fig. 15-2). Initially, the circuit is dissipative and the two poles lie on the real axis (Fig. 15-3). As G decreases, the poles first coalesce and then separate along the arcs of a circle. This occurs at point A in Figs. 15-2 and 15-3. When $G = -g$, they lie on the imaginary axis. A further reduction in G permits an exponentially increasing output, with the poles moving into the right half plane; the negative conductance now predominates. Eventually they again coalesce (point C in Fig. 15-2) and separate along the positive real axis. Here the circuit operates as a relaxation oscillator. Consider also the plot of the roots of the negative-resistance switching circuit presented in Fig. 11-26.

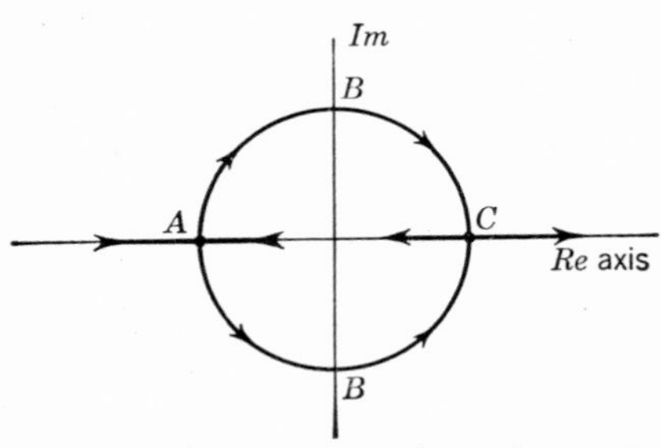

FIG. 15-3. Pole migration along the dashed path of Fig. 15-2 with decreasing values of G. Points of interest correspond to those labeled in Fig. 15-2.

Example 15-1. To place some of the thoughts to be presented in this chapter in their proper perspective, we shall now represent the tuned-plate oscillator, which was treated from the feedback viewpoint in Chap. 14, as a negative-resistance circuit. Consider Fig. 15-4*a* when, in the active region, the grid winding is unloaded. With the proper polarity connections of the feedback coil, the drive voltage becomes

$$e_g = -\frac{M}{L} e_p$$

Substituting into the controlled source of Fig. 15-4*b*, we see that the current flow is proportional to the voltage developed across the two terminals. Hence the controlled source may be replaced by the negative conductance

$$g = -\frac{M}{L} g_m$$

leading to the equivalent model of Fig. 15-4*c*.

For sinusoidal oscillations, this negative conductance must lie within the appropriate region of Fig. 15-2. By lumping r_p together with the external conductance, the restriction on the transconductance is given by

$$\frac{1}{r_p} + G + \sqrt{\frac{4C}{L}} > \frac{Mg_m}{L} > \frac{1}{r_p} + G$$

Figure 15-4*d* illustrates how the negative-resistance region II is bounded by the dissipative segments; region I is where the grid conduction limits the amplification; and region III is where the large-signal amplitude drives the tube into cutoff. Such regions and their bounds are readily found from the piecewise-linear model.

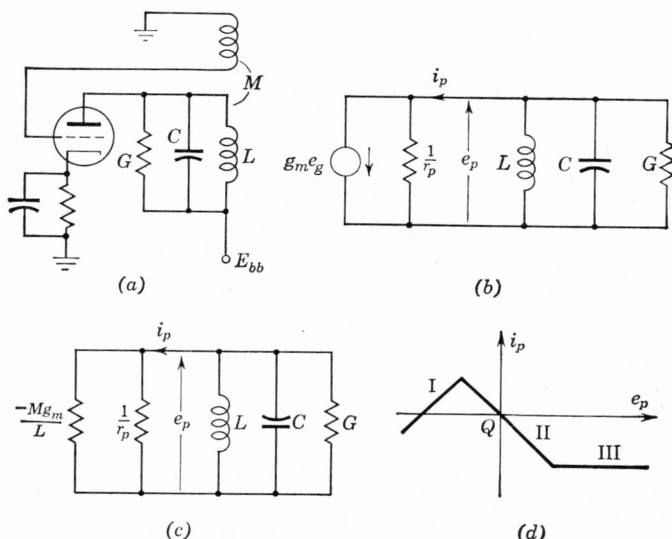

FIG. 15-4. (a) Tuned-plate oscillator; (b) incremental-plate circuit model; (c) equivalent negative-resistance circuit; (d) volt-ampere characteristics as drawn through the quiescent point of operation.

CNLR Oscillator. If a CNLR is employed as the energy source in a negative-resistance oscillator, then the normal mode of operation is satisfied by an external series-resonant circuit (Fig. 15-5). Since this is the dual of Fig. 15-1, the single defining equation is written on a loop basis:

$$L\frac{dI}{dt} + RI + \frac{1}{C}\int I\,dt + v_n = 0$$

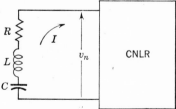

After differentiating and collecting terms, we obtain

$$\frac{di_n{}^2}{dt^2} + \frac{1}{L}\left(R + \frac{dv_n}{di_n}\right)\frac{di_n}{dt} + \frac{i_n}{LC} = 0 \tag{15-7}$$

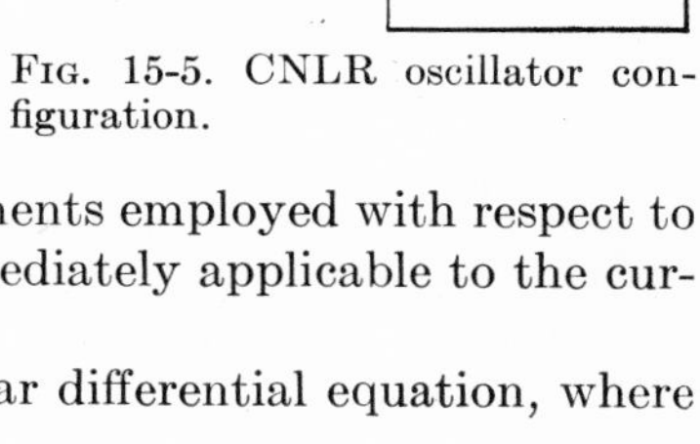

FIG. 15-5. CNLR oscillator configuration.

which is the dual of Eq. (15-2). All arguments employed with respect to the voltage solution of Eq. (15-2) are immediately applicable to the current solution of Eq. (15-7).

For example, the roots of the quasi-linear differential equation, where we define

$$\frac{dv_n}{di_n} \equiv r$$

are now located at

$$p_{1,2} = -\frac{1}{2L}(R + r) \pm j\sqrt{\frac{1}{LC} - \frac{1}{4L^2}(R + r)^2}$$

And the new boundary conditions are defined by the equations

For $\alpha > 0$: $$R < -r$$

For ω real: $$-R + \sqrt{\frac{4L}{C}} > r > -R - \sqrt{\frac{4L}{C}}$$

These should be compared with the conditions previously derived for the VNLR circuit and with the plot of Fig. 15-2.

15-2. First-order Solution for Frequency and Amplitude. In order to keep the nonlinearity in the forefront, Eq. (15-2), defining the complete response of the basic voltage-controlled negative-resistance oscillator of Fig. 15-1, may be rewritten

$$\ddot{v}_n + \frac{G}{C}\left(1 + \frac{1}{G}\frac{di_n}{dv_n}\right)\dot{v}_n + \frac{1}{LC}v_n = 0 \tag{15-8}$$

This is in the form of the Van der Pol nonlinear differential equation

$$\ddot{v} + \epsilon f(v)\dot{v} + \omega_0{}^2 v = 0$$

For almost sinusoidal oscillations, $\epsilon f(v)$ must remain small over the range of interest. When it is zero, the Van der Pol equation reduces to the equation of simple harmonic motion,

$$\ddot{v} + \omega_0{}^2 v = 0$$

which has the solution

$$v = A\cos(\omega_0 t + \phi)$$

If the nonlinear term is large, then Eq. (15-8) can be easily solved only for some specific analytic functions of $\epsilon f(v)$.

To find the frequency and amplitude to a first approximation, we shall apply the method of equivalent linearization. We shall assume that over any single cycle the gross behavior of the system may be represented by an equivalent linear circuit, and we shall neglect any variations taking place during the individual cycle.

Choosing as a suitable trial solution for Eq. (15-8)

$$v_n = E(t)\cos\omega t$$

and substituting into Eq. (15-7) and collecting terms yields

$$\left[\frac{d^2E}{dt^2} - \omega^2 E + \frac{E}{LC} + \frac{G}{C}\left(1 + \frac{1}{G}\frac{di_n}{dv_n}\right)\frac{dE}{dt}\right]\cos\omega t$$
$$- \left[2\omega\frac{dE}{dt} + \omega E\frac{G}{C}\left(1 + \frac{1}{G}\frac{di_n}{dv_n}\right)\right]\sin\omega t = 0 \tag{15-9}$$

For almost sinusoidal oscillations we may further assume that $E(t)$ remains essentially constant over any single cycle of the steady-state response. Since

$$\frac{dE}{dt} \cong 0 \qquad \text{and} \qquad \frac{d^2E}{dt^2} \cong 0$$

Eq. (15-9) reduces to

$$\left(-\omega^2 + \frac{1}{LC}\right) \cos \omega t - \frac{\omega G}{C}\left(1 + \frac{1}{G}\frac{di_n}{dv_n}\right) \sin \omega t = 0 \tag{15-10}$$

To evaluate the average response, Eq. (15-10) is now multiplied by $\cos \omega t$ and integrated over a complete cycle:

$$\int_0^{2\pi} \left(-\omega^2 + \frac{1}{LC}\right) \cos^2 \omega t \, d(\omega t) - \int_0^{2\pi} \frac{\omega G}{C}\left(1 + \frac{1}{G}\frac{di_n}{dv_n}\right) \sin \omega t \cos \omega t \, d(\omega t) = 0$$

If the circuit is adjusted close to the threshold of oscillation (to minimize the distortion of the sinusoid), then the degree of limiting, and hence the nonlinearity, is small. The coefficient of $\sin \omega t \cos \omega t$ in the second integral is this very nonlinearity. It plays a major role in determining the amplitude, but since it is small, it will have a relatively minor effect on the frequency. By assuming that this coefficient is essentially constant over the period, the second definite integral would be identically equal to zero. Consequently, the approximate frequency of oscillation, given by the vanishing of the coefficient in the first integral, is the natural frequency of the tuned circuit

$$\omega_0 = \frac{1}{\sqrt{LC}}$$

We shall now investigate $E(t)$ by rewriting the fundamental circuit equation. With the assumed cosinusoidal solution, Eq. (15-2) becomes

$$-\frac{di_n}{dt} = \left[C\frac{d^2E}{dt^2} + G\frac{dE}{dt} + \left(\frac{1}{L} - \omega^2 C\right)E\right] \cos \omega t - \left(2\omega C\frac{dE}{dt} + \omega G E\right) \sin \omega t \tag{15-11}$$

By again assuming that all coefficients are approximately constant over the cycle, the first expression on the right-hand side of Eq. (15-11) may be eliminated by multiplying through by $\sin \omega t$ and integrating over a complete cycle. The equation of interest reduces to

$$-\omega \int_0^{2\pi} \frac{di_n}{d(\omega t)} \sin \omega t \, d(\omega t) = -\left(2\omega C\frac{dE}{dt} + \omega G E\right) \int_0^{2\pi} \sin^2 \omega t \, d(\omega t) \tag{15-12}$$

The left-hand side of Eq. (15-12) may now be integrated by parts:

$$-\omega \int_0^{2\pi} \frac{di_n}{d(\omega t)} \sin \omega t \, d(\omega t) = -\omega(i_n \sin \omega t) \Big|_0^{2\pi} + \omega \int_0^{2\pi} i_n \cos \omega t \, d(\omega t)$$
$$= \omega \int_0^{2\pi} i_n \cos \omega t \, d(\omega t) \quad (15\text{-}13)$$

But the right-hand side of Eq. (15-13) is proportional to the peak value of the fundamental component of the current flow into the VNLR. Thus the solution of Eq. (15-12) is

$$\omega \pi I_{1m} = -\left(2\omega C \frac{dE}{dt} + \omega G E\right)\pi$$

or

$$-\frac{dE}{dt} = \frac{1}{2C}(I_{1m} + GE) \quad (15\text{-}14)$$

At equilibrium the oscillations are constant, $dE/dt = 0$, and

$$I_{1m} = -GE \quad (15\text{-}15)$$

The amplitude satisfying Eq. (15-15) is found by plotting a describing function, i.e., the fundamental component of the current into the VNLR vs. the applied-voltage excitation, and solving for the intersection with the conductance line. Two typical curves appear in Fig. 15-6.

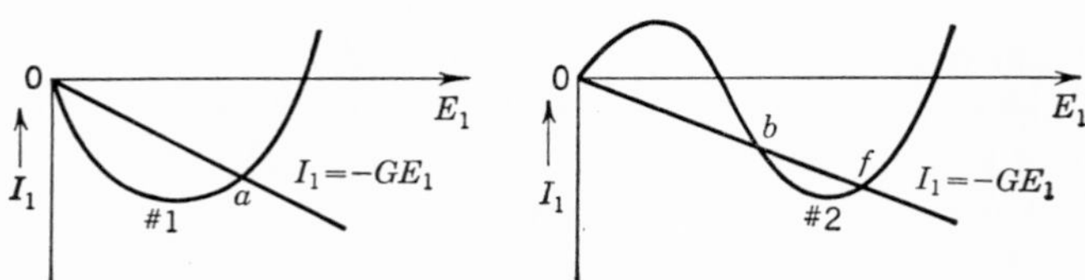

FIG. 15-6. Two describing functions for the basic nonlinear oscillator of Fig. 15-1: curve 1 for a circuit biased in the center of the negative-conductance region, and curve 2 for a circuit biased in the positive-resistance region near the peak point.

Curve 1 appears when the circuit is normally biased within the negative-conductance region. For small signals, the current and voltage are out of phase. As the amplitude of oscillation increases, the operating point is driven into the dissipative regions for a portion of the cycle and the fundamental current begins decreasing. The second curve corresponds to a device normally biased within the dissipative region, such as at point A or B in Fig. 15-1. For small signals, the driving-point impedance is positive and the current is in phase with the applied excitation. A larger amplitude, where the average conductance over a cycle is negative, permits sustained oscillations.

In order to see which of the multiple intersections represent stable points of operation, we return to Eq. (15-14) and consider the effects of a small variation in E about the amplitude satisfying Eq. (15-15).

$$\frac{dE}{dt} = -\frac{1}{2C}\left[I_e + \Delta I + G(E_e + \Delta E)\right]$$

and I_e and E_e are the values at the equilibrium point. From Eq. (15-14) we know that $I_e + GE_e = 0$. Consequently

$$\frac{dE}{dt} = -\frac{1}{2C}\left(\frac{\Delta I}{\Delta E} + G\right)\Delta E \tag{15-16}$$

For stability, any change in E must establish the conditions that will force a return to the equilibrium point. It follows that if the initial perturbation ΔE is positive and momentarily increases the output, dE/dt must be negative in order for the voltage to decrease with time back to the stable amplitude. This is possible only when the term in the parentheses of Eq. (15-16) is positive. The condition for stability becomes

$$\frac{dI}{dE} + G > 0 \tag{15-17}$$

Equation (15-17) says that the total incremental conductance at the stable point must be positive, or in other words, the circuit must appear dissipative with respect to small variations about the equilibrium point.

In order for any oscillator to be self-starting, the origin must be a point of unstable equilibrium. The oscillator of curve 1 will build up to point d, the single stable point. However, if the quiescent point is along the positive-resistance segment, then the origin will be stable and the circuit cannot start by itself (curve 2). Once the circuit is externally excited to, or past, the unstable point b, the build-up will continue to the second point of stable equilibrium, point f.

To evaluate the describing function analytically, the characteristic of the VNLR may be approximated by a power series which is written with respect to the quiescent point.

$$i_n = a_1 v_n + a_2 v_n^2 + a_3 v_n^3 + \cdots \tag{15-18}$$

where the various coefficients are found from the curve. Because of the nature of the external circuit (which is a relatively high-Q tank), only the fundamental component of voltage may be developed across the terminals of the nonlinear element. Furthermore, when the nonlinearity is small, the fundamental is the only current component of interest.

Substituting $v_n = E_1 \cos \omega t$ into Eq. (15-18) and collecting the coefficients of the cos ωt terms results in

$$I_1 = a_1 E_1 + \tfrac{3}{4} a_3 E_1^3 + \tfrac{5}{8} a_5 E_1^5 + \cdots \tag{15-19}$$

For each value of the assumed voltage excitation, the current response term is now known. Cross plotting gives the describing function shown in Fig. 15-6.

The stable amplitude may also be found by realizing that at the threshold of oscillation, the negative conductance of the active element exactly cancels the damping of the tuned circuit. Again, only the fundamental components are of interest; at the harmonics the current and voltage are in quadrature and do not represent power supplied to the tank. From Eq. (15-19), the average conductance of the VNLR over a cycle is

$$G_n = \frac{I_1}{E_1} = a_1 + \frac{3}{4} a_3 E_1^2 + \frac{5}{8} a_5 E_1^4 + \cdots \tag{15-20}$$

Equation (15-20) may be plotted as shown in Fig. 15-7 (the two curves drawn correspond to the two current-describing functions of Fig. 15-6).

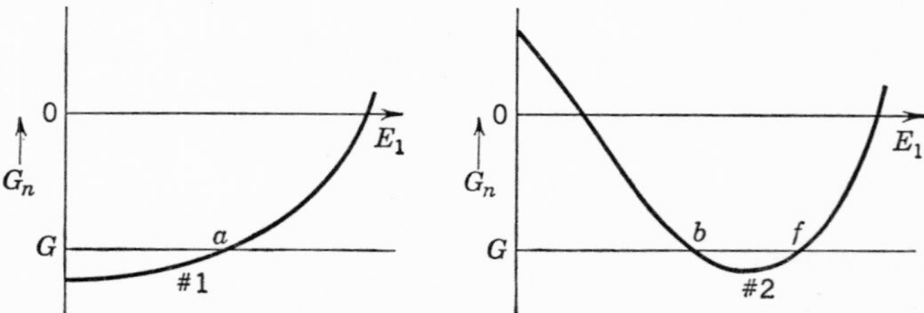

FIG. 15-7. Two possible conductance describing functions. Curve 1 holds when the quiescent point is at the center of the negative-conductance region; curve 2, when the quiescent point is in the positive region near the knee of the curve. These correspond to the current describing functions of Fig. 15-6.

By superimposing the G line on the negative conductance-describing function, the amplitude satisfying $G_n + G = 0$ is finally found.

Example 15-2. A device having the almost symmetrical piecewise-linear characteristics of Fig. 15-8 is used in the basic oscillator circuit of Fig. 15-1. It is initially biased in the center of the negative-resistance region, at Q_1, where $I_o = 40$ ma and $V_o = 20$ volts.

By taking three coordinates on the curve, measured with respect to the Q point, we can construct a cubic that will adequately approximate the characteristic. Choosing the following points: (−10 volts, 0 ma), (−5 volts, 20 ma), and (+5 volts, −20 ma), the approximating polynomial becomes

$$i_1 = -5.33v + 0.0533v^3 \qquad \text{ma}$$

Thus the conductance describing function, as given by Eq. (15-20), is

$$G_{n1} = -5.33 + 0.04E_1^2 \qquad \text{millimhos}$$

and it is plotted in Fig. 15-8*b*. When, for example, the conductance of the tank is 3.5 millimhos, the circuit will oscillate with a peak amplitude of 6.75 volts.

Suppose that the quiescent point is shifted to Q_2, where $V_o = 17$ volts; by how much would the amplitude change? Rather than solve for a new describing polynomial, for the purposes of this discussion we can simply shift the previously derived curve to correspond to the new origin. The shifted curve is defined by

$$i_2 = -5.33(v - 3) + 0.0533(v - 3)^3 + A$$

where the constant A must be included to make $i = 0$ when $v = 0$. This equation reduces to

$$i_2 = -3.89v - 0.48v^2 + 0.0533v^3 \qquad \text{ma}$$

Consequently, the new conductive describing function is characterized by

$$G_{n2} = -3.89 + 0.04E_1{}^2 \qquad \text{millimhos}$$

and the new peak amplitude stabilizes at 3.5 volts.

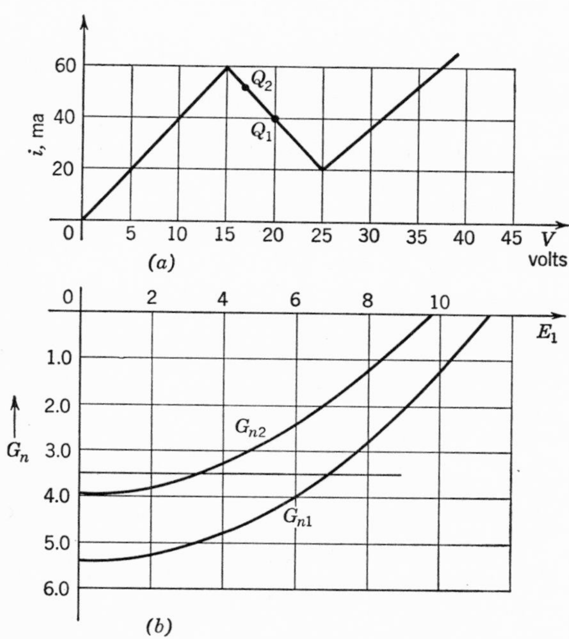

FIG. 15-8. (a) Volt-ampere characteristic; (b) the conductance describing functions for Example 15-2.

15-3. Frequency of Oscillation to a Second Approximation. *First Method.* In order to obtain a more accurate expression as to the frequency of oscillation, we shall now solve the Van der Pol equation with the simple assumption that the voltage waveshape is periodic. This equation is

$$\ddot{v} + \epsilon f(v)\dot{v} + \omega_0{}^2 v = 0$$

where $\omega_0{}^2 = 1/LC$ and where

$$\epsilon f(v) = \frac{1}{C}\left(G + \frac{di_n}{dv_n}\right)$$

for the general circuit of Fig. 15-1. As the first step toward the evaluation of the oscillation frequency, the Van der Pol equation is multiplied by the unknown solution and integrated over the unknown period.

$$\int_0^{2\pi} \ddot{v}v\, d\omega t + \epsilon \int_0^{2\pi} f(v)\dot{v}v\, d\omega t + \omega_0^2 \int_0^{2\pi} v^2\, d\omega t = 0 \qquad (15\text{-}21)$$

Let us now consider each term of Eq. (15-21) individually, starting with the one that contains the system's nonlinearity.

$$F(v) = \epsilon \int_0^{2\pi} f(v)\dot{v}v\, d\omega t \qquad (15\text{-}22)$$

By expanding the volt-ampere characteristic into a power series,

$$i = a_1 v + a_2 v^2 + a_3 v^3 + a_4 v^4 + \cdots$$

the nonlinearity becomes

$$f(v) = G + \frac{di}{dv} = G + a_1 + 2a_2 v + 3a_3 v^2 + \cdots \qquad (15\text{-}23)$$

The necessary assumption of a periodic solution leads to the expression of v and $\dot{v}$ as Fourier series.

$$v = \sum_{k=1}^{\infty} V_k \cos (k\omega t + \phi_n) \qquad (15\text{-}24a)$$

and

$$\dot{v} = -\sum_{k=1}^{\infty} k\omega V_k \sin (k\omega t + \phi_n) \qquad (15\text{-}24b)$$

Consequently $v\dot{v}$ consists solely of terms which are the product of two time-varying signals in quadrature, a sinusoid and a cosinusoid; it does not contain any d-c terms. The substitution of v into Eq. (15-23) and the collection of terms will result in a d-c component and a series of cosinusoidal terms, i.e., the fundamental and all harmonics. The integral of interest [Eq. (15-22)] reduces to the evaluation of various factors of the form

$$\int_0^{2\pi} (\text{dc} + \cos n\omega t)(\cos k\omega t)(\sin m\omega t)\, d\omega t$$

over a complete cycle of the fundamental where k, m, and n are nonzero positive integers. But such an integral is always equal to zero. Thus we have proved that

$$F(v) = \epsilon \int_0^{2\pi} f(v)\dot{v}v\, d\omega t = 0$$

Returning to Eq. (15-21), the first integral may be evaluated by parts:

$$\int_0^{2\pi} \ddot{v}v\,d\omega t = \omega \int_0^{2\pi} \frac{d\dot{v}}{d\omega t} v\,d\omega t = \omega \int_{\omega t=0}^{\omega t=2\pi} v d(\dot{v})$$

$$= \omega v\dot{v}\Big|_{\omega t=0}^{\omega t=2\pi} - \omega \int_{\omega t=0}^{\omega t=2\pi} \dot{v}^2\,dt \tag{15-25}$$

It follows directly from the argument employed with respect to the integral of Eq. (15-22) that

$$v\dot{v}\Big|_{\omega t=0}^{\omega t=2\pi} = 0$$

and as a result

$$\int_0^{2\pi} \ddot{v}v\,d\omega t = -\int_0^{2\pi} \dot{v}^2\,d\omega t \tag{15-26}$$

The right-hand integral may be identified as the mean-square value of the derivative. Equation (15-21) finally reduces to

$$\int_0^{2\pi} \dot{v}^2\,d\omega t = \omega_0^2 \int_0^{2\pi} v^2\,d\omega t \tag{15-27}$$

When the Fourier series of Eqs. (15-24*a*) and (15-24*b*) are substituted into Eq. (15-27), only the squared terms would contribute to the final answer: all cross products integrated over a cycle equal zero. The evaluation of Eq. (15-27), consistent with the assumed periodicity of the solution, results in

$$\tfrac{1}{2}\sum_{k=1}^{\infty} k^2\omega^2 V_k^2 = \tfrac{1}{2}\omega_0^2 \sum_{k=1}^{\infty} V_k^2$$

or

$$\left(\frac{\omega}{\omega_0}\right)^2 = \frac{\sum_{k=1}^{\infty} V_k^2}{\sum_{k=1}^{\infty} k^2 V_k^2} \tag{15-28}$$

Equation (15-28) proves that when limiting introduces distortion terms, the frequency of oscillation is always depressed below the nominal resonant frequency of the tuned circuit, and that the greater the distortion, the greater the frequency depression. This equation is somewhat difficult to use in the form derived, since for small amounts of distortion, $\omega \cong \omega_0$. To simplify the expression, let us consider

$$1 - \frac{\omega^2}{\omega_0^2} = 1 - \frac{\sum_{k=1}^{\infty} V_k^2}{\sum_{k=1}^{\infty} k^2 V_k^2} = \frac{\sum_{k=1}^{\infty} (k^2 - 1) V_k^2}{\sum_{k=1}^{\infty} k^2 V_k^2} \tag{15-29}$$

However,

$$1 - \frac{\omega^2}{{\omega_0}^2} = \frac{(\omega_0 + \omega)(\omega_0 - \omega)}{{\omega_0}^2} \cong \frac{-2\,\Delta\omega}{\omega_0}$$

where the approximation holds when ω is close to ω_0 and where the frequency deviation is $\Delta\omega \equiv \omega - \omega_0$. Furthermore, by restricting the simplification of Eq. (15-29) to signals containing only slight distortion, the fundamental term greatly predominates. Because

$$V_1{}^2 \gg \sum_{k=2}^{\infty} k^2 V_k{}^2$$

the denominator of Eq. (15-29) may be approximated by $V_1{}^2$.

The frequency deviation may finally be expressed in the form

$$\frac{\Delta\omega}{\omega_0} \cong -\frac{1}{2} \sum_{k=2}^{\infty} (k^2 - 1) \frac{V_k{}^2}{V_1{}^2} \tag{15-30}$$

For example, when the VNLR characteristics are symmetrical about the Q point, only odd-harmonic terms will be present in the output. If the principal one is the third harmonic and if it is even 5 per cent of the fundamental,

$$\frac{\Delta\omega}{\omega_0} = -\frac{1}{2} \times 8 \times \left(\frac{0.05V_1}{V^1}\right)^2 = -1.0\%$$

Contributions of the higher-harmonic components will depress the frequency even further.

Second Method. Our second method of finding the frequency depression, because of the nonlinearity of the negative conductance characteristic, will be based on a power balance of the circuit. The ideal negative-resistance device, by its very nature, is unable to store any energy and is also unable to supply any reactive power to the external circuit. Like any characteristic that is a single-valued function of the independent variable, it does not exhibit hysteresis; consequently the line integral of $i\,dv$ over a cycle is

$$\oint i\,dv = 0 \tag{15-31}$$

We shall therefore sum up the reactive power terms at each harmonic and set the result equal to zero. The particular frequency at which this condition is satisfied will be the frequency of oscillation.

As before, the unknown periodic voltage may be expressed as a Fourier series. When it excites the tuned circuit of Fig. 15-1a, the reactive component of the current at each harmonic will be given by

$$I'_k = I_k \sin \phi_k = B_k V_k \tag{15-32}$$

where B_k is the susceptance at the kth harmonic. I'_k is in quadrature with the voltage component of the same frequency. The trajectory traversed on the volt-ampere characteristic, due to this current, is an ellipse having the area

$$A'_k = \pi V_k I'_k = \pi V_k I_k \sin \phi_k$$

This path is shown in Fig. 15-9.

During one period of the fundamental, the harmonic circumscribes this path k times, tracing out the area

$$A_k = \pi k V_k I_k \sin \phi_k = \pi k V_k{}^2 B_k \tag{15-33}$$

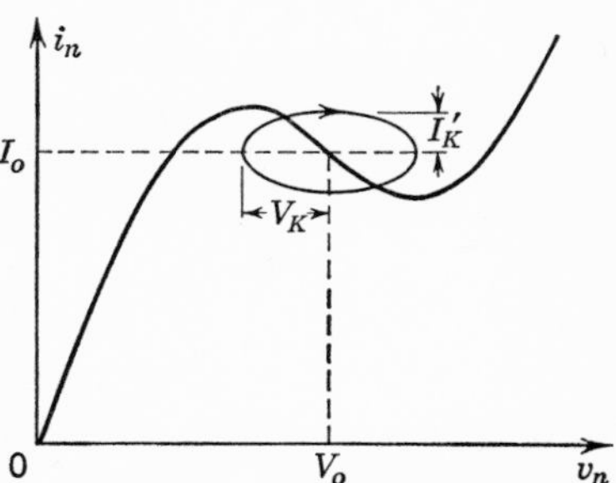

FIG. 15-9. Negative-resistance characteristic showing the path traversed by the harmonic components of voltage and current.

But this is simply $\pi k/2$ times the reactive power. Since no energy is stored by the VNLR, Eq. (15-31) must be satisfied. This condition may now be expressed as

$$\sum_{k=1}^{\infty} A_k = 0 = \pi V_1{}^2 B_1 + \pi \sum_{k=2}^{\infty} k V_k{}^2 B_k \tag{15-34}$$

or, in terms of the reactive power,

$$P_{1R} + \sum_{k=2}^{\infty} k P_{kR} = 0 \tag{15-35}$$

At some sufficiently high harmonic, usually at and above the second, the tuned circuit appears capacitive. In order for Eq. (15-34) to hold, B_1 must have a sign different from that associated with B_2, B_3, etc. This is possible only if the tank appears inductive at the fundamental. We have therefore proved once again that the frequency of oscillation must be below the resonant frequency of the tuned circuit.

The susceptance of the tuned circuit may be expressed as

$$B = C\omega_0 \left(\frac{\omega}{\omega_0} - \frac{\omega_0}{\omega} \right) \tag{15-36}$$

In the vicinity of resonance Eq. (15-36) may be approximated by

$$B_1 \cong 2C\,\Delta\omega$$

and at the harmonics Eq. (15-36) reduces to

$$B_k \cong \omega_0 C \frac{k^2 - 1}{k}$$

Substituting these two terms into Eq. (15-34) and solving results in

$$\frac{\Delta\omega}{\omega_0} = -\frac{1}{2}\sum_{k=1}^{\infty}(k^2 - 1)\frac{V_k^2}{V_1^2}$$

which is identical with Eq. (15-30). Furthermore, since from Eq. (15-34)

$$I_1V_1 \sin \phi_1 = -\Sigma kI_kV_k \sin \phi_k$$

the depression in frequency is also given by

$$\frac{\Delta\omega}{\omega_0} = -\frac{I_1 \sin \phi_1}{2V_1\omega_0C} \tag{15-37}$$

where ϕ_1 is the phase angle of the fundamental current with respect to the fundamental voltage.

Synchronization. The automatic balancing of the circuit, which shifts the frequency to a point where the net reactive power is equal to zero, may be utilized for frequency entrainment or synchronization. Suppose that an external signal that is some rational ratio of the desired fundamental is applied to the basic negative-resistance oscillator. Because the tank is primarily reactive at this frequency, the additional power injected (P_{sk}) will be reactive and Eq. (15-35) will become

$$P_1 + \sum_{k=2}^{\infty} kP_k + kP_{sk} = 0 \tag{15-38}$$

Depending on the phase of the injected signal, the effective reactive power P_{sk} can be either positive or negative; the frequency at which Eq. (15-38) is satisfied may be shifted in either direction.

For example, if P_{sk} is inductive and large enough to cancel the other harmonic terms, then the oscillation frequency could be returned to ω_0. On the other hand, if P_{sk} is capacitive, the net harmonic power is increased and the frequency would be further depressed. Essentially, the injection of this additional power changes the effective susceptance of the circuit.

15-4. Introduction to Topological Methods. Nonlinear systems which are described by a differential equation of the second order may also be studied with the air of various topological constructions. This form of representation is important because it enables us to gain perspective as to the totality of the possible behavior of the system without having to solve the actual differential equation for the time response. The periodic solution will appear as a closed contour on some graph. And as the graphically presented nonlinearity will be used directly—without conversion to an approximating polynomial—grossly nonlinear as well as quasi-linear circuits may be treated. This is not to say that the topological solutions do not have their own limitations; they do. In the course of the following arguments some of the drawbacks will become apparent.

As a convenient starting point, consider the second-order linear differential equation

$$\ddot{x} + b\dot{x} + \omega_0{}^2 x = 0 \tag{15-39}$$

Two initial conditions, which give information as to the initial energy in the system, are necessary for the complete solution; usually the position and velocity at $t = 0$ are specified.

For the simplest case of Eq. (15-39), we set $b = 0$, which reduces the problem to one of simple harmonic motion. The well-known solution for x in terms of time is

$$x = K \cos (\omega_0 t + \phi) \tag{15-40}$$

But in order to evaluate the two constants, we usually also find the derivative.

$$y = \dot{x} = -\omega_0 K \sin (\omega_0 t + \phi) \tag{15-41}$$

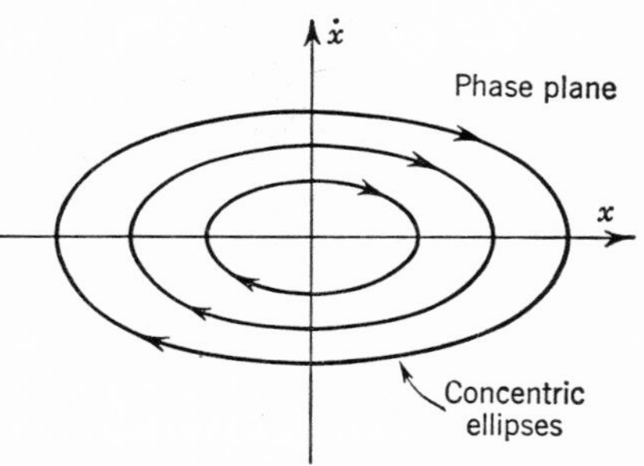

FIG. 15-10. Phase portrait of simple harmonic motion [Eq. (15-39) with $b = 0$].

Since time appears in Eqs. (15-40) and (15-41) merely as a parameter, as an alternative form of presenting the answer, $\dot{x}$ may be plotted as a function of x.

Equations (15-40) and (15-41) are parametric equations of an ellipse. Eliminating t yields, as the solution of the original differential equation,

$$\frac{x^2}{K^2} + \frac{y^2}{\omega_0{}^2 K^2} = 1 \tag{15-42}$$

The starting point of the plot on the x, $\dot{x}$ plane (hereafter called the *phase plane*) is simply the coordinates given by the initial conditions. Since two pieces of information uniquely determine any second-degree curve, one and only one ellipse, satisfying Eq. (15-42), may be drawn through each point on the plane. The totality of all such curves (Fig. 15-10) is called the phase portrait of the system.

Rotation of the trajectory about the origin is always in a clockwise direction. Counterclockwise rotation would indicate a decreasing displacement when the velocity is still positive and an increasing displacement for negative velocities—an obviously impossible situation. Furthermore, these ellipses must cross the x axis at right angles. The x

intercepts are the points at which the velocity changes direction, and consequently they must also be the points of the displacement maxima. The above arguments lead directly to two additional conclusions:

1. All closed paths must encircle the origin.
2. All closed curves correspond to periodic motions.

The equilibrium point of the system is where $\dot{x}$ and $\ddot{x}$ vanish. In this example only the origin is stable, and it therefore is called a singular point.

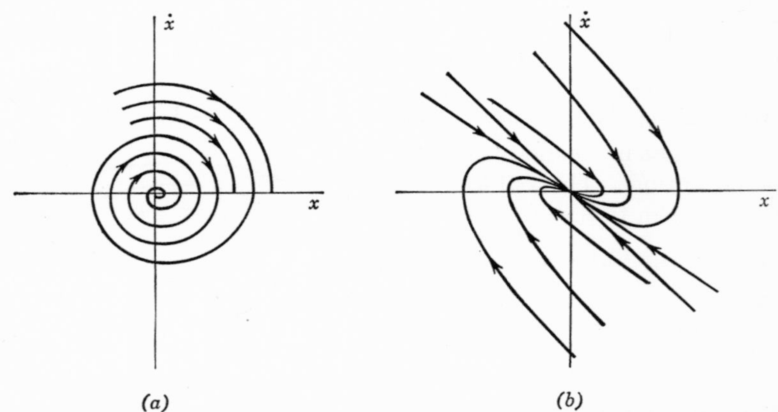

FIG. 15-11. Phase trajectories of the linear second-degree equation. (a) Damped oscillatory response; (b) the aperiodic solution.

If friction (or damping) is included in the system, then $b > 0$ and Eq. (15-39) has two possible solutions.

1. The damped oscillatory wave:

$$x = Ke^{-\alpha t} \cos (\omega_1 t + \phi) \tag{15-43}$$

which exists when the roots are complex conjugates,

$$p_{1,2} = -\alpha \pm j\omega_1$$

The phase portrait corresponding to Eq. (15-43) and its derivative appears in Fig. 15-11*a*. As the oscillatory wave damps out, the trajectory describes a logarithmic spiral about the origin, circling it once for each cycle of the cosinusoidal portion of the solution. Since the spiral eventually terminates at the origin, this singularity is now called a stable focal point.

2. The damped aperiodic wave which corresponds to the overdamped case:

$$x = K_1 e^{-\alpha_1 t} + K_2 e^{-\alpha_2 t} \tag{15-44}$$

The damped aperiodic wave of Eq. (15-44) cannot have more than one point of zero velocity (excluding the trivial point at $t = \infty$). Therefore the phase trajectory will intercept the x axis once—it cannot encircle the origin. In Fig. 15-11*b*, the origin becomes the stable nodal point of the system.

Isocline Construction. The trajectories that represent the solution of the differential equation on the phase plane may be plotted directly from the equation by the method of isoclines. These are the locus of all points in the phase plane where the curve has the same slope. By making the substitution

$$y = \frac{dx}{dt}$$

Eq. (15-39) may be rewritten

$$\frac{dy}{dt} = -by - \omega_0{}^2 x \tag{15-45}$$

But in order to find the slope, Eq. (15-45) will be divided through by y, resulting in

$$S = \frac{dy}{dx} = \frac{dy}{dt}\frac{dt}{dx} = -b - \omega_0{}^2 \frac{x}{y} \tag{15-46}$$

Thus all points having the same slope S lie on a straight line through the origin, satisfying the equation

$$y = -\frac{\omega_0{}^2}{S+b} x \tag{15-47}$$

Once the isoclines are drawn, short-line segments of the appropriate slope may be marked off along each one, as shown in Fig. 15-12. These will serve as guides when drawing the phase portrait. Starting at any initial point, a short section of the curve can be drawn having the slope defined by the isocline passing through the starting point. From the end of the first section, the next section is drawn, and so on, each intersecting the next clockwise isocline with the proper slope until the curve is completed. The totality of the individual segments is the actual phase trajectory satisfying the initial conditions.

Such a construction is carried out in Fig. 15-12 for the damped oscillatory case. For the purpose of illustration, we set $\omega_0 = 1$ and $b = \frac{1}{4}$, reducing Eq. (15-47) to

$$y = -\frac{4}{4S+1} x$$

The initial conditions, which give the starting point of the single trajectory drawn, are $x = -3$ and $\dot{x} = 5$.

Returning to Eq. (15-47), we might observe that the condition of an infinite slope is satisfied along the x axis. This proves the contention that the trajectories cross the x axis perpendicularly.

The most direct path to the stable point would be along an isocline. Since the slope of the trajectory is identical with the slope of the isocline,

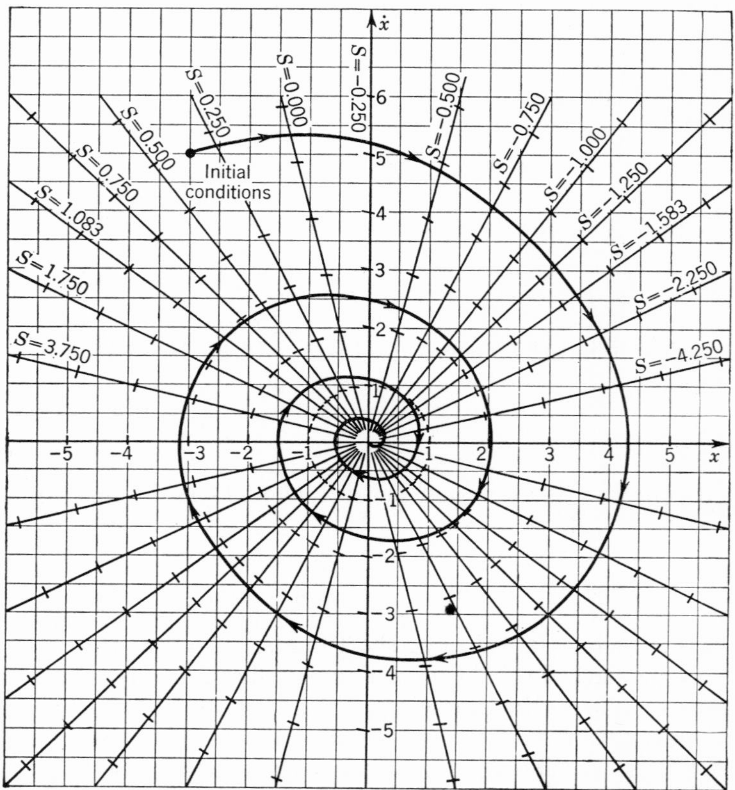

FIG. 15-12. Isocline method of constructing a phase trajectory.

from Eq. (15-47) we see that the necessary condition for such a path is

$$S = -\frac{\omega_0^2}{S + b}$$

But by multiplying out and collecting terms, there results the quadratic

$$S^2 + bS + \omega_0^2 = 0$$

Except that it is a function of S, this quadratic is identical with the characteristic equation from which the roots of the original differential equation (15-39) are found.

Straight lines having a slope equal to the roots are feasible only when these roots are real, i.e., when the response is aperiodic. Two such lines exist on each phase plane as shown in Fig. 15-11*b*. As they head toward the origin, all trajectories approach the line corresponding to the smallest root. It predominates, since it represents the long time decay of the system. The larger root determines the initial rise, and its isocline separates the trajectories that finally approach the origin in the second quadrant from those that terminate in the fourth quadrant.

Unstable Equilibrium. If energy is supplied to the system at the proper rate, for example, by connecting the negative driving-point resistance

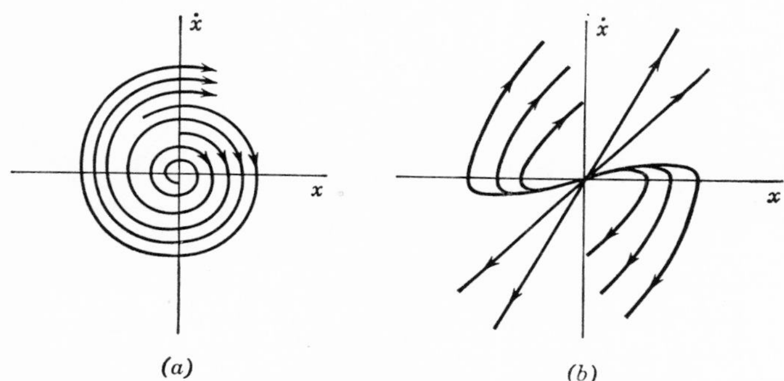

FIG. 15-13. Trajectories for negative damping. (*a*) Increasing oscillatory response; (*b*) increasing aperiodic solution.

across a *GLC* parallel circuit, the amplitude would increase rather than decrease with time. In the region where the circuit may be approximated by a quasi-linear equation, i.e., before limiting, the trajectories would diverge from the singularity at the origin, rotating clockwise as they do so. The two cases of most interest are shown in Fig. 15-13. The increasing spiral represents the build-up of an almost sinusoidal oscillator, and the aperiodic trajectory illustrates the switching path of a multivibrator. If the system has some initial energy, the single trajectory of interest would be the one passing through the point on the phase plane corresponding to the initial conditions. In the case of an increasing exponential, the trajectories will approach the isocline corresponding to the larger root of the second-order equation, regardless of how they diverge from the origin. If we are interested in the response very far away from the point corresponding to the initial conditions, then this particular isocline would closely approximate the path. Of course, nonlinearities in the system may distort the trajectories long before they ever reach this asymptote.

Period and Waveshape. Topological methods may also be employed to convert the trajectory on the phase plane into the equivalent time-varying signal. We can construct a small line segment in the time domain having the slope and position given by the corresponding point on the phase plane. To the end of the first one, a second segment is added, then a third, and so on. As we work our way along the trajectory, the totality of all segments will give a rough approximation to the waveshapes generated. This process is, of course, quite tedious, but necessary where simpler methods cannot yield a satisfactory solution.

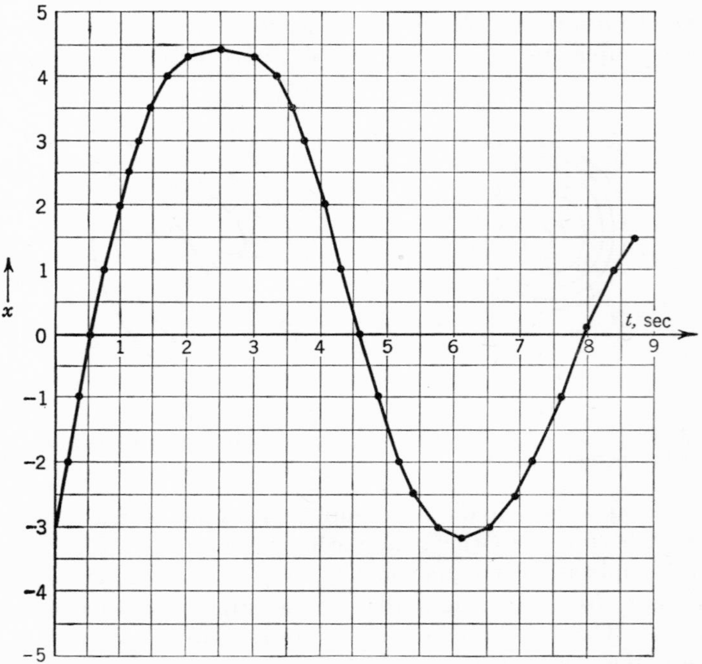

FIG. 15-14. Waveshape constructed from the trajectory of Fig. 15-12.

Figure 15-14 shows just such a construction for slightly more than one complete encirclement of the origin by the trajectory of Fig. 15-12. The initial point of the trajectory was chosen as the start of the construction. Wherever the slope is large, large increments of position are permissible over the associated line segment. Since this section of the curve does not contribute much toward the period, relatively gross approximations are justified. But when the operating point is moving very slowly, the positional increments must be quite close together. To further reduce the timing error, the average slope over each segment of the trajectory was used in the construction of Fig. 15-14.

The timing accuracy of this construction is very poor, and therefore it should be used mainly to identify the waveshape. In the example shown, the time for one complete cycle is almost 1 sec too long.

The time required for the operating point to pass between any two points on the trajectory is found from the line integral:

$$\oint_a^b \frac{1}{y}\,dx = \oint_a^b \frac{dt}{dx}\,dx = \oint_a^b dt = T_b - T_a \tag{15-48}$$

In general, Eq. (15-48) is evaluated by means of a graphical or a numerical integration. For the complete period of any closed contour on the phase plane, the integral becomes

$$T = \oint \frac{1}{y}\,dx \tag{15-49}$$

and it is taken over the complete trajectory.

15-5. Liénard Diagram. As the first step in finding the topological solution of the Van der Pol nonlinear differential equation, we shall normalize the basic equation (15-8) by dividing through by ω_0^2; this leads to the result

$$\frac{d^2v}{d(\omega_0 t)^2} + \frac{\epsilon}{\omega_0} f(v) \frac{dv}{d(\omega_0 t)} + v = 0 \tag{15-50}$$

Since the variables of interest are the voltage across the terminals of the VNLR and its derivative, there should not be any ambiguity or confusion of terms if we redefine $\dot{v} = dv/d(\omega_0 t)$ and rewrite Eq. (15-50):

$$\ddot{v} + \epsilon' f(v)\dot{v} + v = 0 \tag{15-51}$$

And following the procedure outlined in Sec. 15-4, the slope of the trajectory, at each point in the phase plane, will be given by

$$S = \frac{d\dot{v}}{dv} = -\frac{\epsilon' f(v)\dot{v} + v}{\dot{v}} \tag{15-52}$$

The isoclines defined by Eq. (15-52) are no longer straight lines, but are curves which depend on the nature of the nonlinearity. With any given volt-ampere characteristic, $f(v)$ may be evaluated for each value of v. The isoclines are finally constructed, if necessary by plotting individual points.

As this process is extremely tedious, we shall instead turn to the simpler construction developed by A. Liénard. By means of a linear transformation, from the phase plane to the Liénard plane, the problem becomes one of finding the normal to the trajectory and then simply striking an arc to find a segment of the topographical portrait. The transformation chosen is

$$z = \dot{v} + \epsilon' F(v) \tag{15-53}$$

where

$$f(v) = \frac{dF(v)}{dv} \tag{15-54}$$

By differentiating Eq. (15-53) with respect to v and rearranging terms, an alternative expression for the isoclines results:

$$S = \frac{d\dot{v}}{dv} = \frac{dz}{dv} - \epsilon' f(v)$$

Substituting S into Eq. (15-52) leads to

$$\frac{dz}{dv} = -\frac{v}{\dot{v}}$$

From the linear transformation of Eq. (15-53), the slope of the trajectory

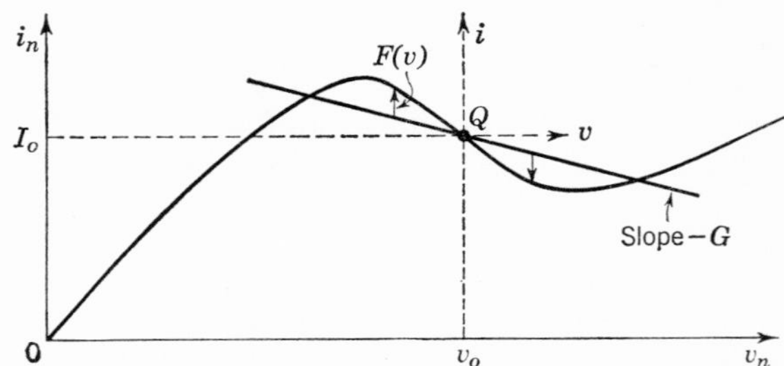

FIG. 15-15. Illustrating the means of evaluating $F(v)$ from the volt-ampere characteristics.

on the Liénard plane finally becomes

$$\frac{dz}{dv} = -\frac{v}{z - \epsilon' F(v)} \tag{15-55}$$

and the slope of the normal to the trajectory is given by

$$N = -\frac{dv}{dz} = \frac{z - \epsilon' F(v)}{v} \tag{15-56}$$

Before we can construct the trajectories we must evaluate $\epsilon' F(v)$. For the basic circuit of Fig. 15-1,

$$\frac{dF(v)}{dv} = f(v) = G + \frac{di}{dv}$$

Integrating both sides with respect to v yields

$$F(v) = Gv + i = i - (-Gv) \tag{15-57}$$

where v and i are measured from the Q point on the volt-ampere characteristics and where $-Gv$ is the conductive load line passing through the Q point. Equation (15-57) says that $F(v)$ is the difference in current between the load line and the characteristic (as shown by the vectors in Fig. 15-15).

In replotting $F(v)$, the ordinate would also be multiplied by ϵ' to scale the curve. This factor is dependent on the design of the tank and may, in fact, be considered a defining parameter.

$$\epsilon' = \frac{1}{\omega_0 C} = \sqrt{\frac{L}{C}} \tag{15-58}$$

The degree of the circuit nonlinearity is proportional to ϵ'; the system becomes quasi-linear for very small values of ϵ' and grossly nonlinear for very large values. We conclude that for an almost sinusoidal oscillator,

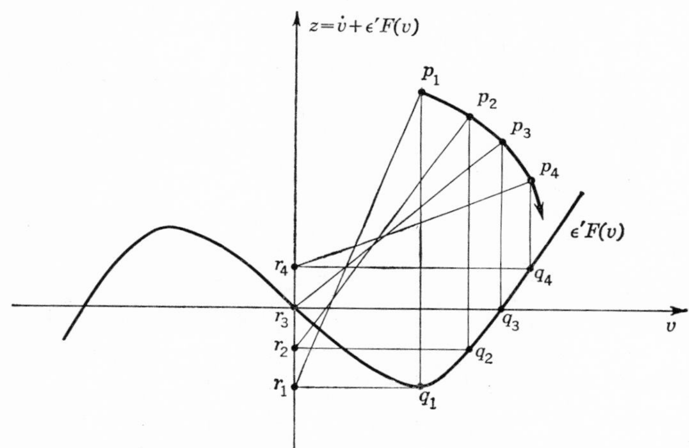

FIG. 15-16. Construction of the Liénard diagram.

L/C should be made as small as possible consistent with the other design requirements. This supports the arguments made earlier with respect to Figs. 15-2 and 15-3.

The final plot of $\epsilon' F(v)$, which serves as the basis for the construction of the Liénard diagram, appears in Fig. 15-16. The procedure followed in constructing first the normal and then the trajectory is based on Eq. (15-56). The various steps illustrated in Fig. 15-16 are:

1. Plot the nonlinearity $\epsilon' F(v)$, following the construction outlined above, on the Liénard plane. This plot cannot be scaled in either coordinate but must be drawn 1:1.
2. At any point on the plane p_1, drop a perpendicular to $\epsilon' F(v)$ at q_1.
3. Draw a line from q_1 to the z axis at r_1.
4. The vertical line segment

$$p_1 q_1 = z_1 - \epsilon' F(v_1)$$

at that particular value of z_1 and v_1. The horizontal line segment

$$q_1 r_1 = v_1$$

Hence, from Eq. (15-56), the hypotenuse of the triangle $r_1p_1q_1$ is the normal to the trajectory passing through point p_1.

5. Strike small arcs intersecting line segment p_1q_1 using point r_1 as the center. These arcs are segments of the various trajectories on the Liénard plane.

6. Starting at any initial point on the plane, strike an arc; from the end of this arc strike another one; and then continue the construction from one point to the next in a clockwise direction until the trajectories converge into a closed contour.

A construction for four points appears in Fig. 15-16, and complete trajectories, cycling to the closed curve representing a periodic solution,

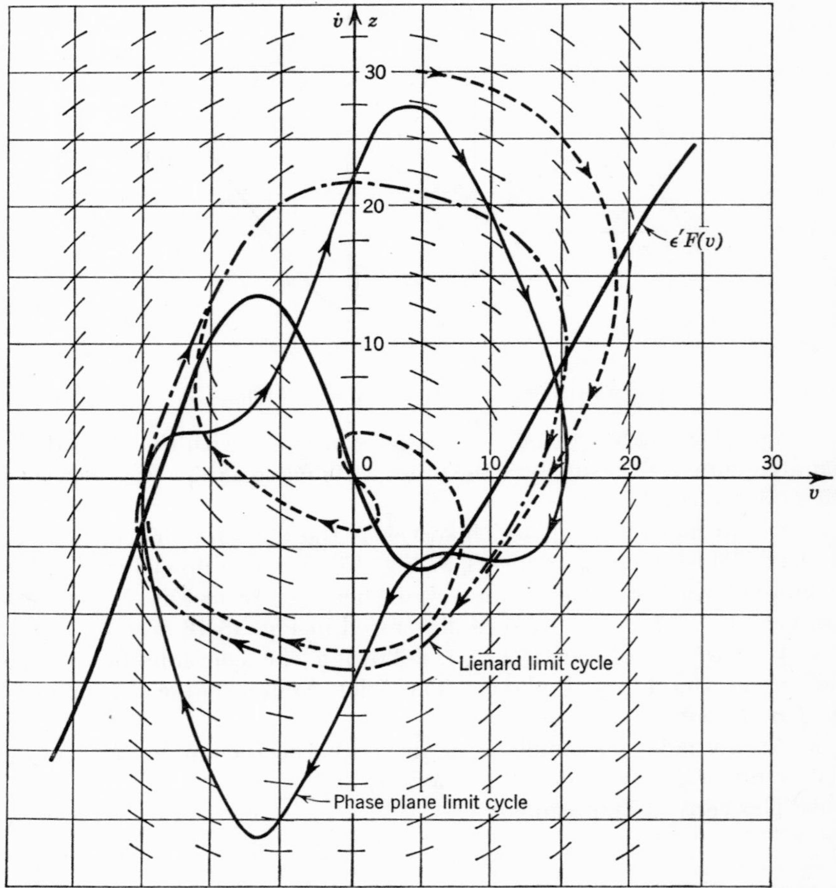

FIG. 15-17. Liénard-plane construction of the trajectory and the limit cycle and the phase-plane limit cycle.

appear in Figs. 15-17 and 15-18. In Fig. 15-17 three different starting points, two close to the origin and one at $z = 30$, $v = 0$, were chosen. By following the procedure outlined above, three trajectories are constructed, and these all eventually form the same closed contour encircling the origin. This curve represents the only periodic solution of the system, and it is called a *limit cycle*. The path leading to the limit cycle,

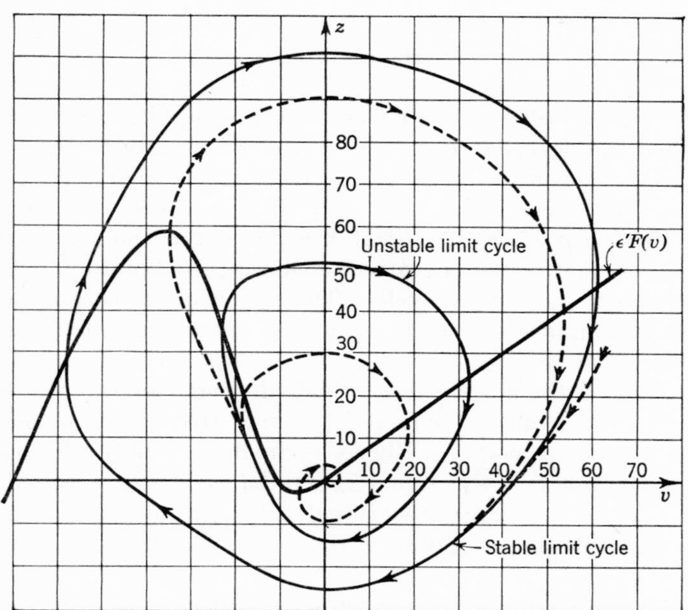

FIG. 15-18. Liénard-plane construction illustrating the conditions yielding both stable and unstable limit cycles.

from any starting point, is the transient portion of the solution. Two trajectories in Fig. 15-17 show the exponential build-up. One, which starts with excessive amplitude, damps down to the final steady-state solution.

The plot on the Liénard plane can be converted into a phase portrait by performing the inverse transformation

$$\dot{v} = z - \epsilon' F(v)$$

which involves subtracting from each point on the Liénard trajectory the value of $\epsilon' F(v)$. This process is also carried out in Fig. 15-17. Because of the large degree of nonlinearity, it leads to the grossly distorted contour shown.

The phase portrait, as well as the Liénard plot of an oscillatory system, will exhibit one or more limit cycles. If all adjacent trajectories converge on one contour (as in Fig. 15-17), then it represents a stable oscillation.

Every unstable equilibrium condition is associated with some closed contour from which the trajectories representing the transient response diverge. It follows that stable and unstable limit cycles separate each other. The origin may also be regarded as a solution which may be either stable or unstable, depending on the nature of the trajectories terminating on it. If the origin is unstable, the circuit is self-starting. If the origin is stable, the circuit must be triggered past the adjacent unstable limit cycle.

Figure 15-18 illustrates the nature of the unstable limit cycle, which arises when the negative-resistance device is normally biased in its dissipative region near the knee of the volt-ampere characteristics. For small signals, the circuit is stable and all trajectories cycle toward the origin. However, after the signal becomes large enough so that the circuit exhibits an average negative resistance, the build-up will proceed toward the next stable limit cycle. These limit cycles correspond to the fundamental amplitudes E_b and E_f in the describing-function solutions of Figs. 15-6 and 15-7.

The shape of the limit cycle, which depends on the size of ϵ' for any given volt-ampere characteristic and frequency, indicates the nature of the time response. When ϵ' is small, the limit cycle approaches a circle or ellipse and the signal generated is almost sinusoidal (Fig. 15-19*a*). When ϵ' is large, the closed trajectory becomes almost rectangular and the time response is that of a relaxation oscillator (Fig. 15-19*b*).

Since the current through a capacitor is proportional to the derivative of the applied voltage, the phase portrait is readily obtained experimentally. The VNLR voltage is applied to the x plates of a cathode-ray oscilloscope and a voltage proportional to the capacitor current to the y deflection circuit.

At this point we might observe that the various topological constructions discussed in this chapter may also be applied to the solution of the negative-resistance switching circuits of Chap. 11. At the low frequencies of operation, the external inductance in the VNLR switching circuit predominates. This corresponds to a very large value of ϵ'. A trajectory similar to that shown in Fig. 15-19*b* would be obtained. Analogous response appears in the CNLR switching circuit. At the higher frequencies, the effective internal energy-storage element of the device plays a more pronounced role, reducing ϵ' and introducing curvature into the trajectory. Thus the phase portrait explains the changes in the behavior of the multivibrator with frequency and even its almost sinusoidal time response when operating at the elevated frequencies.

Furthermore, the phase- or Liénard-plane construction can be used to illustrate the transient switching path between the two states of a bistable circuit. Since the stable points are the nodal points of the system, two constructions would be necessary, one with each singular point as the origin.

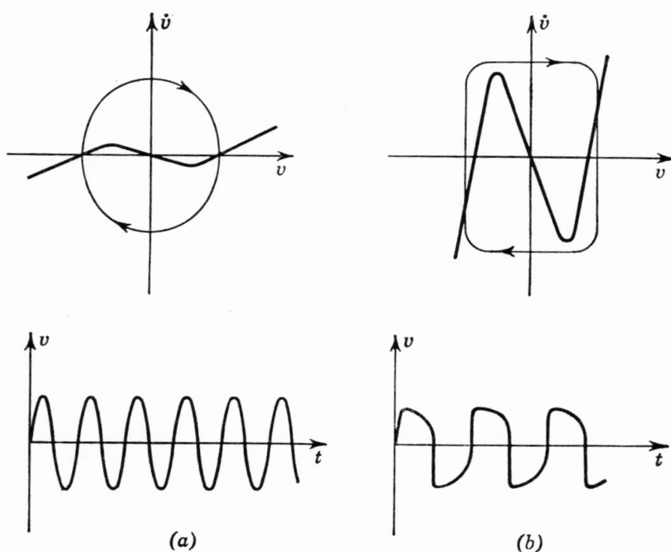

FIG. 15-19. Limit cycles and time response for two values of ϵ'. (a) ϵ' very small—operation as an almost sinusoidal oscillator; (b) ϵ' large—operation as a relaxation oscillator.

15-6. Summary. The complete solution of the nonlinear oscillator, i.e., the waveshape, amplitude, and period, cannot be arrived at by either the topological or the analytic method alone. These two techniques should not be regarded as independent, but rather as complementary: where one is weak, the other is strong. By combining the results, we are able to obtain almost any required information as to the behavior of the system, information which cannot readily be obtained from either method individually.

To find the frequency of oscillation, including the depression due to the harmonic content of the output, we must turn to the analytic solution where an explicit expression was derived [Eq. (15-30)]. However, to evaluate this equation, we must have some knowledge as to the waveshape produced. If this is to be obtained analytically, then the nonlinearity must be expressed as a power series. After the fundamental amplitude is found from the describing function, the harmonic content is evaluated by substituting back into this series. In simple cases, for example, where the volt-ampere characteristic is almost symmetrical, the accuracy requirements are satisfied by approximating the nonlinearity by a cubic polynomial. The coefficients are relatively easy to evaluate. However, in most cases a fifth- or higher-degree equation is necessary for an adequate description, and it becomes extremely tedious to solve for the coefficients. Finally, we should note that the analytic method does not give the waveshape of the output directly, but only as a Fourier series.

On the other hand, the topological solution yields the peak-to-peak amplitude of the stable oscillation quite rapidly but supplies almost no accurate information as to the frequency of operation. A good approximation to the waveshape generated is easily constructed. From it one could find the relative harmonic content of the output either by a graphical integration or by some schedule method.

Suppose that we assume that the period of the waveshape constructed can be scaled to satisfy the frequency found from the analytic expression. Then, from the topological construction, we obtain the waveshape and the harmonic content and use this to find the corrected frequency. Thus each mode of solution is employed where it best serves and, without actually arriving at an analytic expression for the output voltage, we are able to solve the problems posed.

PROBLEMS

15-1. (*a*) Prove that the vacuum-tube Colpitts oscillator may also be treated as a negative-resistance circuit.

(*b*) Convert the negative conductance appearing from plate to ground (found in part *a*) to an equivalent negative conductance across the complete tuned circuit.

(*c*) State the bounding values of g_m for which this circuit will produce an almost sinusoidal output.

15-2. A transistor Hartley oscillator is to be converted into its negative-impedance equivalent circuit. Assume that the transistor has a very large base-to-collector transconductance and that the two coils are not coupled. Make all reasonable approximations. Find the limits of r_c/r'_{11} for which the circuit will function as an oscillator.

15-3. A unijunction transistor (Chap. 11) having $\gamma = 3$, $r_{b1} = 300$, and $r_{b2} = 200$ is biased in its active region and is used as the active element in the CNLR oscillator of Fig. 15-5. The circuit is designed to operate at 50 kc with a tuned circuit that has a loaded $Q = 10$. Specify the limiting values of L and C for which this circuit will function as an oscillator.

15-4. (*a*) Specify the slopes and bounds of the regions of Fig. 15-4*d* if the tube has $\mu = 50$, $r_p = 20$ K, and $r_c = 0$ and if the conductance of the tank is 10^{-4} mho. The plate supply is 100 volts, and the tube is biased in the center of its active region. State all approximations made in the course of the analysis.

(*b*) Will the positive grid loading have any effect other than the reduction in gain? Explain.

(*c*) What limitation must be imposed on the other tank parameters for proper circuit operation if $M = 0.2L$?

15-5. Two negative-resistance characteristics have power-series expansions about the Q point given by

1. $i_n = 3.0v - 0.2v^3 + 0.001v^5$ ma.
2. $i_n = -3.0v + 0.2v^3 + 0.001v^5$ ma.

(*a*) Plot the current describing functions of these two curves on the same graph and find the amplitude of oscillations if $G = 2 \times 10^{-3}$ mho.; if $G = 1 \times 10^{-3}$ mho.

(*b*) Repeat part *a* with respect to the conductance describing function.

15-6. This problem is designed to investigate the response of various negative-resistance oscillators from a consideration of the power-series expansion. Assume that the terms of interest are

$$i_n = a_1v + a_2v^2 + a_3v^3 + a_4v^4 + a_5v^5$$

(*a*) Prove that in order for an oscillator to be self-starting,

$$a_1 < -G$$

(*b*) Prove that

$$a_5 > 0$$

for any values of the other coefficients.

(*c*) Under what conditions will the describing function have a minimum at some nonzero value of E_1? State the answer in terms of the relative size of the coefficients.

(*d*) Under what conditions will the describing function have both a maximum and minimum value of i for some nonzero value of E_1?

15-7. Figure 15-20 shows the piecewise-linear volt-ampere characteristic of a semiconductor device. Find the approximating cubic polynomial holding when the quiescent point is in the center of the negative-resistance region. Solve for the amplitude of oscillation when $R = 400$ and $\sqrt{L/C} = 1{,}000$.

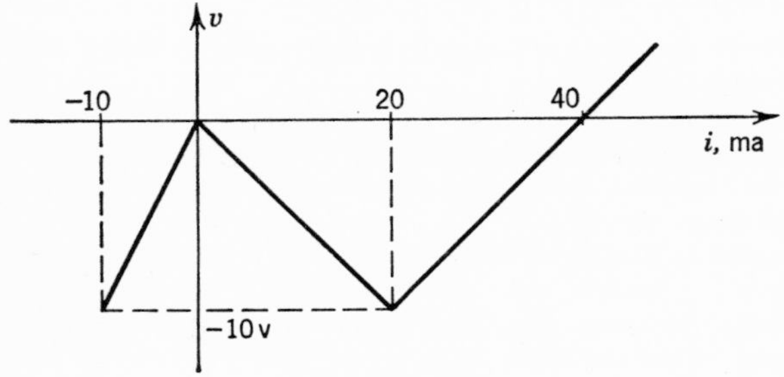

FIG. 15-20

15-8. Express the frequency deviation in terms of the harmonic current components of the VNLR. Give the answer in a form analogous to Eq. (15-30). State the reason for all approximations made in the course of the solution.

15-9. Consider a negative-resistance oscillator using a device described by the polynomial

$$i = -2.0v + 0.5v^3 \qquad \text{ma}$$

(*a*) Find the amplitude of the fundamental term when $G = 1.0$ millimho.

(*b*) Calculate the amplitude of the third-harmonic current component with the assumed sinusoidal excitation found in part *a*.

(c) When $C = 100$ $\mu\mu$f and when $\omega_0 = 10^6$, evaluate the depression in frequency due to the harmonic voltage developed.

(d) Repeat the above calculations for $G = 1.8$ millimhos.

15-10. Use Eq. (15-28) to calculate the approximate depression in frequency if the distortion is great enough so that the terminal voltage is almost a square wave. Even though the answer will be far from exact, it will still give a rough order of magnitude.

15-11. An oscillator with a nominal resonant frequency of $\omega_0 = 10^6$ and a signal amplitude of 20 volts has a 5 per cent third-harmonic and a 1 per cent fifth-harmonic component.

(a) By what percentage will the frequency be depressed?

(b) If $C = 100$ $\mu\mu$f, what is the phase angle of the fundamental?

(c) What is the amplitude of the injected seventh-harmonic component that will just return the frequency to ω_0?

(d) The frequency is to be increased to $1.03\omega_0$ by injecting a second-harmonic signal. What is the necessary amplitude of the synchronizing signal? Calculate the new phase angle at the fundamental.

15-12. Find the phase trajectory of the following single-order system under the conditions given:

$$\dot{x} + bx = 0$$

Plot all trajectories on the same graph and justify any jumps in x that appear.

(a) $b = -5$ and $x(0) = 1$.

(b) $b = -\frac{1}{5}$ and $x(0^-) = -\frac{1}{2}$, $\dot{x}(0^-) = 3$.

(c) $b = +2$ and $x(0) = 10$.

(d) $b = +\frac{1}{2}$ and $x(0^-) = 10$, $\dot{x}(0^-) = -10$.

Find the time response for parts b and d by means of a graphical construction from the phase plane.

15-13. Plot the phase portrait of the following equation on a normalized phase plane; i.e., the coordinates are $\dot{x}/\omega_0$ and x.

$$\ddot{x} + 2A\omega_0\dot{x} + \omega_0^2 x = 0$$

(a) Set $A = 1.1$.

(b) Set $A = 3$.

Pay particular attention to at least one path that falls between the straight-line trajectories.

15-14. Repeat Prob. 15-13 for

(a) $A = -1.1$.

(b) $A = -3$.

15-15. The behavior of an undamped pendulum in the vicinity of its unstable point is defined by

$$\ddot{x} - bx = 0$$

where $b > 0$. In this case the origin is called a saddle point.

(a) Prove that the trajectories are hyperbolas.

(b) Plot two pairs of trajectories when $b = 4$. Sketch the asymptotes and indicate the direction of rotation of all curves.

15-16. Assume that the plot drawn in Fig. 15-17 corresponds to $\epsilon' = 1$. We now wish to consider the response when $\epsilon' = 0.1$ and when $\epsilon' = 10$.

(a) Construct the limit cycle on the Liénard plane for these two cases.

(b) Sketch the approximate waveshapes produced.

(c) By how much does the peak-to-peak amplitude change as ϵ' increases from 0.1 to 1 to 10?

15-17. Accurately construct, out of small line segments, the time-varying signal represented by the limit cycle of Fig. 15-17.

15-18. Plot a Liénard-plane trajectory and the equivalent phase-plane portrait for the oscillator employing a device having the piecewise-linear volt-ampere characteristic of Fig. 15-21. The quiescent point is located at $V_o = 50$ volts and $I_o = 5$ ma, and the tank parameters are $\sqrt{L/C} = 3{,}000$ and $R = 5{,}000$ ohms. Sketch the waveshape.

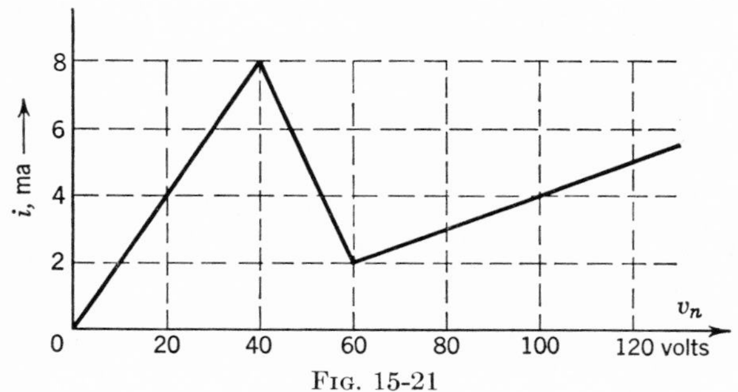

FIG. 15-21

15-19. The load resistance of Prob. 15-18 is changed to 10 K and the Q point to $V_o = 80$ volts and $I_o = 3$ ma.

(*a*) Plot at least two Liénard-plane trajectories showing the transient decay toward the stable point.

(*b*) Is it possible to make this circuit oscillate? Give the expected peak-to-peak output if it is possible. If it is impossible, justify your answer.

15-20. Solve Prob. 15-7 by the method of the Liénard plane.

BIBLIOGRAPHY

Andronow, A. A., and C. E. Chaikin: "Theory of Oscillations," Princeton University Press, Princeton, N.J., 1949.

Belevitch, V.: "Théorie des circuits non-linéaires en régime alternatif," Gauthier-Villars, Paris, 1959.

Edson, W. A.: "Vacuum-tube Oscillators," John Wiley & Sons, Inc., New York, 1953.

Kryloff, N., and N. Bogoliuboff: "Introduction to Non-linear Mechanics," Princeton University Press, Princeton, N.J., 1943.

le Corbeiller, P.: The Nonlinear Theory of the Maintenance of Oscillations, *J. IEE (London)*, vol. 79, pp. 361–378, 1936.

Liénard, A.: Étude des oscillations entretenus, *Rev. gén. élec.*, vol. 23, pp. 901–946, 1928.

Minorsky, N.: "Introduction to Nonlinear Mechanics," J. W. Edwards, Publisher, Inc., Ann Arbor, Mich., 1947.

Oser, E. A., R. O. Enders, and R. P. Moore, Jr.: Transistor Oscillators, *RCA Rev.*, vol. 13, pp. 369–385, September, 1952.

van der Pol, B.: The Nonlinear Theory of Electric Oscillations, *Proc. IRE*, vol. 22, no. 9, pp. 1051–1086, 1934.

NAME INDEX

SUBJECT INDEX